U.S.—JAPAN
BI—LATERAL SEMINAR
IN HYDROLOGY

EAST—WEST CENTER
HONOLULU, HAWAII

JANUARY 11—17, 1971

SYSTEMS APPROACH TO HYDROLOGY

Proceedings of the First Bilateral

U.S.-Japan Seminar in Hydrology

Held at the East-West Center

of University of Hawaii, Honolulu

January 11-17, 1971

Prepared for Publication

by V. Yevjevich

Water Resources Publications
Fort Collins, Colorado
1971

This publication can be purchased for U.S. $12.00 through
WATER RESOURCES PUBLICATIONS
P.O. Box 303, Fort Collins, Colorado 80521 USA

G B
6 5 /
. B5
/ 9 7 /

SYSTEMS APPROACH TO HYDROLOGY

Library Of Congress Catalog Card Number 71-168496

This publication is printed and bound by LithoCrafters, Ann Arbor, Michigan, U.S.A.

The first U.S.-Japan bilateral seminar in hydrology was held at the East-West Center, the University of Hawaii, Honolulu, January 11-17, 1971. The theme of the seminar was, "The Systems Approach to Analysis of Hydrologic Processes and Environments." For the Proceedings of this seminar, the theme has been shortened to "Systems Approach to Hydrology."

Nine papers from Japan and eleven papers from the United States were presented at the seminar. After each paper was presented, with the subject matter of recent research results by contributors, it was discussed by the attending participants. The content of the Proceedings of the seminar is composed of these presented papers, summaries of the discussions, written by the various discussers after the seminar and arranged in alphabetical order, and summaries of the authors' responses to the discussions, also written after the seminar. These discussions provided an opportunity for an exchange of ideas and for an evaluation of the current state of knowledge and research.

The format of the Proceedings is as follows. Each paper is presented in the same order that it was presented in at the seminar. For most papers the text is presented first, followed by the list of symbols and figures, and concluded with discussions and responses. At the bottom of each paper is the sequence number of the paper and the page number within that sequence. At the top, each page of the Proceedings is numbered consecutively. Lists of symbols, with the notations and terms used in the papers, were included with the papers because of the inherent difficulties in trying to standardize all notation and terminology throughout the Proceedings.

During the final session of the actual seminar three topics were brought forth for general discussion by the participants. The three topics were: response hydrology, bridge between scientific and applied hydrology, and relevant future hydrologic research areas. Summaries of these topics, as viewed by some participants, are presented at the end of these Proceedings.

The travel of the U.S. participants and seminar expenses were supported by the U.S. National Science Foundation; the travel expenses of the Japanese participants were supported by the Japan Society for the Promotion of Science. The understanding and support of these two agencies is gratefully acknowledged and appreciated. Acknowledgment and appreciation are also due the East-West Center, and the University of Hawaii, particularly its Water Resources Center, for organizing the seminar. Professor T. Ishihara was the coordinator for Japanese participation, and Professor T. Kishi assisted him in that task. Professor V. Yevjevich was the coordinator for U.S. participation, and Professor S. Lau assisted him in that task.

Although there was no formal editing of the papers in the Proceedings, the mutual cooperation among the participants of the United States and Japan for improving the readability and understanding of each paper was very useful. A Japanese and a U.S. participant reviewed each others paper.

At this first bilateral seminar it was decided that much progress could again be achieved in hydrology for eventual arranging of the second U.S.-Japan seminar of a similar nature in Japan in 1974. The tentative topic proposed by the Japanese participants for this second potential conference is "Conservation, Reclamation, and Control of Hydrologic Environments."

LIST OF PARTICIPANTS

U.S. Participants

1. Dr. V. Yevjevich (U.S. Coordinator)

   Professor-in-Charge of Hydrology
   and Water Resources Program
   Colorado State University
   Fort Collins, Colorado 80521

2. Dr. V. T. Chow

   Professor of Civil Engineering
   Department of Civil Engineering
   University of Illinois
   Urbana, Illinois 61801

3. Dr. J. W. Delleur

   Professor of Hydraulic Engineering
   School of Civil Engineering
   Purdue University
   Lafayette, Indiana 47097

4. Dr. Peter S. Eagleson

   Professor of Civil Engineering
   and Chairman
   Department of Civil Engineering
   Massachusetts Institute of Technology
   Cambridge, Massachusetts 02139

5. Dr. Chester C. Kisiel

   Professor of Hydrology and Water
   Resources
   Hydrology and Water Resources Office
   The University of Arizona
   Tucson, Arizona 85721

6. Dr. Stephen Lau

   Director of Water Resources Center
   University of Hawaii
   Water Resources Center
   Honolulu, Hawaii

7. Dr. Walter L. Moore

   Professor of Civil Engineering
   Department of Civil Engineering
   University of Texas at Austin
   Austin, Texas 78712

8. Dr. Rafael Quimpo

   Associate Professor
   Department of Civil Engineering
   University of Pittsburgh
   Pittsburgh, Pennsylvania 15213

9. Dr. J. Paul Riley

   Associate Professor
   College of Engineering
   Utah State University
   Logan, Utah 84321

10. Dr. William M. Snyder
    Dr. Snyder, with his co-authors,
    submitted the paper which was
    presented at the seminar but
    could not attend it.

    U.S. Department of Agriculture
    Agricultural Research Service
    Soil and Water Conservation
    Research Division
    Southeast Watershed Research Center
    P. O. Box 469
    Athens, Georgia 30601

11. Dr. Timothy D. Steele

Research Hydrologist
U.S. Geological Survey
Water Resources Division
Washington, D. C. 20242

Japanese Participants

1. Dr. Tojiro Ishihara (Japanese Coordinator)

Professor of Civil Engineering
Head of the Data Processing Center
Faculty of Engineering
Kyoto University
Kyoto, 606

2. Dr. Tsutomu Kishi

Professor of Civil Engineering
Faculty of Engineering
Hokkaido University
Sapporo, 060

3. Dr. Akira Murota

Professor of Civil Engineering
Faculty of Engineering
Osaka University
Suita, Osaka, 564

4. Dr. Yoshiaki Iwasa

Professor of Civil Engineering
Faculty of Engineering
Kyoto University
Kyoto, 606

5. Dr. Yutaka Takahasi

Professor of Civil Engineering
Faculty of Engineering
University of Tokyo
Tokyo, 113

6. Dr. Minoru Okuta

Typhoon Research Section
Research Institute of Meteorology
Meteorology Agency
Tokyo, 166

7. Dr. Mikio Hino

Associate Professor of
 Civil Engineering
Faculty of Engineering
Tokyo Institute of Technology
Tokyo, 152

8. Dr. Takuma Takasao

Associate Professor of
 Civil Engineering
Kyoto University
Kyoto, 606

9. Dr. Ryo Kaneko
     Dr. Kaneko submitted the paper
     which was presented at the seminar
     but could not attend it.

Director
National Research Institute of
 Agricultural Engineering
Ministry of Agriculture and Forestry
Hiratsuka, Kanawa

TABLE OF CONTENTS

TABLE OF CONTENTS (cont'd)

TABLE OF CONTENTS (cont'd)

United States-Japan Bi-Lateral Seminar in Hydrology
Honolulu, January 1971

STOCHASTIC HYDROLOGIC SYSTEMS

by Ven Te Chow

Professor of Hydraulic Engineering
University of Illinois
Urbana, Illinois, U.S.A.

SYNOPSIS

Hydrologic phenomena are simulated as stochastic hydrologic systems in terms of mathematical models whose components are represented by stochastic processes. The proposed stochastic hydrologic model is based on a mathematical formulation of the principle of system continuity composed of component stochastic processes of precipitation, runoff, evapotranspiration plus losses and basin storage. Based on various assumptions two stochastic watershed system models are formulated and analysed to illustrate the application of the proposed stochastic hydrologic model. One watershed system model is the annual storm-flood model in which the input hourly rainfall of the annual storm is represented by a first-order nonhomogeneous Markov chain and the annual storm-flood by multiple linear regression. The rainfall and runoff relationship of the watershed is represented by a bivariate Markov process. The other watershed model is the watershed yield model in which the component hydrologic processes of precipitation, runoff, evapotranspiration and basin storage are simulated as stochastic processes by time series to be determined by correlogram and power spectrum analysis. As numerical examples for analysis, the French Broad River basin above Bent Creek, North Carolina is used as the watershed for the annual storm-flood model, and the upper Sangamon River basin above Monticello in east central Illinois is used as the watershed for the watershed yield model.

INTRODUCTION

The natural hydrologic systems are so complex that no exact laws have yet been discovered that can explain completely and precisely the natural hydrologic phenomena. Before such laws can ever be found, complicated hydrologic systems such as watersheds can only be approximated essentially by simulation. In this way the hydrologic system may be treated in various degrees of complexity from deterministic to purely probabilistic and further from probabilistic to stochastic.

Because of the uncertainty involved in the hydrologic behavior, the most suitable simulation is probably by a stochastic hydrologic system. In other words, the behavior of the hydrologic system and the processes which take place in it are considered to vary with a sequential time function of the probability of occurrence. In this simulation, the hydrologic phenomenon changes with the time in accordance with the law of probability as well as with the sequential relationship between its occurrences.

From a systems viewpoint, a physical system is a system in the real world. A sequential system is a physical system which consists of input, output and some working medium (matter, energy, or information) known as throughput passing through the system. A dynamic system is a physical system which receives certain quantitative inputs and accordingly acts concertedly under given constraints to produce certain quantitative outputs. The hydrologic system is physical, sequential, and dynamic in nature; and thus can be so simulated.

In recent years, research on mathematical simulation of hydrologic systems has been greatly developed. Most proposed mathematical models for simulation purposes deal with only stochastic input or stochastic output, or with both stochastic input and stochastic output, while the system itself through which the throughput passes remains to be treated as deterministic. Such simulated systems may be called "quasi-stochastic." An example of simulating the quasi-stochastic hydrologic system is to treat the rainfall and runoff of a watershed as stochastic, while the watershed proper is simulated by deterministic models.

In the above example, the physiographic features of the watershed actually vary not only seasonally, from spring to summer, to fall and to winter, but also vary weekly and daily due to changing weather conditions as well as in long secular terms due to climatic variation. A true stochastic hydrologic system should therefore also treat the system itself as stochastic.

MATHEMATICAL FORMULATION OF STOCHASTIC HYDROLOGIC SYSTEMS

For the true stochastic hydrologic system, all components of the system can be theoretically described by stochastic processes [Chow, 1967, 1968, 1969, 1970]. In the system, the input, the output and the transformation of input to output may be therefore represented mathematically by time series since these component processes in general change with time and are functions of time. The transformation of input to output is characterized by the physiographical features and hydrologic behavior of the system. All the processes are governed by mathematically simulated stochastic laws rather than by deterministic laws. They may be denoted by $[u_t; t \in T]$ where u_t is a stochastic variable at time t which is a parameter running over an index set T or over the time range under consideration. Thus, the input stochastic process is denoted by $[X_t; t \in T]$ where X_t is the input stochastic variable; the output stochastic process by $[Y_t; t \in T]$ where Y_t is the output stochastic variable; and the throughput stochastic process, representing the transformation of input to output, by $[Z_t; t \in T]$ where Z_t is the throughput stochastic variable. These stochastic processes can be simply denoted by $[X_t]$, $[Y_t]$, and $[Z_t]$ respectively. They may not be considered as independent but as a stochastic vector $[X_t, Y_t, Z_t; t \in T]$ or $[X_t, Y_t, Z_t]$. The theory of time series can therefore be used to formulate the stochastic model of this vector. A rigorous mathematical analysis of this vector would require the use of the theory of multiple time series analysis.

The time parameter t in the stochastic processes may be either continuous or discrete. For practical and analytical purposes and for a possible solution of the mathematically simulated model by digital computers, the stochastic processes are considered as discrete time functions. The index set T represents a length of time long enough to describe the hydrologic phenomenon under consideration. Units of the time parameter t can be chosen in convenient time intervals so that for the integral values of t = 1, 2, ..., T, the stochastic variables define the respective processes in satisfactory detail. It should be noted that the time interval to be chosen for the discrete time parameter will affect the simulated stochastic laws of the processes. In general, smaller time intervals will make the stochastic laws more complex as the magnitude and extent of dependence among the stochastic variables based on the historical hydrologic data of a process will be greater and in more detail.

The input-and-output relationship of a stochastic hydrologic system may be represented mathematically by a system equation:

$$[Y_t] = \phi\{[X_t], [Z_t]\} \tag{1}$$

where $\phi\{[X_t], [Z_t]\}$ is the transfer function that represents the operation performed by the system on the input and the throughput in order to transfer them into output.

In most cases, the input, output and throughput of a hydrologic system are amounts of water, although in certain cases they can be taken as energy or other forms of medium. By the basic principle of system continuity, the output is equal to the input minus the throughput which is the amount of flow in the system. Thus, a single transfer function may be written

$$\phi\{[X_t], [Z_t]\} = [X_t] - [Z_t] \tag{2}$$

Hence, from Eqs. (1) and (2), the hydrologic system equation becomes

$$[Y_t] = [X_t] - [Z_t] \tag{3}$$

For the t-th time interval, or the time interval from t to t+1, Eq. (3) may be written as

$$Y_t = X_t - Z_t \tag{4}$$

where X_t is the input in the t-th time interval, Y_t is the output in the t-th time interval, and Z_t is the change of throughput in the t-th time interval.

In order to demonstrate the use of the above equation, the watershed is taken as a hydrologic system which has the precipitation as its input, the streamflow or runoff as its output, and the change in basin storage, due to mere storage and depletion as well as to evapotranspiration plus other losses, as its throughput. For the watershed, Eq. (4) becomes

$$Y_t = X_t - E_t - S_{t+1} + S_t \tag{5}$$

where X_t is the total amount of precipitation input to the watershed during the t-th time interval, Y_t is the total amount of runoff output from the watershed during the t-th time interval, E_t is the total amount of evapo-transpiration plus other losses during the t-th time interval, S_t is the basin storage at time t, and S_{t+1} is the basin storage at time t+1.

To illustrate the application of the proposed mathematical formulation of stochastic hydrologic systems, two stochastic watershed hydrologic system models will be analysed: an annual storm-flood model and a watershed yield model.

AN ANNUAL STORM-FLOOD MODEL

The annual storm-flood is the runoff of a flood produced by an annual storm. The annual storm is a storm which produced the maximum peak discharge of flood flow in a water year. Therefore, for N water years of storm and flood records, there are N annual storms and N annual storm-floods.

The annual storm is treated as the input stochastic process to the watershed system which transforms the annual storm into the annual storm-flood. The stochastic process of the annual storm is denoted by $[X_t; t \in T]$ where the time increment for t in general may be conveniently taken as one hour and T is the duration of the storm considered in the analysis. It is evident that the hourly rainfall process in an annual storm is nonstationary as the probability of transition between the hourly rainfalls of a storm changes with time since the storm began and hence depends on the time of transition. The nonstationary discrete-time process can be described by a nonhomogeneous Markov chain. A previous study by Chow and Ramaseshan [1965] has shown that an autoregressive model based on the first-order Markovian structure of one-step transition probability fits satisfactorily the hourly storm-rainfall data. Therefore, a first-order nonhomogeneous Markov chain can be assumed to represent the stochastic process of the annual storm under consideration. This Markov chain may be written as

$$X_t = \lambda_t X_{t-1} + \varepsilon_t \tag{6}$$

where X_t is the stochastic variable of hourly rainfall in the annual storm, λ_t is the Markov or regression coefficient, and ε_t is the random component of X_t. The subscript t implies that the process is nonstationary as the process and its parameters change with time in the process.

The transition probability of the hourly rainfalls in the annual storm process is

$$g_t(x_t \mid x_{t-1}) = P[X_t = x_t \mid X_{t-1} = x_{t-1}] \tag{7}$$

where the subscript t indicates the nonstationarity and x_t is the variate of the stochastic variable X_t. Thus,

$$p(X_t = x_t) = \sum_{x_{t-1}} P[X_t = x_t \mid X_{t-1} = x_{t-1}]p(X_{t-1} = x_{t-1}) \qquad (8)$$

where $p(X_t = x_t)$ is the probability for $X_{t-1} = x_{t-1}$. Equation (8) implies that the probability of the outcome x_t depends on the probability of its antecedent x_{t-1} and this dependence is represented by the transition probability of Eq. (7).

The annual storm-flood depends not only on the antecedent annual storm-rainfall but also on the corresponding physiographical condition of the watershed. It can therefore be assumed that the hourly flood flow Y_t in the t-th time interval depends upon the hourly rainfall X_{t-1} of the annual storm at the (t-1)-th time interval as well as upon the basin storage S_t at time t. Corresponding to the time increment for hourly rainfalls, the increment of t for flow is also taken as one hour. The process $[Y_t; t \in T]$ can then be suitably described by

$$Y_t = \phi_t(X_{t-1}, S_t) + \varepsilon_t \qquad (9)$$

where $\phi_t(X_{t-1}, S_t)$ is some function of X_{t-1} and S_t to represent the deterministic component of Y_t, and ε_t is a random variable uncorrelated with X_{t-1} and S_t but to provide the random component of Y_t. The subscript t implies that the process and its components are all nonstationary. The length of T is the duration of the flood to be considered in the analysis.

When sufficient data are available, the function $\phi_t(X_{t-1}, S_t)$ can be derived by multiple regression. For the case under consideration, a multiple linear regression is found suitable. Thus, Eq. (9) may be written as

$$Y_t = a_t X_{t-1} + b_t S_t + c_t + \varepsilon_t \qquad (10)$$

where a_t and b_t are nonstationary regression coefficients and c_t is the non-stationary intercept of the linear regression line-of-fit. The random component ε_t may be assumed as normally and independently distributed or as distributed according to a probability law suitable to the given data.

In the analysis of annual storms and annual storm-floods, the evapotranspiration and other losses in the hydrologic process may be ignored because they are insignificant in the relatively short durations of the storms and floods under consideration. Thus, Eq. (5) reduces to

$$S_{t+1} = X_t - Y_t + S_t \qquad (11)$$

The phenomenon of transforming hourly rainfall to hourly flood flow in the watershed system, as influenced by the basin storage, may be described by a one-step bivariate nonhomogeneous Markov process which is represented by a family of two-dimensional stochastic vectors $[X_t, S_{t+1}]$ as

1.5

$$f_t(x_t, s_{t+1} \mid x_{t-1}, s_t) = p_{ij}(t)$$

$$= P[X_t = x_t, S_{t+1} = s_{t+1} \mid X_{t-1} = x_{t-1}, S_t = s_t] \quad (12)$$

where $p_{ij}(t)$ is the transition probability of the bivariate process from state i at t-1 to state j at t. By Eq. (11), the above equation becomes

$$p_{ij}(t) = P[X_t = x_t, X_t - Y_t + S_t = s_{t+1} \mid X_{t-1} = x_{t-1}, S_t = s_t] \quad (13)$$

By the conditional probability theorem [Papoulis, 1965], the above equation can be expressed as

$$p_{ij}(t) = P[X_t = x_t \mid X_{t-1} = x_{t-1}, S_t = s_t]$$

$$P[X_t - Y_t + S_t = s_{t+1} \mid X_{t-1} = x_{t-1}, S_t = s_t, X_t = x_t]$$

$$= P[X_t = x_t \mid X_{t-1} = x_{t-1}, S_t = s_t]$$

$$P[Y_t = s_t + x_t - s_{t+1} \mid X_{t-1} = x_{t-1}, S_t = s_t, X_t = x_t] \quad (14)$$

Since X_t depends only on X_{t-1} but not on S_t as indicated by Eq. (6), and also since Y_t does not depend on X_t but on X_{t-1} as indicated by Eq. (9), the above equation then becomes

$$p_{ij}(t) = P[X_t = x_t \mid X_{t-1} = x_{t-1}]P[Y_t = y_t \mid X_{t-1} = x_{t-1}, S_t = s_t] \quad (15)$$

Since Eq. (9) assumes that the flood flow Y_t is a function of X_{t-1} and S_t, the transition probability of the hourly flood flows for the annual storm-flood process is

$$h_t(y_t \mid x_{t-1}, s_t) = P[Y_t = y_t \mid X_{t-1} = x_{t-1}, S_t = s_t] \quad (16)$$

where x_{t-1}, y_t and s_t are respectively the variates of the variables X_{t-1}, Y_t and S_t. Thus, the probability of the flood flow is

$$p(Y_t = y_t) = \sum_{x_{t-1}, s_t} P[Y_t = y_t \mid X_{t-1} = x_{t-1}, S_t = s_t]p(X_{t-1} = x_{t-1}, S_t = s_t)$$

$$= \sum_{x_{t-1}, s_t} h_t(y_t \mid x_{t-1}, s_t) \, p(X_{t-1} = x_{t-1}, S_t = s_t) \quad (17)$$

1.6

From Eqs. (7) and (16), Eq. (15) gives

$$p_{ij}(t) = g_t(x_t \mid x_{t-1}) h_t(y_t \mid x_{t-1}, s_t) \qquad (18)$$

Let the two-dimensional state vector $[X_t, S_{t+1}]$ of the bivariate Markov process assume discrete values $\delta[X_t, S_{t+1}]_k$ which can be represented by a point in a two-dimensional plane. The coordinates of this point are X_t and S_{t+1}. If X_t can assume discrete states m = 1, 2, ..., M, where each state represents a convenient range of hourly rainfall amounts, and S_{t+1} can assume discrete states n = 1, 2, ..., N, where each state represents a convenient range of hourly basin storages, then the state vector $[X_t, S_{t+1}]$ can assume MN discrete states, i.e., K = MN.

Following Eq. (12) the transition probability of the bivariate process from state i at t-1 to state j at t is

$$f_t(x_t, s_{t+1} \mid x_{t-1}, s_t) = p_{ij}(t), \quad i,j = 1, 2, ..., K \qquad (19)$$

which is nonstationary since it is a product of two nonstationary probability functions as indicated by Eq. (18). For each t = 1, 2, ..., T, there will be a stochastic matrix of size K. Hence, there will be T stochastic matrices, each of size K, for the proposed bivariate process.

Now, assume the initial probability for the bivariate process, $p_j(0)$ for j = 1, 2, ..., K. Since the initial rainfall is always zero, only the probability of the initial basin storage should be assumed. The absolute probability of the bivariate Markov process can be derived inductively by the total probability theorem [Papoulis, 1965] as follows:

$$p_j(1) = \sum_{i=1}^{K} p_i(0) \, p_{ij}(1) \qquad \text{for } j = 1, 2, ..., K$$

$$p_j(2) = \sum_{i=1}^{K} p_i(1) \, p_{ij}(2) \qquad \text{for } j = 1, 2, ..., K$$

$$\cdots$$

$$p_j(t) = \sum_{i=1}^{K} p_i(t-1) \, p_{ij}(t) \qquad \text{for } j = 1, 2, ..., K \qquad (20)$$

where $p_j(t) = p(X_t = x_t, S_{t+1} = s_{t+1})$ and the state j refers to the state of the state vector $[X_t, S_{t+1}]$.

From the joint probability, the marginal probability of the basin storage S_{t+1} can be calculated by

$$p(S_{t+1} = s_{t+1}) = \sum_{x_t} p(X_t = x_t, S_{t+1} = s_{t+1}) = \sum_{x_t} p_j(t) \qquad (21)$$

where the summation is over all values of x_t for $m = 1, 2, \ldots, M$. The expected basin storage at time t may be computed by

$$E(s_t) = \sum_{n=1}^{N} p(S_t = s_{tn})s_{tn} \qquad (22)$$

where s_{tn} is the basin storage in state n, $n = 1, 2, \ldots, N$.

Summing up the transition probability $p_{ij}(t)$ of Eq. (18) over all the values of x_t,

$$\sum_{x_t} p_{ij}(t) = \sum_{x_t} g_t(x_t \mid x_{t-1})h_t(y_t \mid x_{t-1}, s_t)$$

$$= h_t(y_t \mid x_{t-1}, s_t)\sum_{x_t} g_t(x_t \mid x_{t-1})$$

$$= h_t(y_t \mid x_{t-1}, s_t) \qquad (23)$$

Substituting this equation in Eq. (17), the probability distribution of the flood flow Y_t is

$$p(Y_t = y_t) = \sum_{x_t, x_{t-1}, s_t} p_i(t-1)p_{ij}(t) \qquad (24)$$

where $p_i(t-1) = p(X_{t-1} = x_{t-1}, S_t = s_t)$ is, as shown by Eq. (20), the absolute probability of the bivariate process being in state i at time t-1, and $p_{ij}(t)$ is, as shown by Eq. (19), the transition probability of the bivariate process from state i at t-1 to state j at t.

The annual storm-flood model is represented by Eq. (11) in which the components X_t, Y_t and S_t are expressed by Eqs. (6), (10) and (11) itself, respectively, and their probabilities by Eqs. (8), (24) and (21), respectively. When this model is available or its parameters are determined from historical hydrologic data, the model can be used to compute sequential hydrologic data if the initial hydrologic conditions are given. For example, if the initial hourly rainfall and basin storage are known, the subsequent hourly rainfalls, basin storages and flood flows can be calculated. In general, if $X_{t-1} = x_{t-1}$ and S_t are given, the values of $X_t = x_t$ and $Y_t = y_t$ and their probabilities can be computed respectively by Eqs. (6) and (10) and by Eqs. (8) and (24). Having determined $X_t = x_t$ and $Y_t = y_t$ and with S_t already given, S_{t+1} can be computed from Eq. (11) and its probability by Eq. (21). It can be therefore seen that when the state of the hourly rainfall at any time t and the hourly basin storage at t+1 are given, the stochastic variables of hourly rainfalls, basin storages and flood flows and their probabilities can be computed in subsequent times.

As a numerical example, the French Broad River basin in North Carolina, U.S.A. with a size of 676 sq. mi. is chosen as the hydrologic system. Twenty seven annual-storm records (1935-62) and hydrographs of the corresponding floods are available for the analysis. In this analysis, T is taken as 100 hrs. with time increments of one hour. Thus, the stochastic processes of the hourly rainfalls and flood flows are respectively $[X_t;$ $t = 1, 2, \ldots, 100]$ and $[Y_t; t = 1, 2, \ldots, 100]$. Since the basin storage is a relative quantity in the model and only its change in a given time interval, $S_{t+1} - S_t$, is significant, the initial basin storage may be assumed to be zero; that is, $S_o = 0$ and $p(S_o \neq 0) = 0$. Based on this assumption, the stochastic process of the hourly basin storage $[S_t; t = 1, 2, \ldots, 100]$ can be computed by Eq. (11).

From the given data of $[X_t, Y_t, S_t; t = 1, 2, \ldots, 100]$, the Markov chain of the annual storm is computed by Eq. (6). The first 20 hours of the regression coefficient λ_t and the standard deviation σ_t of the random component ε_t, assuming normally distributed with zero mean, are listed in Table 1. Statistical tests have shown that the assumed first-order Markov chain is a satisfactory model. It can be seen that the assumed process is definitely nonstationary.

Table 1. Parameters of the first-order Markov chain of annual storms
(Only values of the first 20 hours are shown as sample)

t	λ_t	σ_t	t	λ_t	σ_t
1	-	-	11	1.133	.101
2	.846	.072	12	.568	.112
3	.810	.063	13	.667	.101
4	.907	.064	14	1.150	.113
5	.344	.049	15	.521	.072
6	.942	.056	16	.785	.060
7	.832	.063	17	.661	.106
8	.793	.058	18	.557	.057
9	1.058	.089	19	.831	.085
10	.630	.095	20	.945	.063

The transition probabilities of the hourly rainfalls in the annual storm can be computed by a transition count method. The hourly rainfall at any given time t is given M = 10 discrete states. The number of hourly rainfalls of amount falling in each state is counted. The transition probabilities between state i at time t and state j at t+1 are computed for all states i, j = 1, 2, ..., 10 and all t = 1, 2, ..., 100 hr. The computed transition probabilities are therefore represented by 100 matrices of size 10 for the nonstationary stochastic process. Table 2 shows the matrix of the hourly rainfall for 10 states at t = 20 hr. Statistical tests have shown that the stochastic process of the annual storms under consideration cannot be treated satisfactorily as stationary.

From the given data of $[X_t, Y_t, S_t; t = 1, 2, \ldots, 100]$, the multiple linear regression of the hourly flood flow is computed by Eq. (10). Table 3 lists, for the first 20 hours, the parameters a_t, b_t and c_t and the standard deviation σ_t of the random component ε_t, assuming normally distributed with zero mean. The adequacy of the assumed linear regression has been tested statistically to be satisfactory. Figure 1 shows the computed hydrograph by Eq. (10) as compared with the observed hydrograph for the annual storm-flood of the year 1938.

1.9

Table 2. The transition probability of the hourly
rainfall for 10 states at t = 20 hr.

i \ j	1	2	3	4	5	6	7	8	9	10
1	1.00	0.00	0.00	0.00	0.00	0.00	0.00	0.00	0.00	0.00
2	0.20	0.80	0.00	0.00	0.00	0.00	0.00	0.00	0.00	0.00
3	0.00	0.25	0.50	0.25	0.00	0.00	0.00	0.00	0.00	0.00
4	0.00	0.45	0.11	0.33	0.00	0.11	0.00	0.00	0.00	0.00
5	0.00	0.00	0.00	0.75	0.25	0.00	0.00	0.00	0.00	0.00
6	0.00	0.00	0.00	0.00	0.00	0.00	0.00	0.00	0.00	0.00
7	0.00	0.00	0.00	0.00	0.00	0.00	0.00	0.00	0.00	0.00
8	0.00	0.00	0.00	0.00	0.00	0.00	0.00	1.00	0.00	0.00
9	0.00	0.00	0.00	0.00	0.00	0.00	0.00	0.00	0.00	0.00
10	0.00	0.00	0.00	0.00	0.00	0.00	0.00	0.00	0.00	0.00

Table 3. Parameters of the multiple linear
regression of annual storm-floods
(Only first 20 hours are shown)

t	a_t	b_t	c_t	σ_t
1	–	–	–	–
2	.024	-.025	.006	.003
3	.021	-.013	.006	.003
4	.024	-.008	.005	.003
5	.010	.001	.005	.004
6	.001	.002	.005	.004
7	-.002	.004	.004	.004
8	-.004	.004	.004	.004
9	-.011	.005	.004	.004
10	-.013	.004	.006	.004
11	-.007	.003	.006	.005
12	-.014	.004	.005	.005
13	-.021	.005	.006	.005
14	-.013	.004	.006	.005
15	-.027	.004	.008	.005
16	-.025	.004	.009	.005
17	-.009	.003	.009	.006
18	-.021	.003	.010	.006
19	-.016	.003	.010	.006
20	-.016	.003	.009	.006

The probability of the hourly flood flows could be computed by
Eq. (24) if a computer of sufficient storage capacity would be available.
The probability curves so computed and to be plotted with flood flows vs.
time for various probabilities may be called "stochastic hydrographs."

1.10

Having computed the hourly rainfalls and flood flows, the hourly basin storages are computed by Eq. (11). For the computation of their probabilities, the basin storage at any given time t is given N = ›14 discrete states. The number of discrete states of the bivariate Markov process is K = MN = 10 x 14 = 140. The nonstationary transition probabilities of this process are computed by Eq. (18). The absolute probability of the bivariate system can be computed by Eq. (20), provided the initial probability distribution of $p_i(0)$, i = 1, 2, ..., K is specified. In this analysis, the initial probability distribution is assumed for 14 discrete states at 0.30; 0.25; 0.10; 0.05; 0.05; 0.05; 0.05; 0.03; 0.03; 0.02; 0.02; 0.02; 0.02; 0.01 for n = 1, 2, ..., 14 respectively. Other initial probability distributions could be also assumed for comparative studies. Finally, the probability of the basin storage is computed by Eq. (21). Figure 2 shows the curves for this probability at t of various times. These curves indicate that the basin storage process is nonstationary. The nonstationarity is more outstanding during the initial periods of the annual storm and particularly in very low states. As the time continues, the process appears to approach more or less stationarity.

A WATERSHED YIELD MODEL

In analysing the yield of a watershed, the year may be divided into twelve months and monthly values of precipitation, runoff, evapotranspiration, and basin storage are used in the analysis. As the time increment is relatively long, the evapotranspiration process cannot be ignored. The model may be therefore represented by Eq. (5). In this model, the component processes of precipitation, runoff, evapotranspiration and basin storage are treated as time series; i.e., $[X_t, Y_t, E_t, S_t; t \in T]$. The types of time series commonly used in hydrology are moving average, sum-of-harmonics, and autoregression such as a Markov chain [Dawdy and Matalas, 1964]. The choice of an appropriate time series for a given hydrologic process is not an easy task because the three models all exhibit fluctuations commonly observed on hydrologic data. One analytical approach which can help to select the best model is the analysis of the sample correlogram.

The correlogram is a graphical representation of the serial correlation coefficient r_k as a function of the lag k, where the values of r_k are plotted against respective values of k. The formula for the computation of r_k can be found in many books on statistics. The correlogram provides a theoretical basis for distinguishing among the three types of fluctuating time series. It has been proved analytically that if the time series is simulated by moving-average for random elements of extent m, then the correlogram will show a decreasing linear relationship and vanishes for all values of k > m. For the sum-of-harmonics, the correlogram itself is a harmonic with periods equal to those of the harmonic components of the time series and it will therefore show the same oscillations. In the case of autoregression, the correlogram will show a damping oscillating curve. In the case of a first-order Markov process with a serial correlation coefficient r_1, it will oscillate with period unity above the abscissa with a decreasing but nonvanishing amplitude if r_1 is negative [Dawdy and Matalas, 1964].

Another diagnostic tool for the analysis of time series in the frequency domain, which can help develop an appropriate time series for the hydrologic process, is the power spectrum analysis. From books on advanced statistics, an estimate of the power spectrum is given as

$$\hat{f}(\omega) = \frac{1}{2\pi} (C_o + 2 \sum_{k=1}^{T-1} C_k \cos k\omega) \qquad (25)$$

where C_k is the autocovariance for a time lag k. This estimate is called the "raw spectral estimate" because it does not give a smooth power spectral diagram. To adjust for the smoothness, it is common to use the "smoothed spectral estimate" in the form

$$\hat{f}(\omega) = \frac{1}{2\pi} [\lambda_o(\omega)C_o + 2 \sum_{k=1}^{m} \lambda_k(\omega)C_k \cos k\omega] \qquad (26)$$

where $\lambda_k(\omega)$ are selected weighting factors and m is a number to be chosen much less than T. A commonly used weighting factor is the "Tukey-Hamming" weights [Blackman and Tukey, 1959]:

$$\lambda_k(\omega) = 0.54 + 0.46 \cos \frac{\pi k}{m} \qquad (27)$$

where m is taken as less than T/10.

The significance of the spectrum is that it exhibits less sampling variations than the corresponding correlogram. Consequently, the estimated spectrum would provide a better evaluation of the various parameters involved in a time series. If the generating process contains periodic terms, the frequencies of these terms will appear as high and sharp peaks in the estimated spectrum and the height of the peaks will give a rough indication of the magnitude of variance from the data including these frequencies.

From Eqs. (25) and (26), the raw and smoothed spectral estimates may be written respectively as

$$L(\omega_t) = \frac{1}{2\pi} (C_o + 2 \sum_{k=1}^{m-1} C_k \cos \frac{\pi k t}{m} + C_m \cos \pi t) \qquad (28)$$

and

$$U(\omega_t) = \frac{1}{2\pi} (\lambda_o C_o + 2 \sum_{k=1}^{m-1} \lambda_k C_k \cos \frac{\pi k t}{m} + \lambda_m C_m \cos \pi t) \qquad (29)$$

Substituting Eq. (27) for the Tukey-Hamming weights in Eq. (29) and simplifying,

$$U(\omega_t) = 0.54 \ L(\omega_t)$$

$$+ \frac{0.23}{2\pi} [C_o + 2 \sum_{k=1}^{m-1} C_k \cos \frac{\pi k}{m}(t+1) + C_m \cos \pi(t+1)]$$

$$+ \frac{0.23}{2\pi} [C_o + 2 \sum_{k=1}^{m-1} C_k \cos \frac{\pi k}{m}(t-1) + C_m \cos \pi(t-1)] \qquad (30)$$

1 .12

As the raw spectral estimates can be represented by Eq. (28), Eq. (29) may be written as

$$U(\omega_t) = 0.23 \ L(\omega_{t-1}) + 0.54 \ L(\omega_t) + 0.23 \ L(\omega_{t+1}) \qquad (31)$$

Computer programs have been written to compute the smoothed spectral estimates by Eq. (31).

As a numerical example for the analysis, the watershed chosen as the hydrologic system is the upper Sangamon River basin of 550 sq. mi. in size, above Monticello, Illinois, and located in ease central Illinois. The areal average monthly precipitations in inches, based on data from six rain-gages at various locations and times in and around the watershed from September 1914 to September 1965, are used as the historical hydrologic inputs to the watershed system. The monthly streamflow records for the Sangamon River at Monticello, Illinois, are used as the historical hydrologic outputs of the watershed system extending from September 1914 through September 1965. The monthly potential evapotranspirations from September 1914 to September 1965 are computed by a method proposed by Hamon [1961] which has been tested in Illinois [Jones, 1966] with satisfactory results and the computation and the data requirement are rather simple.

Since the values of monthly precipitation X_t and monthly runoff Y_t are known from the historical records, it is obvious from Eq. (5) that if the record for the basin storage S_t were known then the record for the actual monthly evapotranspiration E_t could be easily established. On the other hand, if the record of E_t were known and an initial value of S_t were assumed, then the record of S_t could also be established. Unfortunately neither S_t nor E_t can be computed in a direct manner.

It is known, however, that in late September and early October of each year in Illinois the amount of surface water on the watershed and the soil moisture are at a minimum. Especially in the case of very low amount of precipitation during the months of August, September and October, the basin storage must be the lowest. This lowest amount of storage can be considered as the reference point of the basin storage. In other words, the basin storage is taken as zero at the beginning of the month of October of the year having very low precipitation during the months of August, September and October. In the present analysis, this happens to be the case of the year of 1914.

Once the initial stage of the basin storage is established, the following procedure may be followed to establish the records of basin storage and actual evapotranspiration:

If $S_{t-1} + X_t - Y_t \geq E_{pt}$ where E_{pt} is the potential evapotranspiration for the t-th time interval, then the actual evapotranspiration $E_t = E_{pt}$. Thus, the intiial storage S_t for the next time interval can be computed by Eq. (5).

If $S_{t-1} + X_t - Y_t < E_{pt}$, then $E_t = S_{t-1} + X_t - Y_t$ and Eq. (5) gives $S_t = 0$.

In the analysis, the stochastic processes of precipitation, basin storage and evapotranspiration may not be treated independently of each other but they are considered as a three-dimensional vector or a multiple time series, assuming:

(a) Each stochastic process consists of two parts; namely, one deterministic and the other random and uncorrelated to the deterministic part and the parts of other processes.

(b) The deterministic part of each stochastic process consists also of two parts; one part depending only on time and the other part depending on the vector of the stochastic processes of precipitation, basin storage and actual evapotranspiration at previous time intervals.

Based on the above assumptions, the first step is to determine the deterministic part of each process which depends on time. From the experience in hydrology and the exhibition of hydrologic data, the deterministic part appears to be a periodic function rather than a polynomial of time. Hence, the sample correlograms are computed for each process to test the existence of harmonic components in the process. In this analysis, T is the length of the records equal to 612 months and k is from zero to T/10, say 60. The correlograms for precipitation, basin storage and evapotranspiration are shown in Fig. 3. For all three processes these correlograms are oscillating without any indication of damping, thus revealing the presence of harmonic components in all the processes.

In order to determine the periods of the harmonic components, the power spectrum for each of the processes are computed by Eq. (31). The computed smoothed spectra for precipitation, basin storage and evapotranspiration are shown in Fig. 4. The sharp peaks exhibited in these spectra indicate a significant amount of the variance with the periodicities of 12-month and 6-month which are appropriate for use in the time series. The proposed model for the watershed system is a combination of the sum-of-harmonics and the autoregression time series. Since the results of the correlogram and spectral analyses indicate the presence of the 12-month and 6-month periodicities, the general model for the hydrologic stochastic processes may be written in the form

$$U_t = c_1 + c_2 \sin \frac{2\pi t}{12} + c_3 \cos \frac{2\pi t}{12}$$

$$+ c_4 \sin \frac{4\pi t}{12} + c_5 \cos \frac{4\pi t}{12} + U_t' \tag{32}$$

where c_1, c_2, c_3, c_4 and c_5 are the coefficients to be estimated and U_t' is the residual stochastic process with zero mean. The coefficients are determined by the least-square method. The term U_t' represents the residual stochastic process which may be assumed random with their means equal to zero.

With the hydrologic processes of precipitation, basin storage and evapotranspiration being determined, the runoff process may be formulated from Eqs. (31) and (32) as

$$Y_t = 0.8036 + 0.5024 \sin \frac{\pi t}{6} + 1.7778 \cos \frac{\pi t}{6} - 0.0303 \sin \frac{\pi t}{3}$$

$$+ 0.6064 \cos \frac{\pi t}{3} + 0.5786 \sin \frac{\pi(t-1)}{6} - 2.3821 \cos \frac{\pi(t-1)}{6}$$

$$+ 0.5583 \sin \frac{\pi(t-1)}{3} - 0.1366 \cos \frac{\pi(t-1)}{3} + X_t' - E_t' - (S_t' - S_{t-1}') \tag{33}$$

1.14

where X'_t, E'_t and S'_t are residual stochastic processes of X_t, E_t and S_t, which, as an approximation, are assumed uncorrelated to each other, but for further refinement of the model may depend on each other.

CONCLUSIONS

The analysis of the two stochastic watershed system models has demonstrated that hydrologic phenomena can be simulated by stochastic system models provided certain assumptions are to be made. In order to improve the system models, these assumptions have to be further modified and refined to meet the requirements of individual cases although certain refinement may be restricted by the increased effort of computation that will outstrip the computer capability. By means of stochastic hydrologic system models it becomes possible to quantify the hydrologic phenomenon and to generate stochastic hydrologic data. The stochastic hydrologic system models can be incorporated with economic and other relevant functions to form water resources system models, thus providing a rational basis for realistic and economic planning, design and operation of water resources projects. For instance, the annual storm-flood model may be found particularly useful in the study of flood-control projects and the watershed yield model may be used as a valuable tool to deal with water-supply and irrigation projects which may consider year long availability of water resources.

ACKNOWLEDGMENTS

This study is part of a continuing research program on stochastic hydrology directed by the author at the University of Illinois since 1962. Most hydrologic data used in the study were collected by Dr. S. Ramaseshan and Mr. Gonzalo Cortes-Rivera, and the analyses were performed largely by Drs. T. Prasad and S. J. Kareliotis. A portion of the study is the result of a research project on "Stochastic Analysis of Hydrologic Systems" sponsored by the U.S. Office of Water Resources Research and supported by funds provided by the U.S. Department of the Interior as authorized under the Water Resources Research Act of 1964, P.L. 88-379 Agreement No. 14-01-0001-1632.

REFERENCES

Blackman, R. B., and Tukey, J. W., "The Measurement of Power Spectra," Dover Publications, Inc., New York, 1959.

Chow, V. T., A general report on new ideas and scientific methods in hydrology (Simulation of the hydrologic behavior of watersheds), Proceedings, International Hydrology Symposium, Fort Collins, Colorado, 6-8 September 1967, pp. 50-65.

Chow, V. T., Hydrologic systems for water resources management, Conference Proceedings of Hydrology in Water Resources Management, Water Resources Research Institute Report No. 4, Clemson University, Clemson, South Carolina, March 1968, pp. 8-22.

Chow, V. T., Stochastic analysis of hydrologic systems, Research Report No. 26, Water Resources Center, University of Illinois, Urbana, Illinois, 1969; or P.B. No. 189791, Clearinghouse for Federal, Scientific and Technical Information, U.S. Department of Commerce, Springfield, Virginia, 1969.

Chow, V. T., Systems approaches in hydrology and water resources, in "The Progress of Hydrology," Proceedings, The First International Seminar for Hydrology Professors, Vol. 1, pp. 490-509, 1970.

Chow, V. T., and Ramaseshan, S., Sequential generation of rainfall and run-off data, Proceedings, American Society of Civil Engineers, Journal of Hydraulics Division, Vol. 91, No. HY6, pp. 205-223, July, 1965.

Dawdy, D. R., and Matalas, N. C., Analysis of variance, covariance, and time series, Section 8-III, Part III in "Handbook of Applied Hydrology," ed. by V. T. Chow, McGraw-Hill Book Co., New York, 1964, p. 8-85.

Hamon, W. R., Estimating potential evapotranspiration, Proceedings, American Society of Civil Engineers, Journal of Hydraulics Division, Vol. 87, No. HY3, pp. 107-120, May 1961.

Jones, D. M. A., Variability of evapotranspiration in Illinois, Illinois State Water Survey Circular 89, 1966.

Papoulis, A., "Probability, Random Variables, and Stochastic Processes," McGraw-Hill Book Co., 1965.

LIST OF SYMBOLS

a_t = a linear regression coefficient at time t.

b_t = a linear regression coefficient at time t.

C_k = autocovariance for time lag k.

c_t = nonstationary intercept of the linear regression line-of-fit.

c_1, c_2, c_3, c_4, c_5 = coefficients.

E_{pt} = potential evapotranspiration.

$E(s_t)$ = expected basin storage at time t.

E_t = total evapotranspiration plus other losses during t-th time interval.

f_t = transition probability of the bivariate process.

$\hat{f}(\omega)$ = raw estimate of power spectrum.

g_t = a transition probability function.

h_t = a transition probability function.

K = product of M and N.

k = time lag.

$L(\omega_t)$ = raw spectral estimate.

M = total number of discrete states.

m = a discrete state; upper limit of k.

N = total number of discrete states.

n = a discrete state.

p = probability function.

$p_i(t)$ = a probability function for i = 1, 2, ... at time t.

$p_{ij}(t)$ = transition probability of the bivariate process from state i at t-1 to state j at t.

$p_j(t)$ = a probability function for j = 1, 2, ... at time t.

r_k = serial correlation coefficient.

S_t = basin storage at time t.

s_t = variate of S_t.

s_{tn} = basin storage in state n.

T = index set of time, or time range under consideration.

t = time.

U'_t = residual stochastic process.

$U(\omega_t)$ = smoothed spectral estimate.

U_t = stochastic variable at time t.

X_t = input stochastic variable, or total precipitation during t-th time interval.

x_t = variate of X_t.

Y_t = output stochastic variable, or total runoff during t-th time interval.

y_t = variate of Y_t.

Z_t = the change of throughput in t-th time interval.

δ = discrete value of the state vector of the bivariate Markov process.

ε_t = random component of X_t.

$\lambda_k(\omega)$ = Turkey-Hamming weight.

λ_t = Markov or regression coefficient at time t.

σ_t = standard deviation at time t.

18

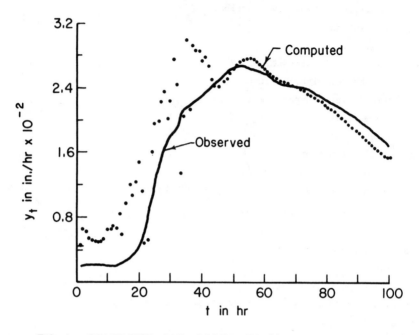

FIG. 1 COMPUTED AND OBSERVED HYDROGRAPHS FOR YEAR 1938

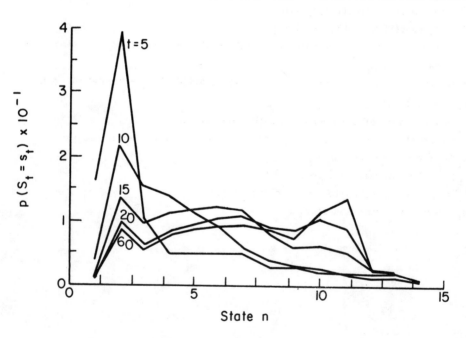

FIG. 2 PROBABILITY CURVES OF BASIN STORAGE

1.18

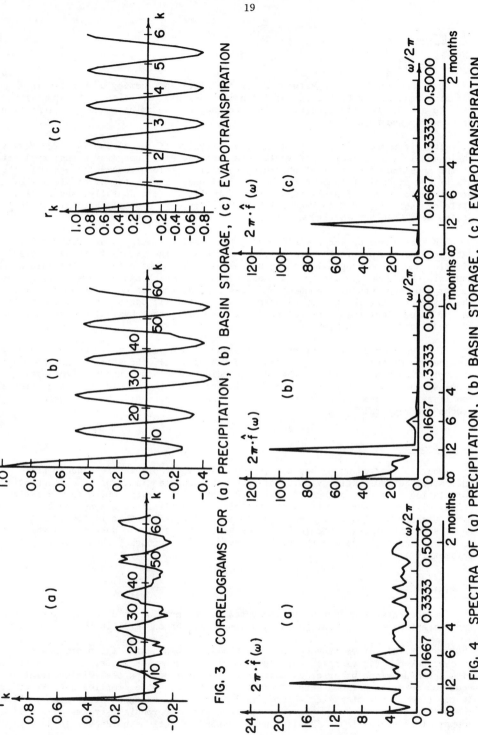

FIG. 3 CORRELOGRAMS FOR (a) PRECIPITATION, (b) BASIN STORAGE, (c) EVAPOTRANSPIRATION

FIG. 4 SPECTRA OF (a) PRECIPITATION, (b) BASIN STORAGE, (c) EVAPOTRANSPIRATION

DISCUSSION

J. W. DELLEUR

Dr. Chow is to be congratulated for the excellent summary of outstanding research done at the University of Illinois under his direction. The speaker would like to ask Dr. Chow to comment on the accuracy of the results and the limitations of the proposed models.

The first model is concerned with hourly value of annual storms. The Markov chain model is well known. It would seem that the difficulty for actual application of the model would be that of obtaining sufficiently long records to evaluate the transition probabilities both in the rainfall model and in the bivariate Markov process used in the rainfall-runoff transformation. (Incidentally, shouldn't the title of Table 2 read "The Transition Probability of the Hourly Rainfall in 10 States at t = 20 hr" instead of "in state 10 at t = 20 hr"?)

In the second or water yield model, the cyclic components are removed from the data in order to obtain the stochastic residuals of the rainfall, the evapotrans-piration and the conceptual storage processes. It is not clear why the harmonic analysis should not be limited to those components which can be physically explained as certainly the annual component and possibly the semi-annual component. It is true that by increasing the number of harmonics a better fit can be obtained, but it may be argued that this does not necessarily explain the physical process involved in the deterministic component.

The runoff model is expressed as the sum of a harmonic component obtained by a combination of the harmonic components of the rainfall, the storage and the evapo-transpiration plus the sum of the corresponding residuals. Has the stochastic model so obtained been compared to the simpler model that could be derived from the runoff series alone, by expressing it in terms of a periodic component and a stochastic residual?

P. S. EAGLESON

What is the reasoning behind your decision to ignore the reasonably well-understood deterministic dynamics of catchment behavior in favor of a stochastic formulation of system behavior? This requires, in order to duplicate the system's relatively long memory, very many transition probabilities and consequently a very difficult computational problem - not to mention the fact that it obscures the physics of the process. Would it not be better to model the determinism where it is strong and to introduce the system uncertainties through probabilistic system parameters?

C. KISIEL

My comments or questions are prompted by research on aridland streams. Perhaps the comments are irrelevant to the hydrologic situation in Illinois.

1. Useful information on the deterministic components of the process seem to be overlooked. For example, the one-step bivariate Markov process is not consistent with the hydrograph behavior as defined by the nonlinear partial differential equation describing flood wave movement. The lag-one model implies a first-order linear time-invariant system whose kernel function is an exponential decay. Visual inspection of many hydrographs even in temperate or perennial streams does not support this contention. Should linear response functions hold over large-time

intervals of months and years?

2. Randomness, in part, enters the process because the fresh excitation has a random time of occurrence and random amplitude. The latter information is a function of space-time precipitation and runoff processes. Once the disturbance at a station is observed, a first-order approximation would be to model it in a deterministic manner. A logical direction, it seems to me, for hydrologic research, would be to consider explicitly those factors that are "truly" random and those that are "strongly" deterministic in a useful manner.

3. The sum-of-harmonics process does seem to be a bit arbitrary for some hydrologic environments in that pure sinusoidals, when summed, simply reconstruct a large part of the seasonal pattern in the water yield model. Hence, the residual term may lack physical significance and simply be a fitting error term. In fact, some "negative flows" may arise in the subsequent use of the model for simulation purposes.

4. In the determination of S_t and S_{t-1} some deterministic hypotheses must be invoked. It is not clear that this quantity is an independently derived quantity.

5. What independent checks exist for predictions of the model? For example, were independent sets of field data used to evaluate model predictions either for simulation of equally-likely sequences or for short-term forecasting?

M. OKUTA

In the example of flood, the time unit of rainfall as input is the same as for discharge. Is it necessary to use the same time unit? I think, if the time unit of discharge is an hour, it may be better for the time unit of rainfall to be shorter than one hour, say 10 min., 20 min., or 30 min. During the heavy rainfall, the intensity may vary significantly during ten minutes or lower time intervals. The flood flow is produced by rainfall having high intensity variation, with response of basin to rainfall dependent on catchment and streams characteristics.

J. PAUL RILEY

1. In your presentation you suggested that the term watershed was not entirely satisfactory because it does not seem to imply subsurface storage. Perhaps the word "catchment" which is used extensively in the British literature might be a more definitive term in this regard.

2. Figure 1 does not show close agreement between observed and computed values in the rising portion of the hydrograph. Because of the random component in your model a close agreement would not necessarily occur.

3. The term "throughput" as used in the early part of the paper needs a little more consistent definition.

4. On the question of models which require large amounts of data, even though adequate computing capability might be available, there are other considerations, such as the time and expense involved in obtaining large values of field data even with telemetered data acquisition systems, which limit the amount of data which might be used in developing a model.

5. Your model is predictive in the sense that for a particular rainfall, the model can generate a range of flows for a given probability range.

6. It is realized that the model is still in the development stages but I am troubled by the rather minor consideration given to the deterministic component of

the model. For example, coefficients are evaluated for Equation 29 for a particular watershed by a fitting procedure to observed data. This approach, it seems, loses much of what we already knew about the system. For instance, it is no longer possible to readily predict changes system responses resulting from changes on the watershed. As Dr. Eagleson suggests, an alternative procedure is to incorporate fundamental and physically based processes into a quasi-deterministic model, and to include stochastic relations for the deterministic parameters of the model.

V. YEVJEVICH

The term "throughput" is not clearly distinguished from the fluctuation of the stored water inside the system. The variable Z_t is used both as the total throughput and later, after Eq. 4, as the rate of this throughput.

By using the Markov-chains approach for rainfall, with discrete states for the variable, the question arises how the number of selected states influence the final results.

Rainfall is considered in the text as a simple but nonhomogeneous Markov chain and the explanation given for this nonhomogeneity is that the hourly rainfall proces in a storm is a nonstationary process. It is difficult to find other reasons for this nonhomogeneity of Markov chains, or for the rainfall to be considered as a nonstationary process, except for the daily and yearly periodicities in parameters of rainfall data.

RESPONSE BY V. T. CHOW

The author wishes to thank all the discussers for their valuable comments and constructive discussions.

In response to Dr. Delleur's discussion, the accuracy of the results and the limitations of practically all hydrologic models depend on the reliability and quantity of the historical record which is used to fit the models. The proposed model is more refined than most models and is therefore suffering more of such limitations.

The harmonic analysis, like any simulation analysis, does not physically explain any natural process; instead it is used only to interpret the natural phenomena. If the physical process involved in the deterministic component were fully understood, then the physical law thus formulated could be used to explain the physical process.

If other comparative stochastic models were available, the proposed model could be compared with them.

In response to Dr. Eagleson's discussion, the knowledge of deterministic dynamics at present can only be used to describe the behavior of very simple catchments. When the complex and complicated behavior of natural catchments were fully understood, then the catchment behavior could be modeled or described by physical, chemical, biological, and any other laws that could be fully understood and formulated.

In response to Dr. Kisiel's discussion, the watershed flow cannot be compared with flood waves because the latter are confined only in the channel. Furthermore, the proposed model does not use either a kernel function or a linear convolution integral.

If we really know the truly random and strongly deterministic factors, then the proposed model should be modified accordingly.

The proposed model, like any simulation model, is in fact a fitting model. If we know the physical significance of the residual term, then it becomes deterministic and can be described by a physical law. If negative flows did occur, the model could be modified to eliminate them if necessary.

The quantity S_t is not an independently derived quantity, as it depends on previous quantities.

The proposed models have been just developed. As mentioned in the paper, further modification that may result from field applications and further research is possible.

The response to discussion by M. Okuta is as follows.

It is possible to modify the time units for the rainfall amount and the corresponding flood flows in order to meet a particular situation. However, the shorter the time unit the longer will be the computation time.

In response to Dr. Riley's discussion, my suggestion for a better term is "hydrological unit." The word "catchment" is commonly used as a drainage basin which does imply surface drainage but not subsurface storage.

Figure 1 does not have to show a close agreement between observed and computed values, because the computed values are randomly generated.

The paper clearly defined Z_t as the change of throughput in the t-th time interval and S_t as the basin storage or the total throughput at time t.

The question on large amounts of data applies to the use of any model which attempts to provide a refined simulation.

The proposed model, like any stochastic model, is predictive on a probability basis.

The proposed watershed yield model does give a major consideration to the deterministic component of the model by simulating it with harmonics. If fundamental and physical knowledge on the deterministic component were known, it could be used to substitute the harmonics.

In response to Dr. Yevjevich's discussion, the paper clearly defines Z_t as the change of throughput in the t-th time interval. The total throughput or the basin storage at time t is represented by S_t. Therefore, the change of throughput or the basin storage during the t-th time interval is equal to $S_{t+1} - S_t$.

In the Markov matrix computation, the number of selected states will influence the computation results in the same way as the number of digitized numbers will influence the results in any digital computer solution. The larger the number of selected states, or the larger the number of digitized values, more refined results will be obtained. However, the number of selected states is limited by the available data as well as the available computation time.

The nonhomogeneity of the hourly rainfall process in a storm is clearly demonstrated in Table 1 in which the parameters are shown to vary with time.

United States-Japan Bi-Lateral Seminar in Hydrology

Honolulu, January 1971

TRANSFORMATION SYSTEM IN FLOOD RUNOFF PHENOMENA

By

Tojiro Ishihara

Professor of Civil Engineering

and

Takuma Takasao

Assistant Professor of Civil Engineering

Kyoto University, Kyoto, Japan

Synopsis :

The purpose of this study is to generalize the flood runoff process in a river basin as a dynamical transformation system. On the basis of hydraulic study on rainwater behavior, the runoff process in a relatively small basin is classified and analyzed with a quasi-deterministic approach. As a result, three equivalent transformation systems are found to exist in the flood runoff process for various conditions of rainfall and basin surface. These systems nonlinear time invariant (NTI) in which the effective rainfall is equal to the rainfall excess; nonlinear time invariant (NTIc) varies spatially as well as timely; and nonlinear time variant (NTV) in which the area of runoff occurrence varies with time and the effective rainfall is the rainfall excess plus the maximum intensity of subsurface runoff over the area. For these three transformation systems, three fundamental patterns can be identified in actual runoff processes namely: NTI, NTIc and NTIc ~ NTV involving the system transformation. The characteristics of each pattern is analyzed, the transformation operator from rainfall to runoff is presented, and the significance of the nonlinearity of runoff is disclosed in the light of system dynamics. The results obtained in this research play an important role in runoff analysis of a river basin as small as several hundred square kilometers in size and may serve as a basis for a generalized runoff theory.

2 .1

1. Introduction

Since L.K. Sherman's study of unit-graph method in 1932, numerous studies on flood runoff caused by storm rainfall have been carried out by many researchers. All these studies can be classified into three groups: (1) empirical studies based on hydrologic data processing [1], (2) mathematical derivations based on the hypothesis of linearity such as that used in the unit-graph method [2, 3], and (3) theoretical analyses and syntheses of the runoff system by systems approach [4, 5, 6].

The authors have also studied the flood runoff systems based on hydraulic and systems concepts to be described below. In order to construct a generalized flood runoff theory, the hydraulic mechanism of rainwater within the whole runoff process, and the establishment of the interrelationships among the mechanisms and subsystems involved in a flood runoff system must be examined. This paper describes, as a part of the authors' study, the quasi-deterministic analysis of the transformation system from rainfall to runoff and the macroscopic law of the system.

Physically sepaking, the transformation system in the flood runoff phenomenon contains various sequential phases such as the averaging of rainfall over time and space, the infiltration of rainwater, and the rainwater flow near basin surface. In order to construct a universally valid theory of flood runoff, we assume the space invariant of rainfall. Furthermore, we focus our attention on the behavior of rainwater flow on the surface near the mountain slope, because it represents the basic phenomenon of a flood runoff, especially for the runoff of a relatively small basin. For these respects, various hydraulic mechanisms of rainwater flow and their relationships are described. As a result, the fundamental runoff patterns as generated from the interior hydraulic mechanisms are derived and their characteristics are discussed from a universal point of view.

---

[1]   Crawford, N.H., and R.K. Linsley: The Synthesis of Continuous Stream Flow Hydrographs on a Digital Computer, Dept. of Civ. Eng., Stanford Univ., 1962.

[2]   Nash, J.E. : The Form of the Instantaneous Unit Hydrograph, J. Geophys. Res., Vol. 64, No. 1, 1959.

[3]   Dooge, J.C.I. : A General Theory of the Unit Hydrograph, J. Geophys. Res., Vol. 64, No. 1, 1959.

[4]   Kulandaiswamy, V.C. : A Basic Study of the Rainfall Excess-Surface Runoff Relationship in a Basin System, Ph. D. Thesis directed by V.T. Chow, Univ. of Illinois., 1964.

[5]   Amorocho, J., and G.T. Orlob. : Nonlinear Analysis of Hydrologic Systems, Univ. Calif. Water Resources Center, Contribution. No 40, 1961.

[6]. Eagleson, P.S. : A Distributed Linear Model for Peak Catchment Discharge, Proc. Internat. Hydrology Symposium, IASH, Ft. Collins, Colo., USA Vol. 1, 1967.

2. Hydraulic mechanisms of subsystems in the flood runoff system

2-1. Prompt subsurface flow

A. Zone of hydrologic activity (A-layer).

The mountain slopes in a river basin can be classified primarily into two types according to their surface configuration: slopes covered with porous surface stratum that has high permeability such as in a well vegetated or well forested basin; and slopes having no porous surface stratum such as in a non-vegetated basin.

By field measurement of the soil moisture near basin surface, Dreibelbis found that the surface stratum has the depth of several decimeters and high porosity. He termed this "zone of hydrologic activity" because of the soil moisture variation [7]. The result of this measurement also confirmes the existence of A-layer which had been assumed by us as the major reason for the occurrence of prompt subsurface flow [8].

B. Prompt subsurface flow

Considering that the rate of rainwater that penetrates into the A-layer is usually more than several hundred millimeters per hour, all the rainwater falling on the surface will penetrate during the initial period of rainfall. Therefore, the rainwater supplied subsequently to the A-layer is equal to the rainfall excess.

By using the equations of continuity and dynamics of flow, in which the law of Darcy is applied, the fundamental equation of prompt subsurface flow can be written as follows [9]:

$$kH\frac{\partial^2 H}{\partial x^2} + k\left(\frac{\partial H}{\partial x} - \sin\theta\right)\frac{\partial H}{\partial x} - \gamma\frac{\partial H}{\partial t} = -r_e \tag{1}$$

in which k is the coefficient of permeability, γ the non-capillary porosity, H the flow depth, θ the inclination angle of the slope, x the distance from the upstream end of the slope, t the time, r_e the rainfall-excess intensity defined as $r_e = r - i$, r the rainfall intensity, and i the infiltration rate into the sub-stratum under the A-layer. Equation (1) is a nonlinear partial differential equation of advective diffusivity. Since it can be assumed in an actual river basin that $\partial H/\partial x /\sin\theta \ll 1$, Eq. (1) will approximately become a quasi-linear equation. Moreover, the diffusion term can be ignored in the equation, because it can be shown from the approximate solution of second order that the order of diffusion term is less than of the advection term [9]. Under these assumptions, the approximate solution of Eq. (1) is given as below.

---

[7]   Dreibelbis, F.R.: Some Aspects of Water shed Hydrology as Determined from Soil Moisture Data, Geophys. Res., Vol. 67, No. 9, 1962.

[8]   Ishihara, T. and Takasao, T.: A Study on the Subsurface Runoff and Its Effects on Runoff Process, Trans. JSCE, No. 79, 1962 (in Japanese).

[9]   Takasao, T.: Occurrence Area of Direct Runoff and Its Variation Process, Rep. DPRI, No. 6, 1963 (in Japanese)

On the characteristics

$$\chi - \chi' = f \cdot (t - t') \tag{2}$$

the following relation must be satisfied:

$$\gamma H = R_e(t) - R_e(t') \tag{3}$$

In the above equations, χ' and t' are the values of coordinates representing the initial point of characteristics on the $\chi - t$ plane, $f = (k/\gamma)\sin\theta$, and $R_e(t) = \int_0^t r_e(s)ds$. The non-capillary porosity γ seems to be independent of the intensity of rainfall and the time. After studying the experimental results obtained from the laboratory tests at Kyoto University on runoff by the use of artificial rainfall and characterized by the soil structure [10].

2-2. Effective rainfall and occurrence area of overland flow

The effective rainfall should be defined as the rainfall which supplies the overland flow effectively, and the occurrence area of overland flow as the area in which the overland flow occurs over the A-layer. These are two elemental factors in the runoff process, which must be both evaluated; namely, the soil condition of a slope and the rainfall condition.

For a slope with no A-layer, the intensity of effective rainfall r_f is equal to that of rainfall excess r_e, and the occurrence area of overland flow F is the whole drainage area A. For a slope with A-layer, the runoff phenomenon becomes considerably complicated, and two different phases of runoff will occur, depending on whether or not the water surface in the A-layer reaches its limit. This limit is given from Eqs. (2) and (3) by the following relation:

$$R_e(t) - R_e\left(t - \frac{L}{f}\right) = \gamma D \tag{4}$$

in which L is the length of the slope and D the thickness of the A-layer. This simple relation is very important as will be explained in the next chapter, and may be called the transition condition of the system change.

If the value of the terms on the left hand side of Eq. (4) is always less than γD, the overland flow may occur only in temporary streams or gullies distributed on the slope. The effective rainfall which supplies the overland flow is equal to the sum of the rainfall excess which directly supplies the streams and the seepage of rainwater from the saturated zone of the A-layer into the overland flow. The average intensity of effective rainfall r_f per unit area, for practical purposes of runoff analysis, is given as

$$r_f = \frac{1}{A}\left(A_e r_h + A_o r_e\right) \tag{5}$$

in which $A_e = 2NL_d H$, where N is the number of temporary streams per unit area, L_d the average length of the streams, r_h the seepage rate of rainwater to the streams, and A_o the area covered by the streams. Defining the effective rainfall as that given by Eq. (5), it must be noted that the occurrence area

---

[10]   Takasao, T. and Kishimoto, S.: An Experimental Study on the Runoff Process of Rainfall, Rep. DPRI, No. 4, 1961 (in Japanese).

of overland flow is replaced by the whole drainage area, and that the average intensity of effective rainfall r_f varies from point to point corresponding to the water depth H in the A-layer. The runoff in this regime is called the subsurface runoff.

If the rainfall intensity becomes greater and the condition, $H \leq D$, is not maintained, the overland flow occurs also over the A-layer. The occurrence area of overland flow over the A-layer varies with time, corresponding to the variation of the intensity of rainfall excess. The distance ξ_o from the upstream end of a slope to the initial point of occurrence area is, using Eqs. (2) and (3),

$$R_e(t) - R_e(t - \frac{\xi_o}{f}) = \gamma D ,$$

$$\xi_o < L \tag{6}$$

The A-layer under the occurrence area of overland flow must be fully saturated and, therefore, $r = r_e$ within this region. Accordingly, by the condition of continuity, the occurrence area of overland flow becomes

$$F = (1 - L_r)A , \qquad L_r = \frac{\xi_o}{L} \tag{7}$$

2-3. Overland flow

Since the overland flow on the mountain slope is assumed to be approximately uniform, the equations of motion and continuity become, respectively.

$$h = K q^p \tag{8}$$

$$\frac{\partial h}{\partial t} + \frac{\partial q}{\partial x} = r_f \tag{9}$$

in which h is the water depth of overland flow, q the discharge rate per unit width, and

$$K = (\frac{n}{\sqrt{\sin\theta}})^p \tag{10}$$

In Eq. (10), n is the Manning roughness coefficient and p the numerical constant equal to 0.6. The applicability of the Manning formula to overland flow has been ascertained by laboratory tests carried out at Kyoto University and other places, but the value of n varies widely with the surface condition of the slope. According to the experimental results, the value of n for overland flow on a bare slope or a temporary stream distributed over the surface stratum is 0.01~0.03 ($m^{-\frac{1}{3}}$.sec) and the value on a vegetated surface is 0.3~0.4 ($m^{-\frac{1}{3}}$ sec). This difference of n due to the surface condition is remarkable [10].

Applying the theory of characteristics to Eqs.(8) and (9), the solution is as follows [11], [12]. On the characteristics

$$x - \xi = \frac{1}{pK} \int_{\tau}^{t} ds \left[\int_{\tau}^{s} \frac{I_f}{K} dz + \{ g(\xi, \tau)^p \} \right]^{\frac{1}{p} - 1} \tag{11}$$

the following relation must be satisfied:

$$g = \left[\int_{\tau}^{t} \frac{I_f}{K} ds + \{ g(\xi, \tau)^p \} \right]^{\frac{1}{p}} \quad \text{or} \quad g = \int_{\xi}^{x} I_f dz + g(\xi, \tau) \tag{12}$$

in which $g(\xi, \tau)$ is the discharge rate at the point (ξ, τ) , which represents the starting point of characteristics under consideration on the $x - t$ plane. Letting $\xi = \xi_0$, Eqs. (11) and (12) give the desired solution for overland flow on the A-layer mentioned earlier.

3. Flood runoff pattern and its characeristics

By the hydraulic mechanism of rainwater flow on a mountain slope as explained above, the runoff process of storm flood in a river basin can be classified from the view point of symbolic dynamics and analyzed in a quasi-deterministic way [13].

3-1. Runoff process and transformation system

The storm-runoff process is stochastic and the transformation from rain-fall to discharge at a gauging station constitutes an ensemble of stochastic transformations. This ensemble has a non-deterministic property which in-volves a certain regularity or law as the ensemble averages over time and space.

Thus, the time change of direct runoff, dQe/dt , at a gauging station in any river basin may be represented by the following nonlinear stochastic functional form:

$$\frac{dQ_e^p}{dt} = g \left[(I_f(t) - \frac{d\tau}{dt} I_f(\tau))/K , \int_0^t P(Q_e, E, t : t') E(t') dt' \right] \tag{13}$$

The first term in the functional form in Eq.(13) can be derived form Eq.(12). It expresses the influence of effective rainfall I_f , within a certain finite time interval $(t - \tau)$, on the time change of the discharge rate at the present state. The finite time-interval varies with time because of the nonlinearity of overland flow and the variation property of the occurrence area of direct runoff. This time change of the time-interval plays an important role in explaining the fundamental characteristics of runoff process as it will be explained later.

[11]   Ishihara, T. and Takasao, T.: Fundamental Researches on the Unit Hydrograph Method and Its Application, Trans, JSCE, No. 60, Extra Papers (3-3), 1959 (in Japanese).

[12]   Wooding, R.A.: A Hydraulic Model for the Catchment Stream Problem, J. Hydrol., Vo. 3, 1965.

[13]   Ishihara, T. and Takasao, T.: A Study on Runoff Pattern and Its Characteristics, Bull, DPRI, No. 65, 1963

The following relation is obtained form Eqs.(11) and (12):

$$\frac{d\tau}{dt} = 1 - \frac{d}{dt}\left\{K(L - \xi_c(\tau))^b\left(\int_\tau^t f(s)\,ds/(t-\tau)\right)^{b-1}\right\} \qquad (14)$$

Let us call this, $d\tau/dt$, "lag change".

The second term in the functional form in Eq. (13) may be regarded as the departure from the time change of discharge rate determined by the first term, which has a certain statistical distribution. The characteristics of this distribution may depend on the entire history of the runoff, especialy on the geometric characteristics of a channel distribution; and the statistical variables may have some interrelation with each other. For these considerations, the second term representing the statistical departure from the first term is expressed formally in Eq.(13), in which the statistical vector E , changing with time, has a certain probability p influenced by the state in the past, the statistical vector and the present time.

Although the transformation system from rainfall to discharge is stochastic, the first step in determining the system structure is to find out the equivalent systems in respect to dynamics, and to understand the mechanism and the characteristics of these systems by the deterministic way which is suggested implicitly in the first term in the functional from in Eq.(13). The statistical evaluation of the departure from the determination by the first term constitutes the second step, which is meaningless without performing the first step.

Thus, in subsequent sections, the approach to runoff analysis is quasi-deterministic, and L and K in Eqs.(4) and (10) are defined as the representative values of a basin.

3-2. Equivalent transformation system

From the mathematical point of view, the system of transformation from a physical state or quantity, such as input I_e , to another state or quantity, such as output, Q_e , may be generally represented by the following differential--difference equation of the functional form:

$$\sum_{i=0}^{N} a_i \frac{d^i Q_e}{dt^i} = g\left[\sum_{i=0}^{N-1} b_i \frac{d^i I_e}{dt^i}, \sum_{i=0}^{N-1}\sum_{j=0}^{N} c_i \frac{d^i I_e(t-t_j)}{dt^i}, t\right] \qquad (15)$$

$$0 \leq t_o < t_1, \cdots\cdots < t_j < t_{j+1} < \cdots\cdots < t_n$$

in which N and n are integers; a_i , b_i and c_i the coefficients; and $t-t_j$ the time-interval.

The transformation system is characterized by coefficients, a_i , b_i and c_i , and by the difference between time-intervals, $t_{j+1} - t_j$, in Eq.(15). Thus, four equivalent transformation systems, in respect to dynamics, can be classified as follows:

    (i)   Linear time-invariant system (LTI)
            a_i, b_i, c_i and $(t_{j+1} - t_j)$ = const.
    (ii)   Linear time-invariant system (LTV)
            a_i, b_i, c_i or $(t_{j+1} - t_j) = f_n(t)$
    (iii)   Nonlinear time-invariant system (NTI)
            a_i, b_i, c_i or $(t_{j+1} - t_j) = f_n(Q_e, dQ_e/dt)$
    (iv)   Nonlinear time-variant system (NTV)
            a_i, b_i, c_i or $(t_{j+1} - t_j) = f_n(Q_e, dQ_e/dt, t)$

These classifications may be suitable to a quasi-deterministic system such as runoff phenomena, and can be understood physically depending upon (a) whether the character of a system varies with time(LTV and NTV)or not (LTI and NTI), and (b) whether it is influenced by the input, such as the intensity of rainfall(NTI and NTV), or not(LTI and LTV).

Since the characters of the four transformation systems classified above are essentially different from each other, the determination of the interior dynamic structure in the runoff process must be based upon the clear classification of the equivalent transformation systems of runoff to be determined by the basin characteristics and the rainwater flow behavior.

The runoff process in an actual basin varies with the conditions of both the surface soil and the rainfall, as stated in the previous chapter. In a river basin with no A-layer, no prompt subsurface flow occurs, and the occurrence area of runoff phenomena does not vary with time. Therefore, the transformation system in such a basin is time invariant. On the other hand, in a river basin with A-layer, two different conditions may arise, depending upon whether or not the occurrence area of surface runoff is limited in the temporary streams, and the transition condition is given by Eq.(4). Furthermore, the effective rainfalls for the two conditions are different from each other in their evaluation. In addition, since the numerical constant p in Eqs.(10), (11) and (12) is equal to 0.6 for overland flow, each dynamic transformation system of runoff is nonlinear.

Table 1 shows the result of the above discussion on the equivalent transformation system of runoff, representing the relation between the surface stratum condition and the transformation system. In this table, $\overline{f_h}$ represents the average seepage rate f_h over the area, $\overline{f_a}$ is $(f_h)_{max}$, and NTI_c system represents the region of subsurface runoff, in which subscript c shows that the effective rainfall f_f varies with time and space.

3-3. Runoff pattern

Because of the existence of three equivalent transformation systems, as shown in Table 1, three fundamental patterns in runoff process result, as tabulated in Table 2. Subscripts e , i and s of Q represent the values of direct runoff, subsurface runoff and surface runoff, respectively. When NTV transformation system develops it is always associated with NTI_c system as shown as($NTI_c + NTV$) in Table 2.

Fig. 1 shows the runoff patterns and the transformation systems schematically. The actual runoff process is always in the area enclosed by the solid line, in any basin and under any condition of rainfall. The area covered by the dotted line, LTI , is the system in which the method of runoff analysis based on linear time-invariant assumption such as unit-graph method is valid.

NTI pattern occurs in a basin with no A-layer($D=0$)such as a barren basin, in which the dynamic property is relatively simple. However, a basin with no A-layer is scarcely ever found among the usual mountain basins.

Mountains are generally well vegetated, and have a A-layer stratum ($D>0$). The runoff process in such basins is very complicated, and the system analysis plays a particularly vital role. If the transition condition given by Eq.(4) is not satisfied, the system and the runoff pattern are both NTI_c . If the transition condition is satisfied, but the runoff pattern is$NTI_c \sim NTI$, the transformation systems change as $NTI_c \rightarrow (NTI_c + NTV) \rightarrow NTI_c \rightarrow (NTI_c + NTV) \cdots \rightarrow NTI_c$, in which the arrows represent the system transition as shown in Fig. 1.

Thus, the broken line in Fig. 1 may be called "the window of system transition". The number, the time positions, and the size of the window greatly influence the configuration of runoff, particularly during a flood, and are determined by using the transition condition of Eq.(4).

3-4. Lag as transformation operator

The runoff pattern depends on the character of the transformation system, in which the most fundamental factor is the lag. Here, the lag must be defined as the transformation operator in physical significance, which relates rainfall to discharge. With this consideration, the time-interval $(t-\tau)$ of the propagation of disturbance on the characteristics represents the lag determined by the interior structure of each pattern of overland flow defined by Eqs.(11) and (12), because the discharge rate at any time and any point on the $x \sim t$ characteristic plane can be essentially calculated by using the effective rainfall r_f during the time-interval $(t-\tau)$. That is, putting $T_c = t - \tau$, the discharge rate of direct runoff Q_e can be expressed from Eq.(13) as follows:

$$ Q_e = (F/T_c) \int_{T_c} r_f \, dt \tag{16} $$

Therefore, the lag T_c becomes the transformation operator.

Next we will discuss the lag in some detail. The elapsed time at a gauging station of discharge may be on the whole classified into two domains, depending upon respectively whether or not the disturbances created at the upstream end of a representative slope reach the station. The former domain may be defined as disturbance domain $(D. D.)$ and the latter as non-disturbance domain $(U. D.)$. Further $(U. D.)$ and $(D. D.)$ are each divided into two domains depending upon whether the effective rainfall is supplied entirely or partly to the characteristics representing the rainwater disturbance. These two domains are marked by the subscripts I for entirely supplied and II for partly supplied.

Denoting the time which expresses the boundary between $(U.D.)$ and $(D.D.)$ by t_s , and the time which represents the cessation of effective rainfall by t_e the relation between t and the corresponding τ becomes as follows [from Eqs.(11) and (12)]:

For $t \leqq t_s \, ((U.D.)_I \; or \; (U.D.)_{II})$ $; \; \tau = 0$

For $t_s \leqq t \leqq t_e \, ((D.D.)_I)$ $: \; t - \tau = K \{ L - \xi_o (\tau) \}^p / r_{tm}^{1-p}$ (17)

For $t_e < t \, ((D.D.)_{II})$ $: \; (t_e - \tau)^{1/p - 1} \{ (t - t_e) + p (t_e - \tau) \}$

$$ = p K^{1/p} \{ L - \xi_o (\tau) \} / r_{fm}^{1/p - 1} \tag{18} $$

in which

$$ r_{tm} = \int_\tau^t r_f \, dt / (t - \tau) \quad , \quad r_{fm} = \int_\tau^t r_f \, dt / (t_e - \tau) $$

In these equations the origin of time must be taken at the initial time of each transformation system. Fig. 2 shows the transformation patterns.

3-5. Representative values of basin characteristics

A question will arise concerning the characteristics of representative values of basin, L and K . These values are the criteria of a basin representing the length and the effect of roughness and inclination angle of a basin, respectively. Each value is to be divided into two parts, representing respectively,

the mountain slope and the channel. This division of L may be independent
of K , and vice versa, because of their physical significance. So, the
subscripts b and c to the values will be used for the mountain slope and
channel, respectively.

L_b , K_b and L_c , K_c determine not only the lags in the mountain slope
and the channel but also the discharge rate at a gauging station as expressed
by Eq.(16). Therefore, the effects of mountain slope and channel on the runoff
relation can be evaluated from a comparison of each lag.

For the sake of simplicity, we will discuss here the case of the time
domain $(D.D.)_I$ in NTI system. It must be noted that we compare the two lags,
t_b and t_c , corresponding to the same part of rainfall as shown in Fig. 3.
From Eq.(17) corresponding to $(D.D.)_I$ in NTI , t_b and t_c are expressed as
follows:

$$t_b = K_b L_b^p / r_{tm}^{1-p} \tag{19}$$

$$t_c = K_c L_c^p / g_m^{1-p} \tag{20}$$

in which $K_c = \{n_c (sin\theta_c)^{-1/2} K_1^{3/2}\}^p$, and $p = 3/(2Z+3) \approx 0.6$, supplemented
with the hydraulic radius R equal to $K_1 A_c^Z$ and the cross-sectional area
And g_m , being the discharge rate per unit width of slope averaged over t_c ,
must be represented as follows, for the reason mentioned before:

$$g_m = r_{tm} L_b \tag{21}$$

Consequently, the effects of mountain slope and channel on the runoff relation
is expressed in the form of the ratio of the two lags, using Eqs.(19), (20)
and (21); that is,

$$S_t = t_c/t_b \approx K_c L_c^p / K_b L_b \tag{22}$$

Since S_t is influenced only by the basin characteristics but not by the
rainfall condition, we can define S_t as an important non-domensional value
which represents the relation between the characteristics of a basin and the
runoff.

Using Eq.(22), it can be seen that the value of S_t is considerably
smaller than unity in a river basin less than several hundred square kilo meters
in area, and that it is not necessary to take account of the effect of stream
channels on the runoff pattern, because of the fact that $p = 0.6$ and $K_b > K_c$,
which are derived from the experimental results on overland flow as stated in
the previous chapter.

Thus, we may consider that the representative values of a basin, L and
K , are mainly influenced by the characteristics of the mountain slope.
Assuming a quasi-uniform distribution of mountain slope characteristics, it may
be possible to analyze the runoff process from the universal point of view by
using the results in previous section.

If the value of S_t is not less than unity, such as in a larger basin, we
are forced to take account of the effect of stream channels even in the quasi-
deterministic sense. A study of this hydrologic problem is now in progress.

3-6. Characteristics of runoff pattern and the peak flow

It has been explained previously that the lag is the fundamental factor
representing the character of the transformation system. Accordingly the characters of individual runoff patterns can be visualized through investigation of

the characteristics of the lag. In this regard we will discuss briefly the characters of runoff patterns, especially the peak flow, and show some examples of application.

A. Nonlinearity

First of all, the nonlinearity of runoff phenomenon depends on the order of the time variation of T_c as transformation operator, and can be evaluated from the structure of the lag change $d\tau/dt$ as defined by Eq.(14).

If the lag change is always zero in the entire time domain at a gauging station, the propagation velocity of rainwater flow is constant and the transformation system is time invariant. In this case, a method of runoff analysis based on the assumption of linear time-invariant, such as the unit-graph method, becomes an effective tool. The actual runoff phenomenon, however, is not linear, as stated in previous sections. Accordingly, the evaluation of nonlinearity is very important for the flood runoff, especially in a small **basin**, because of the nonlinear effects of channel storage and other factors. The larger the time-variation of lag change becomes, the stronger the effect of nonlinearity results. As a result, the linear relationship between rainfall and discharge is unsatisfactory and the method of runoff analysis becomes very complicated.

The nonlinearity of the NTI pattern depends only on the nonlinearity of the overland flow. The effective rainfall f_f is equal to the rainfall excess f_e and there is substantially no effect on distributing them, so that the time variation of the effective rainfall is larger than that of NTI_c . Moreover, since the roughness for overland flow is usually small in a basin having the NTI system, the nonlinear effect is very strong. This is the reason why the runoff is very intense in such a basin.

In a basin with surface stratum, either NTI_c or $NTI_c \sim NTV$ pattern will appear depending on the rainfall condition.

As the rainwater falling on a ground is stored temporarily in the A-layer for NTI_c , the range of time-variation of f_f is small. For this reason, the effect of nonlinearity appears to be relatively weak.

The transformation systems for the $NTI_c \sim NTV$ pattern pass through the windows which represent the system transition from NTI_c to $(NTI_c \sim NTV)$, and vice versa. Hence the nonlinearity of the $NTI_c \sim NTV$ pattern depends on the nonlinear characters of overland flow and the system change. Since the index of the occurrence area of overland flow, $\xi_c(\tau)$, corresponding to the $(NTI_c + NTV)$ system acts to increase the nonlinear character of the runoff process, the configuration of runoff changes radically at the window and, therefore, the nonlinear character of system change becomes most important in the $NTI_c \sim NTV$ pattern.

As mentioned above, the nonlinear structure of runoff phenomena is very complicated even in the case of $S_t \ll l$, owing to the deviations of rainfall and basin characteristics. By the system approach stated in previous sections, however, it may be possible to disclose the structure and to obtain the basic knowledge by which we may discuss the applicability of many methods for runoff analysis hitherto presented, and construct a new method from the view point of dynamics.

B. Peak flow

a) Peak flow

Next we will discuss the relationship between the peak discharge and its lag. According to the approach in previous sections, the time of peak t_p at a gauging station must be in the time domain $(D.D.)_I$, if $(D.D.)_I$ develops. If $(D.D.)_I$ does not develop, t_p is to be in the domain $(U.D.)_{II}$, and may appear near the boundary of $(U.D.)_{II}$ and $(D.D.)_{II}$ because the potential energy of water stored in channels may become maximum at this time. The peak for the pattern of NTI_c or $NTI_c \sim NTV$ is always the former case. The latter case seldom arises in the NTI pattern and the significance of the concentration time usually used as a criterion of the lag of peak flow becomes suitable in this case only.

The peak t_p for the $NTI_c \sim NTV$ pattern must be in $(D.D.)_I$ for the $(NTI_c + NTV)$ system, and the occurrence area F of overland flow on the A-layer varies with time. It is convenient for a practical runoff analysis to assume that the area is constant and equal to the whole area A of a river basin and that the average intensity of side-seepage from the surface stratum, being the maximum value $\bar{I_a}$ of the effective rainfall I_f in NTI_c, is converted to the variant quantity I_v. This conversion can be given by the condition that the same discharge appears at the same time in both gauging stations of the variant field F and the constant field A. Using Eqs.(11) and (12), I_v becomes approximately, in the neighbourhood of the peak of runoff,

$$I_v = \bar{I_a} - L_r(I_e + \bar{I_a})\qquad(23)$$

In the $NTI_c \sim NTV$ pattern, replacing the effective rainfall I_f by the equivalent effective rainfall I_f^* after putting $F = A$, the peak discharge of this pattern can be evaluated easily since

$$I_f^* = I_v + \bar{I_a}\qquad(24)$$

The above replacement of the effective rainfall can be applied to NTI_c, because the change of the occurrence area of overland flow in NTV is equivalent physically to that of the depth of the stored water in the A-layer in NTI_c. In this case, however, L_r is not the one determined by Eq.(7) but a length representing the variation of the stored water depth. For these considerations, L_r applicable to the two patterns for $D > 0$ is expressed as follows [14], from the continuity condition and the simple assumption on the configuration of stored water depth:

$$L_r \doteq \varphi(t)^{-1}\left(\int_0^t b\varphi(s)ds\right)\qquad(25)$$

in which $\varphi(t) = exp(-\int_0^t a\,dt)$, $a = 2(1/\gamma D)(I + \bar{I_a})$ and $b \doteq 2(1/\gamma D)(\bar{I_a} + i)$. Although the above treatment of the equivalent effective rainfall I_f^* is theoretically not strictive, it seems convenient practically, especially in the analysis of the runoff from a rainfall which has a complicated hourly distribution. The values of $\bar{I_a}$ and γD of the basin can be estimated by the following relations derived by the hydraulic procedure on the recession curve of the subsurface runoff.

$$\left. \begin{array}{l} \gamma D = \{e^{\lambda_2(t_2-t_1)} i_c/\lambda_2\} \\[2mm] \bar{I_a} = (1-\delta)\lambda_2 \gamma D \end{array} \right\}\qquad(26)$$

in which λ_2 is a constant, t_2 and t_1 are the cessation times of subsurface runoff and surface runoff, respectively ($t_1 = t_d$, the cessation time of rainfall, for no surface runoff), i_c is the final infiltration capacity, and $\delta = A_\circ/A$. In NTI_c, $I_f = I_e$.

Using Eqs.(11) and (12) and inserting the equivalent effective rainfall r_f^* , the occurrence condition of the peak of runoff for $(v.v.)_I$ is

$$(dT_c/dt)_{t=t_p} = 0 \qquad (27)$$

The relation between the initial time τ_p and the arrival time t_p of the characteristics is

$$r_f^*(\tau_p) = r_f^*(t_p) \qquad (28)$$

Fig.4 is the schematic representation of Eq.(28). Accordingly, the arrival time interval T_{pc} on the characteristics concerning the peak discharge becomes, from Eq. (17), as follows:

$$\left. \begin{aligned} T_{pc} &= KL^p/r_{mp}^{1-p} \\ \\ r_{mp} &= \int_{T_{pc}} r_f^* dt/T_{pc} \end{aligned} \right\} \qquad (29)$$

Discontinuity of the $T_{pc} \sim r_{mp}$ relation may arise in the neighbourhood of $r_{mp} = \bar{f_a}$, because the significance of L_r is different for NTI_c and $(NTI_c + NTV)$. The maximum discharge rate of runoff Q_{ep} is given by

$$Q_{ep} = r_{mp} A \qquad (30)$$

When the time of peak t_p is in $(v.v.)_{II}$ of the NTI system, the lag corresponding to the peak flow is equal to the concentration time. Using Eq.(18), putting $\tau = 0$ and $\xi_o = 0$, t_p is given by

$$t_p = pLK^{1/p}/R_e(t_d)^{1/p-1} + (1-p)t_d \qquad (31)$$

in which t_d is the duration time of rainfall excess. The maximum discharge is expressed as follows, ignoring the final infiltration capacity:

$$Q_{ep} = A R_e(t_d)/t_d \qquad (32)$$

b) Applications

Some applications of the theory on peak flow are shown by several examples in this paper. Example I is an application to many flood runoffs in one basin, and Example II to runoffs in many basins in which runoff patterns seem to be the same.
  (i) Example I (Peak flow of Yura River basin at ONO)
  The upstream part of the Yura River basin above ONO gauging sation (Kyoto Prefecture) is 346 km^2 in area and 40 km in length of the main channel and is well vegetated. From these basin characteristics, St is less than unity and the runoff pattern shows NTI_c or $NTI_c \sim NTV$ for any rainfall condition.
  Using the relation of Eq.(26), the values of $\bar{f_a}$ and r_D for this basin are estimated as 6 mm/hr, and 120 mm, respectively [14]. Applying these values to Eq.(25), r_f^* are calculated from Eqs.(23) and (24). Applying the occurrence condition of peak flow, Eq.(28), to r_f^* , the relations of $T_{pc} \sim r_{mp}$ and $Q_{ep} \sim r_{mp}$ are obtained as shown in Figs. 5 and 6. The calculated values are in

---

[14] Ishihara, T., Ishihara, Y., Takasao, T. and Rai, C.: A Study on the Runoff Characteristics of Yura River Basin, Rep. DPRI, No. 5B, 1962 (in Japanese).

good agreement with the theoretical relation expressed by the solid line in the figures. It is remarkable that the discontinuity of the $T_{pc} \sim \bar{r}_{mp}$ relation occurs in the neighbourhood of $\bar{r}_{mp} = \bar{r}_a$, and the theoretical estimation of the system transition stated in the previous article is verified.

(ii) Example II (Peak flows of many basins in Illinois)

Morgan and Johnson selected twelve river basins located in Illinois, with areas ranging from 10 to 101 square miles, and obtained their runoff data in order to determine their unit graphs [15]. The following conditions for the runoffs in the selected basins may be possible: (1) St is less than unity, (2) the basins have surface stratum as in an usual mountainous basin, and (3) as the value of δD of a usual basin is in the range from 100 to 150 mm, the patterns of the runoffs shown in Table 3 are NTI_c , and are simple cases because $ft_d \ll L$. From these assumptions, the time interval $t_p - t_d$ can be expressed as follows by modifying Eq.(17):

$$ t_p - t_d = K L^p (Q_{ep} A^{-1})^{1-p} \tag{33} $$

Assuming a uniform distribution of the mountain slope characteristics, the values of $K L^p$ for the selected basins are not so different. Fig. 7 shows the relation between $t_p - t_d$ and $(Q_{ep} A^{-1})^{0.4}$, using values in Table 3. This result indicates that the assumptions mentioned above and Eq.(33) are good.

4. Conclusions and discussion

In this paper, the storm runoff during a flood has been described as a transformation system from rainfall to discharge, and it has been pointed out that three fundamental patterns exist in the runoff process and their characteristics are mainly determined by the nonlinearity and the variation properties of the occurrence area of runoff phenomena. The results obtained in this paper play an important role in the runoff analysis of a river basin as small as several hundred square kilometers in area. In a larger basin, we still face the problem of the effects of channels distributed in the river basin on the flood runoff process in an even quasi-deterministic manner.

A study on the flood runoff process and its theoretical modeling in a channel distribution system will be presented at the discussion time of this seminar.

[15] Morgan, E.P. and Johnson, M.S.: Analysis of Synthetic Unit-graph Method, Proc. ASCE, HY5, 1962.

Supplement Paper "A Suggested Approach to Flood Peak Runoff Process in Channel Distribution System" by Tojiro Ishihara and Takuma Takasao.

The paper "Transformation Systems in Flood Runoff Phenomena" discusses the transformation system of the flood runoff in a relatively small basin, in which the parameter St , representing the ratio of the lag time of the mountain slope and to that of the stream is smaller than unity. In a larger basin, however, the effect of the stream flow in the channels distributed over a river basin on the flood runoff process should be considered additionally. We would like therefore to take this opportunity to briefly discuss this problem. The basic idea is that the flood hydrograph near the peak at a gaging station can be estimated through both the network structure of the channel distribution and the confluent process of peak flows.

Channel distribution system and flood peak

The channel distribution system can be represented by a set of the ordered channels C_u ; i.e., $\{C_1, C_2, \cdots C_u, \cdots C_k\}$, in which C_u is the set of channels of order u , C_1 is the unit cells and C_R is the channel of trunk number k .
C_u is also the set of the channels classified by the confluent number i, and can be expressed as $C_u = \{\sum_{i=1}^{N_u-1} (_iC_u)\}$, in which $_iC_u$ is the channels of order u having the confluent point number i and N_u the number of the channels of order u.
From the view point of the flood runoff analysis, C_u is the transformation system in which the input is the output from C_{u-1} and it is transfered to become the output C_u , or the input to C_{u+1} .
When we assume the output from C_1 , as a set of impulses, the transformation process of C_u $(u=2,3,\cdots,k)$ is the compound event consisting of the topological property of C_u , the distribution of the metric values of C_u , and the confluent process of the peak pulses in C_u . Then, the flood peak from C_u , which is the set of pulses, becomes a pulse function on time domain by the compound event and equals the flood hydrograph near the peak.

Stochastic property of channel distribution

1) Channel distribution laws.

Three statistical laws on the structure of the ordered channels have been proposed as follows [1];

$$\frac{1}{4} law : N(C_u)/N(C_{u+1}) = 4$$

$$\frac{1}{2} law : N(_iC_u)/N(C_u) = (1/2)^i, \quad (i=1,2,\cdots, N_{u-1})$$

$$\frac{3}{4} law : N(_vC_u)/N(C_u) = \frac{3}{4} \cdot \left(\frac{1}{4}\right)^{v-u-1}, \quad (v=u+1, u+2, \cdots k)$$

where $N(C_u)$, $N(_iC_u)$ and $N(_vC_u)$ are the number of the channels of order u, the number of the channels of order u having the confluent point number i, and the number of channels of order u joining the channels of higher order than $(u+1)$, respectively.

[1]   Ishihara, T. Iwasa, Y. and Takasao, T; Stochastic Study of Channel Distribution in River Basins, Proc. IHS, September 1967.

2) Statistical characteristics of network and metric value.

The values of the expectation and the variance of the network can be obtained by the statistical laws for channels:

$$E(N_{u+1}(C_u)) = 3$$
$$Var(N_{u+1}(C_u)) = 2 \tag{1}$$

The most important metric value of a basin is the catchment area with respect to the flood runoff. By the definition, the catchment areas A_u and A_{ui} corresponding to C_u and iC_u are expressed as

$$A_{u+1} = \{A_{u+1}, i\} = \{ja A_u\} \tag{2}$$

where j is the number of A_u joining iC_{u+1} and a is a parameter which is equal to $R_a/3$ (R_a is the area ratio).

Then, the probability density function $P(A_{u+1})$ of A_{u+1} , which is a compound distribution consisting of the statistical laws of channel network and the distribution property of A_u , can be expressed as follows :

$$P(A_{u+1}) = \sum_{i=1}^{N_u-1} P(n=i) \cdot p((i+1)a A_u) \tag{3}$$

From Eqs. (2) and (3) and the statistical law of compound distribution, the expectation and the variance of A_{u+1} become

$$E(A_{u+1}) = E(j) E(a A_u)$$
$$= 3 E(a A_u) \tag{4}$$
$$Var(A_{u+1}) = Var(j) E^2(a A_u) + Var(a A_u) \cdot E(j)$$
$$= 2 E^2(a A_u) + 3 Var(a A_u)$$

and the variation coefficient of A_{u+1} , or C_{Au+1} , is

$$C_{Au+1} = \sqrt{\frac{2}{9} + \frac{1}{3} C_{Au}^2} = \sqrt{\frac{1}{9}(1-(\frac{1}{3})^{u-1}) + (\frac{1}{3})^{u-1} C_{A_1}^2} \tag{5}$$

Correspondence of flood peak to its time

The expectation of the peak value and its occurrence time of the output pulse function from C_u , $E(g_{pu})$ and $E(\tau_{pu})$, can be obtained, considering the confluent process of the pulse within C_u , as

$$E(g_{pu}) = a(2 + P_{u-1}) E(g_{pu-1})$$
$$E(\tau_{pu}) = E(\tau_{pu-1}) + 2 E(\tau_{u-1}) \tag{6}$$

2.16

where p_{u-1} is the confluent ratio of the pulses within C_u and $E(\tau_{u-1})$ is the mean propagation time of the peak pulses of the intervals of the confluent points within C_u, $E(\tau_{u-1})$ can be represented as follows by the kinematic wave theory:

$$E(\tau_{u-1}) = p \, \overline{\ell}_{u-1} \cdot \overline{K}_{u-1} / E^{1-p}(g_{pu}) \qquad (7)$$

in which p = 0.6, $\overline{\ell}_{u-1}$ is the mean interval length of confluent points within C_u, and $\overline{K}_{u-1}$ is

$$\overline{K}_{u-1} = (\overline{n}_{u-1} \cdot \overline{S}_{u-1}^{2/3} / \sqrt{\sin \overline{\theta}_{u-1}})^p \qquad (8)$$

where $\overline{n}_{u-1}$, $\overline{S}_{u-1}$ and $\sin \overline{\theta}_{u-1}$ are the mean of the roughness coefficient, the hydraulic radius, and the slope of C_u, respectively.

(2) Relationship between g_{pu} and τ_{pu}

Assuming $p_u \doteqdot 1$, the peak and its occurrence time of output from $_iC_{u+1}$, $g_{pu+1, i}$ and $\tau_{pu+1, i}$ can be expressed as

$$g_{pu+1, i} = (i+1) \, a \, g_{pu}$$
$$\tau_{pu+1, i} - \tau_{pu} = i \, E(\tau_u) \qquad (9)$$

From the above equations, the relationship of g_{pu} and τ_{pu} is represented aproximetely by

$$g_{pu+1} = \gamma_{u+1} \, \tau_{pu+1} + \beta_{u+1}$$

where $\gamma_{u+1} \doteqdot E(g_{pu})/E(\tau_u)$ $\qquad (10)$

$$\beta_{u+1} = (1 - \frac{E(\tau_{pu})}{E(\tau_u)}) - E(g_{pu})$$

The above relationship is based on the assumption of the same velocity of the peaks within $_iC_u$ $(i=1,\cdots N_{u-1})$, which is a linear piece-wise assumption. According to this assumption, the relationship of g_{pu} and τ_{pu} becomes linear and biunique.

(3) Variance of pulses.

The magnitude of the pulse function g_{pu} is the set of output pulses from $_iC_u$, i.e. $g_{pu+1} = \{ g_{pu+1, i} \}$. Then the probability density function of the set of the pulses is, assuming $p_u \doteqdot 1$,

$$P_r(g_{pu+1}) = \sum_{i=1}^{N_u-1} (\frac{1}{2})^i P_r((i+1) \, a \, g_{pu}) \qquad (11)$$

2 .17

From the above equation, the variance of $\mathcal{G}_{pu+1}$ becomes

$$Var(\mathcal{G}_{pu+1}) = 2E(a\mathcal{G}_{pu}) + 3\,Var(a\mathcal{G}_{pu}) \qquad (12)$$

Further, we can get the relationship between the variances of $\mathcal{G}_{pu+1}$ and $\mathcal{T}_{u+1}$ as follows, from Eq.(10):

$$Var(\mathcal{G}_{pu+1}) = \eta_u^2 \, Var(\mathcal{T}_{pu+1}) \qquad (13)$$

By this relationship, the variance of the magnitude can be expressed on a time domain.

Hydrograph near the peak

We may assume that the density functions of $\mathcal{G}_{pu}$ and A_u are nearly the same, considering the correspondence of both values. Further, since it has been known that the density function of A_u is lognormal, we may assume that the density function of $\mathcal{G}_{pu}$ near the peak of pulse function is normal for the sake of convinience. From these assumptions and the linear and biunique relationship of $\mathcal{G}_{pu}$ and $\mathcal{T}_{pu}$, the pulse function on the time domain can be expressed as follows:

$$\mathcal{G}_{pu} = E(\mathcal{G}_{pu}) \cdot Exp\left\{-(\mathcal{T}_{pu} - E(\mathcal{T}_{pu}))^2 / 2\,\sigma_{\mathcal{T}_{pu}}^2\right\} \quad (14)$$

This function is equal to the hydrograph near the peak. The standard deviation $\sigma_{\mathcal{T}_{pu}}$ is the effective width of Eq.(14) on the time domain, and so Eq.(14) should be considered as the shape of hydrograph within $|E(\mathcal{T}_{pu}) - \mathcal{T}_{pu}| \leq \sigma_{\mathcal{T}_{pu}}$.

The sharpness of the hydrograph is represented by $\sigma_{\mathcal{T}_{pu}} / E(\mathcal{G}_{pu})$ as a measure:

$$\sigma_{\mathcal{T}_{pu}} / E(\mathcal{G}_{pu}) = \sigma_{\mathcal{G}_{pu}} / \eta_u \cdot E(\mathcal{G}_{pu}) \qquad (15)$$

$$= C_{Au} / \eta_u = (R_L / R_K R_a^{2-b})^{u-2} \cdot C_{Au} / \eta_2$$

where R_L is the stream length ratio, $R_K (= \bar{K}_u / \bar{K}_{u+1})$ the roughness, and R_a slope ratio.

The above relationship may be sewed as a basis of the analysis of the channel distribution effect on the flood peak. The above approach to the analysis of the flood runoff system is still in progress, and its application to the flood control practice by the grouping the dams is also continuing.

LIST OF SYMBOLS

A : Drainage area

A_c : Cross-sectional area

A_e : Occurrence area of the subsurface runoff, $2 N \cdot L_d \cdot H$

A_o : Area covered by the temporary streams

a : is equal to $2(\frac{1}{p_D})(r + \bar{r}_a)$

b : is equal to $2(\frac{1}{p_D})(\bar{r}_a + i)$

Subscript b : to values used for the mountain slope

Subscript c : to values used for the channel

D : Thickness of the A-layer

$(D.D)_I$ or : Disturbance domain which the effective rainfall is supplied
$(D.D)_I$ entirely or partly

E : Statistical vector

F : Occurrence area of overland flow

f : Constant, $(\frac{K}{f}) \sin \theta$

H : Flow depth

h : Water depth of overland flow

i : Infiltration rate into the sub-stratum under the A-layer

i_c : Final infiltration capacity

K : Constant, representing the effect of roughness and inclination
    angle in a basin, $(\frac{n}{\sqrt{\sin \theta}})^r$

L : Length of the slope

L_d : Average length of the streams

L_r : Ratio of L to ξ_o

LTI : Linear time-invariant system

LTV : Linear time-variant system

N : Number of temporary streams per unit area

NTI : Nonlinear time-invariant system, in which the effective rainfall
    is equal to the rainfall excess

NTI_c : Nonlinear time-invariant system, in which the effective rainfall
    varies with time and space

NTV : Nonlinear time-variant system

n : Manning roughness coefficient

p : Numerical constant equal to 0.6

Q_e : Direct runoff

Q_{ep} : Maximum discharge rate of the direct runoff

q : Discharge rate per unit width

R : Hydraulic radius, $K_1 A_c^z$ (k_1, z, constants)

2.19

$R_e(t)$: Integral of the rainfall excess intensity, $\int_o^t r_e(s)ds$

r : Rainfall intensity

$\bar{r}_a$: Maximum value of the effective rainfall r_f in NTI_c

r_e : Rainfall excess intensity

r_f : Intensity of effective rainfall

r_f^* : Equivalent effective rainfall after putting $F=A$

r_h : Seepage rate of rainwater to the streams

r_{mp} : Average intensity of the equivalent effective rainfall within the arrival time interval T

r_v : Variant quantity, representing the apparent intensity of the subsurface runoff

S_t : Ratio of the two lags of mountain slope and channel, t_c/t_b

T_c : Lag time, $t - \tau$

T_{pc} : Arrival time interval on the characteristics concerning the peak discharge

t : Time

t_d : Duration time of excess rainfall

t_e : Cessation time of effective rainfall

t_p : Time of peak at a gauging station

t_s : Time which expresses the boundary between (U.D) and (D.D)

t_1 : Cessation time of surface runoff

t_2 : Cessation time of subsurface runoff

$(U.D)_1$ or : Non-disturbance domain which the effective rainfall is supplied
$(U.D)_x$ entirely or partly

x : Distance from the upstream end of the slope

x',t' : Values of coordinates representing the initial point of characteristics on the $x - t$ plane

$\phi(t)$: is equal to $\exp(-\int_o^t a\,dt)$

λ_2 : Recession coefficient of the subsurface runoff

κ : Coefficient of permeability

γ : Non-capillary porosity

θ : Inclination angle of the slope

ξ_o : Distance from the upstream end of a slope to the initial point of occurrence area

δ : Ratio of A to A

Table I. Classification of equivalent transformation system in runoff process.

Condition of surface stratum			Transformation system
$D=0$	$\xi_0=0,$	$r_f=r_e$	NTI
$D>0$ $\left\{\begin{array}{l}\\\\\end{array}\right.$	$\xi_0=0,$	$r_f \doteqdot \overline{r_h} = A e r_h A^{-1}$	NTI_c
	$\xi_0=f_n(t,r),$	$r_f=r_e+\overline{r_a}$	NTV

Table 2. Fundamental runoff patterns derived from transformation system

Transformation system				Runoff pattern
NTI	$\xi_0(\tau)=0,$	$F=A$	$Q_e=Q_s$	NTI
NTI_c	$\xi_0(\tau)=0,$	$F=A$	$Q_e=Q_t$	NTI_c
$NTI_c \rightarrow (NTI_c+NTV)$ $\rightarrow NTI_c \cdots\cdots \rightarrow NTI_c$	$\left\{\begin{array}{l}\xi_0(\tau)=0,\\ \xi_0(\tau)=f_n(t,r),\end{array}\right.$	$\begin{array}{l}F=A,\\ F=(1-\\ L_r(\tau))A,\end{array}$	$\begin{array}{l}Q_e=Q_t\\ \text{(for } NTI_c)\\ Q_e=Q_s\\ \text{(for NTV)}\end{array}$	$\left.\begin{array}{l}\\\\\\\end{array}\right\}$ $NTI_c \sim NTV$

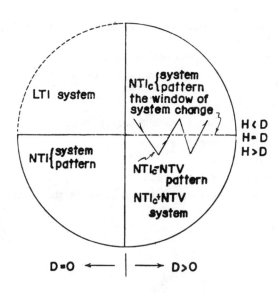

Fig.I. Diagram representing the relation of equivalent transformation systems and runoff patterns.

2 .21

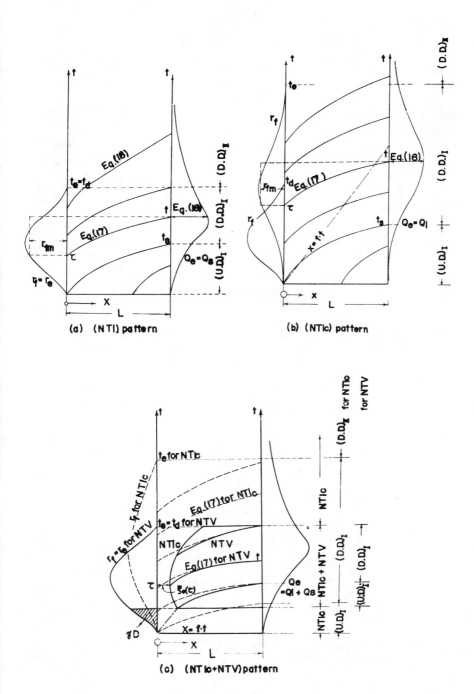

Fig. 2. Schematic representation showing the characteristics
of transformation system in each pattern.

2.22

46

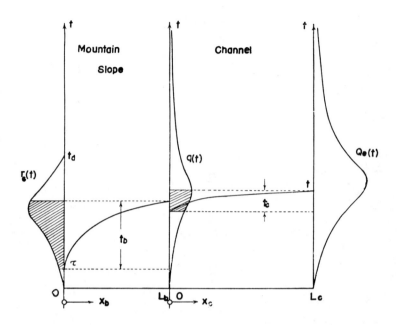

Fig. 3. Schematic representation showing propagation states of rainfall
disturbance on mountain slope and channel, for NTI system.

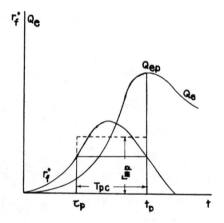

Fig. 4. Schematic representation illustrating the relation between equivalent
rainfall, the occurring time of maximum discharge, and the propagation
time of peak flow T_{pc} .

2.2^3

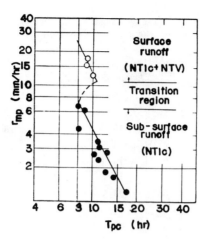

Fig.5. Relation between the propagation time of peak flow and mean intensity of equivalent rainfall at ONO in Yura River basin.

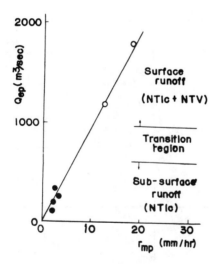

Fig.6. Relation between the maximum discharge of direct runoff and mean intensity of equivalent rainfall,at ONO in Yura River basin.

48

Table 3. Characteristics of selected basins and runoffs
(After Morgan and Johnson).

Basin No.	Name	A, in square miles	L_c, in miles	t_d, in hours	t_p, in hours	Q_{ep}, in cubic feet per second
1.	Hickory Creek	10.1	4.9	1	2.0	1040
2.	Canteen Creek	22.5	10.1	1	3.0	2530
3.	Big Creek	32.2	15.6	2	10.0	1570
4.	Indian Creek	37.0	18.8	2	12.0	1700
5.	Pay Creek	39.6	11.7	1	5.0	4010
6.	Money Creek	45.0	23.8	2	16.0	1280
7.	Farm Creek	60.9	17.3	1	3.0	9350
8.	Mill Creek	62.5	19.9	1	8.0	4920
9.	W. Br. Salt Fork	71.4	16.8	2	12.0	2140
10.	Hadley Creek	72.7	16.8	1	4.0	9430
11.	W. Bureaue Creek	83.3	19.6	2	4.0	5730
12.	E. Bureau Creek	101.0	23.3	2	4.0	5740

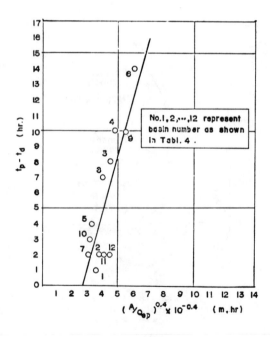

Fig.7. Relation between the maximum discharge of direct runoff and
its occurence time, for twelve river basins in Illinois.

2 .25

DISCUSSION

V. T. CHOW

I assume that the term "quasi-deterministic" has the same or similar meaning as the term "quasi-stochastic" which is used in my paper.

The use of kenimatic-wave theory and the one-dimensional hydro-dynamic equations is a first approximation to the watershed system. At the University of Illinois we are using two-dimensional high-order hydro-dynamic equations which provide a better model for the type of watersheds commonly encountered in the United States.

According to the experimental data obtained at the University of Illinois,* we found that Manning's roughness coefficient is inadequate for overland flows. Therefore, a new parameter describing the overland flow roughness should be developed and introduced in the analysis.

---

*T. E. Harbaugh and V. T. Chow, "A Study of the Roughness of Conceptual River Systems or Watersheds," Proceedings, XIIth Congress of the International Association for Hydraulic Research, Sept. 11-14, 1967, Fort Collins, Colorado, U.S.A., pp. 9-17.

P. S. EAGLESON

Do I understand that you recommend the use of the kinematic wave method for catchments in which the ratio of "overland" flow to streamflow characteristic times is less than one? In such cases the streamflow predominates in the system behavior and we are talking about floodrouting. This is just the type of situation for which the kinematic wave method is least applicable since it does not account for the dispersion of the flood wave as it moves down the river.

C. KISIEL

1. Deterministic models of the runoff process are apparently proposed as a basis for reducing the amount of data required about the transformation mechanisms. Stochastic models, on the other hand, tend to rely on the available data and rather simple lumped model hypotheses. Deterministic models tend to require more data about detailed space-time variation of parameters (roughness, permeability, slope, transitions from one flow regime to another, porosity, points of initiation of overland flow, and so on). Given this premise, how important in the authors' view is the tradeoff (in economic terms) between the cost of getting the required data to implement the deterministic models and the accuracy of model predictions (in relation to managerial use of the predictions)?

2. How variable would the graph in Figure 5 be if a sample of 20 to 50 different storms were analyzed?

RESPONSE BY T. TAKASAO

The response to discussion by V.T. Chow is as follows.

The use of kinematic wave theory and the Manning's roughness coefficient, we would like to point out our basic approach for constructing the runoff model. First, the transformation system of flood runoff should be mainly constructed

2 .26

from two subsystem which are the plane or the mountain slope system and the channel network system. Thus, the flood runoff system becomes multidimensional. Next, the flood runoff model should contain the main hydrodynamic propagation processes such as surface flow and subsurface flow. For these two points, the important thing for the construction of the flood runoff model are the evaluation of the relative effects to the total system of the subsystems or the propagation processes and of the lumped scale of the subsystems; the order of the equation is not so important. Manning's formula is only a rough approximation of the flow resistance, and Manning's coefficient is a stochastic parameter. In our laboratory experiments on the overland flow useing artificial rainfall equipment Manning's formula agreed well with the resistance law of the observed overland flow on the different bed conditions. Part of the overland flow on the natural basin surface, however, may do not follow the Manning formula. However, from the results of our experiment and using the meaning of Manning's formula mentioned above, we believe Manning's formula as applied to the overland flow in the total flood runoff system is applicable.

The response to discussion by P. Eagleson is as follows.

The comment on the limitation of the kinematic wave method is quite correct. The concept of kinematic wave is appropriate for the construction of a total runoff system model that consists of many river segments and the variances of the channel network structure, where the metric values of the river basin dominate the dispersion effect of the stream flow in a channel. (See discussion paper "A suggested approach to flood peak runoff process in channel distribution system".) To analyze the flood flow itself in a channel which is an element or subsystem of the runoff system, the dispersion effect of the stream flow should be considered and the high order hydrodynamic equation should be treated.

The response to discussion by C. Kisiel is as follows.

It is not easy to answer the question about the trade off between the cost and the time collecting the data and the accuracy of the model, but this problem may be very important in a real river project and should be studied. Next, the question about the meaning of Figure 5 is not so important because the slope of the real line in this figure is theoretical.

2 .27

United States-Japan Bi-Lateral Seminar in Hydrology
Honolulu, January 1971

THE STRUCTURE OF INPUTS AND OUTPUTS OF HYDROLOGIC SYSTEMS*

by Vujica Yevjevich

Professor-In-Charge, Hydrology and Water
Resources Program, Civil Engineering
Department, Colorado State University,
Fort Collins, Colorado, USA

Synopsis

A brief analysis leads to the conclusion that all water inputs and outputs of
hydrologic environments are periodic-stochastic processes. To make a basic
structural analysis of hydrologic processes possible, ten hypotheses are given.
Complex hydrologic processes of inputs and outputs, such as river flow and precipitation time series, are composed of periodic components in several parameters
and an independent stochastic component. Periodicities in the mean and standard
deviation may or may not be proportional. Techniques for making inferences about
significant harmonics are outlined for both cases. Non-parametric and parametric
methods of removing these periodicities from a series are given and the autocorrelation coefficients of standardized series are shown to be periodic also.
To obtain the independent stochastic components of the second-order stationarity,
periodicities in the mean, standard deviation, and autocorrelation coefficients
can be removed. Complex hydrologic series are not third-order stationary either.
The shapes of distributions of stochastic independent components for discrete
series of small time units (say one day) require the fitting of probability density
functions of an unfamiliar type to hydrology.

THE STRUCTURE OF INPUTS AND OUTPUTS OF HYDROLOGIC SYSTEMS

1. Introduction

Hydrologic environments are places on earth where liquid, gaseous, or solid
forms of water, as inputs and outputs, may be stored. Boundaries and initial
conditions of environments must be clearly defined whenever a systems approach is
used to study their responses. The inputs and outputs as time series (or space-
frozen time processes), and the interior properties of environments as they change
in space and time (or time-frozen space processes and the changing responses with
time) are defined as hydrologic processes. In the water cycle, oceans and seas
can be considered hydrologic environments that supply water to the atmosphere and
thus to continents and receive the return precipitation and continental surface and
subsurface runoff. The atmosphere also can be considered a hydrologic environment
with moisture inputs and outputs. Continental surfaces, underground acquifers,
inland bodies of water, plants, and soils are environments with complex water inputs,
environmental compositions, responses, and outputs.

This environmental trinity, input - response - output, in combinations, mutual
dependences and feedbacks is defined as the hydrologic system. When investigations

*The research project "Hydrologic Stochastic Processes," from which this paper is
produced, is supported by the U.S. National Science Foundation, Grant GK-11444.

consider this trinity they represent the systems approach to analysis of hydrological processes and environments.

Because energy inputs, storage, and outputs of all environments are basic causative factors determining the water processes along the water cycle, the general characteristics of water cycle must closely follow the characteristics of energy inputs, storage and outputs. Considering just energy, all hydrologic environments are closed systems except the solar radiation input to the earth and earth irradiation into the space. Practically speaking the solar energy input over a unit area of given orientation at the uppermost atmosphere is a deterministic periodic process. Without atmosphere, a river basin of given orientation and position would receive the potential daily energy, as demonstrated in Fig. 1 for five watersheds, which all are deterministic periodic processes.[1] However, the measurements of radiation income at a unit area shows a deterministic periodic and a stochastic combination. The stochastic part is produced by the randomness in atmospheric transparency (or opacity) for incoming solar radiation, with this transparency a periodic-stochastic space and time process. The irradiation of earth to space is a periodic-stochastic process, much of which consists of stochasticity. All other energy inputs and outputs are in closed systems, namely any energy output of an environment is an energy input to another environment. Thus, for water processes, all hydrologic environments are closed systems, with water output of one environment input into another. Because energy inputs and outputs decide when and where water is going along the water cycle, all hydrologic time processes must be periodic-stochastic processes.

Hydrologic environments can be considered completely natural, natural with a minimum of man-made effects such as rural river basins, natural with significant man-made effects such as urban river basins, and predominately man-made systems with several man-made reservoirs, conveyance structures, controls, etc. All transitions exist from a natural to a predominately man-reshaped environment. Inputs, environmental properties, responses, and outputs may be similarly classified. This paper is concerned with natural environments, though the approach and conclusions can be extended to any other environment, including time series of water uses, highly controlled by man.

Hydrologic inputs and outputs are either liquid, gaseous, or solid water, or their combinations, dissolved matter in water either as solids or gases, suspended matter in flowing water, and materials carried along with water at its liquid-solid and liquid-gaseous interfaces, such as bed load, air entrainment, etc. In a systems approach to analyzing hydrologic processes and environments it is useful to well define inputs and outputs.

Hydrologic data and information contained in data should be distinquished as well as the hypotheses underlying the extraction of information from data and methods used for this extraction. The subject of this paper are the hypotheses that are justified for the analysis of hydrologic inputs and outputs, as well as the methods used to extract and describe the information.

[1] Lee, Richard, Evaluation of Solar Beam Irradiation as a Climatic Parameter of Mountain Watersheds, Colorado State University Hydrology Paper No. 2, August 196

3.2

2. General hypotheses

Hydrologic experience, hydrologic environmental analysis of energy and water fluxes, the geophysical history of environments, and the structure of environmental responses lead the writer to postulate 10 hypotheses for the structural analysis of hydrologic input and output processes, for no analysis and mathematical description of these processes can be better than the underlying hypotheses.

(1) Continuous hydrologic time processes are periodic-stochastic, in which the deterministic astronomic periodicities introduce the cyclicity in parameters of these processes, while various sources of randomness in environmental responses introduce the stochasticity.

(2) Nearly all random variation (noise) of a process is allocated to the independent stochastic component, while only the randomness as sampling errors within the estimated parameters is left in periodic components and the stochastic dependence models. Periodicities as deterministic functions (signals) are only in certain parameters (mean, variance, autocorrelation coefficients, skewness and kurtosis coefficients, etc.). For any parameter, ν, its periodicity in a process $x_{p,\tau}$ presented as a discrete series is defined as

$$\nu_\tau = \mu_\nu + \sum_{j=1}^{m} C_j \cos \left(\frac{2\pi j \tau}{\omega} + \theta_j \right) , \tag{1}$$

in which ν_τ is the value of ν at a position τ, $\tau = 1,2,\ldots,\omega$, with ω the basic period (year, day); μ_ν is the mean of ω values of ν_τ of the $x_{p,\tau}$-process, $p = 1,2,\ldots,n$ with n the number of periods ω in the series (n equals the years or days in an observed series); m is the total number of harmonics with amplitudes C_j significantly different from zero out of $\omega/2$ possible harmonics in the periodic process; j denotes the sequence of significant harmonics, and θ_j is the phase of the j-th harmonic. In estimating ν_τ by sample values v_τ of the periodic parameter ν, and fitting Eq. (1) to v_τ by computing the significant C_j-values, the v_τ-ν_τ differences, as sampling variations, become part of the stochastic component.

The opposite hypothesis is

$$\nu_\tau = \mu_\nu + \sum_{i=1}^{s} C_{p,\tau}^i \cos \left(\frac{2\pi \tau i}{\omega} + \theta_{p,\tau}^i \right) , \tag{2}$$

in which $C_{p,\tau}^i$ and $\theta_{p,\tau}^i$ are random variables inside harmonics of a periodic parameter, and s is the number of harmonics, each with a random amplitude and random phase. This hypothesis is disregarded, however, because it complicates the understanding and description of parameter variation inside the period ω, and it introduces too many usually mutually dependent random variables. Figure 2 shows daily means as a ν_τ parameter, with the periodic component of Eq. (1) and $m = 5$, and the periodic component of Eq. (2) and $s=1$, for a wet, average, and dry year of the Merced River at Pohono Bridge, Yosemite, California.

(3) By removing from the series the periodic-deterministic components in the most important parameters, the hypothesis is that the stochastic component can be made stationary. If periodicities in the mean, standard deviation, and autocorrelation coefficients are removed, the remaining stochastic component becomes second-order stationary. If all periodicities in parameters of third-order are removed, the stochastic component becomes third-order stationary, and so on for higher orders.

(4)   Non-homogeneity (mainly man-made) or systematic errors (inconsistency) are identified, described, and removed prior to the structural analysis of input, output and response processes.

(5)   Methods of analysis are such that the sampling biases, long-range sampling trends, sampling cyclicity, unrepresentative extremes for the sample, etc. have a minimum effect on information extracted from data in the form of mathematical models and their estimated parameters.

(6)   When feasible, regional hydrologic information is used to improve models and increase the accuracy of estimated parameters in extracted information of an individual series.

(7)   The reliability of methods should not depend on the selected time units of discrete series, say whether the series has one-day, 3-day, 7-day, 14-day, 1-month, or a 3-month time unit.

(8)   The models and estimated parameters contain nearly all statistical information that a sample can produce.

(9)   In the models the number of parameters to be estimated is balanced against the reliability of their estimation.

(10) Because basic periodicities in hydrology are known in advance, all harmonics of deterministic periodic components are also known in advance.   Therefore, estimation is limited for amplitudes and phases (or the equivalent pair of Fourier coefficients) for known frequencies of harmonics.

3.   Periodic components in the mean and standard deviation

The estimates of the population means at any discrete position τ of the periodicity ω from n values of the $x_{p,\tau}$-series, with $\tau = 1,2,\ldots,\omega$ and $p = 1,2,\ldots,n,$ are

$$m_\tau = \frac{1}{n} \sum_{p=1}^{n} x_{p,\tau} \; . \tag{3}$$

The estimates of the population standard deviations are

$$s_\tau = \left[\frac{1}{n} \sum_{p=1}^{n} (x_{p,\tau} - m_\tau)^2 \right]^{\frac{1}{2}} , \tag{4}$$

if n is sufficiently large. However, if a periodic component μ_τ is fitted to the ω values of μ_τ, with the proper significance tests for amplitudes significantly different from zero, the unbiased estimates of population standard deviations then become

$$s_\tau =' \left[\frac{1}{n-1} \sum_{p=1}^{n} (x_{p,\tau} - \mu_\tau)^2 \right]^{\frac{1}{2}} . \tag{5}$$

The non-parametric method of separating the periodic components of the mean and the standard deviation from the series gives

$$\varepsilon_{p,\tau} = \frac{x_{p,\tau} - m_\tau}{s_\tau} , \tag{6}$$

3 .4

in which m_τ and s_τ are estimated by Eqs. (3) and (4), respectively. This method is most commonly used. When Δt is large (1 month), the non-parametric method is justified because the differences $\mu_\tau - m_\tau$ and $\sigma_\tau - s_\tau$, with μ_τ and σ_τ the fitted periodic functions to m_τ and s_τ respectively, are either zeros or very small under proper tests for significant harmonics. However, when Δt is small (1 day), the estimates of all 730 values of m_τ and s_τ by Eqs. (3) and (4) can not be accurate. Using 730 statistics is awkward, requiring lengthy computer time for processing of data, storage of statistics, and simulation of large samples. This also means perpetuating the evident sampling variations. Thus the fitting of periodic functions μ_τ and σ_τ to m_τ and s_τ by proper tests becomes unavoidable. Based on experience, it is expected that the variance of differences between population periodic functions for the mean and the standard deviation and the fitted periodic functions μ_τ and σ_τ is much smaller than the variance of differences between the population periodic functions and the estimates m_τ and s_τ. For limited number of significant harmonics, as the usual case is, say 4-8 in each of μ_τ and σ_τ, the number of parameters to estimate and use is 16-32, instead of 730 for daily time series. This approach then permits using the parametric method for separating periodicities of the mean and standard deviation from the series by

$$\varepsilon_{p,\tau} = \frac{x_{p,\tau} - \mu_\tau}{\sigma_\tau} . \tag{7}$$

Basic difficulties arise in applying proper statistical tests. Techniques are not available for testing the significance of harmonics in the complex hydrologic periodic-stochastic processes. Most tests available relate to the model

$$x_{p,\tau} = \mu_\tau + \varepsilon_{p,\tau} , \tag{8}$$

composed of the sum of periodic and stochastic parts. To the writer's knowledge, there are no testing techniques available when $x_{p,\tau}$ has several periodic parameters and Eq. (8) is not satisfied. Two cases arise in hydrologic series, first s_τ and m_τ, or consequently σ_τ and μ_τ, are proportional, or $\sigma_\tau / \mu_\tau = \eta_\tau \approx \eta$, with η a constant, and secondly η_τ is not a constant but a periodic or some other function changing with τ. In the first case Eq. (7) can be expressed as

$$x_{p,\tau} = \mu_\tau (1 + \eta \, \varepsilon_{p,\tau}) = \mu_\tau \, \varepsilon^*_{p,\tau} , \tag{9}$$

in which $\varepsilon^*_{p,\tau} = 1 + \eta_\tau \, \varepsilon_{p,\tau}$ has the mean unity and the variance $\eta 2$, a component without the periodicities in the mean and standard deviation. This can be reduced to Eq. (8) by logarithmic transformation:

$$\ln x_{p,\tau} = \ln \mu_\tau + \ln \varepsilon^*_{p,\tau} . \tag{10}$$

The case of Eq. (10) is often satisfied in hydrology, mostly for precipitation series and sometimes for runoff series with flows resulting only from rainfall, or with no accumulation and melting of snow and ice.

To test whether s_τ and m_τ are proportional, the ω coefficients of variation are estimated by $\hat\eta_\tau = s_\tau / m_\tau$, and the null hypothesis is $E(\hat\eta_\tau) = \eta = \sigma_x / \mu_x$. The constant η is estimated by $\hat\eta = s_x / m_x$, with m_x and s_x

the overall mean and standard deviation of the available $x_{p,\tau}$ -series. Replacing the yet unknown μ_τ in Eq. (9) by the computed m_τ then

$$\varepsilon^*_{p,\tau} = \frac{x_{p,\tau}}{m_\tau} , \qquad (11)$$

which has no periodicity in the mean and standard deviation. The ω sample coefficients of variation, $\hat{n}_\tau$, each estimated by n values of $\varepsilon^*_{p,\tau}$ at given positions τ , have the expected value $E(\hat{n}_\tau) = n$ and variance[2]

$$\sigma^2_\eta = \frac{\mu^2(\mu_4-\mu_2^2)-4\mu\mu_2\mu_3 + 4\mu_2^3}{4\mu^4\mu_2 n} , \qquad (12)$$

in which $\mu = \hat{n}$ is the mean coefficient of variation, and μ_2, μ_3 and μ_4 are the central moments of the ω values of n_τ estimated by the ω values of $\hat{n}_\tau$, assuming the $\varepsilon^*_{p,\tau}$-variable is independent in sequence. Since n_τ-values of the $\varepsilon^*_{p,\tau}$-variable may be highly sequentially dependent, the ω-values of $\hat{n}_\tau$ should be reduced to an effective sample length, ω_e , for testing whether the distribution of the ω values of $\hat{n}_\tau$ values differs significantly from the approximate normal distribution of n_τ with the variance given by Eq. (12). A first approximation to computing ω_e is by using the first serial correlation coefficient r_1 of the ω values of $\hat{n}_\tau$ by

$$\omega_e = \omega \frac{1-r_1}{1+r_1} . \qquad (13)$$

Then a chi-square test is performed for the $\hat{n}_\tau$-frequency distribution determined from their ω values, but using (ω_e-2) as the number of degrees of freedom for the chi-square distribution in testing the goodness of fit by an approximate normal sampling distribution of n_τ , with $E(n_\tau) \approx s_x/m_x$, and the variance of n_τ given by Eq. (12). If this approximate chi-square test indicates accepting the null hypothesis, then using Eq. (10) for that series is also acceptable. For this case Fisher's test for significance of harmonics is applicable, provided the logarithms of $\varepsilon^*_{p,\tau}$ in Eq. (10) are approximately normal, and the effective sample size of the $\ln \varepsilon^*_{p,\tau}$-series is used. The Fisher critical test statistic, g_c, is then given for a probability significance level, P, by [3]

$$P = s(1-g_c)^{s-1} - \frac{s(s-1)}{2} (1-2g_c)^{s-1} +\ldots$$

$$+ (-1)^{k-1} \frac{s!}{k!(s-k)!} (1-sg_c)^{s-1} , \qquad (15)$$

with k the greatest integer less than $1/g_c$, $s = N/2$, the number of harmonics and $N = n\omega$ the sample size. In most cases, the first term on the right side of

[2] Cramer H., Mathematical Methods of Statistics, Princeton University Press, 1959 printing, page 358.

[3] Fisher, R.A., Tests of Significance in Harmonic Analysis, Contributions to Mathematical Statistics, F. Wiley and Sons, New York 1950, paper no. 16, p. 16. - 16.59.

3 .6

Eq. (15) gives a sufficiently accurate g_c for a given P and s. For normal dependent series of $\ln \varepsilon^*_{p,\tau}$ approximately of the first-order autoregessive linear model, with ρ_1 estimated by the first serial correlation coefficient, $r_1(\ln \varepsilon^*_{p,\tau})$ the effective sample size of $\ln \varepsilon^*_{p,\tau}$ for testing the harmonics in $\ln \mu_\tau$ is

$$N_e = n\omega \ \frac{1-\rho_1}{1+\rho_1} \ , \tag{16}$$

and s in Eq. (15) is $s = N_e/2$. The amplitudes of harmonics in $\ln x_{p,\tau}$ are estimated by using the Fourier coefficients

$$A_j = \frac{2}{n\omega} \sum_{p=1}^{n} \sum_{\tau=1}^{\omega} (\ln x_{p,\tau} - \overline{\ln x_{p,\tau}}) \cos \frac{2\pi j\tau}{\omega} \tag{17}$$

and

$$B_j = \frac{2}{n\omega} \sum_{p=1}^{n} \sum_{\tau=1}^{\omega} (\ln x_{p,\tau} - \overline{\ln x_{p,\tau}}) \sin \frac{2\pi j\tau}{\omega} \ , \tag{18}$$

with

$$C_j^2 = A_j^2 + B_j^2 \ . \tag{19}$$

The harmonics with the highest C_{max}^2 is first tested for significance by

$$g_1 = \frac{C_{max}^2}{2s_x^2} = \frac{C_{max}^2}{\sum_{j=1}^{m} C_j^2} \ , \tag{20}$$

in which s_x^2 is the variance of $\ln x_{p,\tau}$. If $g_1 > g_c$, this harmonic has $C_j > 0$, and is significant. An approximation for the second, third,..., largest C_j^2 then proceeds by

$$g_i = \frac{C_i^2}{2s^2 - \sum_{j=1}^{i-1} C_j^2} \tag{21}$$

with $i < 2,3,...$, where i is the sequence of decreasing values of C_j^2. For the first value $g_i < g_c$, that and the remaining harmonics are not significant.

The second, and the most realistic and general, case in hydrology is when s_τ and m_τ are not proportional. To use Eqs. (15) through (21) for inferring the significant harmonics in the mean and the standard deviation is neither correct nor reliable. However, an approximation can be made by considering all harmonics of the m_τ- and s_τ-series in their sequential order of C_j^2 until either a given percentage of the variances of m_τ and s_τ are explained (say P = 95%), or the number of significant harmonics is less than a maximum of six, whichever is first satisfied. If these six harmonics explain less than a given percent of variances of m_τ and s_τ (say less than P = 5%), they may be considered as non-periodic. More detailed but also more complex significance tests are not discussed in this paper.

Figures 3 and 4 give the mean, m_τ, and the standard deviation, s_τ, of the daily flow series of the Merced River at Pohono Bridge, Yosemite, California, for a 40-year period of observations (n=40, ω=365), as well as the fitted periodic components μ_τ with five harmonics and σ_τ with four harmonics, respectively, by using the second approximate method of selecting the significant harmonics. Figure 5 shows the coefficient of variation, $\hat{\eta}_\tau = s_\tau/m_\tau$ versus τ for the same river, and visually infers that the $\hat{\eta}_\tau$-series is different from sampling fluctuation of $\hat{\eta}_\tau$ about the constant value $\hat{\eta}$. The case of the Merced River daily flow series is given to illustrate a complex hydrologic time process.

Two conclusions are usually drawn in hydrology from the spectral density graphs of time series: (1) which frequencies show the largest values of spectral densities, or equivalent to the estimates of significant frequencies, and (2) which of them have significant amplitudes. Because all major frequencies for harmonics are known in advance, as ω is known, and because the conclusion about significant harmonics is usually based on the validity of Eqs. (8) or (9), the inferences from the spectral graphs may be very unreliable and should be used cautiously.

By using the periodic functions μ_τ and σ_τ, and Eq. (7), their removal produces the $\varepsilon_{p,\tau}$-series which still is not a second-order stationary process because of periodicities in covariances or in autocorrelation coefficients. The mean of μ_τ must be m_x as the estimate of the general mean μ_x. However, by using σ_τ in Eq. (7) instead of s_τ of Eq. (6), the variable $\varepsilon_{p,\tau}$ of Eq. (7) has the mean zero and the variance close to by not exactly unity. Therefore, one is tempted to compute the mean and standard deviation of $\varepsilon_{p,\tau}$, and if they depart from zero and unity, one is attempted to standardize $\varepsilon_{p,\tau}$ by using these two additional parameters.

4. Periodic components in autocorrelation coefficients

The variable $\varepsilon_{p,\tau}$ of Eq. (6), Eq. (7), or Eq. (10) is often assumed in hydrologic practice to be second-order stationary. However, it has the periodicity in autocorrelation coefficients more often than not. The computation of the correlogram of $\varepsilon_{p,\tau}$ by neglecting the periodicity ω may lead to erroneous conclusions and procedures in simulating large samples. Besides, if a sampling upward or downward trend, or the sampling pseudo-cyclicity is present in $x_{p,\tau}$-series they greatly affect the shape of the general $\varepsilon_{p,\tau}$-correlogram. To avoid this bias and to study and remove the periodicity in autocorrelation coefficients, they are estimated for each position τ, just as m_τ, s_τ and $\hat{\eta}_\tau$ are estimated, namely by

$$\rho_{k,\tau}(\varepsilon_{p,\tau}) = \frac{\text{cov}(\varepsilon_{p,\tau} \, \varepsilon_{p,\tau+k})}{(\text{var } \varepsilon_{p,\tau} \text{ var } \varepsilon_{p,\tau+k})^{\frac{1}{2}}} \tag{22}$$

which is estimated by

$$r_{k,\tau}(\varepsilon_{p,\tau}) = \frac{\sum\limits_{p=1}^{n}\left[\varepsilon_{p,\tau} - \frac{1}{n}\sum\limits_{p=1}^{n}\varepsilon_{p,\tau}\right]\left[\varepsilon_{p,\tau+k} - \frac{1}{n}\sum\limits_{p=1}^{n}\varepsilon_{p,\tau+k}\right]}{\left[\sum\limits_{p=1}^{n}\left(\varepsilon_{p,\tau} - \frac{1}{n}\sum\limits_{p=1}^{n}\varepsilon_{p,\tau}\right)^2\right]^{1/2}\left[\sum\limits_{p=1}^{n}\left(\varepsilon_{p,\tau+k} - \frac{1}{n}\sum\limits_{p=1}^{n}\varepsilon_{p,\tau+k}\right)^2\right]^{1/2}} \quad , \quad (23)$$

with $k = 1,2,\ldots;$ $\tau = 1,2,\ldots,\omega$ and $\varepsilon_{p,\tau}$ a standardized variable.

Figure 6 shows the graphs $r_{k,\tau}(\varepsilon_{p,\tau})$ for $k = 1,2,3$, and 20, versus τ for the Merced River, similarly as given for the mean, standard deviation, and coefficient of variation. Because several $r_{1,\tau}$, $r_{2,\tau}$, and $r_{3,\tau}$ values are near the upper boundary of unity, the periodicity in them is not so visually obvious as it is for $r_{20,\tau}$. For $r_{1,\tau}$, $r_{2,\tau}$, and $r_{3,\tau}$ the periodic functions $\rho_{1,\tau}$, $\rho_{2,\tau}$, $\rho_{3,\tau}$ are fitted and plotted also in Fig. 6. The statistical inference of significant harmonics in the periodic autocorrelation coefficients is complex and needs more theoretical development. In this absence, the testing and fitting of $\rho_{k,\tau}$ is made by a split-sample technique of $r_{k,\tau}$-series, and only a limited number of major harmonics is used. The fit of $\rho_{k,\tau}$ to explain 95% of variation of $r_{k,\tau}$, or the use of up to six first harmonics, whichever is satisfied first is a practical and simple method of determining the significant harmonics in $r_{k,\tau}$.

The periodicity of autocorrelation is easily explained by physical factors. Rainfall may have different characteristics during various seasons and a periodicity in autocorrelation coefficients of daily precipitation series. Daily evaporation and daily water storage in a river basin are the main sources of large autocorrelation in daily runoff series. Since they respond differently to rainfall input and snowfall accumulation and melting, the river basin response and the time series dependence must be, therefore, a function of seasons. Difficulties encountered by some present methods of simulating large samples of hydrologic time series may stem from these periodicities in autocorrelation coefficients.

The general m-th order autoregressive (Markov) linear dependence scheme, which has some good physical justifications is,

$$\varepsilon_{p,\tau} = \sum\limits_{j=1}^{m} \alpha_{j,\tau}\, \varepsilon_{p,\tau-j} + \xi_{p,\tau} \quad , \quad (24)$$

with $\alpha_{j,\tau}$ the autoregression coefficients at the position τ, which are dependent on the $\rho_{k,\tau}$-coefficients. Any of the first three linear models, m=1, m=2, and m=3 of Eq. (24) usually satisfies the observed data. The component $\xi_{p,\tau}$ of Eq. (24) results in a second-order stationary and independent stochastic component.

The coefficients $\alpha_{j,\tau}$ are expressed in function of $\rho_{k,\tau}$ for a given τ. For m=1, $\alpha_{1,\tau} = \rho_{1,\tau}$, or it is the first autoregressive (Markov) model. For the second-order model, m=2,

$$\alpha_{1,\tau} = \frac{\rho_{1,\tau} - \rho_{1,\tau}\rho_{2,\tau}}{1 - \rho_{1,\tau}^2} \quad ; \quad \alpha_{2,\tau} = \frac{\rho_{2,\tau} - \rho_{1,\tau}^2}{1 - \rho_{1,\tau}^2} \quad (25)$$

and for the third-order model, m=3,

3.9

$$\alpha_{1,\tau} = \frac{(1-\rho_{1,\tau}^2)(\rho_{1,\tau}-\rho_{3,\tau}) - (1-\rho_{2,\tau})(\rho_{1,\tau}\rho_{2,\tau}-\rho_{3,\tau})}{(1-\rho_{2,\tau})(1-2\rho_{1,\tau}^2+\rho_{2,\tau})}, \tag{26}$$

$$\alpha_{2,\tau} = \frac{(1-\rho_{2,\tau})(\rho_{2,\tau}+\rho_{2,\tau}^2-\rho_{1,\tau}^2-\rho_{1,\tau}\rho_{3,\tau})}{(1-\rho_{2,\tau})(1-2\rho_{1,\tau}^2+\rho_{2,\tau})}, \tag{27}$$

and

$$\alpha_{3,\tau} = \frac{(\rho_{1,\tau}-\rho_{3,\tau})(\rho_{1,\tau}^2-\rho_{2,\tau}) - (1-\rho_{2,\tau})(\rho_{1,\tau}\rho_{2,\tau}-\rho_{3,\tau})}{(1-\rho_{2,\tau})(1-2\rho_{1,\tau}^2+\rho_{2,\tau})}. \tag{28}$$

By using the three models of Eq. (24), with m=1,2, and 3, the determination coefficients, or the percentages of explained variance of $\varepsilon_{p,\tau}$ by its auto-regressive part of Eq. (24) are given by

$$D_1 = \frac{1}{\omega}\sum_{\tau=1}^{\omega}\rho_{1,\tau}^2, \tag{29}$$

$$D_2 = \frac{1}{\omega}\sum_{\tau=1}^{\omega}\frac{\rho_{1,\tau}^2+\rho_{2,\tau}^2-2\rho_{1,\tau}^2\rho_{2,\tau}}{1-\rho_{1,\tau}^2}, \tag{30}$$

and

$$D_3 = \frac{1}{\omega}\sum_{\tau=1}^{\omega}\left(\frac{\rho_{1,\tau}^2+\rho_{2,\tau}^2+\rho_{3,\tau}^2+2\rho_{1,\tau}^3\rho_{3,\tau}+2\rho_{1,\tau}^2\rho_{2,\tau}^2+2\rho_{1,\tau}\rho_{2,\tau}^2\rho_{3,\tau}}{1-2\rho_{1,\tau}^2-\rho_{2,\tau}^2+2\rho_{1,\tau}^2\rho_{2,\tau}}\right.$$

$$\left. - \frac{2\rho_{1,\tau}^2\rho_{2,\tau}+4\rho_{1,\tau}\rho_{2,\tau}\rho_{3,\tau}+\rho_{1,\tau}^4+\rho_{2,\tau}^4+\rho_{1,\tau}^2\rho_{3,\tau}^2}{1-2\rho_{1,\tau}^2-\rho_{2,\tau}^2+2\rho_{1,\tau}^2\rho_{2,\tau}}\right) \tag{31}$$

in which $\rho_{1,\tau}$, $\rho_{2,\tau}$ and $\rho_{3,\tau}$ are estimated by the first three values, $r_{1,\tau}$, $r_{2,\tau}$ and $r_{3,\tau}$ respectively.

The use of the average values of $\bar\rho_{1,\tau}$, $\bar\rho_{2,\tau}$, and $\bar\rho_{3,\tau}$ in Eqs. (29) through (31) gives approximate results. To fit data of $r_{k,\tau}$, the model of Eq. (24) can be approximately tested by computing D_1, D_2, and D_3. If $D_2 - D_1$ is less than one percent of D_1, and $D_3 - D_1$ is less than two percent of D_1, the first-order model should be selected. If $D_2 - D_1$ is greater than one percent of D_1, but $D_3 - D_2$ is less than one percent of D_2, the second-order model should be selected. Otherwise, the third order model is appropriate.

The $\varepsilon_{p,\tau}$-series of Eq. (24), computed from the selected model, and using the corresponding coefficients $\alpha_{j,\tau}$ estimated by $a_{j,\tau}$, and $a_{j,\tau}$ by $r_{k,\tau}$ of Eqs. (25) through (29), is now the second-order independent stationary process, and therefore ready for further investigation.

3.10

5. Bias resulting from the use of general correlogram of $\varepsilon_{p,\tau}$-series

Figure 7 shows the average annual discharge series of the Merced River. It is easy to infer visually that there is a sampling upward trend in annual flows. Similarly, Fig. 8 shows the annual peak discharge series of the Merced River. The three largest peaks occurred in the fall, as a combination of rainfall and snow melt, while all others occurred in the snow-melt spring-summer season. The three highest peaks are evidently from a different population of flood producing conditions than the other peaks.

The general correlogram of the $\varepsilon_{p,\tau}$-series, obtained by neglecting the τ-positions, is given in Fig. 9 for the daily flow series of the Merced River. The first serial correlation coefficient r_1 is 0.80 in this correlogram, while the average of 365 values of $r_{1,\tau}(\varepsilon_{p,\tau})$ is 0.95. Using of the first- or second-order Markov model, based on the general correlogram, would grossly underestimate the time dependence characteristics, both by their absolute values and by the type of dependence. By fitting a Markov first-order model to the $\varepsilon_{p,\tau}$-series, with $\rho_1 = 0.80$ as a constant in Eq. (24), the $\xi_{p,\tau}$-series can be computed. For this new approximately second-order independent stationary series the spectral graph for frequency range 0.00-0.50, is given in Fig. 10. The expected spectral density is $E(v_d) = 2.0$. Only for small frequencies are the densities larger than 2.00, they then fall suddenly to smaller values than 2.00 and then randomly fluctuate about $E(v_d) = 2.00$ for most frequencies. The sampling trend of Fig. 7 may be responsible for this pattern, while the three very large values of peak discharges of Fig. 8 may have affected $\rho_1 = 0.80$ so that it is much smaller than the average 0.95 of $\rho_{1,\tau}(\varepsilon_{p,\tau})$. Therefore, by using either the $\rho_{k,\tau}(\varepsilon_{p,\tau})$ periodic components or their average values, if they are not periodic, instead of using $r_k(\varepsilon_{p,\tau})$ or the general correlogram, some sampling biases may be removed, the most important auto=correlation coefficient are more realistically estimated, and their sequential patterns follow the expected patterns of the physical process.

6. Third-order stationarity of $\xi_{p,\tau}$-series

To test whether the $\xi_{p,\tau}$-series has periodicities in the third-order para-meters, the two most practical parameters to use are the skewness coefficient defined by

$$\beta_\tau (\xi_{p,\tau}) = \frac{\mu_{3,\tau}(\xi_{p,\tau})}{[\mu_{2,\tau}(\xi_{p,\tau})]^{3/2}} \tag{32}$$

with $\mu_{3,\tau}$ and $\mu_{2,\tau}$ the second and third central moments, and the product of the three consecutive values of $\xi_{p,\tau}$, defined by

$$\rho_{\tau,\tau+1,\tau+2} = \frac{1}{n-2} \sum_{p=1}^{n-2} \left[(\xi_{p,\tau} - \frac{1}{n-2}\sum_{p=1}^{n-2}\xi_{p,\tau})(\xi_{p,\tau+1} - \frac{1}{n-2}\sum_{p=1}^{n-2}\xi_{p,\tau+1}) \right.$$
$$\left. (\xi_{p,\tau+2} - \frac{1}{n-2}\sum_{p=1}^{n-1}\xi_{p,\tau+2}) \right] . \tag{33}$$

Figure 11 shows $\hat{\beta}_\tau$, the estimated skewness coefficients of $\xi_{p,\tau}$ of Eq. (24) by using the first autoregressive model, and the average value 0.95 of $r_{1,\tau}(\varepsilon_{p,\tau})$. It shows that the third-order stationarity is not satisfied. Tests, however, may be performed to accept or reject the hypothesis of the third-order stationarity. It is often feasible to use the three parameter distributions for the $\xi_{p,\tau}$-variable in such a way that their lower boundary is a periodic parameter, which may take care of the periodicity in the skewness coefficient.

7. Second-order stationary model

The method outlined in this paper for the analysis of inputs and outputs permits the identification, estimation, and removal from the rest of a series the periodicity in any parameter, and the reduction of an independent stochastic component to the desired or justified order of stationarity. All information is given as mathematical models and their coefficients are estimated from data. For the second-order independent stationary stochastic component, the model is

$$x_{p,\tau} = \mu_\tau + \sigma_\tau \left(\sum_{j=1}^{m} \alpha_{j,\tau} \varepsilon_{p,\tau-j} + \xi_{p,\tau} \right) \tag{34}$$

with μ_τ , σ_τ and $\alpha_{j,\tau}$'s periodic, and

$$\varepsilon_{1,1}=\xi_{1,1}; \varepsilon_{1,2}=\alpha_{1,1}\varepsilon_{1,1} + \xi_{1,2}; \varepsilon_{1,3}=\alpha_{1,1}\varepsilon_{1,2} + \alpha_{2,1}\varepsilon_{1,1} + \xi_{1,3},$$ etc. up to $\varepsilon_{1,m-1}$.

For the case of third-order stationarity, $\xi_{p,\tau}$ may have the probability distribution $F(\xi_{p,\tau}; \alpha,\beta,\gamma_\tau)$, with γ_τ the periodic lower boundary, or a similar approach can be used for dealing with the periodicities in the parameters of Eqs (32) and (33). By simulating a very large sample of $\xi_{p,\tau}$- series in Eq. (34), and using the estimated periodic functions μ_τ , σ_τ , and $\alpha_{j,\tau}$'s , large samples of the $x_{p,\tau}$-series may be generated by Eq. (34). Various methods are available for testing hypotheses to determine if the new samples have the same statistical properties as the original $x_{p,\tau}$-sample.

8. Distribution of independent stochastic component

The component $\xi_{p,\tau}$ has a very large sample, $N = n\omega$. For daily flows and $n = 40$ in case of the Merced River, $N = 14,600$ values; for its monthly flows $N = 40 \times 12 = 480$. The $\xi_{p,\tau}$-component is then well described by its fitted probability distribution function, with a limited number of parameters (usually 2-6). This distribution function contains all information about the stochasticity of a $x_{p,\tau}$-series and is the basis for the simulation of large samples of $x_{p,\tau}$.

Unfortunately, for small Δt of discrete series (say 1-day, 2-day, 3-day, 7-day values) the frequency density curves are particular distributions, as shown by Fig. 12 of the $\xi_{p,\tau}$-series of daily flows for the Merced River. To fit well a probability density function, it is necessary to go beyond the classical probability distribution functions in hydrology, such as normal, lognormal, and various gamma distribution functions. Pearson types of functions, gamma functions with various transformations (Laguerre polynomials, Chebishev polynomials, etc.) are necessary.

The fitting of normal, lognormal, and gamma probability density functions to the $\xi_{p,\tau}$-variable is usually satisfactory for discrete series with a large Δt (say $\Delta t = 14$ days, a month, 3 months). The distributions of the $\xi_{p,\tau}$-series are bounded on the left side. As $x_{p,\tau}$ is a positively valued variable, so for $(x_{p,\tau})min = 0$, Eq. (34) gives,

3 .12

$$(\xi_{p,\tau})_{\min} = -\left(\frac{\mu_\tau}{\sigma_\tau} + \sum_{j=1}^{m} \alpha_{j,\tau} \, \varepsilon_{p,\tau-j}\right)_{\max} \quad , \tag{35}$$

in which $1/\eta_\tau = \mu_\tau/\sigma_\tau$. To obtain $(\xi_{p,\tau})_{\min}$ the values $\varepsilon_{p,\tau-j}$, $j = 1,2,\ldots,m$, and η should be as large as possible while $x_{p,\tau}$ is at a minimum. Because of this physical lower boundary, the lognormal and gamma distributions with three parameters are attractive probability functions to fit, provided the $\xi_{p,\tau}$-frequency distributions are of the shape of these functions. Besides, the lower boundary γ_τ as the third parameter may be treated as periodic parameter, to take care of periodicities in the third-order parameters.

The fitting three-parameter lognormal probability density function is

$$f(\xi) = \frac{1}{\sigma_n(\xi-\xi_o)\sqrt{2\pi}} \exp\{-[\ln(\xi-\xi_o) - \mu_n]^2/2\sigma_n^2\} \quad , \tag{36}$$

with μ_n the mean of $\ln(\xi-\xi_o)$, σ_n the standard deviation of $\ln(\xi-\xi_o)$, and ξ_o the lower boundary, constant or periodic. The lower boundary is estimated by

$$\left(\sum_{i=1}^{N} \frac{1}{\xi_i-\xi_o}\right)\left\{\frac{1}{N}\sum_{i=1}^{N} \ln^2(\xi_i-\xi_o) - \left[\frac{1}{N}\sum_{i=1}^{N} \ln(\xi_i-\xi_o)\right]^2 - \right.$$

$$\left. - \frac{1}{N}\sum_{i=1}^{N} \ln(\xi_i-\xi_o)\right\} + \sum_{i=1}^{N} \frac{\ln(\xi_i-\xi_o)}{\xi_i-\xi_o} = 0 \quad , \tag{37}$$

in which $\ln$ is the symbol for natural base of logarithms, ξ_i is a short designation for $\xi_{p,\tau}$, and $N = n\omega$.

In order to test how well Eq. (36) fits the $\xi_{p,\tau}$- empirical frequency distribution, the chi-square test can be applied. If ν class intervals with equal probabilities $1/\nu$ are used in the chi-square test, the normal standard distribution gives the corresponding class limits, t_j , for probabilities j/ν , $j = 0,1,2,\ldots,\nu-1$; then the class limits of $\xi_{p,\tau}$ are obtained by

$$\xi_j = \xi_o + e^{\sigma_n t_j + \mu_n} \quad . \tag{38}$$

The three parameter gamma probability density function is

$$f(\xi) = \frac{1}{\beta\Gamma(\alpha)}\left(\frac{\xi-\xi_o}{\beta}\right)^{\alpha-1} e^{(\xi-\xi_o)/\beta} \tag{39}$$

in which α, β, and ξ_o are parameters, with ξ_o the lower boundary, constant or periodic. The maximum likelihood method gives the estimate of the lower boundary as

3 .13

$$\frac{1 + \sqrt{1 + \frac{4}{3} A}}{1 + \sqrt{1 + \frac{4}{3}A} - 4A} - \left(\frac{1}{N} \sum_{i=1}^{N} \xi_i - \xi_o\right) \frac{1}{N} \sum_{i=1}^{N} \frac{1}{\xi_i - \xi_o} = 0 \quad , \tag{40}$$

in which

$$A = \ln\left[\frac{1}{N} \sum_{i=1}^{N} \xi_i - \xi_o\right] - \frac{1}{N} \sum_{i=1}^{N} \ln(\xi_i - \xi_o) \quad . \tag{41}$$

The parameter α is estimated by

$$\alpha = \frac{1 + \sqrt{1 + \frac{4}{3} A}}{4A} - \Delta\alpha \tag{42}$$

with the correction factor $\Delta\alpha$ given by

$$\Delta\alpha = 0.04475 (0.26)^{\alpha} \tag{43}$$

which is an approximation; the parameter β is estimated by

$$\beta = \frac{1}{\alpha} \left(\frac{1}{N} \sum_{i=1}^{N} \xi_i - \xi_o\right) \quad . \tag{44}$$

For the goodness of fit test of the three-parameter gamma distribution to the $\xi_{p,\tau}$-variable, with $N = n\omega$, the number ν of class intervals with equal probabilities $1/\nu$ is used. The class limits ξ_j of these intervals are determin by the inverse of the integral

$$\frac{j}{\nu} = \frac{1}{\beta^{\alpha} \Gamma(\alpha)} \int_{\xi_o}^{\xi_j} (\xi - \xi_o)^{\alpha - 1} e^{-(\xi - \xi_o)/\beta} d\xi \quad , \tag{45}$$

in which ξ_o, α and β are estimated by Eqs. (40) through (44).

For frequency density curves of the type of Fig. 12, which are common for smal Δt (say $\Delta t = 1$ day, 2 days, 7 days), the double-branch two-parameter gamma functi with each branch having $0 < \alpha < 1$, has then the left branch equation

$$f(\xi_o - \xi) = \frac{P}{\beta_1^{\alpha_1} \Gamma(\alpha_1)} (\xi_o - \xi)^{\alpha_1 - 1} e^{-(\xi_o - \xi)/\beta_1} \quad , \tag{46}$$

for $\xi < \xi_o$, and the right branch equation

$$f(\xi - \xi_o) = \frac{1-P}{\beta_2^{\alpha_2} \, \Gamma(\alpha_2)} \, (\xi - \xi_o)^{\alpha_2 - 1} \, e^{-(\xi - \xi_o)/\beta_2} \, , \tag{47}$$

for $\xi > \xi_o$. Six parameters should be estimated: ξ_o (the mode), P (the probability of all values $\xi_{p,\tau} \leq \xi_o$), α_1 and β_1 for the left branch, and α_2 and β_2 for the right branch. The left branch no longer has a lower boundary as the physical conditions imply. This is not a serious disadvantage because the convergence of the left branch tail to zero is rapid. For Fig. 12, the estimate of ξ_o is the position of the sharp peak, and the estimate of P is the area to the left of this peak. The estimates of α_1, β_1, α_2, and β_2 are then made by using the maximum likelihood method.

9. Concluding remarks

The above structural analysis, based on the hypotheses outlined earlier, defers significantly from the autoregressive approach. This approach relates $x_{p,\tau}$ for a given τ to the values $x_{p,\tau-1}$, $x_{p,\tau-2}$,..., (say a January value related to the December, November,..., values) by an autoregressive scheme. In general, there are ω regression equations and $m\omega$ autoregressive coefficients, with m the order of autoregression equation, $m=1,2,...$. This approach is feasible as long as ω and m are small. If $\omega = 12$ months, and $m = 3$, 12 equations and 36 coefficients are required. However, if $\omega = 365$ days, and $m = 3$, 365 autoregression equations and 1095 coefficients are required. This is a reason why the autoregression approach was never successfully applied to daily flow series, or to discrete series with time units smaller than a month.

The autoregression approach to a direct analysis of the $x_{p,\tau}$-series requires as many random variables as there are time units Δt, or positions τ in the periodicity ω . For monthly time series, 12 random variables, one for each month, should be investigated to determine good reliability in the estimation of the stochastic variation. For a three-parameter probability density function, fitted to each of the 12 variables, 36 parameters must be estimated. For a daily time series this direct autoregression approach does not seem practical because it would require 365 random variables and 1095 parameters. As soon as these random variables are assumed to be identically distributed along some or all τ-positions, the departure from reality may be significant. In general, this type of departure may be the reason many practitioners are sceptical about the reproducibility of the basic properties of observed series by simulated large samples.

In contrast to the autoregression method, the approach outlined in this paper permits a complete mathematical description of input and output time series of a hydrologic environment conceived as a system. Selected models are tested for goodness of fit, with their parameters properly estimated. To summarize, this approach has the following general advantages.

(1) Information contained in a sample series is extracted and presented in the most condensed form.

(2) Simulation of large sample series by the data generation (Monte Carlo) method is simplified because only independent stationary stochastic variable needs to be simulated, with further linear and/or trigonometric transformations and an added trigonometric function, determining the simulated $x_{p,\tau}$-series.

(3) Sufficient data are available for accurately fitting a probability density function to the frequency distribution of the independent stationary stochastic component.

(4) The stochastic component may be made stationary of any order which is justified by the desired or required accuracy.

(5) The effects of sampling biases are reduced to a minimum.

(6) Models of input and output series may be convoluted or studied in an appropriate way to obtain a representative response function of the system.

(7) The physical background can be studied in order to validate the selected models and estimated parameters.

LIST OF SYMBOLS

$a_{j,\tau}$	the estimates of $\alpha_{j,\tau}$
A_j	Fourier coefficient of the j-th harmonic
B_j	Fourier coefficient of the j-th harmonic
C_j	the amplitude of the j-th harmonic
D_1, D_2, D_3	the determination coefficients of the linear autoregressive schemes for $m = 1$, 2, and 3
$f(\xi)$	the probability density function for $\xi_{p,\tau}$
g_1, g_i	Fisher's testing parameters for significant harmonics
j	the sequence of harmonics of a periodic parameter
k	the lag in autocorrelation
m	the order of the linear autoregressive dependence of $\varepsilon_{p,\tau}$
m_x	the mean of m_τ
m_τ	the estimated means along $\tau = 1,2,\ldots,\omega$
n	the number of years in a sample of a time series
N	the sample size $N = n\omega$
p	the sequence of years, $p = 1,2,\ldots,n$
P	probability of values greater or smaller than a given value
r_1	the sample first serial correlation coefficient
$r_{k,\tau}$	the estimates from the sample of $\rho_{k,\tau}$
s_x	the mean of s_τ
s_τ	the estimated standard deviations along $\tau = 1,2,\ldots,\omega$
v_τ	the estimate of v_τ
$x_{p,\tau}$	discrete series value at the position τ inside the year, and p-th year
α	the shape parameter of the Gamma distribution
$\alpha_{j,\tau}$	the j-th linear autoregressive coefficient at $\tau = 1,2,\ldots,\omega$
β	the scale parameter of the Gamma distribution
$\beta_\tau(\xi_{p,\tau})$	the skewness coefficient of $\xi_{p,\tau}$ for $\tau = 1,2,\ldots\omega$
$\varepsilon_{p,\tau}$	the random variable with m_τ and s_τ, or μ_τ and σ_τ, removed
$\varepsilon^*_{p,\tau}$	the random variable with mean unity and variance η^2
η	the coefficient of variation

3 .16

r_τ the periodic function of C_v , coefficient of variation

θ_j the phase of the j -th harmonic

μ_i $i = 2, 3, 4,$ the central moments

μ_n the mean of logarithms of $(\xi_i - \xi_o)$ with $\xi_i = \xi_{p,\tau}$

μ_x the mean of μ_τ

μ_ν the symbol for the mean of the parameter ν

μ_τ the periodic function of the means

ν the symbol for any time series parameter

ν_τ the periodic function of the parameter ν along $\tau = 1,2,\ldots,\omega$

ξ_o the lower boundary of $f(\xi)$

$\xi_{p,\tau}$ the independent second-order stationary random variable

ρ_1 the population first serial correlation coefficient

$\rho_{k,\tau}$ the k -th autocorrelation coefficient at the positions $\tau = 1,2,\ldots,\omega$

$\rho_{\tau,\tau+1,\tau+2}$ the third-order dependence parameter

σ_n the standard deviation of logarithms of $(\xi_i - \xi_o)$ with $\xi_i = \xi_{p,\tau}$

σ_x the mean of σ_τ

σ_τ the periodic function of the standard deviations

τ the time position (interval) inside the year

ω the number of values τ in a period (year)

3 .17

68

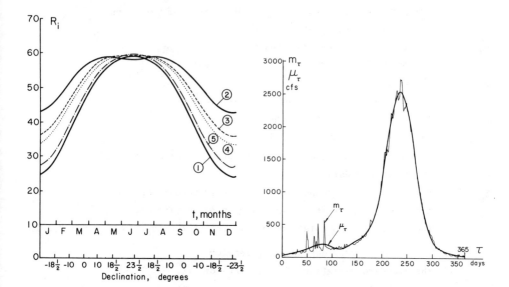

Fig. 1. Deterministic periodic process of potential daily radiation index, R_i, for five small river basins with different slopes and orientation at Fernow Experimental Forest, West Virginia, with an annual index: (1) 45.6, (2) 54.0, (3) 51.4, (4) 50.4, and (5) 47.3 .

Fig. 3. The estimated means (m_τ) and the fitted periodic component (μ_τ) in the 365 means of daily flows series of the Merced River.

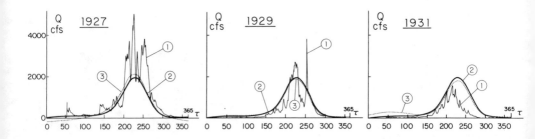

Fig. 2. The fitted deterministic periodic component of daily means (2), the fitted periodic component for daily means with amplitudes and phases as random variables (3), and the daily flows of a wet year (left graph), an average year (center graph), and a dry year (right graph), as lines (1), for the Merced River at Pohono Bridge, Yosemite, California.

3 .18

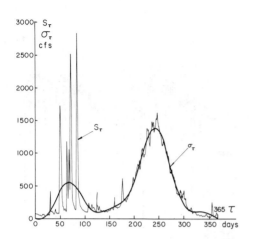

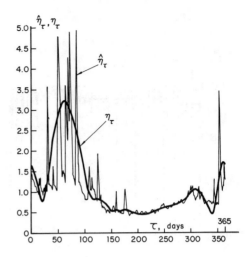

Fig. 4. The estimated standard deviations (s_τ) and the fitted periodic component (σ_τ) for the 365 standard deviations of daily flows series of the Merced River.

Fig. 5. The estimated coefficients of variation $(\hat{\eta}_\tau)$ and the fitted periodic component (η_τ) for the 365 coefficients of variation of daily flow series of the Merced River.

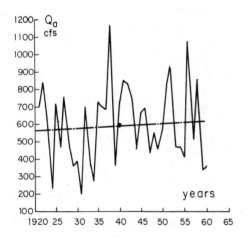

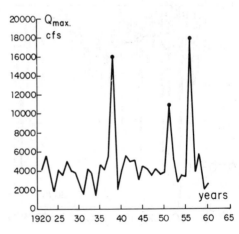

Fig. 7. The annual average discharge series of the Merced River, with an upward trend.

Fig. 8. The annual peak discharge series of the Merced River, with three large autumn floods.

3 .19

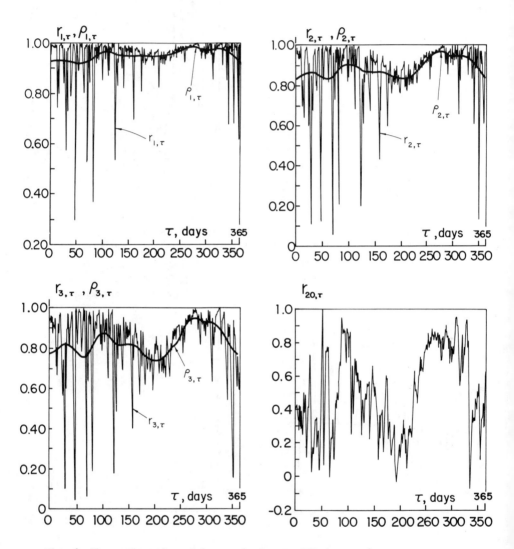

Fig. 6. The estimated serial correlation coefficients $(r_{1,\tau},\ r_{2,\tau},\ r_{3,\tau},$ and $r_{20,\tau})$ and the fitted periodic components $(\rho_{1,\tau},\ \rho_{2,\tau},$ and $\rho_{3,\tau})$ for serial correlation coefficients of daily flow series of the Merced River.

71

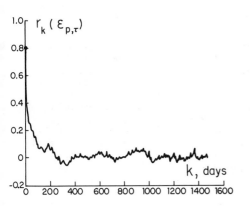

Fig. 9. The general correlogram, r_k, of the standardized $\varepsilon_{p,\tau}$-series (with removed periodicities in the mean and standard deviation) of daily flow series of the Merced River.

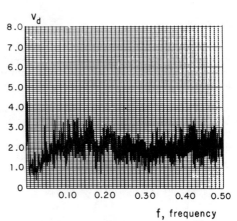

Fig. 10. The spectral density graph of the independent $\xi_{p,\tau}$-series obtained by using the first Markov Model in Eq. (24) and $\rho_1 = 0.80$.

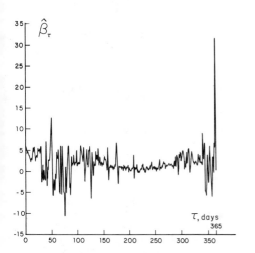

Fig. 11. The estimated skewness coefficients $(\hat{\beta}_\tau)$ of the independent second-order stationary stochastic component, for daily flow series of the Merced River.

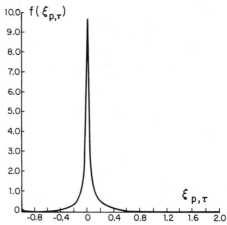

Fig. 12. The frequency density curve of the independent second-order stationary component of the daily flow series of the Merced River.

3.21

DISCUSSION

J. W. DELLEUR

The speaker would like to comment on the author's oral criticism on the application of communication engineering procedures such as spectral analysis to hydrologic problems. All methods should, of course, be used with caution when applied in a context different from that for which they were originally intended.

Spectral analysis is superfluous if it is used only for the identification of cyclic components. These, as the annual component, are usually known a priori because of the astronomic periodicities, as stated in the author's second hypothesis. However, spectral and cross-spectral analyses have other important applicati Just to cite a few, the spectral analysis of the residuals can be useful in the selection of an appropriate model as well as in the estimation of the model parameters, or in the study of crossing problems and of their related statistics. Cross spectral analysis provides a powerful method to relate two time series such as rainfall and runoff by means of a simple linear regression, a laged regression, or a continuous or discrete transfer function. These applications have been discussed and tested by the speaker.[1]

Finally, the speaker would like to ask what is the justification for the comm usage of more harmonics in the fitting of periodic components to means and to standard deviations than the number of harmonics that can be physically identified It is interesting to notice that Plate[2] is criticizing the work of Quimpo[3] in this particular respect.

---

[1] Delleur, J. W., and Bernier, J.: "Développements Récents en Matière d'analyse de Chroniques d'événements Hydrologiques: Liaison en Chaine, Théorie du Renouvelleme Analyse Spectrale," Societe Hydrotechnique de France Les Models Mathematiques en Hydrologie de Surface, Paris, November 1970.

[2] Plate, Erich J.: "Limitations of Spectral Analysis in the Study of Wind-Generate Water Surface Waves," International Symposium on Stochastic Hydraulics, Pittsburgh (May 31-June 2, 1971).

[3] Quimpo, R. G.: "Autocorrelation and Spectral Analyses in Hydrology," Proc. ASCE, Vol. 94, Journal Hydr. Div., p. 363 (1968).

P. S. EAGLESON

1. Are there not natural periodicities other than 24 hours and 12 months which should be included in your model? I am thinking particularly about the (quasi) periodicity represented by the circumferential propagation of jet stream instabilities and the low pressure centers associated with these. Because of the variability in this "period" the spectrum will show a bump rather than a spike of course.

2. Instead of using your model for "dependent" hydrologic variables such as streamflow would it not produce a greater accounting for the deterministic content to
a. model the "independent" or input variable (rainfall in this case) as you suggest and then
b. pass this signal through a model of the system (catchment in this case) t generate the dependent signal? This also allows manipulation of the system to simulate man's past or proposed activities?

T. ISHIHARA

This paper proposes an interesting and effective method for simulating the input information into the water resources system. The basic idea in this paper was presented by Quimpo, R.G. and Yevjevich, V. at 1967 and is developed in detail at this time. We have a few comments for this paper. At first, the hypothesis is given that the reliability of methods should not depend on the selected time units of discrete series. But, we found that the stochastic laws depended on the selected time units and the periodicities of the precipitation and the river discharge series did not always appear in one-day time unit. On this point, Prof. Chow also notes that the time interval to be chosen for the discrete time parameter will affect the simulated stochastic laws of the processes. Under these considerations, we think the method of approach should depend on the selected time units and the different time unit series cannot be estimated sufficiently by the same method. Second, the problem is a choice of the sample size. If the characteristics of the model would depend on the used sample size, it has a risk to simulate the input information with such the instable characteristics for a long time in future. Lastly, in the future the stochastic models such as proposed in this paper may become very important in the field of hydrology. Would you please tell us your opinions on the subject and the limitation of their application?

C. KISIEL

The word periodic has distinct mathematical meaning. If T is the period of the phenomenon and $f(t)$ its amplitude, then a periodic process exists when $f(t) = f(t + T) = f(t + 2T) = \ldots = f(t + nT)$. Because this is seldom true in natural processes, the word oscillatory as defined by M. G. Kendall in Advanced Theory of Statistics (Volume III) is more correct. I must admit that for some phenomena the distinction may have little importance for management purposes, but to push the notion of periodicity too hard is a deception. One might argue that a periodic model arises largely because of the mathematical analysis imposed on the data.

On page 15, it is stated that the approach permits "a complete mathematical description of input and output time series of a hydrologic environment conceived as a system." This is a rather strong conclusion that excludes other conceptualizations. The approach does not allow for multiple inputs, for oscillatory behavior that results independently of astronomic processes, and for the inclusion of alternate stochastic models of the state transitions from one time period to the next.

Given the formulation proposed in this paper, how well are important properties such as runs, crossings, and extremes preserved? Have simulations been performed and checked with independent sets of data?

Experience with stochastic models of streamflow indicates that extremes are underestimated because model parameters have an historical bias. I do not see where the proposed approach extricates us from the "curse" of historical bias. That uncertainty has implications certainly for important management decisions on water resources.

The suggestion is left that spectral analysis has no further use in hydrology for detecting "periodicities." That would be correct if astronomic processes were the sole forcing "function" of interest to hydrologists. Beat frequencies arise in nature as do biennial oscillations in atmospheric phenomena whose implications to hydrologic predictions are not fully understood as yet. Furthermore, cross-spectral analysis has utility in system identification of hydrologic processes. Such use has not been fully appraised. Human activity imposes certain rhythms on observed processes such as water level fluctuations in a well used for irrigated agriculture or minical water supply. Time series techniques can aid in the study of such activity.

A. MUROTA

I want to state my opinion about the nature of stochastic components.

As hydrologists, our basic idea is that in river flow sequences, high and low flows, belong to different populations because of their linearity and nonlinearity

In water resources system, one of the most fundamental subjects is the estimation of variation of river flow sequences over a long term. In order to set up a simulation model of input data in water resources systems, stochastic properties o river flow sequences should be analyzed. This writer has treated both monthly ri flow sequences as a long term variation and five-day river flow sequences as a sho term variation for the purpose of providing the operation of a reservoir with input data.

I. Simulated monthly river flows should preserve not only probability distri butions, but also serial correlations of the sequences in good agreement with thos of observed flows because successive occurrence of high flows or extremely low flo seriously affects water utilization.

Our correlation analyses originate from the idea that the population of month river flows consists of groups of high and low flows which differ in serial correla tion. While high flows over a certain limited magnitude may be assumed random in their occurrence, i.e. autocorrelation coefficient $\rho \doteq 0.0$, low flows have persist in their occurrence, i. e. the value of ρ should be significant. Therefore, it is unsatisfactory to apply usual linear regression relationships to the simulation of monthly river flows.

From this point of view, the author proposes a nonlinear simulation model, wh has two population groups of a nearly zero value of autocorrelation coefficient fo high flows and significant larger values for low flows.

From our results of river flow simulation, it is concluded that the proposed nonlinear model naturally gives higher accuracy to replication of autocorrelation than the linear model, but autocorrelation characteristics are not so significant on the distribution parameters of river flows. For the accumulated total flows from June to September when high flows frequently occur, their distribution curve simulated by the nonlinear model shows a better fit to that of observed flows, especially for extreme low and high flows, than the usual linear model. This may be because the linear model uses too large values of autocorrelation coefficients for high flows and too small values for low flows.

With respect to the mechanism of persistency of low flows that results in different stochastic properties for high and low flow sequences, the writer has investigated whether autocorrelation characteristics of monthly flows are caused by self-persistency of precipitations or by storage effect in the watershed. According to autocorrelation analyses of monthly rainfalls, the differences in autocorrelation between heavy and weak rainfalls that have been recognized for riv flow sequences are not so obvious. It is concluded, therefore, that the different properties of autocorrelation between high flows and low flows might be due not to randomness of heavy rainfalls and persistency of weak rainfalls, but to a storage effect in the water shed or nonlinearity of rainfall-runoff relationship, for example, direct runoff being so intense that the storage effects are negligible for heavy rainfalls.

3 .24

II.   In practical water resources development, river flows are regulated through system elements, for example, by the reservoir operation. For the reservoirs having limited regulation capacity, stochastic process of inflow to the reservoir has to be made clear for a shorter time unit than a month. Accordingly, the problem to be investigated is how the short term variations of river flows are related to flows in a longer time scale.

An elementary procedure of statistical treatment of 5-days flow may be initiated by taking N samples of the same k-th 5-days flow in the month of N years of observed data. Such sampling, however, naturally neglects the tendency that meteorological phenomena show a different phase lag and have a different duration time from year to year. On the assumption that the river flow sequences in a time unit of 5-days would be fairly affected by the meteorological condition or runoff process with some large time scale, the writer took the direction that statistical analyses should be performed on the deviation of each 5-days flow from the monthly mean flow. The deviated components from this monthly mean 5-day flow involve neither trend nor seasonal periodicity and should have pure randomness.

The writer classified 5-day flow data into statistically different groups using the criterion of the flow of 40 m^3/sec. This critical value has been determined from analyses which show that frequency of occurrence of high flows greater than $40 m^3$/sec approximately coincides with frequency of heavy rainfalls and typhoon precipitations that have strong randomness.

Because the high and low flow belong to different populations, deviations of high flow and low flow also would not be statistically homogeneous. To homogenize these samples of deviations, we adopt the variables which are deviated components divided by the monthly mean 5-day flow except for high flow data. Frequency distributions of these variables show more symmetrical shapes and narrower ranges than for those cases using the deviated flows from N-years mean flow. In addition, 5-day flow sequences of these components are serially independent and vary about the monthly mean 5-day flows.

By using the stochastic properties of monthly and 5-day flow sequences, a simulation model can be constructed by the following procedures.

1.   The sequences of monthly mean flows can be synthesized by a nonlinear simulation model.

2.   When the monthly mean flow is given, the sequences of the 5-day flows that deviate from the mean flow can be computed within the month.

3.   To the sequences of monthly mean flows obtained by 1, the deviated components obtained by 2 are added and then the sequences of 5-day flows can be simulated.

References

Murota, A., Kanda, T., "A Stochastic Analysis of River Flow Characteristics in the Kizu River Basin," Technology Reports of the Osaka University, Vol. 18, October, 1968.

Murota, A., Kanda, T., "A Stochastic Model to Simulate Monthly River Flow Sequences," the 13th Congress of the International Association for Hydraulic Research, August, 1969.

Murota, A., Kanda, T., "Stochastic Properties of Monthly and 5-Days River Flow Sequences and their Applications to River Flow Simulation," Technology Reports of the Osaka University, Vol. 21 March, 1971 (in printing).

R. G. QUIMPO

My question is relative to the need for spectral analysis in determining the significant frequencies in a hydrologic process. Through the interaction of their components, many physical systems (a structure or a machine), have a natural frequency. This natural frequency is, in general, different than those which may be attributed to astronomical phenomena. Is it thus possible that the components of a hydrologic system can so combine, resulting in a natural frequency different from those which are due to the 365-day and 24-hr. cycles? If so, would this not require some prior method of identifying the frequency?

J. PAUL RILEY

In your 4th hypothesis you indicate that non-homogeniety (mainly man-made) is identified, described, and removed. If man-made changes can be removed, presumably they also could be identified, described, and added in instances where the model might be employed to predict the effect of proposed man-made changes upon the syste

T. D. STEELE

I have three brief questions:

(1) What is the meaning and significance of the results of figure 2?

(2) How was the upward trend in annual mean flows shown in figure 7 determine Is the slope of the line (upward trend) statistically significant as was inferred in the paper?

(3) Intuitively, it would seem that annual flood peaks similar to those noted in figure 8 could be observed at other stations which would lack the causal inter- pretation given for the Merced River case. Would you care to comment on this?

RESPONSE BY V. YEVJEVICH

The response to discussion by J. W. Delleur is as follows.

In my oral discussion I warned that spectral analysis as used by the communi- cation engineers should not be transferred indiscriminately into hydrology, for the following reasons. First, hydrologic series do not fulfill a simple condition of a sum of periodic and stochastic components. The composition shows periodi- cities in many parameters with a stationary stochastic component as exemplified by Eq. (34) in my paper. What does the continuous spectrum of that $x_{p,\tau}$ variable really measures in this case? Second, communication engineers have introduced the Wiener-Khinchine transforms for computing spectral densities from autocorrelation functions. Returning to Fourier transforms of original series, however, as exemplified by Fast-Fourier Transforms, saves computer time enormously. Was it really necessary, except for educational objectives, to go through the Wiener-Khinchine transforms and then later return to the much more efficient FFT? Third, some communication engineers claim that it is easier to see properties of stochastic processes in the frequency domain than in the lag domain. This is simply a problem of education and learning how to read spectra or correlograms. Fourth, while probabilists extensively use distributions of mixed random variables to fit physical reality, the trend seems to have been in using only the continuous spectrum. When complex series have known periodicities with an added stochastic component, the mixed spectrum of the line-spectrum should be used for harmonics of these periodicities and continuous variance densities for the stochastic part. Fifth, one can ask what the cross-spectral densities measure more than the cross-correlation functions tell, particularly if both series are of the type of Eq. (34).

The question of associating harmonics with real physical cycles is a misleading concept, mainly transferred from other disciplines into hydrology. Why should periodicities in nature be sine and cosine functions? In reality, a given number of harmonics is used only as a description of the shape of real periodicities of nature. Trying to find a physical explanation for every harmonic is a danger of translating indiscriminately techniques from one discipline to another.

The response to discussion by P. S. Eagleson is as follows.

It is questionable whether there are processes in the atmosphere and oceans that can induce periodicities in hydrologic processes beyond astronomic cycles. Also, it is not easy to visualize how the stochastic phenomena of jet streams and low and high pressure centers can induce regular cyclicity.

Instead of modeling the independent component in runoff theory, it is theoretically feasible to model the independent stochastic component in precipitation and then pass it through the system of a catchment environment. However, as many papers have shown during this seminar, precipitation over a catchment area has significant errors and the responses of the system are not simple. The general response of a real catchment is not only a function of time but also of other factors, with seasonality and stochasticity playing significant parts. Besides, the nonlinearity of systems is rather a rule than an exception. Assuming that precipitation does not change with time but that catchment factors do change by man-induced effects, then this second approach of simulation becomes attractive. On the other hand, the runoff series usually well indicates the impact of changes, and they can be identified and corrected for, and then applied to a sample of runoff series.

The response to discussion by T. Ishihara is as follows.

The time series of natural hydrologic phenomena are usually either continuous or intermittent but nevertheless continuous processes. When a time interval Δt is selected for discretization of such a series, the basic properties of series should not change. The selection of a greater Δt can be conceived as a summation or averaging of random variables of smaller Δt. By the central limit theorem, the summation of random variables changes the parameters and/or distribution and time dependence but not necessarily the basic characteristics of time series. This point of view is justification for the hypothesis in this writer's paper that the method and basic results of time series analysis should not depend on the time interval, Δt. All analyses by this writer of daily precipitation series show they are periodic. How is it possible to have periodic monthly precipitation series without having periodicity of daily series? However, it is admitted that for short samples the large sampling variation of daily series do not permit as simple a detection of periodicity in parameters of daily precipitation series as does the small variation of monthly precipitation. From experience the writer has found that the means and standard deviations for daily precipitation for each day of the year, the number of storms for each part of the season of the year, and the water yield per storm in each part of the season of the year are all periodic-stochastic processes.

3 .27

Because of a large random component in daily precipitation, and usually sma
samples, the detection of periodic components in parameters requires a refined
procedure, which is what the writer was attempting to accomplish by his paper.
Basically, simulating series by the Monte Carlo method should not depend on
whether Δt is 1 day, 3 days, 7 days, 15 days, or a month.

As to the writer's self-criticism of the outlined method of analyzing
hydrologic time series, the basic problem is that in most runoff time series
parameters of higher order than two are not stationary. Any future refinements c
series analysis will likely require the study of the third and fourth order
parameters for periodicity. However, by obtaining with time longer samples of
precipitation and runoff data and by using the regional information on data from
many stations, the information becomes available for study even of the third and
fourth order nonstationarity in parameters.

The response to discussion by C. Kisiel is as follows.

Whether the periodicity in hydrologic parameters are called periodic,
oscillatory or cyclic processes is a question of semantics and preferences. It
is sufficient to look at the mean values and standard deviations of the incoming
sun's radiation at a ground station for every day of the year to be convinced tha
there is a basic astronomic cyclicity or periodicity at the energy level which i
the moving motor of all hydrologic processes on the earth. If this fact is not
acceptable as sufficient justification for mathematical modeling of periodic-
stochastic processes, then the method of how to study the nonstationarity of
hydrologic stochastic processes will consistently be in doubt.

Advocating as complete a mathematical discription of hydrologic time serie
as feasible does not imply conclusiveness nor the exclusion of other conceptuali
zations. Basically, all methods used in the analysis of hydrologic series can b
divided into two groups: those that study series as nonstationary processes,
and those that separate the deterministic-periodic part of a series from the
stochastic part of given order of stationarity. From the writer's experience
it seems that the second conceptual approach is more advantageous, for the simpl
reason that it is much easier to treat mathematically, analyze in detail, and
relate the results to physical reality.

Trying to preserve the runs and crossings, range, surplus and deficit,
and extremes in the analysis of the series belongs to the first concept of treat
series as nonstationary processes. The writer is not convinced that extremes mu
be underestimated because model parameters might have a historical bias. It is
not the writer's intention to imply that the spectral analysis has no further us
in hydrology. What is implied, as stated in the response to the discussion by
J. Delleur, is that the line spectrum should be used for astronomic periodicitie
the continuous spectrum for the stochastic parts or series, and a mixed (line
and continuous) spectrum for the periodic-stochastic processes. The writer will
glad to study in detail and test statistically the claims of biannual periodicit
in atmospheric phenomena. One should not forget history, once many of the
"periodicities" inferred from the stochastic processes of short length series
were not confirmed.

The response to discussion by A. Murota is as follows.

The characteristic of the approach described by Professor Murota is an
analysis of hydrologic series as a nonstationary process. This approach is base
on the assertion that high flows and low flows have different time dependences,
and that river basin systems are nonlinear. However, even in a stationary
dependent process of highly skewed variables one would find that the correlatior
looks different for high and low values, particularly because of differences in

79

sampling variations. In accepting this assumption, one should ask is it legitimate to have one model for high flows and another model for low flows without any transitions between the two. Simulating monthly flows, usually with high periodicity in monthly means, and adding the 5-day "noise" about the simulated monthly values has the following characteristics. By computing individual monthly values, some seasonal variation in 5-day flows is smoothed out. The deviations of 5-day flows from the monthly values are highly mutually dependent and this must be reproduced in simulated 5-day flows. A constraint is imposed that the simulated 5-day flows for six consecutive values should have means zero.

In summary the approach by Professor Murota is basically one of a multitude of possible approaches in treating hydrologic series from the start as nonsta-tionary processes, and simulating them by preserving nonstationarity in one way or another.

The response to discussion by R. Quimpo is as follows.

As in the case of the response to the discussion by P. Eagleson, it is difficult for this writer to visualize how various hydrologic environments, in their natural state, can induce new periodicities beyond the reshaping of astronomical periodicities by modifying the amplitudes and shifting the phases of the harmonics that describe the input periodicites. The question whether the responses of hydrologic environments to various inputs, considering as hydrologic environments all environments along which the general water cycle occurs, deserves a severe and critical evaluation.

The response to discussion by J. P. Riley is as follows.

Many hydrologic time series exhibit both nonhomogeneity (man-made or produced by natural disruptions) and inconsistency (systematic errors) in their basic parameters. Certain statistical techniques and analyses of the prevailing environment and station history may be used to discover this nonhomogeneity and/or inconsistency in order to properly describe and remove them from the series. In this way either the virgin series are obtained or the series are reduced to the present or future conditions of the environment. This topic is considered outside the framework of the paper, even though it is one of the most important current hydrologic problems both in theory and in practice.

The response to discussion by T. D. Steele is as follows.

The approach of analyzing periodicities in hydrology by assuming the amplitude of any given harmonic a random variable is illustrated by Fig. 2. This would imply that for a 12-month harmonic the amplitude is larger in wet years and smaller in dry years than for the average year.

The trend shown in Fig. 7 is statistically nonsignificant. It is shown as a sampling bias rather than as nonhomogeneity in data. Usually this sampling trend is shown at most of the surrounding stations. The idea is that the sampling trend should not be perpetuated by the generation method.

The most attractive way to distinguish in Fig. 8 the three large floods that occur in the fall from all other smaller floods that occur in the spring from snowmelt is that there are two types of population that produce floods. The large fall floods have a smaller chance of occurring but they have very large variance. When these conditions in a river basin occur, it is judicious to study separately the fall and the spring floods.

3.29

United States-Japan Bi-Lateral Seminar in Hydrology

Honolulu, January 1971

A STUDY OF LONG RANGE RUNOFF SYSTEM RESPONSE BASED ON INFORMATION THEORY

By

Tojiro Ishihara

Professor of Civil Engineering

and

Shuichi Ikebuchi

Graduate Student, Department of Civil Engineering

Kyoto University, Kyoto, Japan

Synopsis :

Long-range runoff phenomena are essentially stochastic processes. To understand them, we must know not only their deterministic characteristics but also the statistical laws involved in the system of transition between precipitation and river discharge. This paper proposes methods for the analysis and synthesis of a long-range runoff response based on the ideas and techniques of information theory.

First, statistical properties of daily precipitation and river discharge series are discussed through their correlation analysis ; then, after time-invariant linearization of the runoff system according to the physical mechanisms in the runoff phenomena, the unit-impulse response function is derived from the Wiener-Hoph equation. We have designated this as the "statistical unit hydrograph". Next, statistical unit hydrographs that take into account both the variations of the water content in the subsurface stratum during the rainy season, and also the daily snow melt water input to the system in the snow melt season are proposed. Finally, the results of these procedures are applied to the Yura River basin with good agreement among the natural stream records.

1. Introduction

Because a long-range runoff system is essentially stochastic, for the analysis and synthesis of the system, we must find not only its deterministic characteristics but also the statistical laws which operate in the transition system from precipitation to river discharge.

The methods for this are classified into two groups : parametric models, and stochastic models. Parametric models are represented by the Stanford Watershed Model type [1], or by ones which are based on linear and nonlinear system theories.

The former are practical for computer use, but the choice of the parameters and their physical significance are a problem in themselves ; moreover, a great amount of data is necessary to determine their coefficients. With respect to the linear system theory, most studies are applied to the flood runoff systems [2], [3], [4], but there seems to be a limit in their direct application because of the nonlinearity of such runoff systems. Also in the application of the theory to a long-range runoff response [5], rainfall runoff and snow melt runoff are not separated even though their different runoff mechanisms and the nonlinear transformation method of the precipitation seems to lack physical significance. On the other hand, some investigators have applied the Wiener nonlinear theory to runoff systems [6], [7], but it is still difficult to make this application practical. Stochastic models are based on time series and frequency analyses. They are important in practice for the design of water resource systems but they do have such problems as high sampling variations of frequency distribution and an independent approach to precipitation and river discharge series which ignores the rainfall runoff mechanism.

The methods described above are currently used for studying long-range runoff responses. However, the dynamic mechanism of a runoff system response has not been completely explained, so satisfactory results have not yet been obtained.

The authors are interested in information theory, especially in Wiener's filtering theory, and have been investigating how to apply this theory to long-range runoff systems [10]. Assuming that the subsurface(interflow)and the ground water runoff components are dominant in a long-range runoff system response, and that they are approximately linear systems, we have emphasized the following points. First, the surface runoff component should be separated from the actual runoff system because it is nonlinear and it occurs for short times. Second, the stationary randomness of the daily precipitation series should be verified and the runoff system made time-invariant and linear.

In this paper the statistical properties of the daily precipitation and river discharge series are discussed by using correlation analysis. After the time-invariant linearization of the runoff system is made according to the physical mechanisms of the runoff phenomenon, the unit-impulse response function is derived from the Wiener-Hoph equation. We have designated this response as the "statistical unit hydrograph". Next, the statistical unit hydrographs for the rainy season and for the snow melt season are derived. Lastly, the results of these procedures are applied to the Yura River basin.

[1]   Crawford, N.H., and R.K. Linsley : The Synthesis of Continuous Streamflow Hydrographs on a Digital Computer, Dept. of Civ. Eng., Stanford Univ., 1962.

[2]   Nash, J.E. : The Form of the Instantaneous Unit Hydrograph, J. Geophys. Res., Vol.64, No.1, 1959.

[3]   Dooge, J.C.I. : A General Theory of the Unit Hydrograph. J. Geophys. Res., Vol.64, No.1, 1959.

[4]   Eagleson, P.S. : Optimum Discrete Linear Hydrologic Systems with Multiple Inputs, M.I.T, Hydrodynamic Laboratory, No.80. August, 1965.

[5]   Hino, M. : Introduction to the Information Theories on Hydrology, Part I, II, III, Tec. Report Nos. 4 and 6, Dept. of Civil Eng. Tokyo Institute of Technology, 1968.

[6]   Amorocho, J., and G.T. Orlob. : Nonlinear Analysis of Hydrologic Systems Univ. Calif. Water Resources Center, Contribution. No.40, 1961.

4 .2

2. Statistical Properties of Precipitation and River Discharge Series

2-1. The Wiener filtering theory and its application to a runoff system.

In the Wiener filtering theory it is assumed that the input to a system consists of a random signal plus a random noise, each of which is stationary in the sense that its statistical properties do not vary with time and the system is time-invariant linear. For the time-invariant linear system under consideration, the linearly predicted output function, $q(t)$, is

$$q(t) = \int_{-\infty}^{t} f(\tau) \cdot h(t-\tau) d\tau \qquad (1)$$

in which $f(t)$ and $h(t)$ are the input function and the unit-impulse response function, respectively. Actually, it is impossible to make $q(t)$ coincide with the observed output function, $q^*(t)$, because of the existence of the noise. So, to minimize the difference between $q(t)$ and $q^*(t)$, Wiener introduced the mean-square error as a statistical criterion and derived the Wiener-Hoph equation from Euler-Lagrange calculus of variations :

$$\int_{-\infty}^{\infty} h(t) \cdot \Phi_{11}(\tau-t) dt - \Phi_{12}(\tau) = 0 \qquad (\tau \geq 0) \qquad (2)$$

in which $\Phi_{11}(\tau)$ and $\Phi_{12}(\tau)$ are the autocorrelation function of the input and the crosscorrelation function between the observed input and the output, respectively [11].

Then, for a long-range runoff system response, the daily precipitation, $R(i)$, the daily river discharge, $Q(i)$, and the transformation system in the runoff, $H(k)$, will correspond to $f(t)$, $q^*(t)$, and $h(t)$, respectively. In practice, precipitation input $R(i)$ is lumped together and represented by the average precipitation as measured at certain locations. Under such considerations, Eq.(2) is expressed as being of the following discrete type.

$$\Phi_{RQ}(\tau) = \sum_{k=0}^{m} H(k) \cdot \Phi_{RR}(\tau-k) \qquad (3)$$

[7] Jacoby, S.L.S. : A Mathematical Model for Nonlinear Hydrologic Systems, Geophys. Res., Vol 71, No.20, 1966.

[8] Julian, P.R. : A Study of the Statistical Predictability of Stream-Runoff in the Upper Colorado River Basin, Colorado Univ., 1961.

[9] Quimpo, R.G., and V. Yevjevich. : Stochastic Description of Daily River Flows, Proc. Internat. Hydrology Symposium, IASH, Ft. Collins, Colo., USA, Vol.1, 1967.

[10] Takasao, T., and S. Ikebuchi. : A study of Long Range Runoff System Based on Information Theory, Dis. Prev, Res. Inst., Kyoto Univ. Annuals No.12, 1969. (in Japanese)

[11] Wiener, N : Extraporation, Interporation and Smoothing of Stationary Time Series, John. Wiley, New York. 1949.

4 .3

in which $\Phi_{RR}(\tau)$ and $\Phi_{RQ}(\tau)$ are given by Eqs.(4) and (5),

$$\Phi_{RR}(\tau) = \frac{1}{N-\tau} \sum_{i=1}^{N-\tau} R(i) \cdot R(i+\tau) \tag{4}$$

$$\Phi_{RQ}(\tau) = \frac{1}{N-\tau} \sum_{i=1}^{N-\tau} R(i) \cdot Q(i+\tau) \tag{5}$$

where, N is the number of days for the period considered, and m is the number of days the precipitation measurably influences river discharge.

In its application to a runoff system, it is important that the precipitation series be a stationary random process and that the system be time-invariant and linear. Thus, it is necessary to verify the stationary randomness of the precipitation series.

2-2. Stationarity of the precipitation series.

When the differences of the mean, variance, and autocorrelation coefficients among subseries of the series are relatively small, we may generalize that the series is approximately a stationary random process. In this paper, autocorrelation coefficients are particularly important, and from their shapes we can verify the stationarity of the daily precipitation series.

2-3. Time-invariant linearization of the runoff system.

Once the stationarity of the daily precipitation series has been verified, it is then necessary to make the runoff system time-invariant and linear.

Because the runoff system is a time-lag system, the crosscorrelation coefficient $\varphi_{RQ}(\tau)$ between precipitation and runoff series given by Eq.(6)

$$\underset{\tau}{\text{Max}}\, \varphi_{RQ}(\tau) = \frac{1}{N-\tau} \sum_{i=1}^{N-\tau} R(i) \cdot Q(i+\tau) \Big/ \sqrt{\left(\frac{1}{N-\tau} \sum_{i=1}^{N-\tau} R(i)^2\right) \cdot \left(\frac{1}{N-\tau} \sum_{i=1}^{N-\tau} Q(i)^2\right)} \tag{6}$$

takes the maximum value at $\tau = \tau_m$. This value τ_m is called the equivalent lag-time of the runoff system and gives us a criterion to make the runoff system time-invariant. The method for linearizing the runoff system is by separating the surface runoff component from actual runoff, separating the precipitation that is supplied to the surface runoff component from the observed precipitation, and separating the surface runoff component from the observed river discharge. The separation method is explained in the next chapter.

3. Statistical Unit Hydrograph as the Transformation Operator.

The unit-impulse response function as the transformation operator is obtained by solving Eq.(3) after verifying the stationarity of the daily precipitation series and making the runoff system time-invariant and linear. We call this function the "statistical unit hydrograph" and subsequently write it as SUH. Of course, we must rewrite R(i) and Q(i) in Eqs.(4) and (5) as Re(i) and Qe(i), respectively, where Re(i) and Qe(i) are the effective daily precipitation and the river discharge series after linearization.

3-1. SUH by the uniform separation method.

From the shapes of $\varphi_{RR}(\tau)$ and $\varphi_{RQ}(\tau)$, we first divide a water year seasonally into Winter (Dec.~Feb.), Spring (Mar.~May), Summer (Jun.~Aug.),

and Fall (Sep.~Nov.). Furthermore, to linearize the system, we separate
out the surface runoff component by the uniform separation method. The
procedure is as follows. From the observed daily precipitation series R(i)
and the river discharge series Q(i), separate any excess part more than the
value $\gamma \cdot D$ representing the saturation of the porous subsurface stratum and
the maximum value $\gamma_a \cdot A$ of the subsurface runoff, respectively, in which
γ , D , γ_a , and A are the effective porosity, the depth, of subsurface stratum,
the maximum intensity of subsurface runoff and the basin area, respectively.

Accordingly, the effective daily precipitation series Re(i) and the
effective river discharge series Qe(i) are expressed :

$$R_e(i) = R(i) \qquad\qquad R(i) < \gamma \cdot D \quad \Big\} \quad (7)$$
$$\qquad = \gamma \cdot D \qquad\qquad R(i) \geq \gamma \cdot D$$

$$Q_e(i) = Q(i) \qquad\qquad Q(i) < \gamma_a \cdot A \quad \Big\} \quad (8)$$
$$\qquad = \gamma_a \cdot A \qquad\qquad Q(i) \geq \gamma_a \cdot A$$

The values of $\gamma \cdot D$ and $\gamma_a \cdot A$ of the basin in question can be estimated by the
following relations derived from the recession curve of subsurface runoff.

$$\gamma \cdot D = \left\{ e^{\lambda_2 (t_2 - t_1)} - 1 \right\} f_c / \lambda_2$$
$$\qquad\qquad\qquad\qquad\qquad\qquad\qquad\qquad\qquad \Big\} \quad (9)$$
$$\gamma_a \cdot A = \lambda_2 \cdot \gamma \cdot D \cdot A$$

in which λ_2 is the recession coefficient of the subsurface runoff, t_2 and t_1
are the cessation times of subsurface and surface runoff respectively, and
f_c is the final infiltration capacity [12].

Considering that the dominant components in the long-range runoff are
the subsurface(inter flow)and the groundwater runoff components, this
separation method is convenient for practical runoff analysis. However,
applying the results of this method to an actual river basin, we find that
a water year should be divided into rainy and snow melt seasons, and that both
the variation of the water content in the subsurface stratum in the rainy
season and the amount of snow melt water in the snow melt season as input to
the system should be considered.

3-2. SUH of the rainy season.

In the rainy season, it is important to consider the initial loss
component L(i), in addition to the surface runoff component NL(i), for
estimating the effective daily precipitation Re(i). Figure 1 shows a
schematic representation of the distribution of the water content in the
subsurface stratum. In Fig. 1, W_s , W_c and W_a are the saturated water
content, the capillary saturated water content, and the adsorbed water
content, respectively.

For practical runoff analysis, we define the runoff zone as the
domain $W_c \sim W_s$ and the initial loss zone as the domain $W_a \sim W_c$. Furthermore,
we suppose that the water content W(i) in the runoff zone and in the initial
loss zone decreases with the succesion of no rainfall days as follows.
In the runoff zone,

[12] Ishihara, T., Ishihara, Y., Takasao, T., and C. Rai. : A Study on the
Runoff Characteristics of Yura River Basin, Dis. Prev. Res. Inst.,
Kyoto Univ. Annuals, No.5, 1962. (in Japanese)

$$W(i) = \left\{ W(i_o) + f_c/\alpha \right\} e^{-\alpha(i-i_o)} - f_c/\alpha \tag{10}$$

and in the initial loss zone,

$$W(i) = W(i_o) e^{-\beta(i-i_o)} \tag{11}$$

in which $W(i_o)$ and $W(i)$ are the water contents in the day i_o and i respectively, and α and β are the constants of each zone.

In practice this procedure will start when the water content $W(i)$ is near the lowest level in the initial loss zone, and the effective daily rainfall $Re(i)$ is estimated as the rainfall amount contained in the runoff zone, considering the observed rainfall $R(i)$ and the above calculated water content $W(i)$. That is to say,

when $W(i) \leq W_c$

i) $L(i) = R(i)$, $NL(i) = 0$ if $W(i) + R(i) \leq W_c$

ii) $L(i) = W_c - W(i)$, $NL(i) = 0$ if $W_c < W(i) + R(i) < W_s$ (12)

iii) $L(i) = W_c - W(i)$, $NL(i) = W(i) + R(i) - W_s$ if $W(i) + R(i) \geq W_s$

when $W(i) > W_c$

i) $L(i) = 0$, $NL(i) = 0$ if $W(i) + R(i) \leq W_s$

ii) $L(i) = 0$, $NL(i) = W(i) + R(i) - W_s$ if $W(i) + R(i) > W_s$ (13)

Consequently, $Re(i)$ is given, with the above $L(i)$ and $NL(i)$, as

$$Re(i) = R(i) - L(i) - NL(i) \qquad , \tag{14}$$

and in a day of no rainfall, $Re(i)$ equals zero.

On the other hand, with respect to river discharge, $Qe(i)$ is the same as that described in 3-1. Therefore, SUH of the rainy season is calculated from the above $Re(i)$ and $Qe(i)$.

3-3. SUH of the snow melt season.

The SUH in winter and spring was first calculated from the snowfall in terms of water and river discharge by the uniform separation method. However, the SUH thus calculated differed greatly from year to year. The snow melt runoff system is shown in Fig.2. The temperature, the rainfall, the wind, the subterranean heat, and so on are typical snow melt factors. Since the surface is covered with snow and the greater part of the snow melt water flows through this snow layer, its properties are analogous to that of subsurface runoff through the subsurface stratum. Thus, transformation system II will be regarded as a time-invariant linear system so that we can calculate SUH from the snow melt water and the river discharge.

To estimate the amount of daily snow melt water, the daily mean temperature T and the daily rainfall R are chosen as snow melt factors because they are easy to measure. The relation between the amount of daily snow melt water M and these factors is assumed to be

$$M = M_T + M_R = C \cdot T + R \cdot T/80 \qquad (T \geq 0) \tag{15}$$

4.6

in which M_R represents snow melt caused by rainfall, and this is added to the snow melt M_T caused by the temperature when it rains under $T \geq 0$; C is a constant ; and 80 (cal/g) is the heat of fusion of ice. **Furthermore**, the relations among T, R, and height h are assumed to be

$$T(h_i) = T(h_o) - \mu \cdot (h_i - h_o) \tag{16}$$

$$R(h_i) = R(h_o) + \lambda \cdot (h_i - h_o) \tag{17}$$

in which h_o and h_i are the height of the observation station and the mean height of the divided regions based on the height ; μ is the decreasing rate of the temperature ($°c/100m$) ; and λ is the increasing rate of the rainfall (mm/100 m).

Consequently, after calculating the amount of snow melt M_i in each region separately with Eqs. (15), (16), and (17), the amount of the daily snow melt water in the whole basin M(mm/day) can be expressed as

$$M = \sum_{i=1}^{n} A_i \times M_{in} \left(C \cdot T_i + R_i \cdot T_i / 80, \; S_i \right) / A \tag{18}$$

in which A_i and A are the basin area of region i and the whole basin area, respectively, and the snow content S_i is given as the product of its depth and density. Of course, when it rains under $S_i = 0$, the rainfall R directly corresponds to M.

In the end, SUH in the snow melt season is calculated from the above value M and the river discharge Q(i).

3-4. SUH of the subsurface and groundwater runoff systems.

In the methods described above, there still remain some problems, such as the peak values of the SUH differ from year to year and the accuracy of prediction is unsatisfactory, especially in the lower stages of river discharge. These problems result from that the separation of surface runoff from observed hydrographs is still unsatisfactory and the subsurface and groundwater runoffs are considered as the same runoff system in spite of their different linearities. So we improved and modified the SUH method by the following approach. The major improvement and modification are to separate the groundwater runoff from the subsurface runoff and to estimate the SUH for each runoff system. For practical purposes, we proposed the following procedures.

1) The decrease of soil moisture in runoff zone due to the supply of water to the subsurface and groundwater runoffs, is represented by Eq.(10), the daily decrease of soil moisture, $DW(i)$ $(=W(i)-W(i+1))$, is divided into the components $R_S(i)$ and $R_G(i)$, supplied to the subsurface and groundwater runoffs respectively. In this case, because the maximum value of the component supplied to the groundwater runoff is equal to the final infiltratio rate, f_c ,

$$\begin{aligned} R_S(i) &= DW(i) - f_c & \text{if } DW(i) - f_c \geq 0 \\ R_G(i) &= f_c & \\ R_S(i) &= 0 & \text{if } DW(i) - f_c < 0 \\ R_G(i) &= DW(i) & \end{aligned} \tag{19}$$

On the other hand, the soil moisture in the initial loss zone decreases according to the same equation as Eq.(11).

2) Next, estimating the recession coefficient γ_3 of the groundwater runoff from the observed hydrographs and assuming the peak lag time tpG (in most cases, tpG = one day) and the duration time T_G (for the groundwater runoff over a long period of time, T_G = 40~50 days is suitable for practical purposes), we decide the unitgraph $h_G(\tau)$ of groundwater runoff, under the condition of $\sum_{\tau=0}^{T_G} h_G(\tau) = 1 - p$, where p is the loss rate discharged into the deeper groundwater layer and other basins.

3) We can now predict the groundwater runoff $Q_G^*(i)$ by the following equation.

$$Q_G^*(i) = \sum_{\tau=0}^{T_G} h_G(\tau) \cdot R_G(i-\tau) \tag{20}$$

When the series $Q_G^*(i)$ do not agree with observed groundwater hydrograph, the value of parameter p may be changed. This process is repeated until $Q_G^*(i)$ is judged to be an adequate representation of groundwater hydrograph.

4) Once the optimal parameter p* was decided, the subsurface runoff $Q_S(i)$ is given as the difference between $Q_G^*(i)$ and observed river discharge $Q(i)$. When the difference is larger than maximum value of subsurface runoff, the excess part is separated as the surface runoff. In this case, the maximum value DW_{max} is given as the maximum decrease of soil moisture.

$$DW_{max} = (1 - e^{-\alpha}) \cdot W_s + (1 - \alpha - e^{-\alpha}) f_c / \alpha \tag{21}$$

5) Lastly, we estimate the statistical unit hydrograph $h_S(\tau)$ of the subsurface runoff, from $R_S(i)$ and $Q_S(i)$. Therefore, the subsurface runoff $Q_S^*(i)$ is predicted by the following equation.

$$Q_S^*(i) = \sum_{\tau=0}^{T_S} h_S(\tau) \cdot R_S(i-\tau) \tag{22}$$

where T_S is the duration time of subsurface runoff. The flow chart of the above procedures is shown in Fig. 3.

4. Application to the Yura River Basin and Discussion of Results.

4-1. General remarks about the basin and the research data.

General information about the Yura River basin is shown in Fig.4. The basin is 1,882 km^2 in area, 140 km is the length of the main channel, and it is extensively covered by vegetation. Climatically, there is considerable precipitation, especially snowfall in the winter ; the annual precipitation in the upstream area is much greater than in the downstream area.

The data analyzed and discussed in this paper are summarized in Table 1. In this table, the areal precipitation was obtained by the Thiessen method for the precipitation gauging stations. The computations were done by the FACOM 230-60 computer at the Data Processing Center, Kyoto University.

4-2. Verification of the stationarity of the daily precipitation series.

To verify the stationarity of the daily precipitation series R(i), we divide a water year seasonally and calculate the mean, standard deviation and autocorrelation coefficient in each season. The results obtained at the Ashiu station are shown in Table 2 and Fig. 5. From them, we may conclude that R(i) is approximately a stationary and independent random process because of $\varphi_{RR}(\tau) \doteqdot 0$ for $\tau \geq 1$. The results obtained at the Arakura, Kado, and Fukuchiyama stations were the same as those at Ashiu. Consequently, the stationarity of the daily precipitation series was verified over the whole basin.

4-3. Time-invariant linearization of the runoff system.

The value τ_m is used as a criterion for making the runoff system time-invariant. The cross-correlation coefficient $\varphi_{RQ}(\tau)$ was calculated by Eq.(6). According to Fig. 6, even though τ_m is equal to one day for all seasons, the correspondence between R(i) and Q(i) is strong in the summer and fall and weak in the winter and spring. Consequently, we should at least divide a water year seasonally into rainy and snow melt seasons to make the system time-invariant.

Let us now determine the values of $\gamma \cdot D$ and γ_a as the basic parameters for linearization. As mentioned in 3-1, $\gamma \cdot D$ and γ_a are

$$\left. \begin{aligned} \gamma \cdot D &= \left\{ e^{\lambda_2 (t_2 - t_1)} - 1 \right\} f_c / \lambda_2 \\ \gamma_a &= \lambda_2 \cdot \gamma \cdot D \end{aligned} \right\} \tag{23}$$

in which t_1, t_2, and λ_2 are estimated from the illustration of the hydrograph after the peak flow on semi-log paper.

Figure 7 shows the recession curves at Ono. From them, $\lambda_2 = 0.050$ $1/hr$ and $t_2 - t_1 = 60$ hrs are obtained. In previous studies, $f_c = 0.27$ mm/hr has already been given [13], so that, substituting the above values into Eq. (23), we can obtain $\gamma \cdot D = 120$ mm, and $\gamma_a \doteqdot 6$ mm/hr at Ono. These results were also obtained at other points.

4-4. Various computations of SUH and their characteristics.

(a) Determining SUH by the uniform separation method.

Figure 8 shows SUH computed by the uniform separation method based on $\gamma \cdot D = 120$ mm, $\gamma_a = 6$ mm/hr and m = 30 days.

From these and other calculations, we can say that (1) in winter, the sets of SUH differ considerably from year to year, especially in the upstream area, so the accuracy of the prediction is unsatisfactory; (2) in spring, they coincide fairly well, especially at the downstream stations and recede slowly compared with those in summer and fall, so their accuracy is unsatisfactory, especially in March; (3) they coincide well from year to year both in summer and fall, except for their peak values, so their accuracy is satisfactory except for large floods; (4) prediction by seasonal SUH is more accurate than that by the average SUH for the entire water year and (5) for $\tau \geq 15$, the SUH is apt to take negative values, which reflects the storage effect of the basin.

The above five points prove that the statistical unit hydrograph method is effective for the analysis and synthesis of a long-range runoff system response. At the same time, they suggest that there still remain some problems to be solved in the separation method.

To solve these problems, the following points are helpful. 1) Because the snow melt runoff is extensive in the winter and spring, especially in

[13] Ishihara, T., Tanaka, Y., and Kanamaru, S. : On the Characteristics of the Unit Hydrograph in Japan, Journal of the Japan Society of Civil Engineers, (JSCE), Vol.14, No.3, March, 1956.(in Japanese)

upstream parts, it is necessary to calculate SUH from the snow melt water and
the river discharge. 2) In summer, there is extensive surface runoff
because of the rainy season in addition to the remaining snowmelt. Moreover,
the loss by evapotranspiration is high. Therefore, it is necessary to
consider the variation of the water content in the subsurface stratum.
3) In the fall, the typhoons over this district cause more surface runoff.
It is necessary to deduce this runoff component completely. 4) A water year
should be divided into a snow melt and rainy seasons to make the system
time-invariant. 5) A value m = 15 days should be taken as the number of
days that precipitation has an influence on the river discharge.

(b) SUH of the rainy season.

By the method described in 3-2, let us first estimate the values of
W_a , W_c , and W_s of Fig. 1. Based on previous studies, we assume
$W_c \doteqdot 60$ mm, $W_a \doteqdot 36$ mm from the relations that $W_c - W_a = 20 \sim 30$ mm and
$W_a = 60 \sim 70$ percent of W_c , and $W_s \doteqdot 180$ mm from $W_s - W_c = 120$ mm.
The value W_s corresponds to the product of the depth and the porosity of
the subsurface stratum with 180 mm the proper value. Furthermore, we assumed
that if there is no rainfall for three days, W_s would decrease and become
W_c ; and if there is no rainfall for five days after that, W_c would become
W_a , but the water content $W(i)$ will not decrease to less than W_a [12],
[13].

Under the above assumptions, $\alpha = 1.106$ /day in the runoff zone and
$\beta = 0.102$ /day in the initial loss zone were obtained. Consequently,we
can compute SUH in the rainy season according to Eqs. (10),(11),(12),
(13),and (14) in 3-2.

Figure 9 shows some results obtained by the above method. The results
coincide fairly well from year to year, especially at Kado and Fukuchiyama,
except that their peak values are much greater than those obtained by the
uniform separation method. But, at Arakura, for 1954 when large floods
occurred , H(k) shows intensive variation and suggests that there still
remain a few problems to be solved in the separation method of the nonlinear component.

(c) SUH of the snow melt season.

Next the method described in 3-3 is applied at Arakura from Jan. to Apr.
in the years 1954, 1955, 1956. Data for analysis are the daily mean
temperature T, the daily precipitation R, and the depth of snow content S
at Ashiu. The zoning of the Arakura basin is shown in Table 3. From various
experimental and theoretical data [14], [15], we assumed that C = 5 mm/°C,
$\mu = 0.6$ °c/100m in Eqs.(15) and (16) and that $\lambda = 1.2$ mm/100m in Eq.(17)
from the relation between the precipitation and the height in this basin.
Snow densities were $\rho = 0.3, 0.4$, and 0.5 g/cm^3 for Jan., Feb., and Mar.,
respectively.

Figure 10 shows SUH derived from the snow melt water calculated under
the above given values and the river discharge. They are fairly uniform from
year to year and indicate that their peak values are relatively small and
that the snow melt water discharge recessions compared with the rainfall
runoff recessions. Therefore, we may conclude that this method is more
accurate than the method of uniform separation of precipitation and river
discharge.

[14] Odashiro, H., and N.Yamaguchi, : Snowmelting Flood of Ishikari River,
Hokkaido Development Bureau, 1966,(in Japanese)

[15] Aoki, Y., and K. Ishizuka. : A Study on the Snowmelting, Proc. of the
22 nd Conf. of JSCE, II-17, 1967.(in Japanese)

4 .10

(d) SUH of the subsurface and groundwater runoff systems.

Once the decrease of soil moisture was calculated according to Eqs.(10), (11), and (19), the SUH of the subsurface and groundwater runoff systems are estimated based on Fig. 3. Figure 11 shows the unitgraphs of groundwater runoff at Arakura, Kado, and Fukuchiyama and Figure 12 shows the linearly predicted groundwater runoff series by their unitgraphs. The prediction of groundwater runoff is very satisfactory and the loss rate in the downstream is small. Next, let us estimate the SUH of subsurface runoff. As the first step, the surface runoff was separated based on DW max described in 3-4. However, considering that the maximum value DW max does not discharge as the subsurface runoff in a moment, the separation of surface runoff should be practically made by the following approach. When $Q_s^*(i)$ predicted by hs (τ) estimated at the first step is smaller than $Q_s(i)$ under the condition of $R_s(i-1) \approx DW_{max}$, the difference between $Q_s^*(i)$ and $Q_s(i)$ should be separated as the surface runoff. The statistical unit hydrographs of subsurface runoff based on this approach are also shown in Fig. 11. They coincide very well every year, not only in the whole shape but also in their peak values. Furthermore, the sum of the predicted subsurface and groundwater runoffs is also shown in Fig. 12.

Finally, in order to summarize each method, we show in Table 4. the correspondence between the observed river discharge and that predicted by each method. Judging from these results, we may conclude that the last method is best.

5. Conclusions

In this paper, the statistical unit hydrograph method has been discussed using the Wiener filtering theory after verifying the stationarity of the daily precipitation series and making the long-range runoff system response time-invariant and linear. The results obtained are summarized as follows.
1) The statistical unit hydrograph method is effective for the analysis and synthesis of long-range runoff system responses and satisfactory agreement is obtained between the observed discharge and the predicted one, making it possible to predict the daily river discharge and to complement the lack of data of river flows. 2) Judging from the accuracy of prediction, the SUH that takes into account variation of water content in the subsurface stratum in rainfall season and the SUH that takes into account daily snow melt water in snow melt season are more effective than the uniform separation method.
3) Furthermore, the SUH method of the subsurface and groundwater runoffs is very effective, especially for the prediction in the lower stages of river discharge. 4) If $\gamma \cdot D$, γ_a , α , and β in rainfall season and C , μ , and λ in snow melt season are known or assumed, these methods may be generally applied to any other basins.

In the future, taking into account the evapotranspiration mechanism about the decrease of the soil moisture in runoff zone, it may be possible to make the statistical unit hydrograph method complete.

LIST OF SYMBOLS

A   : Watershed area

A_i : Area of the divided region i

c   : Constant on the snowmelt caused by temperature

D   : Depth of the subsurface stratum

DW(i) : Daily decreasing rate of the soil moisture content

f(t)   : Input function

f_c : Final infiltration capacity

$H(\tau)$: Unit-impulse response function in the daily discrete type (Statistical Unit hydrograph)

h(t)   : Unit-impulse response function in the continuous type

$h_G(\tau)$: Unitgraph of the groundwater runoff

h_i : Mean height of the divided region i

$h_S(\tau)$: Statistical Unit hydrograph of the subsurface runoff

L(i)   : Initial loss component

M_R : Daily snowmelt water content caused by rainfall

M_T : Daily snowmelt water content caused by temperature

m   : Number of days for which the precipitation influences the river discharge

N   : Number of days for the period considered

p   : Loss rate discharged into the deeper groundwater layer and other basins

Q(i)   : Observed daily river discharge

$Q_e(i)$: Effective daily river discharge.

$Q_G^*(i)$: Predicted discharge of the groundwater runoff

$Q_S^*(i)$: Predicted discharge of the subsurface runoff

q(t)   : Output function

R(i)   : Observed daily precipitation

$R_e(i)$: Effective daily precipitation

$R_G(i)$: Input component supplied to the groundwater runoff

R_i : Daily rainfall of the divided region i

$R_s(i)$: input component supplied to the subsurface runoff

r_a : Maximum intensity of the subsurface runoff

r_3 : Recession coefficient of the groundwater runoff

S_i : Snow content of the divided rigion i, given as the product of snow depth and its density

SUH   : Abridgement of the statistical unit hydrograph

T_G : Duration time of the groundwater runoff

Ti   : Daily mean temperature of the divided region i

T_S : Duration time of the subsurface runoff

t_1 : Cessation time of the surface runoff

t_2 : Cessation time of the subsurface runoff

t_{PG} : Peak lag time of the groundwater runoff

W(i)   : Soil moisture content

4 .12

Wa   : Adsorbed water content

Wc   : Capillary saturated water content

Ws   : Saturated water content

α : Recession coefficient of the soil moisture content in the runoff zone

β : Recession coefficient of the soil moisture content in the initial loss zone

$\Phi_{RQ}(\tau)$: Crosscorrelation function between the daily precipitation series and the river discharge series

$\Phi_{RR}(\tau)$: Autocorrelation function of the daily precipitation series

$\varphi_{RQ}(\tau)$: Crosscorrelation coefficient between the daily precipitation series and the river discharge series

$\varphi_{RR}(\tau)$: Autocorrelation coefficient of the daily precipitation series

λ : Increasing rate of rainfall on the height

λ_2 : Recession coefficient of the subsurface runoff

μ : Decreasing rate of temperature on the height

γ : Effective porosity of the subsurface stratum

τ_m : Equivalent lag time of the runoff system response

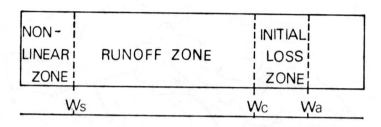

Fig. 1 Schematic diagram of states of water content in the subsurface stratum.

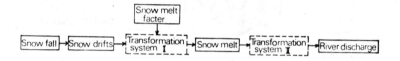

Fig. 2 Block diagram representing the runoff system of snow melt

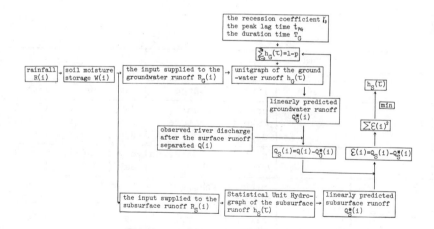

Fig. 3 Flow chart on the SUH of subsurface and groundwater runoffs.

4 .14

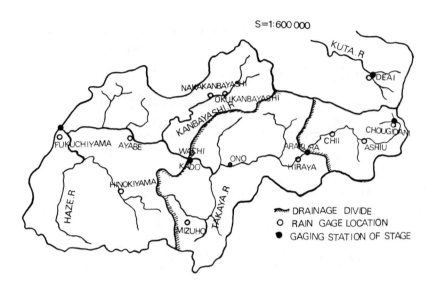

Fig. 4 General data of the Yura River basin.

Table. 1 Analyzed and discussed data.

Gauging station	Catchment area (km²)	Data name	Unit time	Period
Deai	20	river discharge	day	1967.5 - 1968.8
Ashiu		precipitation	day	1956.1 - 1960.12
		mean temperature	day	1956.1 - 1960.12
		depth of snowdrift	day	1956.1 - 1960.12
Arakura	150	areal precipitation	day	1954.1 - 1960.12
		river discharge	day	1954.1 - 1960.12
Ono	354	river discharge	hour	1952 - 1959
Kado	556	areal precipitation	day	1954.1 - 1960.12
		river discharge	day	1954.1 - 1960.12
Fukuchiyama	1157	areal precipitation	day	1954.1 - 1960.12
		river discharge	day	1954.1 - 1960.12

Table. 2 Mean and standard deviation of daily precipitation
at Ashiu station.

Season	Winter(Dec.-Feb.)		Spring(Mar.-May)		Summer(Jun.-Aug.)		Fall(Sep.-Nov.)	
Year	M.V	S.D	M.V	S.D	M.V	S.D.	M.V	S.D
1956	8.11	12.77	7.29	11.54	8.82	19.16	6.57	12.80
1957	6.59	8.66	7.43	11.57	10.11	19.77	5.30	9.98
1958	6.85	9.84	4.45	7.46	8.11	20.39	7.53	14.68
1959	8.28	12.47	6.33	9.13	10.23	34.85	7.69	28.21
1960	7.77	11.34	5.69	9.08	5.50	13.32	9.38	24.46

M.V ; Mean value   S.D ; Standard deviation

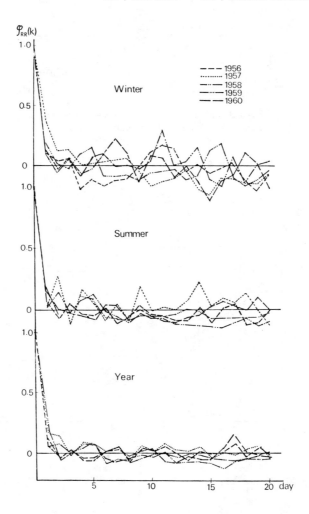

Fig. 5   Autocorrelation coefficients of daily precipitation at Ashui.

4 .16

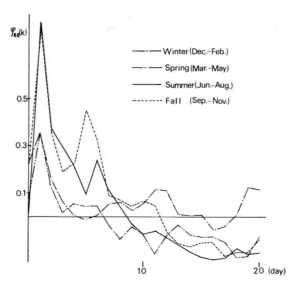

Fig. 6 Cross-correlation coefficients between the daily precipitation
and the river discharge at Arakura.

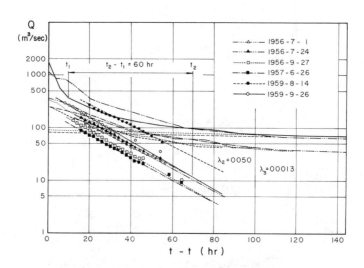

Fig. 7 Recession curves of the subsurface runoff at Ono.

4 .17

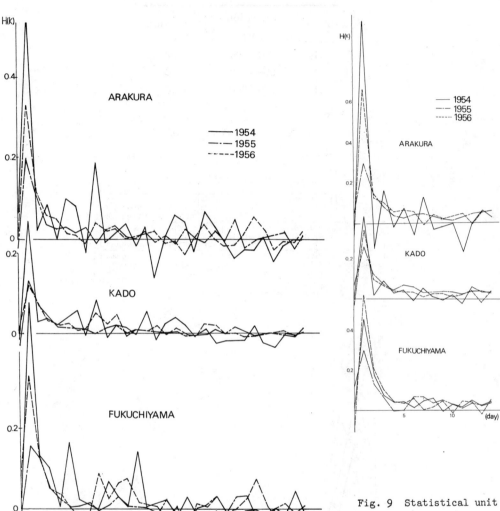

Fig. 8 Statistical unit hydrographs obtained by the
uniform separation method for a summer season.

Fig. 9 Statistical unit
hydrographs representing
variations of water
content in the subsurface
stratum.

4 .18

Table. 3 Zoning of the Arakura basin.

Zone	Elevation (m)	Rate of Occupation (%)
A_1	300~500	32
A_2	500~700	50
A_3	700~900	18

Table. 4 Values of F.

$F = \sum (Q(i) - Q^*(i))^2 / \sum Q(i)^2$; Q(i) : observed (after the surface runoff separated)
Q*(i) : predicted

Watershed	Year	Winter		Spring	Summer			Fall		Annual
		A	C	A	A	B	D	A	B	A
Arakura	1954	0.329	0.413	0.158	0.285	0.262	0.069	0.145	0.138	0.413
	1955	0.450	0.348	0.081	0.133	0.090	0.074	0.091	0.078	0.512
	1956	0.233	0.324	0.225	0.111	0.113	0.076	0.193	0.158	0.728
Kado	1954	0.188		0.084	0.120	0.100	0.108	0.048	0.066	0.189
	1955	0.286		0.046	0.111	0.106	0.116	0.111	0.156	0.658
	1956	0.069		0.155	0.253	0.136	0.078	0.079	0.092	0.610
Fukuchiyama	1954	0.254		0.205	0.133	0.119	0.054	0.050	0.027	0.994
	1955	0.216		0.126	0.138	0.256	0.231	0.193	0.146	0.762
	1956	0.079		0.145	0.120	0.102	0.075	0.076	0.084	0.686

A : by the uniform separation.
B : by the variation of soil moisture content.
C : by the daily snow melt water.
D : by the subsurface and the groundwater runoff.

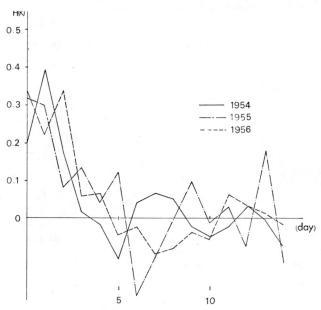

Fig. 10 Statistical unit hydrographs obtained for the daily snow melt water at Arakura.

4 .19

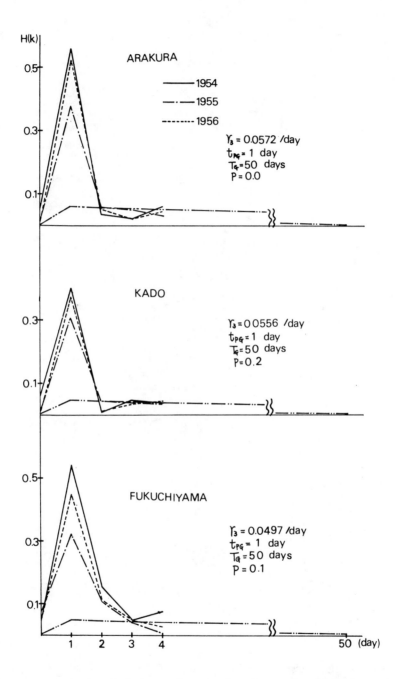

Fig. 11 Statistical unit hydrographs of subsurface and groundwater runoffs.

4 .20

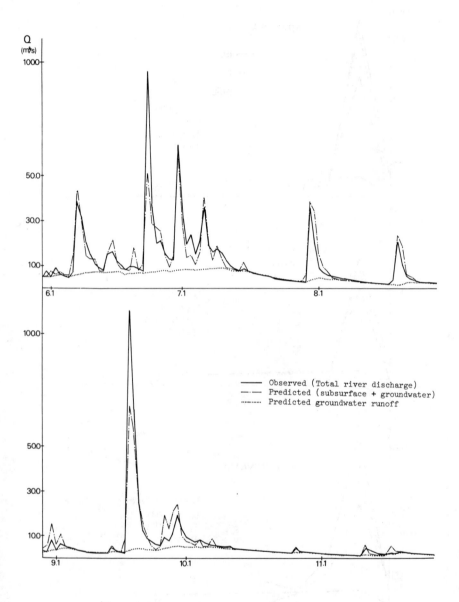

Fig. 12   Comparison between the observed and predicted river discharge
          at Arakura.

4 .21

DISCUSSION   V. YEVJEVICH

The processes studies in this paper are conceived as being composed of random signals plus a random noise. From experience a more realistic hypothesis might be that these processes are composed of a periodic signal in several parameters of the rainfall process with random noise added by using a proper mathematical methodology.

The selection of m , the number of days for which the rainfall influences the groundwater discharge, should have a clearer explanation. Figure 6 could imply that selecting m = 15 is a relatively short value.

The analysis of daily rainfall data is based on the assumption of independence, though most precipitation stations show that daily rainfall has the first serial correlation coefficients in the range between 0.15 and 0.40. The number of storms and the water yield per storm in a short interval are periodic functions with the day and the year as the periods. To consider hourly or daily rainfall inputs as independent processes may be only the first approximation.

Since the rainfall and snowfall--snowmelt seasons in a river basin are not clearly divided, the same intervals of the year may have either rainfall or snowfall conditions prevailing, so it is difficult to easily apply the techniques outlined.

RESPONSE BY T. ISHIHARA

The response to questions by V. Yevjevich are as follows.

1) Randomness of daily rainfall series. The processes in most meteorological phenomena are composed of the periodic and random components, and as for the rainfall process, the monthly and 10-days rainfall series have the same characteristics. From our correlogram analysis and others, however, in the daily rainfall series the pre-eminent periodicities do not appear and so it is natural that the input series are conceived as being composed of a random signal plus a random noise.

2) Selection of m, the number of days for which the rainfall influences the groundwater discharge. The value of m is selected based on the time that the crosscorrelation coefficients between rainfall series and river discharge series become nearly zero. Figure 6 in the final manuscript shows that m = 10-15 is a good selection and also figure 8 shows that selecting m > 15 seems to be lack of physical significance, because the statistical unit hydrographs take mostly negative values in such days as m > 15.

3) Independence of daily rainfall series. Though the daily rainfall series in the special short period as the rainy spell in early summer (June, in Japan) may be dependent on each other, the input rainfall series may be generally considered to be independent in four seasons (winter, spring, summer and fall) or two seasons (rainfall and snowfall seasons). In fact, the test of significance on the correlograms of figure 5 shows that the serial correlation coefficients for k $\geq$ 1 are not significant in most years.

4) Division of rainfall and snowfall-snowmelt season. Though it is difficult to divide both seasons clearly, the rainfall and snowfall-snowmelt seasons may be practically divided based on the crosscorrelation coefficients between the precipitation and river discharge series. The crosscorrelation coefficients in summer and fall show strong responses from rainfall to river discharge and differ from those of winter and spring, and this characteristic is remarkable at the upperstream region as Arakura station. By the crosscorrelation coefficients, therefore, we may estimate the season and region that the snowfall-snowmelt is predominant.

United States-Japan Bi-Lateral Seminar in Hydrology
Honolulu, January 1971

NONLINEAR RUNOFF KERNELS OF HYDROLOGIC SYSTEM

By   Mikio Hino, Associate Professor,
      Tooru Sukigara, Graduate Student,
      & Hideo Kikkawa, Professor,
      Department of Civil Engineering,
      Tokyo Institute of Technology,
      O-okayama, Meguro-ku, Tokyo, Japan

SYNOPSIS
      In recent years, great strides have been made in the area of stochastic
hydrology. A lot of quantitative information on hydrologic phenomena has
been derived reasonably from statistical hydrologic data. However, studies
from a point of view of non-linear stochastic process are rather few and not
necessarily successful.
      This paper describes a method of deriving the nonlinear "runoff kernnels"
based on the Wiener theory of nonlinear random process, together with some
discussions on the results of application to a real basin.
      In the appendix, the importance of the probability distribution of rainfall
and runoff data is discussed, stressing that the preliminary processing to
transform these data into random variables with Gaussian probability distribution
will further improve the efficiency of linear or nonlinear stochastic hydrologic
theories.

INTRODUCTION

a) Trends in Recent Development in Hydrology
      In recent years, a rapid development has been made in the field of hy-
drology, resulting in a profound understanding as well as an increase in the
reliability of prediction of complicated hydrologic phenomena. One area of
"new theoretical hydrology" is developed from a microscopic viewpoint considering both a local balance of dynamical forces and motion and a local conservation
of mass (the equations of motion and the continuity equation). Connecting
successively these equations of local balances either by an analytical method
or by a numerical integration, the investigators engaged in this direction
believe that the complete features of hydrologic phenomena may emerge. The method
of this approach is called "Dynamic hydrology" (Eagleson (1970)).[1] The method
invariably belongs, by its nature, to nonlinear theory.
      The other method of approach is from a macroscopic viewpoint, treating
the rainfall-runoff phenomenon as a lumped system. This method may be further
divided into two groups; i.e. the parametric hydrology group where the establishment of a reasonable differential equation to describe hydrologic process
is investigated and the optimum values of parameters involved in the differential

---

1) Eagleson, P.S. : "Dynamic Hydrology", McGraw-Hill, (1970)

equation for a lumped hydrologic system are sought; and, the stochastic hydrology group aiming to derive reasonably and objectively as much information as possible on the basis of the theories of stochastic process.

b) Nonlinear Theory of Lumped Hydrologic System

To the author's knowledge, the nonlinear theories of a lumped hydrologic system are developed in two ways. The one is an extension of the concept of unit hydrograph to include the nonlinear response terms in the convolutional type of integration. The other is a generalization of the so-called storage function method. In this respect, the former method will be called tentatively "response function method", while the latter "storage function method".

At the present time the "storage function method" seems to be alluring since it is more amenable to the analysis of the nonlinearity of hydrologic phenomena and in fact some interesting theories have been published.[2,3,4] However, one must perform numerical integration of the nonlinear differential equation to obtain the final results. On the other hand, the "response function method" would be further informative than the former because it provides us at a glance with a distinctive image of runoff process such as the linear and nonlinear effects, the lag time to peak discharge, the ratios of runoff components (short period overland runoff and long term infiltration-groundwater flow) and so on. Of course, since both methods belong to the category of a lumped system, the linear and nonlinear kernels of the response function method are, in principle, to be derived also from the nonlinear ordinary differential equation of the storage function method, although the kernels are usually determined from data of hydrologic observation or those of simulation.

c) Nonlinear Stochastic Theory

One of fatal points to be defeated in dealing with nonlinear random problems is the scarcity of mathematical tools.[5] Among a few mathematical means available, the Cameron-Martin-Wiener theory seems to be most adequate for our purpose. Cameron & Martin (1947)[6] and Wiener (1958)[7] proposed a new method of investigating a non-linear random process. A random process is expressed as an infinite series of statistical orthogonal functionals. This idea has been applied to turbulence problems by Meecham and Siegel (1964)[8] and later by many other investigators,[9] becoming one of foci in the field of turbulence.

Amorocho (1963)[10] was the first to attempt applying the Cameron-Martin-

---

2) Singh, K.P. : Nonlinear instantaneous unit-hydrograph theory, Proc. ASCE, vol. 90, no. HY2, 313-347 (1964)
3) Prasad, R. : A nonlinear hydrologic system response model, Proc. ASCE, vol. 93, no. HY4, 201-221 (1967)
4) Labadie, J.W. and Dracup, J.A. : Optimal identification of lumped watershed models, Water Res. Res., vol. 5, no. 3, 591 (1969)
5) Hino, M. : Lecture on New Mathematics, Stochastic Theory B-2, J. Japan Soc. Civil Eng., vol. 55 no. 1 (1970)
6) Cameron. R.H. and Martin, W.T. : The orthogonal development of nonlinear functionals in series of Fourier-Hermite functionals, Ann. Math. vol. 48, 385-389 (1947)
7) Wiener, N. : "Nonlinear Problems in Random Theory" MIT Press (1958)
8) Meecham, W. and Siegel, A. : Wiener-Hermite expansion in model turbulence at large Reynolds numbers, Phys. Fluids, vol. 7, 1178-1190 (1964)
9) Kahng, W-H. and Siegel, A. : The Cameron-Martin-Wiener method in turbulence and in Burgers'model: general formulae, and application to late decay, J. Fluid Mech., vol. 41, part 3, 593-618 (1970)
10) Amorocho, J. : Measures of the linearity of hydrologic systems, J. Geophy. Res. vol. 68. no.8, 2237-2249 (1963)

5 .2

Wiener (formerly, erroneously referred to as Wiener-Hermite) expansion to hydrology. Because of difficulty in deriving the nonlinear kernels, he adopted simplified situations such as inputs with step-function configurations, single square pulses, thus refraining from the determination of individual nonlinear kernels.

On the other hand, Jacoby[11] (1966) followed a little different method by the decomposition of input into linear time-lag systems in series with nonlinear no-time-lag systems the output of which produced the approximation to observed runoff. Although he did not restrict the functional forms of input, the nonlinear kernels were not determined explicitly.

d) Summary of the Author's Previous Results (Linear Theory)

This paper is an extension of a paper written by one of authors (M.H.).[12][13] In order to elucidate the advancement made in this paper which will be presented in subsequent sections, the principal achievements of the previous report will be summarized.

a) Two main components of runoff, i.e. the short period overland runoff and the long-term one, emerge decisively by computing the cross-correlation $C_{io}(\tau)$ or the cross-spectrum, $S_{io}(f)=C(f) + iQ(f)$, of rainfall and runoff.

b) The degree of nonlinearity of rainfall-runoff process can be estimated from the coherence function of rainfall and runoff, $\gamma^2(f)$,

$$\gamma^2(f) = \frac{C^2(f) + Q^2(f)}{P_{ii}(f)\,P_{oo}(f)} \tag{1}$$

where $C(f)$ and $Q(f)$ are the real part and the imaginary parts of the cross-spectrum, respectively and $P_{ii}(f)$ and $P_{oo}(f)$ mean the spectra of rainfall and runoff, respectively.

c) The optimal prediction linear kernel is shown analytically to be a weighted sum of each component which constitute the cross covariance. If the rainfall may be considered to be white noise which has the δ-function type of autocorrelation, the optimum prediction function is exactly identical with the cross covariance function divided by the rainfall magnitude, k,

$$K(\tau) = \frac{C_{io}(\tau)}{k} \tag{2}$$

where $k = \int_{-\infty}^{\infty} C_{ii}(\tau)\,d\tau$ and $C_{ii}(\tau)$ denotes the autocorrelation of rainfall.

d) Application of the linear prediction technique in the transformed domain after a nonlinear transformation of hydrologic data greatly improves the predictability of the theory.[14]

This paper explains firstly the delay-filter or multiple cross correlation method. Then, the method is applied to daily rainfall-runoff problems since daily

11) Jacoby, S.L.S. : A mathematical model for nonlinear hydrologic system, J. Geophy. Res., vol. 71. no. 20, 4811-4824 (1966)
12) Hino, M. : Improvement of the flood predictability by the application of the information theory, Proc. 4th Symposium of Disaster Prevention Science, 53-55 (1967)
13) Hino, M. : Runoff forecasts by linear predictive filter, Proc. ASCE, vol. 96, no. HY3, 681-702 (1970)
14) Hino, M. : Runoff forecasting by variable transformation, Proc. ASCE, no. HY4, 871-878 (1970)

rainfall is nearly a white noise random variable. Discussion is made on the results of application. The importance of the probability distribution of rainfall and runoff data is pointed out and a suggestion is made on the pre-liminary processing to transform those data into random variables with Gaussian probability distribution.

WIENER'S THEORY ON NONLINEAR STOCHASTIC PROCESS

A random input to a nonlinear response system is assumed to be white noise (with Gaussian probability distribution). The random input is denoted by $x(t, \alpha)$ where t is time and α denotes a stochastic parameter. The Wiener theory of nonlinear stochastic process gives the output, $y(t, \alpha)$, in the form of a series of orthogonal functions as

$$y(t, \alpha) = \sum_n G_n [K_n(t+\tau_1, t+\tau_2, \cdots, t+\tau_n), \alpha] \tag{3}$$

where the Gn's are orthogonal functionals expressed in terms of nonlinear kernel $K_n(\tau_1, \tau_2, \cdots, \tau_n)$ as equation (2)

$$G_n(K_n, \alpha) = \int_{-\infty}^{\infty} \cdots \int_{-\infty}^{\infty} K_n(\tau_1, \tau_2, \cdots, \tau_n) \, dx(\tau_1, \alpha) dx(\tau_2, \alpha) \cdots dx(\tau_n, \alpha)$$
$$- C_2^n k \int_{-\infty}^{\infty} \cdots \int_{-\infty}^{\infty} K_{n-2}(\tau_1, \cdots, \tau_{n-2}) dx(\tau_1, \alpha) \cdots dx(\tau_{n-2}, \alpha)$$
$$+ \cdots \tag{4}$$

In hydrologic problems, these unknown orthogonal functionals or rather the unknown kernels should be determined. Let $y_k(t)$ be an output, for the same input x(t), from another known non-linear system which is composed of the known kernels, $H_n(\tau_1, \tau_2, \cdots; \tau_n)$,

$$y_k(t, \alpha) = \sum_n G_n [H_n(t+\tau_1, t+\tau_2, \cdots, t+\tau_n), \alpha] \tag{5}$$

Make the product of the output from the unknown system and that from the known one excited by the same input

$$r(t, \alpha) = \sum_m \sum_n G_m [K_m(t+\tau_1, \cdots, t+\tau_m), \alpha] \times G_n [H_n(t+\tau_1, \cdots t+\tau_n), \alpha] \tag{6}$$

Taking into account the orthogonality of the functionals Gn's, the time averaged value of equation (6) is written

$$\lim_{T \to \infty} \frac{1}{2T} \int_{-T}^{T} r(t, \alpha) \, dt$$

$$= \sum_n n! \int \cdots \int K_n(\tau_1, \tau_2, \cdots, \tau_n) H_n(\tau_1, \tau_2, \cdots, \tau_n) \, d\tau_1 d\tau_2 \cdots d\tau_n \tag{7}$$

Original idea of Wiener is to constitute the known kernels in terms of the procducts of the Laguerre functions $(lu(\gamma))$

$$H_n(\tau_1, \tau_2, \cdots, \tau_n) = \prod_{i=1}^{n} lu_k(\tau_i) \tag{8}$$

Thus, the known orthogonal functionals are expressed by the Hermite polynomials in the Laguerre functions and the unknown functional system is given by the development in terms of sums of products of the Laguerre functions.

Another skillful method of deriving the nonlinear kernels has been devised by Lee & Schetzen (1965).[15] A parallel row of delay-filters is considered. The outputs, $y_k(t)$, of the delay-filter of a k-dimension is

$$y_1(t) = \int_{-\infty}^{\infty} \delta(\tau - \sigma) x(t - \tau) d\tau = x(t - \sigma)$$

$$y_2(t) = \int_{-\infty}^{\infty} \int_{-\infty}^{\infty} \delta(\tau_1 - \sigma_1) \delta(\tau_2 - \sigma_2) x(t - \tau_1) x(t - \tau_2) d\tau_1 d\tau_2 \tag{9}$$

$$= x(t - \sigma_1) x(t - \sigma_2)$$

$$\cdot \quad \cdot \quad \cdot \quad \cdot$$

where $\delta(\tau)$ means the Dirac δ-function.

Now, multiply the output of the unknown system, $y(t)$, by the output of the delay filter, $y_k(t)$. The averages of the products become

$$\overline{y(t)\, y_1(t)} = \int_{-\infty}^{\infty} K_1(\tau_1)\, k\, \delta(\sigma - \tau_1) d\tau_1 = k\, K_1(\sigma) \tag{10}$$

$$\overline{y(t)\, y_2(t)} = 2\, k^2 K_2(\sigma_1, \sigma_2) + h_0 k\, \delta(\sigma_1 - \sigma_2) \tag{11}$$

where

$$h_0 = \overline{y(t)} \tag{12}$$

$$k = \int_{-\infty}^{\infty} \overline{x(t) x(t - \sigma)}\, d\sigma \tag{13}$$

Therefore, the unknown kernel functions of lower order are determined by the mean products of the output or the cross- and the triple- correlation functions, as follows;

$$K_1(\sigma) = \frac{1}{k} \overline{y(t) y_1(t)} = \frac{1}{k} \overline{y(t) x(t - \sigma)} \tag{14}$$

$$K_2(\sigma_1, \sigma_2) = \frac{1}{2k^2} \overline{y(t) y_2(t)} = \frac{1}{2k^2} \overline{y'(t) x(t - \sigma_1) x(t - \sigma_2)} \tag{15}$$

where

$$y'(t) = y(t) - h_0 \tag{15A}$$

APPLICATION TO HEAVY DAILY RAINFALL AND FLOOD[16]

Since the Wiener theory is developed on the assumption that the input (rainfall in our case) is a Gaussian white noise, the direct applications of the theory to individual heavy hourly-(or short period) rainfalls, as conducted by Jacoby and Amorocho, would yield unsatisfactory results. In order to satisfy

15) Lee, Y.W. and Schetzen, M. : Measurement of a non-linear system by cross-correlation, Int. J. Control, vol. 2, no. 3, 237-254 (1965)
16) Kikkawa, H., Hino, M. and Sukigara, T. : Study on a nonlinear prediction of rainfall-runoff system, Tech. Rep. no. 9 Dep. Civil Eng., Tokyo Inst. Tech., June (1970)

this basic assumption, it is most appropriate to apply the theory to daily rainfall-runoff problems, because daily rainfalls are considered to be a white noise. Strictly speaking, the random input in Wiener's theory should be a white noise with Gaussian probability distribution. A preliminary data processing is advisable to transform raw data to Gaussian random variables. This problem is discussed in an Appendix.

Daily hydrologic data on the watershed of the Kannagawa river for a period more than a decade from 1948 to 1960, are analyzed, grouping them into successive three years as was done in the previous linear analysis. The groups have fortunately such characteristics as light, moderate and heavy rainfalls. These data which were obtained by T. Takenouchi and others[17] are one of the most reliable hydrologic data available in Japan.

As already shown, the auto-correlation and the spectrum of rainfall are, respectively, the δ-function type and the white-noise spectrum. The rainfall-runoff cross-correlations peak at one day lag and decrease at first rapidly and then slowly (as shown in Fig. 3). However, the three individual curves differ considerably depending on the intensity of rainfall. That is to say, the heavier the rainfall, the more rapid the decrease in cross-correlation becomes. This shows undoubtedly the strong nonlinearity of runoff phenomenon. Generally speaking, the delay time (detention period) for the maximum input-output cross-correlation would also shift towards a shorter lag-time. In our discrete treatment, however, one day is the shortest time unit, thus no shift of the peak correlation appears.

There is a speculation that the nonlinear analysis even of the second order would exceedingly improve the predictability of daily runoff for the Kanna-gawa basin. The reasoning is that the simple nonlinear transform of rainfall of the type[14] $f_i' = f_i^2$, has greatly increased the accuracy of forecasting of flood runoff.

Consequently, the characteristics of the second-order runoff kernel together with the contributions to the improvement of predictability will be investigated in this paper.

The second order nonlinear kernel for heavy rainfall group $K_2(\sigma_1, \sigma_2)$, has been computed from the triple cross-correlation of daily rainfall-runoff by a digital computer HITAC 5020E (HITACHI INDUSTRY Co.). The graph of $K_2(\sigma_1, \sigma_2)$ (Fig. 4), has a high peak at $\sigma_1 = \sigma_2 = 1$ day and almost flat plain of nil-level for other region except 3 small humps at about σ_1 or $\sigma_2 = 10$ days. The sharp high peak is an evidence of the strong nonlinearity of the second order for short period overland runoff. The gentle humps may be regarded partly as the weak nonlinearity effect for long period runoff. But, rather it is decided to be a pseudo nonlinearity, caused by an interaction between the periodicity of the rainfall autocorrelation at $\tau = 10$ day and runoff. The groundwater runoff of about 10 days delay would necessitate too fast velocity of seepage flows.

In computing of the value of k defined by equation (12) and proceeding to the calculation of predicted runoff, there arises a question as to whether the small humps of $C_{ii}(\tau)$ for τ larger than two days are meaningful enough to be included in the integration of k. Also how precise can the functional form of $C_{ii}(\tau)$ between $\tau = 0$ and $\tau = 1$ be estimated, for the rough discrete time unit of $\Delta\tau = 1$? In order to avoid the uncertainly involved in the computation of k-value, it is suggested to adopt a suitable multiplication factor β. In the following example, a factor of $\beta = 2.0$ is applied tentatively. Also, it is to be noted that the linear kernel determined in this paper and that of the previous paper are not necessarily identical. The former kernel has been obtained as the cross-correlation function devided by the value of k; while, the latter from the solution of the Wiener-Hopf integral equation.

---

17) Takenouchi, T. and others : Hydrological data on the basin of Kannagawa river, Public Works Research Institute and Construction Office of Simokubo Dam, Ministry of Construction, (1962)

5 .6

Flood prediction for the heavy rainfall group was made by using the following formulas,

$$f_0(t) = f_{o1}(t) + f_{o2}(t) \tag{16}$$

$$f_{o1}(t) = \int_{-\infty}^{\infty} K_1(\tau_1) x(t - \tau_1) d\tau_1 \tag{17}$$

$$f_{o2}(t) = \int_{-\infty}^{\infty}\int_{-\infty}^{\infty} K_2(\tau_1, \tau_2) x(t - \tau_1) x(t - \tau_2) d\tau_1 d\tau_2$$
$$- k \int_{-\infty}^{\infty} K_2(\tau_2, \tau_2) d\tau_2 \tag{18}$$

where $f_{o1}(t)$ means the runoff determined from the linear kernel only, while $f_{o2}(t)$ is the result of nonlinear prediction. Figure 5 shows a comparison between predicted flows and observed data. The prediction errors are defined by

$$\varepsilon(t) = f_d(t) - f_{o1}(t) \quad \text{or} \quad \varepsilon(t) = f_d(t) - \{ f_{o1}(t) + f_{o2}(t) \} \tag{19}$$

Figure 6, power spectrum of prediction error, clearly demonstrates how the flood prediction is improved by the method developed above. It is to be noted that the decrease in prediction error is remarkable for whole frequency region, although the method of nonlinear variable transformation[14] improved errors only for higher frequency region.

CONCLUSION

A simple method of deriving the nonlinear kernels of stochastic process by Wiener and Lee and Schetzen has been explained. The method has been applied to a daily rainfall-runoff process. It is shown that the short period runoff component shows strong nonlinearity at a short lag-time, while a weak nonlinearity is also found for the long term runoff component. The predictability for heavy daily rainfall has been shown to be increased considerably.

APPENDIX-IMPORTANCE OF PROBABILITY DISTRIBUTION AND PROPOSAL OF PRERIMINARY TRANSFORM OF RANDOM VARIABLE

Correlation and spectrum analysis has become one of the most prevailing methods of analysis of stochastic process. Especially, the concept of spectrum is powerful. Many practical measures of random process such as numbers of zero-crossing, numbers of peaks, probability of exceeding, forecasting and so on are derived from the spectrum as if it were a magician's hat (if and only if the random variables are a Gaussian). The Gaussian probability distribution is one of the most familiar encountered in practical cases and the presumption of it allows us the utilization of some fertile results of statistical theories, the random noise theory which has been established by Rice and further extended to wave statistics by Longuet-Higgins & Cartwright. However, it is sometimes forgotten or passed over that the concepts of correlation and spectrum are expressions of the second-order moment of random variables, containing no information on the higher-order moments nor those of the probability distribution.

For instance, the deviation of individual runoff from a mean value is asymmetric and the probability distribution is far from Gaussian. Consequently, to take merely the second-order moments overlooks some important indices of statistical characteristics.

The straightforward application of Cameron-Martin-Wiener's nonlinear random theory to a hydrologic system, even if the input is white noise, is not advantagious since the theory is constructed on the assumption that the input is Gaussian white noise. A better agreement between the nonlinear runoff prediction and the observed data as described above would be rather fortuitous. Consequently, a preliminary processing of raw hydrologic data to transform them into random variables with a Gaussian probability distribution is preferable. The idea of treating variables in a transformed domain has been already shown useful in another case.[14]

Let the probability distribution density of a random variable x be $P(x)$. Transformation of x into y by a function

$$y = f(x) \qquad\qquad (A1)$$

$$\text{or} \quad x = f^{-1}(y) = g(y) \qquad\qquad (A2)$$

is applied. Then, the probability distribution density of a new variable y becomes

$$\widetilde{P}(y) = P(x) \;/\; \frac{df}{dx}$$

$$= P(g(y))\frac{dg}{dy} \qquad\qquad (A3)$$

This is equivalent to a requirement that

$$\widetilde{P}(y)\, dy = P(x)\, dx \qquad\qquad (A4)$$

The problem is to derive a functional relation of transformation $y = f(x)$ which yields the Gaussian distribution $P(y)$. A practical way is to determine the relation between x_k and y_k from the following equation,

$$\int_{-\infty}^{x_k} P(x)dx = \int_{-\infty}^{y_k} \frac{1}{\sqrt{2\pi}\,\sigma} \exp\left(-\frac{y^2}{2\sigma^2}\right) dy \qquad\qquad (A5)$$

where $x_k = \cdots, x_0,\; x_0 + \Delta x,\; x_0 + 2\Delta x,\; \cdots$

The technique of transformation of probability distribution density permits us the following two method of nonlinear analysis;

1) Only the non-Gaussian input variables $x(t)$ are transformed to new ones $\widetilde{x}(t)$ with the Gaussian probability distribution. Then, the nonlinear response relationships is investigated between the transformed input $\widetilde{x}(t)$ and the original output.

2) Both the non-Gaussian input $x(t)$ and the output (not necessarily white noise) $y(t)$ are transformed into a domain where the transformed random variables $\widetilde{x}(t)$ and $\widetilde{y}(t)$ have Gaussian probability density functions. In the transformed domain a linear response relation may exist between the variables,

$$\widetilde{y}(t) = h(t) * \widetilde{x}(t) \qquad\qquad (A6)$$

where asterisk means convolution. The inverse transform from $\widetilde{y}(t)$ to $y(t)$ yields the nonlinear kernels and the orthogonal functionals which identify the nonlinear system.

LIST OF SYMBOLS

$C(f)$ = real part of cross spectrum
$C_{ii}(\tau)$ = autocorrelation of rainfall
$C_{io}(\tau)$ = cross-correlation of rainfall and runoff

f   = frequency

$f_d(t)$ = desired output, i.e. observed runoff

$f_i(t)$ = rainfall

$f_o(t)$ = output

$f_{o1}(t)$ = runoff estimated by linear prediction

$f_{o2}(t)$ = runoff component estimated from nonlinear kernels

g(x)   = a function

$G_n(K_n)$ = orthogonal functionals, eqs. (3) and (4)

h_o = average output, eq. (12)

$H_n(\tau_i)$ = known kernel

k   = rainfall magnitude, eq. (2) or eq. (13)

$K_1(\sigma)$ = linear runoff kernel, eq. (14)

$K_2(\sigma_1, \sigma_2)$ = the second order nonlinear kernel, eq. (15)

P(x)   = probability distribution density function

$P_{ii}(f)$ = spectrum of rainfall

$P_{oo}(f)$ = spectrum of runoff

Q(f)   = imaginary part of cross-spectrum

$r(t,\alpha)$ = product of the output from the unknown system and that from the known one excited by the same input, eq. (6)

$S_{io}(f)$ = C(f) + iQ(f) = cross-spectrum of rainfall and runoff

t   = time

x   = input variable

y   = output variable

α = stochastic parameter

β = modification parameter

$\gamma^2(f)$ = coherence function, eq. (1)

$\delta(\tau)$ = Dirac's δ-function

$\varepsilon(t)$ = prediction error, eq. (19)

$\sigma, \sigma_1, \sigma_2$ = time-delay variable

τ = time or time-delay variable

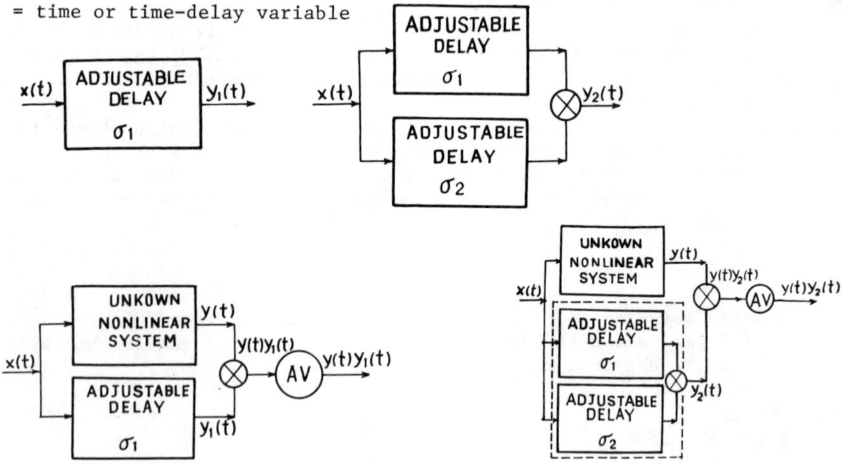

Fig. 1 : The delay-filter systems for calculation of the muticorrelation and the nonlinear kernels.

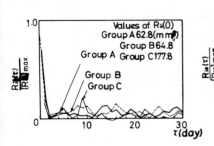

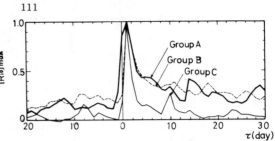

Fig. 2 : The autocorrelation coefficients of rainfall.

Fig. 3 : The cross-correlation functions of rainfall and runoff.

$$K_2(\sigma_1, \sigma_2) = \frac{1}{2 \kappa^2} \overline{(f_0(t) - \overline{f}_0) \, x(t-\sigma_1) x(t-\sigma_2)}$$

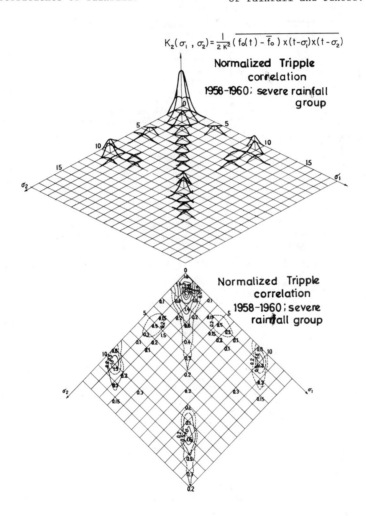

Fig. 4 : The second-order nonlinear kernels.

5 .10

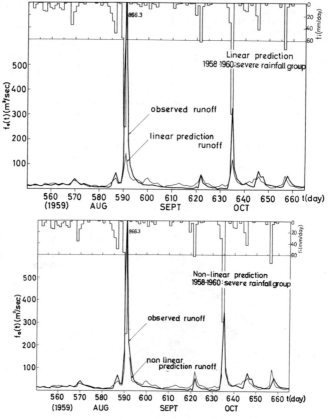

Fig. 5 : An example of runoff prediction.

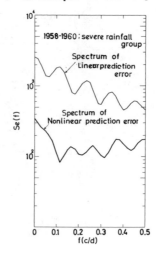

Fig. 6 : Spectra of prediction errors of linear and nonlinear predictions for heavy rainfall.

5 .11

DISCUSSION

V. T. CHOW

With reference to Fig. 6 the comparison of analyses between the linear and nonlinear assumptions may lead to the explanation of the linear and nonlinear characteristics of the physical phenomenon, although such interpretations may not be easy to make. However, the proposed method may be a possible tool.

P. S. EAGLESON

For my own information does this non-linear approach guarantee the satisfaction of continuity? It seems as though the successive kernels bear different units and I wonder how mass conservation is accounted for.

C. KISIEL

1. Concerning Figures 2 and 3, other than identifying storms as light, moderate or heavy, what kinds of storms produced the observed runoff -- for example, cyclonic, convective, typhoon, etc.?

2. What independent tests were made on the nonlinear predictors as applied to independent sets of rainfall?

R. G. QUIMPO

My comment is relative to the transformation of variables to achieve normality and thus apply Wiener's theory. This has been quite a problem, especially in simulation studies. For skewed distributions, the Wilson-Hilferty transform, suggested by Thomas and Fiering, has been used in many studies.

The difficulty in using Eq. A-3 is that $y = f(x)$ and hence $\frac{df}{dx}$ is usually unknown. The procedure suggested in Eq. A-5 is cumbersome because it requires storing a table in the computer and finding the corresponding values of x and y is time-consuming and computationally expensive. In this regard, I would like to call your attention to the Johnson distributions which are discussed in detail by Hahn and Shapiro*. This is of the form

$$y = \gamma + \eta\phi(x, \epsilon, \lambda) \quad \eta > 0, \ \lambda > 0, \ -\infty < \gamma < \infty, \ -\infty < \epsilon < \infty$$

where y is normally distributed, and depending on values of γ, η, ϵ and λ, the probability distribution of x could take different shapes. The types of distribution that x could take covers the whole range of Pearson's skewness-kurtosis' plot and so, x can be distributed symmetrically, positively or negatively skewed, bounded on one or both sides. The advantage of using this type of distribution is that after values of the parameters are estimated, one automatically obtains a Gaussian variable.

---

*"Statistical Models in Engineering", Wiley and Sons, 1967.

J. PAUL RILEY

1. Figures 5(a) and 5(b) apparently indicate only fitting differences and do not represent independent tests of your models. Your paper would be strengthened by including some plots showing independent tests of your model as a predictice tool.

2. You apparently check conservation of mass through the model by integratin
rainfall input and runoff output. This procedure indicates that your model does
not provide for losses on the watershed which probably is a suitable assumption
for predicting short time runoff in humid regions. However, it is suggested that
this assumption might be clearly indicated by the paper.

V. YEVJEVICH

The assumption of autocorrelation being the δ-function, and the white-noise
spectrum, seems at variance with Figure 3 in the text of this paper. The left
side of this figure shows an average ρ_k of about 0.20, with runoff preceding
rainfall. This positive average value may be explained by the cross correlation
of periodic components in rainfall and runoff. The differences in ρ_k on the
right and left sides of Figure 3 may then be attributed to the true relation of
stochastic components of runoff and rainfall.

Is it possible to assign physical explanations to the two functions, $k_1(\sigma)$
and $k_2(\sigma_1, \sigma_2)$, say by interpreting them as different impulse hydrographs, such
as the surface runoff, ground water flow, snowmelt runoff impulse hydrograph, or
by any other physical conditions? In general, can the mathematical concepts be
given a physical interpretation? Also, if the variables are transformed to better
study the impulse hydrographs, how easily can a physical interpretation be given
to the results obtained?

RESPONSE BY M. HINO

The response to discussion by P. S. Eagleson is as follows.

The condition of mass conservation is checked for the linear model by
the following method that the integrated mean output for a constant mean
annual rainfall should be equal to the observed mean annual runoff.

For the nonlinear model discussed in the main part of my paper, the
mass conservation condition would be approximately retained for rainfall
within the observed range. However, for a hypothetical heavy rainfall, it
will fail.

For the improved nonlinear model proposed in the appendix of my paper,
the condition of mass concervation is always reserved, because the probability distribution is transformed to be symmetrical with respect to zero
mean value, and the mean output for a constant mean value of input is
choosen to be equal to the mean of the observed output.

The dimensions of K_1 and K_2 are different. However, Runoff components
expressed in terms of K_1 and K_2 have the same dimension. Refering to equations
(13), (14), (15), (16), (17) and (18), the dimensions of runoff component
are as follows;

$$[k] = [x \cdot x \cdot t]$$
$$[f_{o1}] = [K_1] \ [x \cdot t] = [y \cdot x/k] \ [x \cdot t] = [y]$$
$$[f_{o2}] = [K_2] \ [x \cdot x \cdot t \cdot t] = [y \cdot x \cdot x/k^2] \ [x^2 \cdot t^2] = [y]$$

The response to discussion by C. Kisiel is as follows.

1)   In Japan, long rainfalls on early summer season which we call "Tsuyu" are caused by the long-staying front; while those in early autumn season are produced by typhoons. Sometimes in summer, heavy storms are brought about by convective rainfalls which cause locally concentrated severe rainfall damage.

2)   The kernels should be identical for different rainfall groups. However, the deviation of real input from the basic assumption of Wiener theory that input is a Gaussian white noise causes slight different forms between them. A preliminary transformation procedure as mentioned in Appendix is expected to give identical kernels of any order. The kernels shown in Fig. 3 and 4 which are derived from the three-year period heavy rainfall group are tested for the other two rainfall groups. The results were satisfactory.

The response to discussion by R. Quimpo is as follows.

The discussion by R. Quimpo may be best responded by asking a question, namely how the functional form $\phi(x, \varepsilon, \lambda)$ can be practically evaluated and its parameters estimated? I would like to express my thanks to Dr. Quimpo.

The response to discussion by J. P. Riley is as follows.

Examples shown in Figures 5(a) and 5(b) are given as results of the linear and nonlinear prediction for the worst case of Group C rainfall, in which the effect of nonlinearity is the strongest. Runoff prediction for other three year period group using the kernels K_1 and K_2 determined from the heavy rain group is shown to give satisfactory results.

The response to discussion by V. Yevjevich is as follows.

1)   Of course, the assumption that the rainfall is a random noise is a rough one. It is advisable to exclude by filtering procedure the long period components when we are concerned with short peiod runoff prediction (shorter than a month).

2)   If you mean components of runoff by the term "physical explanation", I would like to reply that this is the aim of our future study especially for the nonlinear kernels. The physical explanation of the linear kernel is given in my previous paper.

116

ted States - Japan Bi-Lateral Seminar in Hydrology
Honolulu, January 1971

R SYSTEMS ANALYSIS IN HYDROLOGY--THE TRANSFORM APPROACH,
THE KERNEL OSCILLATIONS AND THE EFFECT OF NOISE

by Jacques W. Delleur and Ramachandra A. Rao
Professor and Assistant Professor
School of Civil Engineering, Purdue University, Lafayette, Ind., U.S.A.

SYNOPSIS

The Fourier, Laplace and Z-transforms were used to evaluate the impulsive
response of watersheds from discrete rainfall excess and direct runoff values.
Runoffs for arbitrary storms could then be obtained making use of the convolution
integral. The methods were compared for their accuracy, stability, and computing
time by using a theoretical example. The computed kernel functions (impulsive
responses) for a number of storms showed large oscillations. These could be due
to noise, primarily in the input data and also in the output data. Several digital filters were tested to filter the input, or the output, or both, or to filter
the calculated kernel functions.

INTRODUCTION

A number of deterministic models in hydrology consider the rainfall and runoff as cause and effect. In surface water hydrology it is customary to separate
the ground water component from the surface runoff; the cause and effect relationship is then between the runoff producing rainfall or effective rainfall and the
direct runoff. In 1932 Sherman postulated that there is a linear relationship between effective rainfall (cause) and direct runoff (effect). He defined the unit
hydrograph as the response of the watershed to a specified effective rainfall
input, namely a unit depth of effective rainfall applied uniformly over the catchment in a specified time duration. The limit of the unit hydrograph as the rainfall duration approaches zero is called the instantaneous unit hydrograph (IUH).
J. C. I. Dooge[1] developed the basic theory of the instantaneous unit hydrograph.
This IUH can be thought of as the impulsive response of a lumped, time invariant
linear system. For this type of system the mathematical relationship between the
input and output function is the convolution or Duhamel integral

$$y(t) = \int_0^t x(\tau)h(t - \tau)d\tau \tag{1}$$

where $x(t)$ and $y(t)$ are the input and output functions, respectively, and $h(t)$ is
the impulsive response or the kernel function. Once the kernel function of a
watershed is known, the direct runoff may be calculated for any given rainfall
excess input. For this reason the determination of the kernel function from a
set of observed input and output data is of fundamental importance to the hydrologist. This paper is concerned mainly with the determination of the kernel function by means of the Fourier, Laplace and Z-transforms.

---

[1] Dooge, J. C. I. "A General Theory of the Unit Hydrograph," Journal of Geophysical Research, Vol. 64, 241-256, 1959.

I. - THE TRANSFORM APPROACH

It is well known that for a lumped, time-invariant, linear system initially relaxed, the transform of the output is equal to the product of the transforms or of the input and of the kernel function. The transformed kernel function is thus the ratio of the transforms of the output and of the input functions. The kernel function is finally obtained by inversion of its transform. The practicality of one type of transform versus another depends substantially on the relative ease with which the numerical inversion can be performed.

The Fourier Transform

The Fourier transform pair is defined by the following integrals

$$f(\omega) = \int_{-\infty}^{\infty} f(t)e^{-j\omega t}dt \quad , \quad f(t) = \frac{1}{2\pi}\int_{-\infty}^{\infty} f(\omega)e^{j\omega t}d\omega \quad . \qquad (2,3)$$

By taking the Fourier transform of both sides of eq. 1, it may be shown that the convolution in the time domain is equivalent to the product of the transforms in the frequency domain:

$$Y(\omega) = X(\omega)H(\omega) \quad , \quad H(\omega) = \frac{Y(\omega)}{X(\omega)} \quad . \qquad (4a,4b)$$

where $X(\omega)$, $Y(\omega)$ and $H(\omega)$ are the Fourier transforms of $x(t)$, $y(t)$ and $h(t)$, respectively. By expressing the exponential in the definition of the Fourier transform in terms of trigonometric functions the Fourier transform of the kernel function may be written as

$$. \; H(\omega) = \int_{-\infty}^{\infty} h(t)[\cos \omega t - j \sin \omega t]dt \qquad (5)$$

Defining the real and imaginary parts of the transform by

$$R_h(\omega) = \int_{-\infty}^{\infty} h(t)\cos \omega t \; dt \quad , \quad X_h(\omega) = - \int_{-\infty}^{\infty} h(t)\sin \omega t \; dt, \qquad (6,7)$$

respectively, eq. 5 becomes

$$H(\omega) = R_h(\omega) + j \; X_h(\omega) \qquad (8)$$

As $h(t)$ is a real function of t, it is readily seen that $R_h(\omega)$ and $X_h(\omega)$ are, respectively, even and odd functions of ω. Similarly $R_x(\omega)$ and $R_y(\omega)$, the real parts of $X(\omega)$ and $Y(\omega)$, respectively, are even functions of ω; and $X_x(\omega)$ and $X_y(\omega)$, the imaginary parts of $X(\omega)$ and $Y(\omega)$, respectively, are odd functions of ω.

If $H(\omega)$ is known, $h(t)$ can be evaluated by means of the inversion integral, eq. 3, which may be written as

$$h(t) = \frac{1}{2\pi}\int_{-\infty}^{\infty} H(\omega)e^{j\omega t}d\omega = \frac{1}{2\pi}\int_{-\infty}^{\infty} [R_h(\omega) + j \; X_h(\omega)][\cos \omega t + j \sin \omega t]d\omega$$

$$= \frac{1}{2\pi}\left\{\int_{-\infty}^{\infty} [R_h(\omega)\cos \omega t - X_h(\omega)\sin \omega t]d\omega + j \int_{-\infty}^{\infty} [R_h(\omega)\sin \omega t + X_h(\omega)\cos \omega t]d\omega\right\} \qquad (9)$$

As $R_h(\omega)\sin \omega t$ and $X_h(\omega)\cos \omega t$ are odd functions of ω, the last expression in eq. 9 reduces to

$$h(t) = \frac{1}{\pi}\int_{0}^{\infty} [R_h(\omega)\cos \omega t - X_h(\omega)\sin \omega t]d\omega \qquad (10)$$

6 .2

The kernel function h(t) may be calculated from eq. 10 in which $R_h(\omega)$ and $X_h(\omega)$ are, in turn, calculated with the help of eq. 4b, or more specifically by eqs. 11 and 12, the right hand side of which contain only the real and imaginary parts of the Fourier Transforms of the input and output functions:

$$R_h(\omega) = \frac{R_y(\omega) \cdot R_x(\omega) + X_y(\omega) \cdot X_x(\omega)}{[R_x(\omega)]^2 + [X_x(\omega)]^2} \tag{11}$$

and

$$X_h(\omega) = \frac{X_y(\omega) \cdot R_x(\omega) - R_y(\omega) \cdot X_x(\omega)}{[R_x(\omega)]^2 + [X_x(\omega)]^2} \tag{12}$$

In practical hydrologic computation, the rainfall excess input x(t) and the direct runoff output y(t) are not given in the form of continuous functions, but the values of these functions are given at discrete time intervals. The integrals in the Fourier transform and in its inversion need to be approximated by finite sums. The input and output data are assumed to be specified at the time interval Δt. For the integrals in the time domain the lower limit is taken as zero as the functions x(t), y(t), and h(t) are zero for t < 0, and the upper limit is the maximum time for which the function is defined. The discretized data in the time domain do not contain significant information about Fourier components with periods less than $2\Delta t$. Consequently, it is not necessary to extend the calculation in the frequency domain for frequencies higher than $f_c = (2\Delta t)^{-1}$. This cutoff frequency is called the Nyquist frequency. The lower and upper limits of the integrals in the frequency domain are thus zero and $\omega_c = 2\pi f_c$, respectively.

If $\Delta\omega = 2\pi\Delta f$ is the frequency interval, the Fourier transforms do not contain significant information with a frequency larger than $2\Delta f$. Consequently, the largest period for which the calculations need to be carried is $T_c = 1/(2\Delta f)$. This is a consequence of the sampling theorem in the frequency domain which states that the Fourier transform $f(\omega)$ can be uniquely reconstructed from equidistant samples, provided that $f(t) = 0$ for $|t| > T_c$. This theorem applies to the evaluation of the kernel function h(t) by means of eq. 10, as this function is bounded in the time domain. If the number of sampling points of the rainfall excess hyetograph is N_P, then the rainfall duration is $T_R = (N_P - 1)\Delta t$. Likewise if the number of sampling points in the direct runoff hydrograph is N_Q, the base time of the direct runoff hydrograph is $T_Q = (N_Q - 1)\Delta t$. The base time of the kernel function of the IUH is thus $T_K = T_Q - T_R = (N_Q - N_P)\Delta t$, and the number of points in the base time of the kernel function is $N_Q - N_P + 1$. The frequency interval in the evaluation of eq. 10 is thus $\Delta f = 1/(2T_c) = 1/[2(N_Q - N_P)\Delta t]$. If N_ω is the number of sampling points in $H(\omega)$, the number of intervals is $N_\omega - 1$ which is obtained by dividing the Nyquist frequency by the frequency interval, thus

$$N_\omega - 1 = f_c/\Delta f = 2(N_Q - N_P)\Delta t/(2\Delta t) \quad \text{or} \quad N_\omega = N_Q - N_P + 1 \tag{13}$$

It is thus seen that for the numerical evaluation of the impulsive response(eq.10) the frequency range from 0 to $(2\Delta t)^{-1}$ must be divided into at least $N_Q - N_P$ intervals, where N_Q and N_P are the number of sampling points in the direct runoff output, and in the rainfall excess input, respectively.

Once the kernel function h(t) is evaluated it is often used in the convolution integral, eq. (1), with the original input to regenerate the output as a verification of the correctness of the calculations. The function h(t) may also be convolved with another input to predict the output. As the convolution in the time domain is equivalent to the product of the transforms in the frequency domain the sampling theorem in the frequency domain is useful in determining the discretization requirements. The numerical evaluation of

$$y(t) = \int_0^t x(\tau)h(t - \tau)d\tau = \frac{1}{2\pi} \int_{-\infty}^{\infty} X(\omega) \cdot H(\omega)e^{j\omega t}d\omega \qquad (14)$$

as a sum truncated at the Nyquist frequency can be expected to be correct for $t \leq 1/(2\Delta f)$. As it is desired to have an accurate evaluation of $y(t)$ for the whole interval 0 to T_Q, it is necessary to choose $\Delta f \leq 1/(2T_Q)$ or $\Delta\omega \leq \pi/T_Q$. Thus the number of intervals in the frequency range is $N_Q - 1$, and the number of sampling points in the integrand of eq. 14 is N_Q, where N_Q is the desired number of sampling points in the calculated output. If the calculation is done in the time domain by a finite sum approximating the integral of eq.1, each of the sequences must have at least N_Q sampling points, some of which may be zeros. The matter of the numerical convolution will be discussed later in the light of the Z-transform and the discrete Fourier transform.

The Laplace Transform

The Laplace transform pair is defined by the following two integrals:

$$H(s) = \int_0^{\infty} h(t)e^{-st}dt \qquad , \qquad h(t) = \frac{1}{2\pi j} \int_{\gamma-j\infty}^{\gamma+j\infty} H(s)e^{st}ds \quad . \qquad (15,16)$$

The last equation is known as the Mellin integral formula. The integration is to be performed along the line $\text{Re}(s) = \gamma$. The real number γ is chosen so that it lies to the right of all the singularities of the function $H(s)$, but is otherwise arbitrary. If the function $H(s)$ is known in closed form, the integral of eq. 16 can be evaluated by contour integration along the Bromwich path in the complex plane and by using Cauchy's residue theorem. Alternatively, if $H(s)$ is known as the ratio of two polynomials such that the degree of the denominator is greater than that of the numerator, the inversion integral may be evaluated by Heaviside's expansion formulae.

The difficulty usually encountered in hydrologic application of the Laplace Transform is that the function $H(s)$ is usually not known in closed form, but it is known pointwise only. The classical methods of analysis, therefore, are not applicable, and it is necessary to resort to other numerical procedures for the inversion of the Laplace transform. One approach consists in reducing the Mellin integral of eq. 16 into a Fourier integral. This method has also been called the Laplace-Gamma method, and has been discussed among others by Krylov and Skoblya.[2]

Expressing the Laplace variable s as a complex frequency $s = \gamma + jq$ and considering q as the integration variable, the Mellin integral becomes

$$h(t) = \frac{1}{2\pi j} \int_{-\infty}^{\infty} e^{(\gamma + jq)t} H(\gamma + jq)j \ dq = \frac{e^{\gamma t}}{2\pi} \int_{-\infty}^{\infty} e^{jqt}H(\gamma + jq)dq \qquad (17)$$

Introducing the notations

$$H(\gamma + jq) = G(q) \qquad \text{and} \qquad h(t)e^{-\gamma t} = g(t) \qquad (18,19)$$

---

[2] Krylov, V. I. and Skoblya, N. S. "Handbook of Numerical Inversion of Laplace Transforms," Israel Program for Scientific Translations, 1969. (Translated from Russian).

eq. 17 becomes

$$g(t) = \frac{1}{2\pi} \int_{-\infty}^{\infty} G(q)e^{jqt}dq \tag{20}$$

which is recognized as the inverse Fourier transform of $G(q)$ as defined in eq. 3.

Rewriting the Laplace transform of $h(t)$ of eq. 15 in terms of the complex frequency q, we get

$$H(\gamma + jq) = \int_{0}^{\infty} h(t)e^{-(\gamma+jq)t}dt \tag{21}$$

or

$$G(q) = \int_{0}^{\infty} e^{-\gamma t}h(t)e^{-jqt}dt = \int_{0}^{\infty} g(t)e^{-jqt}dt \tag{22}$$

It is immediately recognized that $G(q)$ is the Fourier transform of $g(t)$ and that eq. 20 and 22 are Fourier transform pairs.

The Fourier transform $G(q)$ may be expressed in terms of its real and imaginary parts. Thus using the notation of eq. 6, 7, and 8

$$G(q) = R_g(q) + jX_g(q) \tag{23}$$

so that, by eq. 10, the inverse of $G(q)$ is

$$g(t) = \frac{1}{\pi} \int_{0}^{\infty} [R_g(q) \cos qt - X_g(q) \sin qt]dq \tag{24}$$

Representing the Laplace transform of the input and of the output by $X(q)$ and $Y(q)$, respectively, the transfer function $G(q)$ can be written as

$$G(q) = \frac{Y(q)}{X(q)} = R_g(q) + jX_g(q) = \frac{R_y(q) + jX_y(q)}{R_x(q) + jX_x(q)} \tag{25}$$

The kernel function $h(t)$ is then obtained by eq. 19:

$$h(t) = \frac{e^{\gamma t}}{\pi} \int_{0}^{\infty} [R_g(q) \cos qt - X_g(q) \sin qt]dq \tag{26}$$

where

$$R_g(q) = \int_{0}^{\infty} e^{-\gamma t} h(t) \cos qt \, dt \quad , \quad X_g(q) = -\int_{0}^{\infty} e^{-\gamma t} h(t) \sin qt \, dt \tag{27,28}$$

The real and imaginary parts of the transfer function are given by equations similar to eqs. 11 and 12 which are then introduced in the right hand side of eq. 26 for the evaluation of $h(t)$. It is thus seen that the inversion integral in complex plane of eq. 16 is replaced by the integral of eq. 26 on the real line which can be performed numerically without difficulty. It can also be shown that the eq. 26 may also be written as

$$h(t) = \frac{2e^{\gamma t}}{\pi} \int_{0}^{\infty} R_g(q) \cos qt \, dq; \qquad h(t) = \frac{2e^{\gamma t}}{\pi} \int_{0}^{\infty} - X_g(q) \sin qt \, dq \tag{29a,29b}$$

The remarks made for Δt and $\Delta \omega$ and for the limits of integration regarding the Fourier transform are still valid for the Laplace transform but with ω replaced by q. Additional remarks, however, are in order regarding γ. The real part of the complex frequency must be to the right of the singularities of $G(q)$. In practice, the locations of these are not known without assuming a mathematical model of the system. However, as the hydrologic system behaves in a manner similar to an overdamped mechanical system, it may be assumed to be stable. Therefore

6.5

γ may be taken as any positive number. In particular, for γ = 0, the Laplace-Gamma method reduces to the Fourier transform.

The magnitude of the transfer function

$$|G(q)| = \left\{[R_g(q)]^2 + [X_g(q)]^2\right\}^{1/2}$$

(30)

may be thought as defining a three-dimensional surface over the (γ, jq) plane. This surface has peaks to the left of the imaginary axis located at the singularities of the transfer function. To the right of these singularities the surface gradually levels towards the (γ, jq) plane. The function $|H(\omega)|$ is a cut of this surface at γ = 0. The function $|G(q)|$ is a cut of this surface for $\gamma \neq 0$. For γ > 0 the amplitudes of G(q) decrease as γ increases. One may, therefore, expect that as γ increases the numerical values of the integral of eq. 26 decrease, which are then multiplied by a proportionally larger coefficient $e^{\gamma t}/\pi$ to obtain h(t). As a consequence, for large values of γ the errors in the evaluation of h(t) will tend to be magnified. It is thus expected that the accuracy of the results will decrease with increasing values of γ.

Z-Transform

The previous methods of systems analysis by the Fourier and Laplace transforms were originally developed for continuous input, output, and transfer functions. The necessary approximations were developed to extend the use of these methods to the analysis of discrete data as they are usually found in hydrology. In contradistinction, the Z-transform was developed specifically for the analysis of discrete data.

The Z-transform pair of a sequence of numbers x(Δt), x(2Δt), ..., x(nΔt), is defined by

$$X(z) = \sum_{n=0}^{\infty} x(n\Delta t)z^{-n} \quad , \quad x(n\Delta t) = \frac{1}{2\pi j} \oint X(z)z^{n-1}dz$$

(31,32)

where z is a complex variable, and the contour integral is evaluated on the unit circle.

The Z-transform may be considered as an extension of the Laplace transform. If the function f(t) is a continuous function which is zero for t < 0, then its discrete sampled function $f^*(t)$ and the Laplace transform of $f^*(t)$ may be written, respectively, as:

$$f^*(t) = \sum_{n=0}^{\infty} f(n\Delta t)\delta(t - n\Delta t) \quad , \quad f^*(s) = \sum_{n=0}^{\infty} f(n\Delta t)e^{-ns\Delta t} .$$

(33,34)

Letting $z = e^{s\Delta t}$ in eq. 34 we retreive eq. 31. It is seen that X(z) is given by an infinite series in powers of z^{-1}.

The Z-transform relationship between input and output sampled in synchronism is similar to the Fourier or the Laplace transform relationships for continuous functions:

$$Y(z) = H(z)X(z) \quad \text{or} \quad H(z) = \frac{Y(z)}{X(z)} ,$$

(35a,b)

where H(z) is the sampled transfer function also known as the pulsed transfer function, and X(z) and Y(z) are the Z-transforms of the input x(nΔt) and of the output y(nΔt), respectively. The pulsed impulsive response H(nΔt) would then be obtained by inversion of H(z). By comparing the definitions of the Laplace

6.6

transform (eq. 15) and of the Z-transform (eq. 31), it is seen that the sampled values of the kernel function $h(n\Delta t)$ and the pulsed impulsive response $H(n\Delta t)$ are related by

$$H(n\Delta t) = h(n\Delta t)/\Delta t \qquad (36)$$

In practice to invert $H(z)$ it is not necessary to use the inversion integral of eq. 32. As $H(z)$ is given as the ratio of two polynomials in z^{-1}, it will suffice to express the ratio in a series in powers of z^{-1} by long division, for which a simple algorithm may be written. The coefficients in the series correspond to the values of the sampled function at the sampling instants. The sampled transfer function may be written, with the help of eqs. 31 and 35b, as

$$H(z) = \frac{y(\Delta t) + y(2\Delta t)z^{-1} + \ldots + y(n\Delta t)z^{-n+1}}{x(\Delta t) + x(2\Delta t)z^{-1} + \ldots + x(m\Delta t)z^{-m+1}} \qquad (37)$$

since for hydrologic data $x(0) = y(0) = 0$. By long division eq. 37 becomes

$$H(z) = H_1 + H_2 z^{-1} + H_3 z^{-2} + \ldots + H_n z^{-n} + \ldots \qquad (38)$$

where

$$H_n = \left\{ y(n\Delta t) - H_1 x(n\Delta t) - H_2 x[(n-1)\Delta t] \ldots - H_{n-1} x(2\Delta t) \right\} /x(\Delta t) \qquad (39)$$

In eq. 38 the H_n are the coefficients of powers of z^{-1}, hence by eq. 31, $H_n = H(n\Delta t)$. The impulsive response sampled at interval Δt is then calculated from eq. 36 as $h(n\Delta t) = H(n\Delta t)\Delta t$.

Similar to eq. 14, the product of two Z-transforms in the z-plane is equivalent to the discrete convolution in the time domain. Thus if $Y(z) = X(z)H(z)$, then

$$y(n\Delta t) = \sum_{m=0}^{n} x(m\Delta t)H(n\Delta t-m\Delta t) = \sum_{m=0}^{n} x(n\Delta t-m\Delta t)H(m\Delta t) \qquad (40)$$

Just as the Z-transform may be thought of as a discrete form of the Laplace transform, so the evaluation of the Z-transform of a finite sequence, $f(n\Delta t)$, at N points equally spaced in the z-plane at angles of $k\Omega$ radians along the unit circle, can be considered equivalent to the evaluation of the discrete Fourier transform. In fact, if in eq. 34 the variable s is replaced by $j\omega$, and ω is discretized at intervals $\Omega = 2\pi/N\Delta t$, and the sum is carried over N terms, the right hand side of eq. 34 becomes identical to the discrete Fourier transform which is defined by eq. 41 and its inverse by eq. 42.

$$F(k\Omega) = \sum_{n=0}^{N-1} f(n\Delta t)e^{-jk\Omega n\Delta t} \quad , \qquad f(n\Delta t) = \frac{1}{N} \sum_{k=0}^{N-1} F(k\Omega)e^{jk\Omega n\Delta t} \qquad (41,42)$$

The spectral samples given by eq. 41 may thus be imagined as vectors perpendicular to the complex z-plane and arranged along the unit circle at angular values of $k\Omega$. As a result, the product of two discrete Fourier transforms is equivalent to the discrete Fourier transform of a circular or periodic convolution of eq. 40 and is not equivalent to a linear or aperiodic convolution as implied by eq. 1. It thus appears that the number of sampling points in the convolution sum is equal to the number of sampling frequencies in the z-plane. Should it be desirable to extend the convolution sum further, then it is necessary to add a sufficient number of zeros to the x or H sequences, or to both, (eq. 40). It may now be seen that the same result applies to the evaluation of the discretized convolution integral. The number of sampling points in the finite sum approximating the convolution integral cannot exceed the number of sampling points in the sequences being convolved. If necessary, these sequences may be extended with as many zeros as necessary to avoid the periodicity effect.

Numerical Experiments

The example chosen for the numerical experiments was suggested by Dooge[3] but was modified so that it would satisfy the continuity equation. The shapes of the input, output, and kernel functions are similar to those found in typical hydrologic problems. The input function is given by

$$x(t) = t(1 - t)e^{1 - t}(e^8 - 41) \quad ; \quad 0 \leq y \leq 1 \quad (43)$$

the output function is

$$e^{9-t} t^3(2 - t)/12 + e^{1-t} (t^2 + 3t + 4) - e(4 - t) \; ; \quad 0 \leq t < 1 \quad (44a)$$

$$e^{9-t} (2t - 1)/12 + (11 - 3t) - e(4 - t) \quad\quad\quad 1 \leq t < 8 \quad (44b)$$

$$(e^{9-t}/12)[12t^2 - 130t + 335 - (t - 8)^2(152 - 14t - t^2)] \quad\quad (44c)$$

$$+ (11 - 3t) \quad\quad\quad 8 \leq t \leq 9$$

and the kernel function is given by

$$h(t) = t(e^{8-t} - 1)/(e^8 - 41) \; ; \quad\quad 0 \leq t \leq 8 \quad (45)$$

The Laplace transforms of the output and input functions were first computed by using the finite difference form of eq. 15, in which the frequency was varied from zero to q_m. By using the real and imaginary parts of the output and input transforms in eq.11 and 12(with ω replaced by q), the real and imaginary parts of the transfer function were computed, which were in turn substituted back into eq. 26 to obtain the response function h(t). The response function was convolved with the input to regenerate the outflow hydrograph. The numerical experiments were conducted to determine the effect of changes in γ (eq. 26) and in q_m on the computational scheme. The following notation is used in the presentation of results:

X(t) – Given input – Theoretical – (eq. 43).
Y(t) – Given output – Theoretical – (eq. 44).
Amplitude – (eq. 30).
H(t) – Theoretical impulsive response, eq. 45.
H1(t) – Response function computed by using eq. 29a.
H2(t) – Response function computed by using eq. 29b.
H3(t) – Response function calculated by Fourier Transform, eq. 10.
H4(t) – Response function computed by using eq. 26.
Z1(t) – Output regenerated by convolving the input with H1(t) – (eq. 1).
Z2(t) – Output regenerated by convolving the input with H2(t) – (eq. 1).
Z3(t) – Output regenerated by convolving the input with H3(t) – (eq. 1).
Z4(t) – Output regenerated by convolving the input with H4(t) – (eq. 1).
q_m – Truncation frequency in numerical evaluation of eq. 26, 29a, 29b.
γ   – A parameter in eq. 26, 29a, 29b.

The effects of changing γ on the evaluation of h(t) are shown in Fig. 1. The results for the Fourier transform (γ=0) and for the Laplace transform (γ=0.1,0.3, 0.6, and 1.0) are shown on the left half of the figure. The ΔT value used for discretizing the input and output data was equal to 0.1, and the trun-

[3] Dooge, J. C. I. "Analysis of Linear Systems by Means of Laguerre Functions," Jour. SIAM (Control) 2(3):396-408, 1965.

cation frequency, $q_m = \Pi/0.1 = 10\Pi$, which is the Nyquist frequency, was used in all the cases. The range $(0, q_m)$ was divided into (N_Q) intervals where N_Q is the number of points defined on the outflow hydrograph. The results are essentially the same for all the non-negative γ values tested. However, if larger γ values are selected, the errors in the computation of integrals in eq. 26, 29a, and 29b increase with an increasing value of γ.

The effect of negative γ values on the behavior of the computational scheme is shown in the right half of Fig. 1. Although the γ values in the Laplace-Gamma method are traditionally selected to be on the positive side of the axis in the complex plane, the only restriction on the selection of the γ values is that they should be to the right of the singularities. However, the negative γ values have the apparent advantage that they do not amplify the errors in the integrals as positive γ values tend to do, and, consequently, this experiment was undertaken. The results of the experiments indicate that the negative γ values introduce higher oscillations in the amplitude values than the corresponding positive γ values. The response functions and the regenerated hydrographs differ negligibly from those computed by using positive γ values shown in the left half of Figure 1.

In general, the kernel functions $H4(t)$ were more accurate and more stable than $H1(t)$ or the $H2(t)$ functions, for all the t values which were considered. When there is a positive outflow or inflow value at $t = 0$, then the results of computation of $H2(t)$ will be erroneous as $H2(t)$ will always be forced to be equal to zero at $t = 0$, according to eq. 29b. These conclusions were also borne out by the analysis of field data, the results of which are not shown here.

The results of varying the truncation frequency, q_m, are shown in Fig. 2. The minimum and the maximum values of the truncation frequency used in the experiment were half and twice the Nyquist frequency or 5π and 20π, respectively. It may be observed in the left side of Fig. 1 that the amplitude spectrum oscillates around zero for frequencies larger than about 3π. It appears, therefore, that the frequencies between 3π and 10π contain very little information, if any. For this reason the integration between 3π and 10π does not improve the results; on the contrary, it may bring in noise which may be present in this frequency band. This conclusion is verified by the fact that the kernel values obtained for $q_m = 10\pi$ have greater discontinuities at $t = 1$ and 8 (Fig. 1, left) than the corresponding computations shown in Fig. 2 (right). The value of $q_m = 20\pi$, or twice the Nyquist frequency, obviously yields erroneous results, as frequencies higher than the Nyquist frequency do not contain any information. The results in the right hand side of Figure 2 show the instabilities introduced by these higher frequencies.

The Z-transform method of computing the response functions was compared to the Fourier transform method for field data. The results for two different watersheds are shown in Fig. 3. The results are essentially the same by both methods. The Z-transform has the advantage that the corresponding computer program to find $h(t$ is much simpler and shorter than those for either the Fourier or the Laplace transforms. As a result the computer time for the Z-transform calculations is considerably less than for the other methods, by a factor of 1/10 approximately.

It could have been anticipated that the results by the Z-transform would be less accurate than those by the Fourier or Laplace transform as each value of the sampled transfer function H_n depends on the previous values (see eq. 39), whereas in the Fourier and Laplace methods, each value of the transfer function is calculated independently and depends on all the values of the input and output functions. At least with the 15 place accuracy of the computer used (CDC 6500) there was no discernible propagation of error by the Z-transform method.

6 .9

II. - THE KERNEL OSCILLATIONS AND THE EFFECT OF NOISE

In the case of actual rainfall excess and direct runoff data, it must be recognized that they contain errors, as is the case in all physical measurements. There is a limit to the precision with which the kernel function can be calculated by means of the transforms. Laurenson and O'Donnell[4] investigated the effect of several types of errors on the calculated unit hydrograph. In addition to the errors or "noise" in the hydrologic data, additional errors are created in the calculation procedures. One source of error is the quantization error of the input and output data. Another source of error is due to the rounding or truncation of products or sums of products. These errors may either be damped or amplified depending upon the realization of the computations. Sampling at a constant interval in the presence of noise does not create a major problem. It is possible to reconstruct a function from its sampled values by interpolation using the sampling theorem. As the coefficients of the interpolation are less than one and decrease rapidly, oscillating in sign, the magnitude of the error of the interpolated function is of the same order of magnitude as the errors affecting the data. It may thus be stated that the reconstruction of a function from its sampled values is tolerant to the presence of noise. But as it will be seen in the following discussion, this is not necessarily true of all the computations involved in the estimation of the kernel function.

Blank, Delleur, and Giorgini[5] found that an error in the kernel is reduced by a factor varying from 1/6 to 1/25 in the resulting output obtained by convolution. Conversely an error in the output would be magnified in the derived kernel. This shows that the kernel function is very sensitive to errors in the output data. Numerical experiments by Blank and Delleur,[6] in which known smooth input and output functions were perturbed by a random noise with an amplitude less than 10% of the maximum signal, resulted in strong oscillations in the kernel function. The amplitude of these oscillations reached 8 times the maximum amplitude of the undisturbed kernel. It is thus apparent that the kernel functions are very sensitive to noise both in the input and output functions. This result justifies the practice of either smoothing the kernel function or of attempting to eliminate the noise in the data. Further observation of the results showed that the frequency of the oscillations in the kernel function was close to the Nyquist frequency. This indicated that the noise was principally in the high frequency range, and that it could be greatly attenuated by means of a low-pass filter.

Digital Filters

A filter may be described as a linear system which has a frequency response with a specified amplitude, $|W(\omega)|$, and phase, $\theta(\omega)$, in the frequency domain. If

---

[4] Laurenson, E. M. and O'Donnell, T. "Data Error Effects in Unit Hydrograph Derivation," Journal of the Hydraulics Division, ASCE, Vol. 95, No. HY6, 1969.

[5] Blank, D., Delleur, J. W., and Giorgini, A. "Oscillatory Kernel Functions in Linear Hydrologic Models," Paper H58, AGU 1970 Annual Meeting (Abstract in EOS, Trans. AGU, Vol. 51, No. 4, April 1970), submitted for publication in Water Resources Research.

[6] Blank, D., Delleur, J. W. "A Program for Estimating Runoff from Indiana Watersheds - Part I. Linear System Analysis in Surface Hydrology and Its Application to Indiana Watersheds," Purdue Water Resources Research Center, Tech. Rept. No. 4, August 1968.

the amplitude is a constant, generally unity, for $\omega < \omega_c$, and is small for $\omega > \omega_c$, then the filter is called a low-pass filter and ω_c is the cutoff frequency. The impulsive response, $w(t)$, of the filter is obviously the inverse Fourier transform of its frequency response function $W(\omega)$. For the continuous filter the relationship between the input data and the output or filtered result is

$$y(t) = \int_0^\infty w(t)x(t-\tau)d\tau \qquad \text{such that} \qquad W(\omega) = |W(\omega)|e^{-j\theta(\omega)} \qquad (46,47$$

has the desired amplitude and phase characteristics. The functions $w(t)$ and $W(\omega)$ are called the data window and spectral windows, respectively, according to the terminology introduced by Blackman and Tukey. For digital filters the convolution integral is replaced by a convolution sum

$$y_t = \sum_{i=-m}^{n} w_i x_{t-i} \qquad (48$$

Filters of this type are called moving averages, and are non-recursive as they do not have any feedback. The filters used in this study are of this type. For discrete filters, the frequency response in terms of $f = \omega/2\pi$ is given by

$$W(k\Delta f) = \sum_{i=-m}^{m} w_i \cos(2\pi i k\Delta f) - j \sum_{i=-m}^{m} w_i \sin(2\pi i k\Delta f) \qquad (49$$

which is the counterpart of Eq. 5 for continuous systems. Note that the phase can be made equal to zero by taking $w_i = w_{-i}$, when the frequency response reduces to

$$W(k\Delta f) = w_0 + 2\sum_{i=1}^{m} w_i \cos(2\pi i k\Delta f) \qquad -\frac{1}{2} \le k\Delta f < \frac{1}{2} \qquad (50$$

The Tukey window[7] (sometimes called hanning) is a low pass filter often used in spectral analysis. Jenkins and Alavi[8] modified the Tukey window to obtain high-pass filter. Its data and spectral windows are given by

$$w_0 = 1 - \frac{1}{m+1} \qquad (51$$

$$w_i = w_{-i} = -\frac{1}{m+1}\left\{\frac{1}{2} + \frac{1}{2}\cos\frac{i\pi}{m+1}\right\}, \qquad i = 1, \ldots m \qquad (52$$

$$W(f) = w_0 + 2\sum_{i=1}^{m} w_i \cos 2\pi i k\Delta f \qquad (53$$

For the filtering of the hydrologic data, a low pass filter is needed with the cut off frequency near the Nyquist frequency. Delleur[9] obtained this type of filter by translation of the frequency response function in the frequency domain

$$W'(f) = W(0.5 - f) = w_0 + 2\sum_{i=1}^{m} (-1)^i w_i \cos 2\pi i k\Delta f \quad . \qquad (5$$

---

[7] Blackman, R. B., and Tukey, J. W. "The Measurement of Power Spectra," Dover 1959.

[8] Alavi, A. S., and Jenkins, G. M. "An Example of Digital Filtering," Applied Statistics, Vol. 14, p. 70, 1965.

[9] Delleur, J. W. "Réflexions sur l'Analyse Spectrale," Laboratoire National d'Hydraulique, Chatou, France, Rept. ST22, Jul. 1969.

It is seen that the low pass filter is simply obtained by multiplying the weight coefficients w_i by $(-1)^i$. This filter will be called the modified Jenkins filter, MJF, and its frequency response is shown in Fig. 4.

A refinement of the Tukey window was suggested by Blackman[7]. The corresponding discrete high pass filter has the following data and spectral windows:

$$w_o = \frac{0.16\ m}{m+1} \tag{55}$$

$$w_i = w_{-i} = -\frac{1}{m+1}\ (0.42 + 0.50\ \cos\frac{i\pi}{m+1} + 0.08\ \cos\frac{2i\pi}{m+1})$$

$$i = 1, 2, \ldots\ m \tag{56}$$

$$W(k\Delta f) = w_o + 2\sum_{i=1}^{m} w_i\ \cos 2\pi i k\Delta f$$

As before a low pass filter with cutoff at the Nyquist frequency may be obtained by replacing w_i by $(-1)^i w_i$. This filter will be called the modified Blackman filter, MBF, and its frequency response is also shown in Fig. 4.

Digital Filtering of Hydrologic Data:

The MJF and the MBF were applied to effective rainfall and direct runoff data from some Indiana watersheds. The determination of the effective rainfall and of the direct runoff is discussed in ref. 6. Figure 5 illustrates the effect of the MJF and the MBF on the data. When the data are filtered, 2m data points, m each at the beginning and at the end, are lost. If the number of data points is large, such as in a hydrograph, this effect is not serious. If it is small, as in a hyetograph, then the volume of rainfall is drastically reduced and is not the same as the volume of runoff. This effect is illustrated in Fig. 5 which shows a comparison of original and filtered rainfall and runoff data for different values of m. In order to circumvent this situation, the volumes of the original rainfall and runoff were computed and the ordinates of the filtered hydrograph and hyetograph were, respectively, multiplied by the following ratios: (volume of the original hydrograph/volume of the filtered hydrograph) and (volume of the original hyetograph/volume of the filtered hyetograph). The hydrographs and hyetographs resulting from this procedure are referred to as "adjusted" data. The adjusted rainfall and runoff data are also shown in Fig. 5. Between the two filters, it can be seen that the MJF causes a lesser distortion of the data than the MBF.

The effects of filtering and "adjusting" both the input and output on the kernel function are shown in Fig. 6. For the storm considered the results of filtering with the MJF and the MBF of different orders indicate that filters with m = 1 are ineffective in eliminating the kernel function oscillations, but with m = 2 the MJF almost completely eliminates the oscillations whereas some oscillations are still in evidence for the MBF. With m = 3, the performance of the MBF is comparable to that of MJF with m = 2. It is interesting to note that for the MJF with m = 3 more high frequency oscillations are present in the filtered response functions than those found with m = 2.

The effects of filtering and "adjusting" only the input, or only the output, or both the input and output on the kernel function, as well as the effects of changes in m on the kernel function behavior are shown in Fig. 7. The MJF was used in all these computations. It can be seen that for m = 1, (Fig. 7 left) filtering only the input will not only not smooth the kernel function but has the adverse effect of increasing the oscillations; whereas filtering only the output or both the input and output eliminates, to a large extent, the oscillations. With m = 7, (Fig. 7 right) filtering the input, or both the input and the output, eliminates the oscillations, with the input filtering results being better. Filtering only the output, on the other hand, is not as effective.

As filtering the input and output data causes the loss of some information and results in the distortion of the data due to their 'adjustment', which may be deemed objectionable, an alternative procedure is to filter the response function itself. Some results of filtering the response functions are shown in Fig. 8. It can be seen that a MJF of order 1 eliminates the oscillations completely. The technique of filtering the kernel functions, however, has been found to be effective only for high frequency oscillations of the kernel function.

Acknowledgement

This research was supported by the Purdue University Water Resources Research Center under the Office of Water Resources Research, Project Numbers OWRR-B-008-IND and OWRR-B-022-IND, (Water Resources Act of 1964, P.L. 88-379). This study is an extension of the work of Blank and Delleur.[6,10] The hydrologic data used in this paper were collected by D. Blank.[10] The Computer programs for the Fourier and Laplace transforms and for the filtering were prepared by Messrs. T. W. Putney and J. R. Parker, and for the Z-transform by Mr. M. T. Lee.

Supplementary Reference

Since the presentation of this paper this work has been extended further by Delleur and Rao.[11]

[10] Blank, D. "Linear System Analysis in Surface Hydrology and its Application to Indiana Watersheds," Ph.D. Thesis, Purdue University, August 1968.

[11] Delleur, J. W., and Rao, R. A. "Characteristics and Filtering of Noise in Linear Hydrologic Systems," International Symposium on Mathematical Models in Hydrology, Warsaw, July 1971.

List of Symbols

f	frequency, cycles per unit of time
$f(t)$	function of time
f_c	Nyquist frequency
$f*(t)$	discrete sampled function of $f(t)$
$f*(s)$	Laplace transform of $f*(t)$
$g(t)$	function defined in eq. 19
$G(q)$	function defined in eq. 18
$h(t)$	impulsive response
H_n	coefficient defined in eq. 39
$H(n\Delta t)$	pulsed impulsive response, i.e. inverse of $H(z)$
$H(z)$	Z-transform of $h(n\Delta t)$
$H(\omega)$	Fourier transform of $h(t)$
i	counter index in eqs. 48 through 56
j	imaginary quantity, $\sqrt{-1}$
n	counter index in eqs. 32 through 42
N	number of sampling points in discrete Fourier transform, eqs. 41, 42
N_P	number of sampling points in rainfall excess hyetograph
N_Q	number of sampling points in direct runoff hydrograph
N_ω	number of sampling points in frequency response $H(\omega)$
q	real part of Laplace transform variable s
q_m	maximum value of q used in numerical calculation
$R_g(q)$	real part of $G(q)$
$R_h(\omega)$	real part of $H(\omega)$
$R_x(\omega)$	real part of $X(\omega)$
$R_y(\omega)$	real part of $Y(\omega)$
s	Laplace variable $= \gamma + jq$
t	time
T_c	period corresponding to the frequency interval Δf
T_K	base time of kernel function
T_Q	base time of direct runoff hydrograph
T_R	rainfall excess duration
$w(t)$	impulsive response of filter
w_i	coefficient in discrete filter, eqs. 52, 56
w_o	coefficient in discrete filter, eqs. 51, 55
$W(\omega)$	frequency response of filter

x(t)	input function, i.e. rainfall excess
x(nΔt)	sampled input function
X(q)	Laplace transform of x(t)
X(z)	Z-transform of x(nΔt)
X(ω)	Fourier transform of x(t)
$X_h(\omega)$	imaginary part of H(ω)
$X_g(q)$	imaginary part of G(q)
$X_x(\omega)$	imaginary part of X(ω)
$X_y(\omega)$	imaginary part of Y(ω)
y(t)	output function, i.e. direct runoff
y(nΔt)	sampled output function
Y(q)	Laplace transform of y(t)
Y(z)	Z-transform of y(nΔt)
z	Z-transform variable
γ	real part of s
δ	Dirac δ function
θ(ω)	phase of filter
τ	time
ω	angular frequency
Ω	2π/NΔt

For the list of notations used in figures, see lower part of page 6.8 .

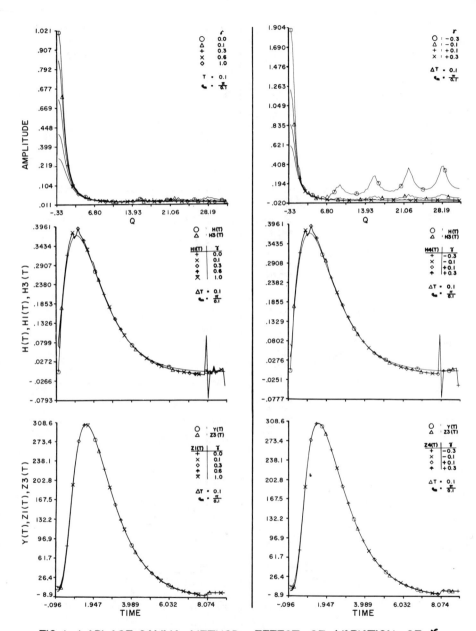

FIG. I LAPLACE-GAMMA METHOD - EFFECT OF VARIATION OF γ

6 .16

132

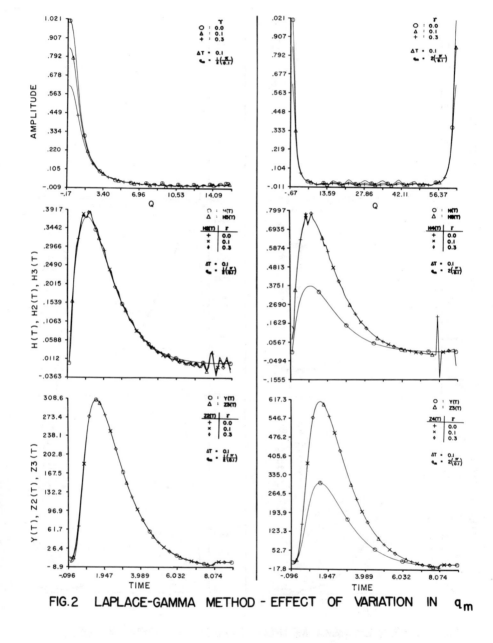

FIG.2 LAPLACE-GAMMA METHOD - EFFECT OF VARIATION IN q_m

6.17

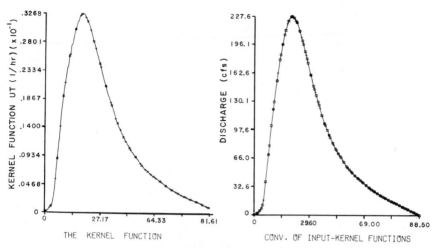

STORM OF 6/22/60 ON CARPENTER CREEK NEAR EGYPT, INDIANA

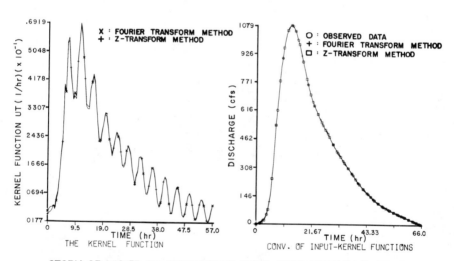

STORM OF 1/16/53 ON MISSISSINEWA RIVER NEAR RIDGEVILLE, INDIANA

FIG. 3. Z-TRANSFORM METHOD

6.18

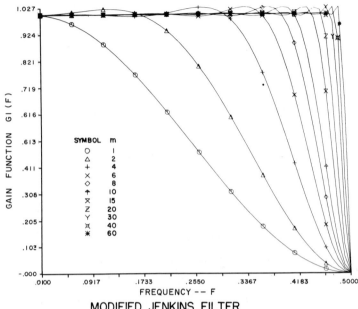

MODIFIED JENKINS FILTER

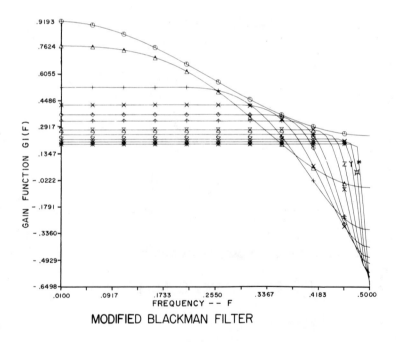

MODIFIED BLACKMAN FILTER

FIG. 4. LOW PASS FILTER FREQUENCY RESPONSE

6.19

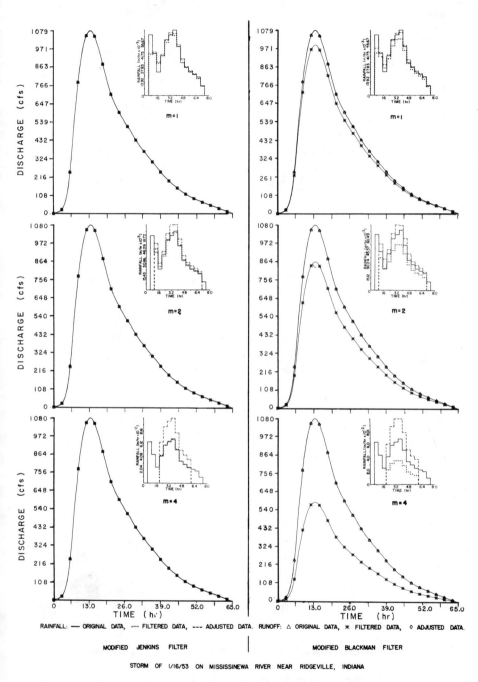

RAINFALL: —— ORIGINAL DATA, ···· FILTERED DATA, - - - ADJUSTED DATA. RUNOFF: △ ORIGINAL DATA, ✳ FILTERED DATA, ◊ ADJUSTED DATA.

MODIFIED JENKINS FILTER　　　　　MODIFIED BLACKMAN FILTER

STORM OF 1/16/53 ON MISSISSINEWA RIVER NEAR RIDGEVILLE, INDIANA

FIG.5 EFFECT OF FILTERING ON THE ORIGINAL DATA

6 .20

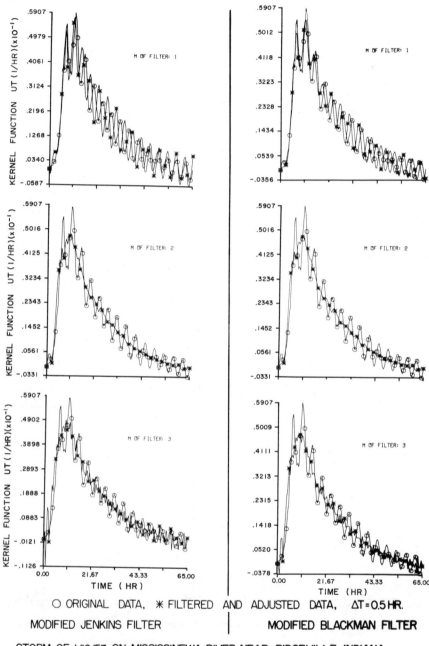

O ORIGINAL DATA, ✳ FILTERED AND ADJUSTED DATA, ΔT=0.5 HR.

MODIFIED JENKINS FILTER | MODIFIED BLACKMAN FILTER

STORM OF 1/16/53 ON MISSISSINEWA RIVER NEAR RIDGEVILLE, INDIANA

FIG. 6.   FILTERING INPUT AND OUTPUT DATA

6.21

137

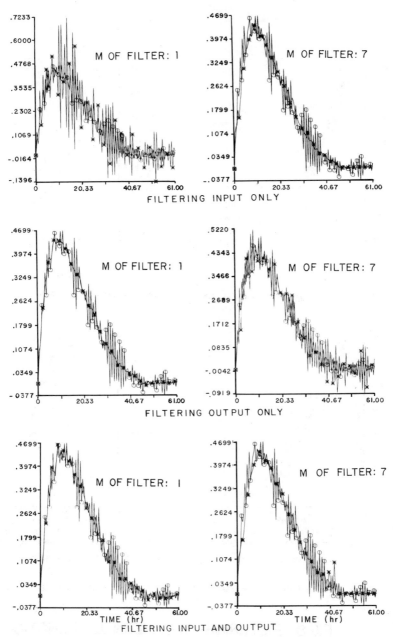

○ ORIGINAL DATA, ✳ FILTERED AND ADJUSTED DATA, ΔT=0.5 HR.

STORM OF 2/17/56 ON MISSISSINEWA RIVER NEAR RIDGEVILLE, INDIANA

FIG.7 EFFECT OF FILTERING ON THE KERNEL FUNCTION (MODIFIED JENKINS FILTER)

6.22

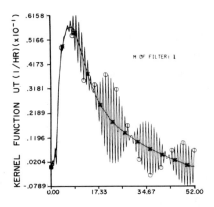

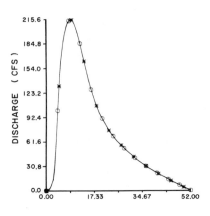

STORM OF 5/16/60 ON CARPENTER CREEK NEAR EGYPT, INDIANA

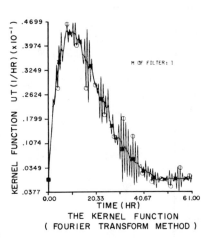

THE KERNEL FUNCTION
(FOURIER TRANSFORM METHOD)

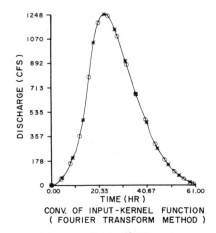

CONV. OF INPUT-KERNEL FUNCTION
(FOURIER TRANSFORM METHOD)

STORM OF 2/17/56 ON MISSISSINEWA RIVER NEAR RICHMOND, INDIANA

○ KERNEL FUNCTION FROM THE ORIGINAL DATA,   ＊ FILTERED KERNEL FUNCTION,   ΔT=0.5 HR.

FIG.8   FILTERING   THE   KERNEL   FUNCTION
(MODIFIED   JENKINS   FILTER)

DISCUSSION

V. T. CHOW

From our experience in employing the transformation techniques, we found that the initial conditions of both input and output (their first and possibly second and higher derivatives) affect the derived kernel functions very greatly. Since there are great errors in determining the rainfall excess and base flow, the initial conditions of the input and output are subject to corresponding errors which would affect the results of the proposed analytical procedures. Therefore, there seems to be an urgent need for research on the effect of input and output initial conditions on the kernel functions.

M. HINO

(1) The discusser would like to ask which is better between methods of solving directly the simultanetous equation of rainfall and runoff, eq. (1), and that of solution in frequency domain, eq. (2)

$$y(i\Delta t) = \sum_m x \ (m\Delta t)h((i-m)\Delta t) \qquad (i = 1,2,\ldots,m) \tag{1}$$

$$Y(\omega) = X(\omega)H(\omega) \tag{2}$$

$$h(t) = \frac{1}{2\pi}\int_{-\infty}^{\infty}H(\omega)e^{i\omega t}d\omega$$

(2) The discusser would like to know about the results of computation of transform of rainfall, runoff and response function in frequency domain $X(\omega)$, $Y(\omega)$, $H(\omega)$. The knowledges of $X(\omega)$, $Y(\omega)$ and $H(\omega)$ would clarify the focus of our interest in dealing with stochastic process.

(3) I believe that the application of the high frequency cut off filter directly to the result of eq. (2) is far more reasonable and more effective than the cut off filtering of the input and output to the hydrologic system, $x(t)$ and $y(t)$.

(4) The instability in the derived kernel function is, the discusser believes, caused by the relatively low intensity of $X(\omega)$ and $Y(\omega)$ in high frequency range. The low level of information necessarily causes the introduction of noise in the process of data transformation. Thus, it is a conventional method of data processing to preliminary "prewhite" before the Fourier or other transformation and to "recolor" after the completion of transformation.

(5) The authors assert that the Z-transform is simpler and shorter in computational time than the Fourier transformation. However, the recent technique of FFT (fast Fourier transform) developed by Cooley and Tucky would further shorten the computational time of Fourier transform. The program of FFT is now available at computing centers.

(6) I am also employing the fitering technique of raw hydrologic data to obtain reasonable information. The results of hydrologic computation published in J. of Hydraulic Division of ASCE were processed through the high and low sharp cut band-pass filter of eq. (3)

$$W(r\Delta\tau) = [\sin(\frac{r\pi}{m} \ f_H) - \sin \ (\frac{r\pi}{m} \ f_L)]/\pi r \ , \tag{3}$$

where m means the maximum lag, f_H and f_L are the cut off frequencies. The filtered data becomes

$$\tilde{X}(i\Delta t) = \sum_r x\{(i-r)\Delta t\}W(r\Delta t) \quad . \tag{4}$$

(7) The filtering processing of raw material data is indispensable to the statistic treatment of random process. The discussions developed by the authors emphasize the importance and meaning of fitering technique usually employed by the investigators in this field.

C. KISIEL

1. How would the kernel derived by transform methods differ from kernels derived by correlation methods?

2. Has the method been evaluated on sequences of events rather than single events?

3. What physical meaning can be attributed to the kernels?

J. PAUL RILEY

The kernel is evaluated on the basis of a single runoff event. If you had a sufficient number of events for a given watershed, you could evaluate the kernel for each event and thereby assign probability levels to various kernels. Differences in kernel values in this case could be reduced by grouping the data, for example, on a reasonal basis.

V. YEVJEVICH

It can be stressed by interpreting the results of this paper that the use of the Z-transform should be the recommended way for estimating a kernel. The implications are that the modified Jenkins Filter is the proper filter to be used to smooth out errors, but the estimates of the information lost and the distortion of data through this filtering need to be evaluated. The selection of the largest frequency and the number of intervals in the frequency domain seems to be dependent on the shape of the kernel (or the parameter γ).

RESPONSE BY J. W. DELLEUR AND R. A. RAO

The analysis was applied to rainfall excess and direct runoff sequences. Both the input and output sequences were thus initially zero and the system is initially relaxed. It is correct that if the analysis is applied to natural rainfall and runoff data, the kernel may depend on the initial conditions as stated in Dr. Chow's discussion. It may be noted in passing that in the formulation of the effective rainfall-direct runoff relationship as differential equations the initial conditions are usually assumed to be zero.

In his first question Dr. Hino is asking if the convolution is most effectively calculated in the time domain or in the frequency domain. Although the two approaches are mathematically equivalent, it appears that for short sequences of data, as is the case in the authors' analysis of single hydrologic events, the convolution in the time domain is more effective. In the analysis of very long series of turbulence or other stochastic processes the convolution in the frequency domain is more effective. For this type of situation, Giorgini and Travis [1] have developed a method called the "short convolution", in which the Fast Fourier Transform (FFT) is used.

The FFT, mentioned in Dr. Hino's fifth question, is a very effective technique particularly for spectral analysis. The authors have used the FFT in the analysis of turbulence signals measured with a hot film anemometer in overland flow with and without rainfall [2]. The signals were discretized at 3 millisecond intervals and the number of samples per record was 32768 $(=2^{15})$. The FFT method proved to be very useful in the analysis of these long time series. In the present study of single storm events on watersheds with areas between 3 and 300 square miles, the number of points is comparatively very small. For watersheds of this size when the rainfall and runoff data were discretized at 30 minute intervals the number of points was usually less than 70 and 300 for the rainfall excess and direct runoff respectively. In one event the input and the output were given by 4 and 19 points, respectively. For small series of this sort the FFT is not advantageous. For this reason the authors used the classical approach of the Fourier, Laplace and Z-transforms.

Dr. Hino's second question concerning the results of the computations of the transforms of the rainfall $X(\omega)$, of the runoff $Y(\omega)$ and of the transfer function $H(\omega)$ is a very important one as it yields an explanation for the oscillatory behavior of the kernel function. The authors have recently shown [3] that the function $|Y(\omega)|$ has usually the appearance of a smoothly decaying function with increasing frequency. The function $|X(\omega)|$ has also a decaying appearance but is usually less smooth than $|Y(\omega)|$. Because of the irregularities in $|X(\omega)|$, the possibility therefore exists for $|H(\omega)| = |Y(\omega)|/|X(\omega)|$ to exhibit a spurious peak at those frequencies where $|X(\omega)|$ is very small compared to $|Y(\omega)|$. The peak in $|H(\omega)|$ in the frequency domain is then translated into an oscillation in $h(t)$ in the time domain. The authors have recently found [3] that these oscillations may be controlled by using the proper combination of discretization step and filtering. The desired filter cutoff frequency may be obtained from the $|H(\omega)|$ plot by observing the frequency of the spurious peak. As indicated in Dr. Hino's fourth question and in the authors' experience, the spurious peaks in the transfer function occurred at relatively high frequencies for which the remainder of the curve of $|H(\omega)|$ had already reached a small value. Consequently, a low pass filter with the cutoff frequency at or slightly below the spurious peak was satisfactory. For this reason the authors experimented only with low pass filters. It is conceivable, however, that the band pass filter may be superior if the spurious peak occurs at a fairly low frequency. In that case the authors

[1]   Giorgini, A. and Travis, J. R. "A 'Short' Convolution", Water Resources and Hydromechanics Lab., School of Civil Engineering, Purdue University. Technical Report No. 26, 1969.

[2]   Kisisel, I. T., Rao, R. A., Delleur, J. W., and Meyer, D. L. "Turbulence Characteristics of Overland Flow - The Effects of Rainfall and Boundary Roughness," Water Resources and Hydromechanics Laboratory, School of Civil Engineering, Purdue University, Technical Report No. 28, Feb. 1971.

[3]   Delleur, J. W. and Rao, A. R. "Characteristics and Filtering of Noise in Linear Hydrologic Systems," International Symposium on Mathematical Models in Hydrology, Warsaw, July 1971.

would prefer to attempt to attenuate the peak by changing the discretization step before filtering.

The technique of "prewhitening" and "recoloring" suggested in Dr. Hino's fourth question is often used in spectral analysis. The technique of prewhitening consists in applying to the data a special filter that will yield a filtered sequence which has a flat or white spectrum. This requires designing a digital filter with a frequency response with peaks where the spectrum of the data has valleys and vice versa. This technique again may be practical for large series, but is impractical for the short series encountered in the analysis of single hydrologic events, because the filter would require too many terms, with the consequent loss of information in very short series. The same is true of the "recoloring" operation which requires the application of a filter which is the reverse of the prewhitening filter.

The authors agree with Dr. Hino's third remark that filtering the kernel function may be more reasonable than filtering the output and input of the hydrologic system. This was proposed by the authors (See Fig. 8). This procedure has the advantage of utilizing all the data available, whereas filtering of the input and output data results in loss of data at the beginning and end of the series and requires an adjustment to maintain the conservation of mass. The authors feel that the combination of proper discretization step and kernel filtering may be the most effective way of eliminating oscillations in the kernel functions.

Dr. Riley's question and Dr. Kisiel's first question have some common aspects. If a sufficient number of events on a given watershed is available, it would be possible to group the kernels on a seasonal basis. Blank [4] has found that the kernels could be grouped according to maximum value and to the time lag, and that these parameters could be correlated to the time of the year. Further work is still in progress in this area.

In answering Dr. Kisiel's first two questions, it must be remembered that the authors addressed themselves to the problem of linear hydrologic system identification for the case of single events. In the case of sequences of events, the spectral analysis approach has been successfully used to develop a linear relationship between rainfall and runoff time series [5].

Dr. Yevjevich's discussion properly summarizes two of the principal findings of the authors' paper, namely a) that the Z-transform is the most economical method of linear system identification from the point of view of computer time, and b) the modified filter applied directly to the input and output data or to the kernel function is very effective in smoothing errors existing in the data or generated by the computational procedure. Filtering the computed kernel has the advantage of eliminating the loss of information and distortion of the data that occurs in filtering short rainfall sequences. In the Laplace transform method the resulting kernel is independent of γ. However, in the computations γ should be taken as a small positive number. The presence of oscillations in the kernel function is related to the number of intervals in the time domain. Further elaboration on this point can be found later in the discussion.

[4] Blank, D. "Linear System Analysis in Surface Hydrology and its Application to Indiana Watersheds," Ph.D. Thesis, Purdue University, Aug.1968

[5] Delleur, J., and Bernier, J. "Développements récents en matière d' analyse des chroniques d'événements hydrologiques: liaison en chaine, théorie du renouvellement, analyse spectrale," to be published, La Houille Blanche.

United States-Japan Bi-Lateral Seminar in Hydrology
Honolulu, January 1971

EFFECT OF AN ERROR IN DISCHARGE MEASUREMENTS ON THE
DETECTION PROCESS IN RUNOFF SYSTEMS ANALYSIS

by   Tsutomu Kishi
Professor, Department of Civil Engineering
Faculty of Engineering
Hokkaido University
Sapporo, Japan

Synopsis

A river basin acts as a low pass filter in the prediction process and becomes an amplifier for high frequency bands in the detection process.

First, theoretical considerations are made about the detection process for a basin of the cascade-connected linear reservoirs. Theoretically speaking, the possibility of obtaining the time function of input depends on the functional form of the output and on the order of the system or the number of linear reservoirs.

An approximate method of calculation by which the Fourier inverse transform of the detected input function is always integrable is presented. Results of calculations using field data are described as illustrative examples. The author points out that the precision of the detected values of the input decreases markedly if even a small error is contained in the measurements of the output.

Then, the author investigates the relation of turbulence characteristics of natural streams to the error in velocity measurements which must be a signigicant factor affecting the total error in discharge measurements. It is pointed out that the error in velocity measurements can be decreased appreciably if the observational period at a point is prolonged by a small fraction of time.

1.   Introduction

The use of the transform methods in runoff systems analysis has been mainly made for the processes of identification and prediction and few attempts have been made for the detection process. However, it becomes often necessary both in practical designs and in research to detect the precipitation, which happens to be missed, from the runoff records and a given system function. To this end, it is important to investigate a methodology of the detection process.

In the prediction process a river basin is a low pass filter. To the contrary, it acts as an amplifier for high frequency bands in the detection process. The rate of amplification would depend on the functional form of output and on the frequency characteristics of the basin system. Since the shorter the duration of a pulse in the output the wider the Fourier spectrum becomes, an error of short duration in discharge measurements would result in the detection process. This fact brings forth various problems which should be studied before the detection process in runoff systems analysis comes into operation.

The total error in discharge measurements in natural streams comes from various origins. The turbulence in streams must be a significant factor among them. The relationship between the error of the mean velocity observed at a point and the period of observation will be derived from the power spectra of velocity fluctuations. This kind of research is an essential basis in obtaining the precise records of stream discharge which are especially necessary in the calculation of the detection process.

7.1

2. Theoretical considerations

Let us consider a basin system which consists of a linear reservoir cascade with n elements. The systems frequency function $G(\omega)$ is given by

$$G(\omega) = \left(\frac{\lambda}{\lambda+j\omega}\right)^n \tag{1}$$

where ω : angular frequency
λ : storage factor (reciprocal of storage constant)
j : imaginary unit
n : number of linear reservoirs

In the frequency domain, the Fourier transform of input $I(\omega)$ is related to the output $Q(\omega)$ with

$$I(\omega) = Q(\omega)/G(\omega) \tag{2}$$

Since the time function of input $I(t)$ must be a causal function, the absolute value of $I(\omega)$ must be square-integrable:

$$\int_{-\infty}^{\infty} |I(\omega)|^2 \, d\omega < \infty \tag{3}$$

Thus, the function $Q(\omega)$ must be at least such that

$$Q(\omega) = o \; \{G(\omega)\} \qquad\qquad (\omega \to +\infty) \tag{4}$$

where o = Landau notation, which means
$Q(\omega)/G(\omega) \to o$ for $\omega \to +\infty$

It is not necessarily true that an arbitrary output function always satisfies condition (4). This will be shown by the following illustrative examples.

Suppose that a triangular pulse shown in Fig. 1 is given as the output at time $t = t_o$. The Fourier transform pair is

$$Q_B(t-t_o) \longleftrightarrow \frac{4\sin^2(\omega B/2)}{B\omega^2} e^{-j\omega t_o} \tag{5}$$

Thus, the time functions of input for the single reservoir system (n = 1) and two cascaded reservoirs system (n = 2) are given by equations (6) and (7), respectively.

single_reservoir_system

$$I(t) = \frac{2}{\pi} \int_o^{\infty} \frac{4\sin^2(\omega B/2)}{\lambda B\omega^2} (\lambda\cos\omega t_o + \omega\sin\omega t_o)\cos\omega t \, d\omega \tag{6}$$

$$t > 0$$

two_cascaded_reservoirs_system

$$I(t) = \frac{2}{\pi} \int_o^{\infty} \frac{4\sin^2(\omega B/2)}{\lambda^2 B\omega^2} [(\lambda^2-\omega^2)\cos\omega t_o + 2\lambda\omega\sin\omega t_o]\cos\omega t \, d\omega \tag{7}$$

$$t > 0$$

7 .2

Equation (6) is integrable because the integrand on the right hand side satisfies condition (4). In Fig. 2 results of numerical calculation for two cases described in the following table are shown. For this problem Laplace transform is more convenient to investigate the functional form of I(t). Indeed, input function I(s) is given by

$$I(s) = Q(s) + \frac{1}{B\lambda} \cdot \frac{1}{s} [e^{-(t_0-B)s/2} - e^{-(t_0+B)s/2}]^2 \qquad (8)$$

Table: Conditions for numerical calculation

	Case 1 (Fig. 2a)	Case 2 (Fig. 2b)
$\lambda(hr^{-1})$	0.1	0.1
$B(hr)$	1.0	1.0
$t_0(hr)$	10.0	20.0
$\Delta\omega(radian/hr)$	0.05	0.05
$\omega_{max}(radian/hr)$	150	150
$I(\omega_{max})/I(\omega)_{max}$	0.009	0.015

ω_{max} means the highest value of frequency over which $I(\omega)$ is truncated. $I(\omega)_{max}$ is the maximum value of $I(\omega)$

Equation (8) shows that I(t) is the sum of the output Q(t) and two successive rectangular pulses with different sign (positive and negative). The height of rectanglular pulses is amplified by the factor $1/B\lambda$.
Since the inverse Fourier transform given by equation (6) is calculated at discontinuities, Gibb's phenomenon[1] appeares in the results of the numerical calculation.

Fig. 2b shows the effect of truncation error.

Contrary to equation (6), however, equation (7) is not integrable as will be easily recongnized.

For the next example we shall consider the output to be a rectangular pulse as shown in Fig. 3. The time functions I(t) are:

single_reservoir_system

$$I(t) = \frac{2}{\pi} \int_0^\infty \frac{2\sin\omega B}{\lambda\omega} (\lambda\cos\omega t_0 + \omega\sin\omega t_0)\cos\omega t d\omega \qquad (9)$$
$$t > 0$$

two_cascaded_reservoirs_system

$$I(t) = \frac{2}{\pi} \int_0^\infty \frac{2\sin\omega B}{\lambda^2\omega^2} [(\lambda^2-\omega^2)\cos\omega t_0 + 2\lambda\omega\sin\omega t_0]\cos\omega t d\omega \qquad (10)$$
$$t > 0$$

It is easily seen that both solutions are meaningless unless the concept of distributions is introduced. For instance, $I(\omega)$ for equation (9) is

---

1) Papoulis, A., "The Fourier Integral and its Application", McGraw-Hill, 1962, p. 30

$$I(\omega) = \frac{2\sin\omega B}{\omega} e^{-j\omega t_0} + \frac{j}{\lambda} 2\sin\omega B e^{-j\omega t_0} \qquad (11)$$

Obviously, the first term of the right hand side is $Q(\omega)e^{-j\omega t_0}$. The transform pair for the second term is obtained by considering the symmetrical character[2]

$$\frac{1}{\lambda}[\delta\{t-(t_0-B)\} - \delta\{t-(t_0+B)\}] \longleftrightarrow \frac{j}{\lambda} 2\sin\omega B e^{-j\omega t_0} \qquad (12)$$

Consequently, the time function $I(t)$ is

$$I(t) = Q(t-t_0) + \frac{1}{\lambda}[\delta\{t-(t_0-B)\} - \delta\{t-(t_0+B)\}] \qquad (13)$$

The function $I(t)$ given by equation (13) is shown in Fig. 3.

As stated above the evaluation of the inverse Fourier transform is not always easy even under relatively simple conditions. Consequently, in the detection process for actual basin systems under more complicated circumstances it is necessary to develop a method of numerical calculation especially suitable for computer calculations.

3. Presentation of a method of numerical calculation

A necessary and sufficient condition for a square-integrable function $A(\omega) \geq 0$ to be the Fourier spectrum of a causal function is the Paley-Wiener condition[3]

$$\int_{-\infty}^{\infty} \frac{|\ln A(\omega)|}{1+\omega^2} d\omega < \infty \qquad (14)$$

Consequently, the absolute value of $I(\omega)$ detected must satisfy condition (14).

A method of numerical calculation which satisfies the Paley-Wiener condition is as follows:

Approximating the output $Q(t)$ by a polygon as shown in Fig. 4a, and differentiating twice,

$$Q(\omega) = -\frac{1}{\omega^2}\{\frac{k_1}{(t_2-t_1)} e^{-j\omega t_1} + \frac{k_2}{(t_3-t_2)} e^{-j\omega t_2} + \cdots\cdots$$

$$+ \frac{k_n}{(t_n-t_{n-1})} e^{-j\omega t_n}\} \qquad (15)$$

$$= -\frac{1}{\omega^2}\{Q_R(\omega) + jQ_X(\omega)\}$$

where $Q_R(\omega)$, $Q_X(\omega)$: real and imaginary part of $-Q(\omega)\cdot\omega^2$

---

2) c.f. 1), p. 14
3) c.f. 1), pp. 215-217

Approximating the impulse response G(t) by step functions as shown in Fig. 4b and differentiating once,

$$G(\omega) = \frac{1}{j\omega} [k_1 e^{-j\omega t_1} + k_2 e^{-j\omega t_2} + \cdots + k_n e^{-j\omega t_n}] \qquad (16)$$

$$= -\frac{1}{\omega} \{-G_X(\omega) + jG_R(\omega)\}$$

where $G_R(\omega)$, $G_X(\omega)$: real and imaginary part of $-G(\omega)\cdot\omega$

Consequently,

$$I(\omega) = \frac{1}{\omega} \cdot \frac{1}{G_R^2 + G_X^2} \{(-Q_R G_X + Q_X G_R) - j(Q_R G_R + Q_X G_X)\} \qquad (17)$$

As will be seen in equations (15) and (16)

$$\left|\begin{matrix} Q_R \\ Q_X \end{matrix}\right| \le \left|\frac{k_1}{t_2 - t_1}\right| + \left|\frac{k_2}{t_3 - t_2}\right| + \cdots \left|\frac{k_n}{t_n - t_{n-1}}\right| \qquad (18)$$

($\equiv M$, a positive finite value)

$$\left|\begin{matrix} G_R \\ G_X \end{matrix}\right| \le |k_1| + |k_2| + \cdots |k_n| \qquad (19)$$

($\equiv N$, a positive finite value)

Therefore

$$|\omega I(\omega)| \le \frac{2MN}{G_R^2 + G_X^2} \qquad (\equiv k, \text{ a positive finite value}) \qquad (20)$$

Thus,

$$A(\omega) = |I(\omega)| \le |k/\omega| \qquad (21)$$

Consequently,

$$\lim_{\omega \to \pm\infty} \frac{|\ln A(\omega)|}{1+\omega^2} = \lim_{\omega \to \pm\infty} \frac{|\ln \omega|}{1+\omega^2} = 0 \qquad (22)$$

The Paley-Wiener condition is, thus, satisfied.

Though the Paley-Wiener condition does not immediately mean that $I(\omega)$ has a causal inverse, it is permissible to regard the inverse transform of $I(\omega)$ as an approximation of a causal function $I(t)$ because an actual runoff system in which $I(t)$ must be a causal function is being considered.

Numerical examples for the Teshio river basin are shown in Figs. 5 and 6. A point to be worthy of note is the fact that much attention should be paid to the high frequency domains of output and basin system function, since the

7 .5

function I(t), in many cases, spreads up to a considerably high frequency domain because of its relatively short duration.

In Fig. 5 the values of G(ω) calculated from two flood records at the Pifuka gaging station[4] are compared. It is found that curves of G(ω) are nearly identical for ω < 0.6 and the system frequency function for this basin can be assigned, if necessary. However, for ω > 0.6 it is difficult to prescribe a precise value of G(ω), since the small fluctuations on the G(ω) curve seem to be rather random. These fluctuations would probably be due to the observational errors contained in I(t) and Q(t). The absolute value of G(ω) for ω > 0.6 is damped so small that the effect of errors in observations would become evident.

A typical example is found in the G(ω) curve for flood No. 1 shown in Fig. 5. A distinct fluctuation in the G(ω) curve is observed for ω between 1.0 and 1.3. In this range of ω, the absolute value of I(ω) is particulary small, so that a small change in the value of Q(ω) has an appreciable effect on the value of G(ω). Indeed, the order of magnitude of $|Q(\omega)|$ in this range of ω is 10^{-1} mm. On the one hand, the total rainfall for flood No. 1 is 23.7 mm. Consequently, if there is an error pulse in the discharge measurement corresponding to approximately 0.5 % of the total effective rainfall, its Fourier spectrum would have the same order of magnitude as $|Q(\omega)|$. Thus, the value of G(ω) is very changeable.

In most cases the systems frequency function G(ω) is damped faster than Q(ω) and I(ω). And, as stated above, it is usually difficult to prescribe the precise value of G(ω) for $\omega > \omega_c$, where ω_c is a truncation frequency. For this reason, a function P(t) which is an approximate estimate of I(t) is plotted in Fig. 6.

The function P(t) is obtained by the following way[5]. If I(ω) is truncated above a constant ω_c and the resulting function is designated by P(ω)

$$P(\omega) = I(\omega) p\omega c(\omega) = 0 \qquad\qquad |\omega| > \omega_c \qquad (23)$$

where $p\omega c(\omega)$: truncation filter

The inverse transform P(t) can be found by expanding P(ω) into a Fourier series in the $(-\omega_c, \omega_c)$ interval:

$$P(\omega) = \sum_{n=-\infty}^{\infty} A_n e^{-jn\pi\omega/\omega_c} \qquad (24)$$

where

$$A_n = \frac{1}{2\omega_c} \int_{-\omega_c}^{\omega_c} P(\omega) e^{jn\pi\omega/\omega_c} d\omega \qquad (25)$$

P(t) is, then, given by

$$P(t) = \frac{\omega_c}{\pi} \sum_{n=-\infty}^{\infty} An \frac{\sin(\omega_c t - n\pi)}{\omega_c t - n\pi} \qquad (26)$$

---

4) Yamaoka, I., Fujita, M, Evaluation of Simulation Models For River Runoff Through Niquist Plots, Proc, Vol. 1, 13th I.A.H.R., Kyoto, 1969, pp. 171-180.
5) c.f. 1) p. 59

From the above we have

$$P\left(\frac{n\pi}{\omega_c}\right) = \frac{\omega_c A_n}{\pi} \tag{27}$$

The function $P(t)$ is related to $I(t)$ by

$$P(t) = \int_{-\infty}^{\infty} I(t) \frac{\sin\omega_c(t-\tau)}{\pi(t-\tau)} d\tau \tag{28}$$

For sufficiently large ω_c we have

$$I(t) \simeq P(t) \tag{29}$$

The values of rainfall detected by the above method are shown in Figs. 6(a) and (b) by the dotted line. Owing to the truncation error the total rainfall detected is not identical with the total rainfall. Then, the detected value was corrected to make the total rainfall detected be equal to the total rainfall[6]. The results are shown in Figs. 6(a) and (b) by the solid line.

4. Considerations to the precision of velocity measurements in natural streams[7]

4.1 Variance-duration curve for the mean velocity

The precision of velocity measurements in natural streams depends on the duration of the observation. The mean velocity U observed at any point during a time T_* is considered as a stochastic quantity the distribution of which is a function of T_*. The relation between the variance of U and the observational period T_* is called as the variance-duration curve and given by

$$C(T_*) = \frac{2C(0)}{T_*^2} \int_0^{T_*} (T_*-\tau)R_E(\tau)d\tau \tag{30}$$

where $\quad C(T_*)$: variance of mean velocity observed during T_*
$\qquad\qquad C(0)$: variance of mean velocity for $T_* = 0$, that is the square of turbulence intensity of the flow
$\qquad\qquad R_E(\tau)$: auto-correlation function of the velocity fluctuation Subscript E designates the Eulerian correlations

For $T_* \gg T_E$, where T_E is the Eulerian integral time scale defined by $T_E = \int_0^\infty R_E(\tau)d\tau$, equation (30) gives

$$\frac{C(T_*)}{C(0)} \simeq 2 \frac{T_E}{T_*} \quad (= 2 \frac{L_x}{UT_*}) \tag{31}$$

---

6) Total rainfall is obtained by (Total runoff height/Runoff coefficient). If the runoff coefficient is a function of total rainfall, it is sometimes the case, all the calculations should be done with the effective rainfall.
7) Kishi, T., Mori, A., and Hirayama, K., Study on the Mechanics of Turbulence in Relation to the Analysis of the Accuracy of Velocity Measurements in natural Rivers, Rept. Faculty of Eng., Hokkaido Univ., July, 1970 (in Japanese)

where L_x is the macro scale of turbulence defined by $L_x = UT_E$.

It is noticed from equation (31) that no other length scale relating to the geometry of the river section is contained in $C(T_*)$ when T_E or L_x/U is considered as the unit of time scale. Equation (31) is an important relation in the consideration of the generalized expressions for turbulence characteristics natural streams.

As is well known, the following relations hold between the auto-correlation function and the power spectrum:

$$R_E(\tau) = \frac{1}{u^2} \int_0^\infty E(f) \cos 2\pi f\tau \, df \tag{32}$$

$$E(f) = 4u^2 \int_0^\infty R_E(\tau) \cos 2\pi f\tau \, d\tau \tag{33}$$

where

$E(f)$: power spectral density of turbulence
f : frequency
u^2 : energy of turbulence, that is square of turbulence intensity

Since $E(0) = 4u^2 T_E$, the relation of $E(f)/u^2 T_E$ v.s. $T_E f$ is the normalized power spectrum of turbulence. When the normalized power spectrum is approximate by an exponential function its functional form should be[8)]

$$\frac{E(f)}{u^2 T_E} = 4 \exp\{-4T_E f\} \tag{34}$$

Substituting equation (34) into equation (30) thru equation (32) and integrating

$$\frac{C(T_*)}{C(0)} = 2 \frac{\tan^{-1}\omega}{\omega} - \frac{\ln(\omega^2+1)}{\omega^2} \tag{35}$$

where

$$\omega = \frac{\pi}{2} \cdot \frac{T_*}{T_E}$$

4.2 Comparison with the field measurements

Velocity measurements were performed in three rivers in Hokkaido --- the Ishikari river, the Chitose river and the Shin river in 1968 and 1969. The Ishikari river at Hashimoto-cho station which is more than 100 m wide and around 3 m deep was selected as an example of large scale channel. The Chitose river at A and B stations which is around 30 m wide and 1 m deep is the example of a moderate channel. The Shin river which is 10 m wide and 0.5 m deep is an example of a small scale channel.

For the normalized power spectra, a comparison of equation (34), shown as a dashed curve, with field measurements is shown in Fig. 7. In spite of a wide range of variety in the geometry of gaging stations equation (34) agrees favorably with the field measurements.

---

8) c.f. 7)

The theoretical variance-duration curve of $C(T_*)/C(0)$ versus T_*/T_E given in equation (35) is compared with field measurements in Fig. 8. The solid line in the figure shows equation (35) and the dotted line shows the asymptotic relation (31). It is seen that equation (35) agrees favorably with the field measurements and equation (31) is also applicable for $T_*/T_E > 15$.

In the discussions so far, the magnitude of the integral time scale T_E or the macro scale of turbulence L_x has not yet been mentioned. These quantities presumably show a complicated dependence on the depth of water. The scale of the vortices in an open channel flow will mainly be controlled by the water depth if the water depth is small. However, if the water depth is large the scale of vortices will be related to the width of the flow as well.
The data of measurements shown in Figs. 7 and 8 were all obtained during a low water period. Therefore, the water depth would be the controlling length of the vortices. Fig. 9 shows the variation of L_x/H , where H is the water depth, with Z/H , where Z is the height above the bottom. Rough values of L_x/H range from 3 to 4, though they increases from the bottom towards the surface. Thus, the rough estimation of T_E is $(3 \sim 4) \cdot H/U$.

4.3 Importance of increasing the precision in velocity measurements

In the previous chapter, the author pointed out that a specially high precision in the output data is necessary in the operation of the detection process. The total error contained in the output measurements comes from various origins. However, there is no doubt that the error in velocity measurements is one of an important factor among them. Especially, for high water the discharge measurements must be of high reliability, since the number of data from which the stage-discharge relationship is derived is usually limited.

With this respect, the author would like to call attention to a blind spot in the hydrometric practive. For instance, in the "Guide to Hydrometeorological Practice", edited by W.M.O in 1965, only a space of nine words which follow is devoted to the observational period in velocity measurements.
"The velocity is observed . . . . . by conuting the number of revolutions of the rotor during a period of not less than 60 seconds.

The author would like to propose the following standard for the observational period in velocity measurements:

$$T_* \geq 5T_E$$

According to the above standard the standard deviation of the observed mean velocity at a point will be decreased to 50 % of the turbulence intensity, that is r.m.s of the velocity fluctuation of the flow. In the present practive of velocity measurements, the observational period for flood runoff would be at longest

$$T_* \simeq T_E$$

If the above evaluation is not wrong, the standard deviation of the observed mean velocity is as great as 90 % of the turbulence intensity. If we wish to decrease the value of standard deviation to 50 % of the turbulence intensity by increasing the number of observation points, the observation points have to be increased more than three times the number of the original points.
As will be recongnized, it is important and useful to enact a standard for the practice of velocity measurements by which the required precision is attained.

7 .9

5. Conclusion

In this paper, mathematical considerations were made for the detection process in runoff systems analysis. The value of the Fourier transform function of the input to be detected should be calculated in the frequency domain with precision up to a high frequency region of ω in order to detect the detailed form of the input function. However, the above is not always easy because the Fourier spectra of the output and the systems frequency function decay to small value in the relatively low frequency region of ω and, consequently, the value of the Fourier spectra are disturbed by various noises in the high frequency domain. The fact that no methods such as the cross-correlation method in the identification process are found to eliminate the effects of noise would be a difficulty in the detection process. This fact will be understood through the examples given in chapter 3. In this meaning, a high precision in the discharge measurements is especially necessary in the detection process and a discussion concerning the hydrometric practice was presented.

Acknowledgement

The author wishes to thank to Mr. Mutsuhiro Fujita, Assistant Professor, Department of Civil Engineering, Hokkaido University, for his cooporation in this study. He performed the numerical calculations shown in Chapt. 3. And the author is also grateful to Professor Isao Yamaoka, Department of Civel Engineering, Hokkaido University, who kindly offered me the runoff data for the Teshio river at Pifuka.

List of Symbols

$A(\omega)$ = square-integrable function;
B = duration of pulse;
$C(T_*)$ = variance of mean velocity observed during T_*;
$E(f)$ = power spectral density of turbulence;
f = frequency;
$G(\omega)$ = systems frequency function;
$G_R(\omega)$, $G_X(\omega)$ = real and imaginary parts of $-G(\omega) \cdot \omega$;
H = water depth;
$I(\omega)$ = Fourier transform of input;
$I(\omega)_{max}$ = maximum value of $I(\omega)$;
j = imaginary unit;
L_x = macro scale of turbulence;
n = number of linear reservoirs;
$P(t)$ = approximate estimate of $I(t)$;
$p\omega_c(\omega)$ = truncation filter;
$Q(\omega)$ = Fourier transform of output;
$Q_R(\omega)$, $Q_X(\omega)$ = real and imaginary parts of $-Q(\omega)\omega^2$;
$R_E(\tau)$ = auto-correlation function of velocity fluctuation;
s = parameter of Laplace transform;
t = time;
T_* = duration of observation;
T_E = Eulerian integral time scale;
U = mean velocity;
ω = angular velocity;
ω_{max} = truncation frequency;
λ = storage factor (reciprocal of storage constant); and
δ = Dirac's delta function.

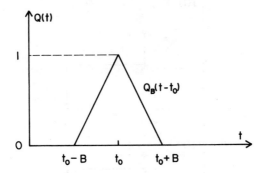

Fig. 1 Triangular pulse in output.

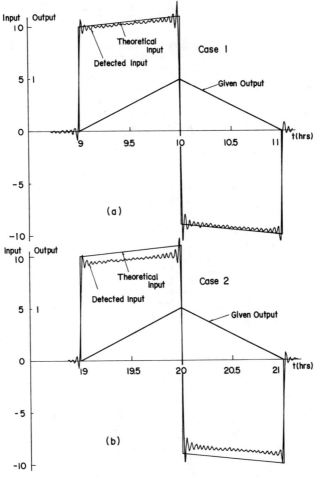

Fig. 2 Comparison of the detected input with theory.
        (Output of triangular pulse; 1st order system)

7 .11

154

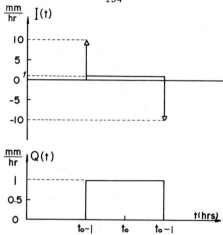

Fig. 3   Rectangular pulse in output and corresponding input
$(\lambda = 0.1 \ hr^{-1}, \ B = 1 \ hr \ in \ Eq.(13))$.

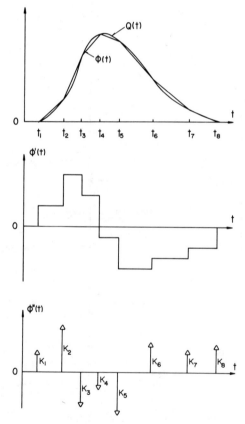

Fig. 4a.   Polygonal approximation of Q(t).

7 .12

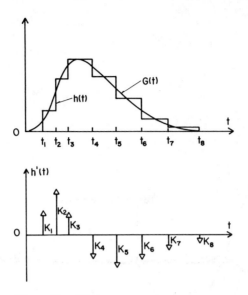

Fig. 4b Step approximation of G(t).

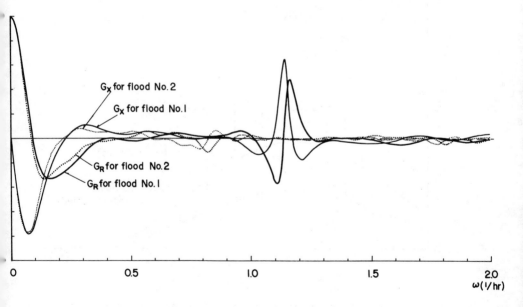

Fig. 5 System frequency function for the Teshio River at Pifuka.

7 .13

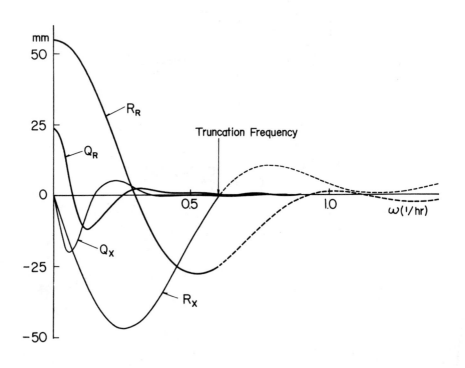

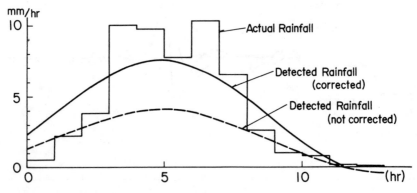

Fig. 6a   Detection process for the Teshio river basin at Pifuka
(flood No. 1)

7 .14

157

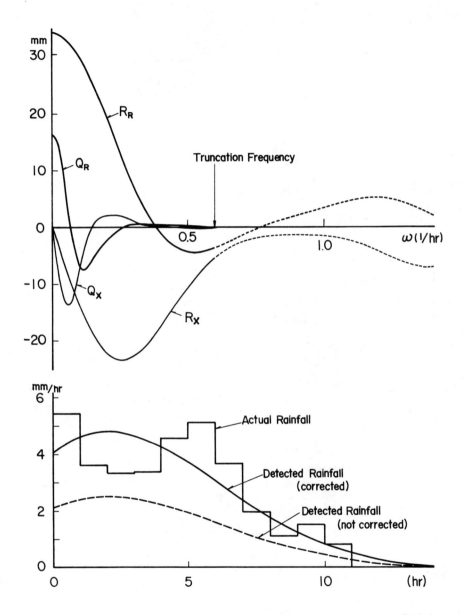

Fig. 6b Detection process for the Teshio river basin at Pifuka
(flood No. 2).

7 .15

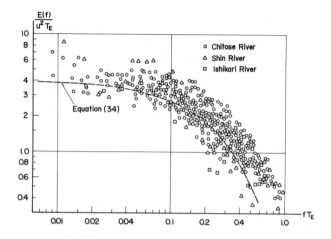

Fig. 7 Spectra of turbulence in natural streams.

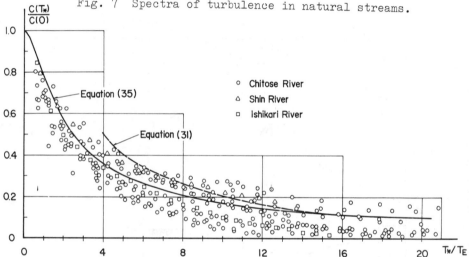

Fig. 8 Variance-duration curve for mean velocity in natural streams

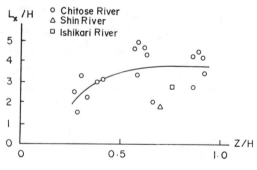

Fig. 9 Relation L_X/H v.s. Z/H.

7 .16

DISCUSSION

V. T. CHOW

In order to improve the theoretical accuracy of the proposed standard for the observational period, it may be desirable to compute T_E from observed data on velocity fluctuation. Then, there will be a need to propose another standard for the measurement of the velocity fluctuation. It is also important to note that there is an upper constraint for the time of measurement. If the time of observation is too long, the measured data at any point will be greatly affected by the rapid change in velocity due to unsteady nature of the flow particularly at flood stages.

J. W. DELLEUR

Dr. Kishi's paper sheds a new light on the application of linear systems in hydrology.

The classical applications have been the derivation of the kernel function and the output prediction for a given input and kernel. Dr. Kishi addresses himself to the important but less studied problem of the input detection and of the error propagation in such calculations. Little is known about error propagation in hydrologic linear system identification and detection. Laurenson and O'Donnell[1] have studied the error sensitivity of several methods of derivation of the unit hydrograph due to errors of different types in the input and output data. Blank, Delleur, and Giorgini[2] have studied the effect of errors in the kernel function on the output. By means of a perturbation analysis they found that for typical circumstances an error in the kernel is reduced by a factor varying from 1/6 to 1/25 in the calculated output. Conversely, it would appear that an error in the output would be magnified in the derived kernel. This point is now confirmed and amplified in Dr. Kishi's paper which shows that rather small errors in the output data may reduce the precision of identified inputs.

The author then bridges the gap between the sciences of hydrology and turbulence as the latter phenomenon may be the source of errors which propagate in the identification of the hydrologic system input. Mandelbrot and Wallis[3] have suggested that the difference between hydrology and turbulence lies in the the difference in the frequencies of interest, say up to one cycle for the former and above for the latter. Dr. Kishi has now added a new concept of unity between the two sciences often regarded as unrelated.

The results of the measurements of turbulence spectra in natural streams shown in Fig. 7 are of a different order of magnitude from those normally measured in water flows in the laboratory with hot-film anemometers. A recent study by the writer and his associates[4,5] shows that for thin free surface flows, most of the energy is contained at frequencies below 10 cycles per second. Similar conclusions have been obtained by Raichlen[6] and by Richardson and McQuivy[7] for measurements in laboratory flumes. Figure 7 shows that most of the energy is contained in frequencies for which

$$f \, T_E < 0.1 \quad \text{or} \quad f < \frac{0.1}{T_E} \quad .$$

If we assume a water depth, H, of 2 meters and a mean velocity, U, of 0.5m/sec, and that the Eulerian time scale is of the order of 5 H/U, then T_E = 20 secs and f = 0.005 cps. This extremely low frequency brings the question as to the appropriateness of the current meter for turbulence measurement in view of the relatively large time constant of this instrument. Some but few measurements of turbulence with hot film anemometers have been made in rivers and in the ocean.

[1] Laurenson, E.M., and O'Donnell, T.: "Data Error Effects in Unit Hydrograph Derivation," Journal of the Hydraulics Division, ASCE, Vol. 95, No. HY6, Nov. 1969

[2] Blank, D.; Delleur, J.W.; and Giorgini, A.: "Oscillatory Kernel Functions in Linear Hydrologic Models," Paper H58, AGU Annual Meeting (Abstract in EOS, Trans. AGU. Vol. 51, No. 4, April 1970), Submitted for publication in Water Resources Research.

[3] Mandelbrot, B., and Wallis, J.R.: "Noah, Joseph, and Operational Hydrology," Water Resources Research, Vol. 4, No. 5, pp. 909, 1968.

[4] Kisiel, I. T.; Delleur, J. W.; and Rao, Ramachandra A.: "Turbulence Characteristics of Overland Flow," to be presented at the International Association for Hydraulic Research, XIV Congress, Paris, Aug. 29-Sept. 3, 1971.

[5] Kisiel, I. T.: "An Experimental Investigation of the Effect of Rainfall on the Turbulence Characteristics of Shallow Water Flow," Ph.D. Dissertation, School of Civil Engineering, Purdue University, Lafayette, Ind., Jan. 1971.

[6] McQuivery, R. S., and Richardson, E. V.: "Some Turbulence Measurements in Open-Channel Flow," Proc. of the ASCE, Journal of the Hydraulics Division, No. HY1, pp. 209-223, January 1969.

[7] Raichlen, F.: "Some Turbulence Measurements in Water," Proc. of the ASCE, Journal of the Engineering Mechanics Division, No. EM 2, pp. 73-97, April 1967.

P. S. EAGLESON

Would you like to comment upon the practical use of this method in the detection process? Several possible uses come to my mind but of course, all require knowledge of the system function.

    a. Filling in missing rainfall records

    b. Evaluating the time distribution of rainfall excess

C. KISIEL

    1. Can you clarify the procedure used to correct the detected rainfall as shown in Figures 6a and 6b?

    2. How representative is the turbulence structure in the river as measured b the current or propeller meter? What effect does this have on the computation of the Eulerian time scale?

    3. What would be the effect of sampling errors in precipitation on the extimation of the system frequency function $G(\omega)$? What effect would nonuniformity of rainfall in space (or non-representativeness of the rain gage) have on the entire detection process?

J. PAUL RILEY

In differentiating measured runoff to estimate rainfall input your model does not provide for losses and storage changes within the system. Sometimes these losses are significant in both short time and long time events. You might give consideration to further generalizing your model by taking into account system losses.

V. YEVJEVICH

The author seems to have reached the conclusion that a much longer time measurement of velocities at a point is more important for the accuracy of the computed river discharge than the number of points measured in a river cross-sectional area. From the sampling theory, an optimum must exist between the time of point velocity measurements and the number of points at which velocities are measured. The time-space trade in these measurements that departs from this optimum should result in a loss of accuracy of the computed discharge.

RESPONSE BY T. KISHI

The response to discussion by V.T. Chow is as follows.

The author presented an approximate expression for T_E

$$T_E \simeq (3 \sim 4) H/Um$$

where   Um = mean velocity
         H = water depth

The value of mean velocity measured in accordance with the present standard, say 60 sec, would be used as a first approximation for Um in the above expression.

However the above expression was derived from the measurements performed in the low water period as stated on page 8 in his paper. And the expression of T_E for the high water has not established.

In this meaning, the author agrees that there is a need to establish a general standard for the measurements of velocity fluctuation.

Response on the discussion by J. W. Delleur and the second question in the discussion by C. Kisiel.

Last year, the author and his colleagues performed the turbulence measurements in open channel flows by the hot film anemometer. The experimental conditions are as follows:

Water depth: $5 \sim 10$ cm ; mean velocity: $40 \sim 60$ cm/sec,
Froude number of flow: $0.5 \sim 0.8$; and flows are all
smooth turbulence.

According to our experimental results, the values of the integral time scale T_E were between 0.1 and 0.2 second and most of the turbulence energy were contained at frequencies below $1 \sim 0.5$ cycles per second. This figues of frequency approximately agree with those obtained from $f = 0.1/T_E$ which was pointed out by Prof. Delleur.

As pointed out by Professors Delleur and Kisiel the velocity spectrum measured by the current meter would not be accurate in the high frequency bands, since the current meter is a kind of the cutoff filter for the high frequency bands.

However, the author thinks that the use of the current meter is permissible for the study of the macro structure of turbulence, since the turbulence energy contained in the high frequency bands is relatively small.

The response to discussion by P.S. Eagleson is as follows.

The author performed this calculations aiming at two items pointed out by Prof. P. S. Eagleson. However, it seemed for the author that his aim failed of sucess so far as the examples shown in Figures 6a and 6b are concerned.

The author presumes that one of the reasons of this would be thw too wide Fourier spectrum of the input. Better results in detection process will be expected if a longer sampling interval for the input data is used instead of the hourly rainfall. The author, basing on the precision of the detected input, finds a way of the future development of this method in considering the relationship between the optimum sampling interval of the input and the duration time of the output.

Response to first and third questions in discussion by C. Kisiel.

1) In the calculations shown in Figs.6a and 6b the values of the runoff coefficient are given. The corrected values of the detected rainfall were calculated by dividing the detected rainfall by the runoff coefficient.

3) In the analysis of the runoff systems the Fourier spectra of the inputs are usually far wide than those of the outputs. Consequently, the systems function is liable to be erroneous in the high frequency bands even when the corosscorrelation method is used. In this meaning, the author thinks that the use of the high-cut filter such as proposed by Prof. Delleur is necessary.

Response to discussion by J. P. Riley.

In the calculation of the short term runoff, for instant the storm runoff, the definitions of the rainfall loss or the methods of separation of the direct runoff from the total runoff change the funtional form of the outputs and, consequently, have effects on the results of calculations. This effect will be appeared mainly in the low frequency bands of the systems function.

In the calculation of the long term runoff the carry-over discharge to the basin is sometimes a difficult factor to treat as well as the rainfall losses.

The response to discussion by V. Yevjevich is as follows.

As stated by Prof. V. Yevjevich an optimum must exist between the time of point velocity measurements and the number of points at which velocities are measured.

However, in most cases, velocities in a river section vary gradually both in transversal and vertical directions. So that, the increase in the number of points would not improve the precision of the discharge measurements appreciably.

On considering the above fact, the author dared to put stress on the importance of the time of point velocity measurements.

UNITED STATES-JAPAN BILATERAL SEMINAR IN HYDROLOGY

Honolulu, January 1971

KERNELS OF STOCHASTIC LINEAR HYDROLOGIC SYSTEMS

By Rafael G. Quimpo
Associate Professor of Civil Engineering
University of Pittsburgh
Pittsburgh, Pa., USA

Synopsis

Using operational methods of analyzing linear systems, kernels corresponding to current stochastic models of hydrologic time series are obtained. It is shown that these models essentially assume the form of the kernel of the linear system in terms of undetermined parameters as contrasted with the approach which requires the solution of the Weiner-Hopf equation.

Markov, second and third order autoregressive models equivalent to two types of self-similar models for a typical river were obtained using a least-square criterion on the kernel. To compare the re-scaled range properties of synthetic data using different generating techniques, 2400 years of record were synthesized for each of five models. Visual inspection of respective re-scaled-range vs. length-of-record plots suggests essentially the same result for the range regardless of which model is used to generate data.

INTRODUCTION

Several models of time series have been proposed for use in simulating the stochastic runoff process. The applicability of these models to other phenomena has given them various interpretations which often obscure the fact that they have a unifying feature in their linear formulation. This paper examines this aspect through the extension of systems concepts which have been given their due cognizance by parametric hydrologists in recent years.

BACKGROUND - SOME ASPECTS OF HYDROLOGIC SYSTEMS ANALYSIS

Deterministic Systems. Man's efforts to understand various processes in the hydrologic cycle has always involved some sort

8 .1

of a system. System analysis therefore is not new in hydrology. Without attempting to trace the history of its use, a hydrologic system will be interpreted as a collection of components that interrelate input to output and in which the variables are concerned with water (1). If the system is well defined, its behavior may be described by a set of simultaneous differential or integro-differential equations. With reference to these mathematical equations, the system could be linear, non-linear, invariant or varying with time, stochastic or deterministic (2). With reference to the system, it can be lumped, that is, the system is taken as a whole or it can be spatially distributed (3). Since this study has the specific purpose of extending the concepts in this very extensive subject to stochastic hydrologic systems, attention will be focused to spatially-lumped, time-invariant linear stochastic hydrologic systems. This train of modifiers seems to be too restrictive to be useful but surprisingly enough, little attention has been devoted to a methodical study of such a model. Progress to less restrictive stochastic models (i.e., time-varying, non-linear models) will be hastened if the simpler ones are well understood. A brief outline of linear deterministic system theory follow.

The input-output relationship in a linear hydrologic system may be represented by

$$\Phi_L[Y(s,t)] = X(s,t) \tag{1}$$

where $Y(s,t)$ is the output or dependent variable, $X(s,t)$ is the input or independent variable, both functions of space and time; and Φ_L is a linear operator. Eq. 1 may be rearranged to

$$Y(s,t) = \Phi_L^{-1}[X(s,t)] \tag{2}$$

in which Φ_L^{-1} is conceived as operating on the input X to obtain the output Y. Φ_L^{-1} is often referred to as the transfer function of the system.

The solution of Eq. 1 is well known as the Green's function or kernel of the system. It is dependent on both time and space. Eagleson (3) discusses various ramifications of such a

1. Dooge, J.C.I., "The Hydrologic System as a Closed System", Proceedings, International Hydrology Symposium, Fort Collins, Colo., Vol. 2, Sept., 1967.

2. Chow, V. T., "Systems Approach to Hydrology and Water Resources", The Progress of Hydrology, Proceedings, 1st International Seminar for Hydrology Professors, Vol. 1, Urbana, Illinois, August, 1970.

3. Eagleson, P. S., "Deterministic Linear Hydrologic Systems", The Progress of Hydrology, Proceedings, 1st International Seminar for Hydrology Professors, Vol. 1, Urbana, Illinois, August, 1970.

system. Assuming separability conditions, he outlines how one may obtain a spatially-lumped system either time-invariant or time varying. In many hydrologic applications, interest is often centered on the output Y, only at some particular point in the system (e.g., at the mouth of the watershed or downstream of a dam). This leads to spatial lumping. Under the assumption of a spatially-lumped time-invariant system, Eq. 1 may be written as a linear differential equation with constant coefficients

$$[a_n D^n + a_{n-1} D^{n-1} + \ldots + a_1 D + a_0] Y(t) = X(t) \qquad (3)$$

where D^k is the differential operator $\dfrac{d^k}{dt^k}$. Eq. 3 is essentially equivalent to formulating the system (basin) as a cascade of linear reservoirs (1).

An alternative formulation of the problem in terms of input-output analysis is given by Chow(2). Assuming a lumped system, the black box approach relates the output and input to the storage S in the system by the continuity equation

$$X(t) - Y(t) = \frac{dS}{dt} \qquad (4)$$

The usual approach is to assume that the storage is related to both the input and output by

$$S = \sum_{p=0}^{N-1} a_{p+1} \frac{d^p Y(t)}{dt^p} - \sum_{m=0}^{M-1} b_{m+1} \frac{d^m X(t)}{dt^m} \qquad (5)$$

so that Eq. 5 into Eq. 4 yields

$$X(t) + \sum_{m=0}^{M-1} b_{m+1} \frac{d^{m+1} X(t)}{dt^{m+1}} = Y(t) + \sum_{p=0}^{N-1} a_{p+1} \frac{d^{p+1} Y(t)}{dt^{p+1}} \qquad (6)$$

or in operator notation

$$[1 + \sum_{i=1}^{M} b_i D^i] X(t) = [1 + \sum_{j=1}^{N} a_j D^j] Y(t)$$

$$Y(t) = \frac{[1 + \sum_{i=1}^{M} b_i D^i]}{[1 + \sum_{j=1}^{N} a_j D^j]} X(t) \qquad (7)$$

Extension to Stochastic Systems. In the above formulation $X(s,t)$ and $Y(s,t)$ may also be random functions of space and time. A lumped system subjected to a stochastic input would thus have an output whose statistical properties are determined by the stochastic properties of the input and the deterministic properties of the system. A more general formulation suggested by Chow is to make the system itself (i.e., parameters describing the system) vary randomly. This formulation is rather dif-

166

ficult to analyze without some knowledge of the probabilistic
law governing the evolution of the system (4). The first formulation will therefore be adopted. For such a stochastic system,
two types of problems are immediately of interest to hydrology-
namely system identification and prediction. The identificaton
problem involves the analysis of paired X- and Y- values to obtain the parameters which describe the system. Prediction involves the use of the model obtained from the identification problem to predict the value of Y given the input X.

Referring to Eq. 1, once the Green's function is determined,
the output corresponding to any input is obtained by convoluting
the input with the Green's function G(u). Thus for the spatially lumped case

$$Y(t) = \int_{-\infty}^{\infty} G(u)X(t-u)\,du \tag{8}$$

Eq. 8 forms the basis of linear unit hydrograph theory as may
easily be seen by writing it in the alternate form

$$Y(t) = \int_{-\infty}^{\infty} G(t-u)X(u)\,du \tag{9}$$

and then letting physical realizability or causality requirements modify the limits of integration resulting in

$$Y(t) = \int_{0}^{t} G(t-u)X(u)\,du \tag{10}$$

Eagleson (3) points out however, that strictly speaking, Eq. 10
is valid only for zero initial conditions which are implied
when it is used to compute direct runoff from precipitation
excess.

Given X(t) and Y(t), the minimum squared error approach to
estimating G(u) under the linearity assumption, involves minimizing the expectation of the square of the errors W(t)

$$E[W^2(t)] = E[\int_{0}^{t} G(u)X(t-u)\,du - Y(t)]^2 \tag{11}$$

If X(t) and Y(t) are assumed stationary, it can be shown (5)
that the G(u) which minimizes $E[W^2(t)]$ must satisfy the Weiner-
Hopf integral equation

$$\Gamma_{xy}(u) = \int_{-\infty}^{\infty} \Gamma_{xx}(u-v)G(v)\,dv \qquad u \geq 0 \tag{12}$$

where

4. Blanc-Lapiere, A., and Fortet, R., Theory of Random Functions,
   Vol. 1, Translated from French by J. Gani, Gordon and Breach,
   New York, 1965.

5. Laning, J. H., and Battin, R. H., Random Processes in Automatic Control, Mc-Graw Hill Book Company, New York, 1956

$$\Gamma_{xy}(u) = E[X(t)Y(t+u)] \tag{13}$$

and

$$\Gamma_{xx}(u) = E[X(t)X(t+u)] \tag{14}$$

The solution of Eq. 12 using Fourier transform techniques, is given in many books in control theory (5). For the analytical solution to be tractable however, simplifying assumptions are made regarding the functional forms of Eqs. 13 and 14. The usual procedure is to assume that $\Gamma_{xy}(u)$ and $\Gamma_{xx}(u)$ have rational transforms. This is the case if $\Gamma_{xy}(u)$ and $\Gamma_{xx}(u)$ are exponential or exponentially-damped cosine functions.

In a rainfall-runoff analysis of a basin in Japan, Hino (6) assumed exponential forms for $\Gamma_{xy}(u)$ and $\Gamma_{xx}(u)$ to arrive at an explicit form for the optimal kernel. While the analytical solution of the Weiner-Hopf equation is desirable in system identification, its use in long-term streamflow forecasting is rather cumbersome. To apply the optimal kernel in prediction requires the synthetic generation of the input process. This in turn, requires a stochastic model for the rainfall and hence another model-fitting procedure. The use of the kernel is ideal for short-term forecasting where historical data may be used for input, but in most hydrologic applications, stochastic models are best suited for long-range assesment of project performance. Short-term forecasts are best approached by using deterministic techniques, i.e., unit hydrograph and flood routing methods (7). If a rainfall model is used as input for long-term prediction, the model is further constrained by the requirement that its autocovariance properties, in particular $\Gamma_{xx}(u)$, must be of the same form as that used in deriving the explicit form of the kernel.

Because of the above, the approach that has been extensively used is not to solve the Weiner Hopf equation but to postulate the form of the kernel function G(u), expressing it in terms of parameters which may be estimated from historical data. Markov, autoregressive (AR) and self-similar (S-S) models of hydrologic time series belong to this approach. This technique has the advantage that after the parameters of the kernel have been de-

6. Hino, M., "Runoff Forecasts by Linear Predictive Filter", Proc. Paper 7146, Journal of the Hydraulics Division, ASCE Vol. 96, HY3, March, 1970

7. Quimpo, R. G., "Stochastic Analysis of Daily River Flows", Proc. Paper 5719, Journal of the Hydraulics Division, ASCE Vol. 94, HY1, Jan, 1968; and Closure, Proc. Paper 6866, Vol. 95, HY6, Nov. 1969.

termined, its application is much more direct. Since the kernel function is not predicated on the input, the resulting model of runoff is more flexible in the sense that any form of the input process may be used. Input processes which are normally and independently distributed, as well as skewed and serially correlated inputs, may be used. The input is constrained only by the requirement that the output must reproduce the statistics of the historical sequence from which the model was derived. The remainder of this paper will concentrate on the kernels of the models using this approach.

For stochastic models, the preferred form of the convolution integral is Eq. 8, instead of Eq, 9. This becomes apparent if Eq. 8 is expressed in its equivalent discrete form and the limits modified to satisfy causality requirements, i.e.,

$$Y_t = \sum_{u=0}^{\infty} G_u X_{t-u} \tag{15}$$

where Y_t, G_u and X_{t-u} are discrete equivalents of $Y(t)$, $G(u)$ and $X(t-u)$ respectively.

Consider now the Markov model (8) in its simplest form. If X_t is the input and Y_t the output, the simple Markov model may be written as

$$Y_t - \rho Y_{t-1} = X_t \tag{16}$$

where ρ is the first autocorrelation coefficient of Y_t. Using the Z-transform (9) such that

$$z^{-k}(Y_t) = Y_{t-k} \tag{17}$$

Eq. 16 may be written in operator notation as

$$Y_t = \frac{1}{[1-\rho z^{-1}]} X_t \tag{18}$$

Expanding the operator in an infinite series, one obtains

$$Y_t = \sum_{k=0}^{\infty} \rho^k z^{-k}(X_t) = \sum_{k=0}^{\infty} \rho^k X_{t-k} \tag{19}$$

---

8. Matalas, N. C., "Some Aspects of Time Series Analysis in Hydrologic Studies", Proceedings, Hydrology Symposium No. 5, McGill University, Canada, February, 1966.

9. Kaplan, W., "Operational Methods for Linear Systems", Addison Wesley Publishing Co., Reading, Mass., 1962

Thus, comparing Eqs. 19 and 15, it can be seen that for the simple Markov model

$$G_u = \rho^u \tag{20}$$

Jenkins and Watts (10) proceed along the same lines and obtain for the second order AR process used by Beard (11) and Quimpo (7)

$$Y_t - a_1 Y_{t-1} - a_2 Y_{t-2} = X_t \tag{21}$$

two kernels, depending on whether the roots λ_1 and λ_2 of the corresponding characteristic equation

$$\rho^2 - a_1 \rho - a_2 = 0 \tag{22}$$

are real or complex. If λ_1 and λ_2 are real and unequal, Jenkins and Watts give

$$G_u = \frac{\lambda_1^{u+1} - \lambda_2^{u+1}}{\lambda_1 - \lambda_2} \tag{23a}$$

If the roots are complex conjugates $\lambda_2 = \lambda_1^* = Re^{i\theta}$

$$G_u = R^u \frac{\sin(u+1)\theta}{\sin\theta} \tag{23b}$$

For the third order AR model

$$Y_t - a_1 Y_{t-1} - a_2 Y_{t-2} - a_3 Y_{t-3} = X_t \tag{24}$$

it can be shown that if the roots $\lambda_1, \lambda_2,$ and λ_3 of the corresponding characteristic equation are all real and unequal

$$G_u = \frac{\lambda_1^{u+1}(\lambda_2-\lambda_3) + \lambda_2^{u+1}(\lambda_3-\lambda_1) + \lambda^{u+1}(\lambda_1-\lambda_2)}{(\lambda_1-\lambda_2)(\lambda_2-\lambda_3)(\lambda_3-\lambda_1)} \tag{25a}$$

If one root λ_1 is real and the other two are complex conjugates $\lambda_2 = \lambda_3 = P\exp(i\psi)$, it can be further shown after some trigonometry that

$$G_u = \lambda^{u+2}\delta^{-2} + P^u \frac{\cos(u+1)\psi\cos\psi - (\lambda_1/P)\sin(u+2)\psi\sin\psi}{1 - (\delta/P)^2\sin^2\psi} \tag{25b}$$

---

10. Jenkins, G. M., and Watts, D. G., Spectral Analysis and its Applications, Holden Day, San Francisco. 1968

11. Beard, L. R., "Simulation of Daily Streamflow". Proceedings, International Hydrology Symposium, Fort Collins, Colo., Vol. 1, 1967, p. 624-632

where

$$\delta^2 = P^2 + \lambda_1^2 - 2\lambda_1 P \cos \psi \qquad (2$$

Eq. 26 is the cosine law. It may be noted that Wold (12)
examined the behavior of the roots of the characteristic equation only up to the second order model. The physical significance of the geometric interpretation in Fig. 1 is yet to be
explained. Corresponding to Eqs. 23 and 25, if multiple roots
occur, kernels may similarly be obtained.

A digression at this point might be helpful to illustrate
how parameters of the stochastic models may be related to models of parametric hydrology. In hydrograph analysis, the continuity equation 4 and the simple reservoir equation relating
storage S to the outflow Y and storage constant K

$$S = KY \qquad (2$$

combine to yield

$$(1+KD)Y = X \qquad (2$$

The similarity between Eqs. 28 and 18 immediately leads to the
obvious conclusion that the autocorrelation coefficient $\rho(\tau)$
and the storage constant K must be related. In fact it can be
shown that

$$K = \frac{-\tau}{\ln \rho(\tau)} \qquad (2$$

where τ denotes time. Using a slightly different approach,
Fiering (13) also relates $\rho(\tau)$ to the storage constant of a
reservoir model for the catchment. Quimpo, following the above
approach, extends this relation to more complex models of basin
storage characteristics (14).

So far, only Markov and autoregressive models have been
examined. It can be shown however, that the self-similar model
of Mandelbrot and Wallis (15) may also be classified under this
category (i.e., models whose kernel forms are assumed). For
example, the Type 1 S-S model is simply

12. Wold, H., A Study in the Analysis of Stationary Time Series
    Almquist and Wiksell, Uppsala, Sweden, 1954.
13. Fiering, M. B., Streamflow Synthesis, Harvard University
    Press, Cambridge, Mass., 1967
14. Quimpo, R. G., "Structural Relation between Parametric and
    Stochastic Hydrology Models", Manuscript in preparation.
15. Mandelbrot, B., and Wallis, J. R., "Computer Experiments
    with Fractional Gaussian Noises, Part III, Mathematical
    Appendix", Water Resources Research, Vol. 5 No. 1, February
    1969.

8 .8

$$Y_t = \sum_{k=1}^{M} G_u X_{t-u} \qquad (30)$$

where X_t is the discrete equivalent of white noise and

$$G_u = \begin{cases} u^{H-0.5} & u = 1 \\ u^{H-0.5} - (u-1)^{H-0.5} & 1 < u \leq M \\ 0 & u > M \end{cases} \qquad (31)$$

The kernel of the Type 2 S-S model may also be written as

$$G_u = \begin{cases} 0 & u < 0 \\ (H-0.5)u^{H-1.5} & 1 \leq u \leq M \\ 0 & u > M \end{cases} \qquad (32)$$

COMPARISON OF MODELS BY SIMULATION

Since the thesis of this study is the unification of current time series models under the systems framework, the kernel functions of the linear models will be compared. Figure 2 shows the kernels of Markov, autoregressive and self-similar models for given parameters. It is seen that the differences among the models may be expressed in terms of (a) rate of decay; and (b) memory of the system. In Fig. 2, it is noted that for the second and third order AR models, only kernels corresponding to Eqs. 23a and 25a respectively, are plotted. Equations 23b and 25b, corresponding to the cases where the roots of the characteristic equations are complex, result in kernels which oscillate about the abscissa. Because of the comparative evaluation which follows, oscillatory kernels were not used. To illustrate how the different kernels could possibly affect the solution of specific problems, the behavior of the re-scaled range corresponding to the models in Fig. 2 was examined. The importance of the re-scaled range has been explored quite extensively by several authors (16, 17, 18, 19). Only aspects directly related to the example will be reviewed.

16. Hurst, H. E., "Long-Term Storage Capacities of Reservoirs", Transactions, ASCE, Vol. 116, 1951 p. 770-799.
17. Chow, V. Y., Discussion of Hurst, "Long-Term Storage Capacities of Reservoirs", Trans. ASCE, Vol. 116,1951,p.800-802.
18. Feller, W., "The Asymptotic Distribution of the Range of of Independent Random Variables", Annals of Mathematical Statistics, Vol. 22, Sept., 1951.
19. Yevjevich, V. M., "The Application of Surplus, Deficit and Range in Hydrology", Hydrology Paper No. 10, Colorado State University, Fort Collins, Colo., 1965.

If Y_t (t=1, 2, ..., N) denote a sequence of equi-spaced values of river discharges, let $C_t = \Sigma_{i=1}^t Y_i$. The range of cumulative flows is defined as

$$R = \max_{1 \leq t \leq N} [C_t - (t/N) C_N] - \min_{1 \leq t \leq N} [C_t - (t/N) C_N] \qquad (33)$$

If SD is the standard deviation of the sample record Y_t, the re-scaled range is defined as

$$R_s = \frac{R}{SD} \qquad (34)$$

It can be shown that under certain assumptions (16), R_s is related to the storage required to supply a uniform draft equal to the mean discharge of the river. R_s is however, a random variable and current studies are focused on its be- havior for different values of N under various assumptions regarding the stochastic properties of Y_t. An indication of this behavior is a plot of R_s as ordinate, versus N. Feller(18) shows that if Y_t is independently and identically distributed

$$R_s = 1.25N^{0.5} \qquad (35)$$

asymptotically, so that on double-log paper, R_s plots against N with slope 1/2. Empirical streamflow data however, yield slopes greater than 1/2 (16). This suggests that stochastic models of streamflow must reflect this departure from the "square -root law". With this background, the kernels in Fig. 2 were used to generate synthetic data whose re-scaled range properties were studied. The kernels shown in the figure were determined using as basis a self-similar model with H=0.633 and M=50. This value of H is typical of many rivers studied using data published by Yevjevich (20), and the value of 50 for M was chosen arbitra- rily as comparable in length to streamflow data currently avail- able. Corresponding to this S-S model, "equivalent" Markov and AR models were obtained, the equivalence being determined by a least-square fitting technique based on the kernel of the basic S-S model.

With the kernels of five models (i.e., Markov, 2nd order AR, 3rd order AR, Type 1 S-S and Type 2 S-S) thus determined, each kernel was used to generate 2400 years of annual flow data. Each synthetic record was then divided into non-overlapping subsets of 100-, 200-, 300-, 400-, 600-, 800-, and 1200-yr and an "R_s analysis" was made on each subset. Figs. 3 and 4 show the results. The crosses denote computed values of R_s and the circles are the means of each set of crosses, corresponding to one value of N. The decreasing number of crosses as N increases reflect

20. Yevjevich, V. M., "Fluctuations of Wet and Dry Years", Part I, Research Data Assembly and Mathematical Models, Colorado State University Hydrology Paper No. 1, Fort Collins, Colo., July, 1963.

the decrease of non-overlapping subsets from 2400 as the size of the subset increases. The solid line in each figure represent the slope H = 0.633 of the basic model. It is remarkable that despite its being the basic model from which all the others were derived, the data generated using the Type 2 self-similar model exhibit quite some scatter about the slope H as seen in Fig. 4b. While it is beyond the scope of this paper to discuss all the ramifications of the R_s analysis, inspection of Figs. 3 and 4 show that the different generating schemes resulted in statistically indistinguishable "R_s vs. N" plots. While this might not be the case if some other statistic of the synthetic data were studied, the above result suggests that for a given river, if the stochastic models is properly fitted, one can use any generating scheme and get essentially the same result for the range.

CONCLUSIONS

The comparative analysis and results of simulation studies above suggest several conclusions concerning aspects of hydrologic time series modeling. Firstly, using linear stochastic models, the problem may be summarized as that of determining the kernel of the corresponding hydrologic system. While this concept is almost axiomatic in parametric hydrology, in the evolution of stochastic hydrologic models, what should have been obvious was obscured.

Secondly, in determining the kernel of a stochastic system, two approaches are possible: (a) solving the Weiner-Hopf equation for the optimum kernel, or (b) assuming the form of the kernel a priori in terms of a set of parameters, solving the parameter estimation problem and then testing the goodness of fit. The first approach, to be tractable, requires the assumption of autocovariance and cross-covariance properties of input and output. Furthermore, its use is cumbersome as it requires the generation of the input process in order to use the kernel for long-range forecasting. For short-term forecasts, historical data may be used as input but experience shows that short-range forecasting is best approached using deterministic methods (i.e., by hydrograph and routing techniques). The second approach, exemplified by current time series models, appears to be more flexible and straightforward.

Finally, the current models of hydrologic time series may be classified under a single system formulation, their differences being explained by the rate of decay of the kernels and memory of the system. Results show that the behavior of the re-scaled range appear to be insensitive to whether a Markov, autoregressive or a self-similar model is used to generate synthetic data.

ACKNOWLEDGMENTS

Work on this paper was supported by the National Science Foundation under Research Grant No. GK-20388. Mr. Jing-yea

Yang, formerly Graduate Research Assistant at the University
of Pittsburgh, programmed all the calculations in this study.

LIST OF SYMBOLS

The following symbols are used in this paper:

AR	autoregressive
a_i	coefficients of differential equation
b_i	coefficients of storage function
c_t	accumulated sum of flows
D^k	differential operator
E	mathematical expectation
G(t)	kernel function
H	parameter in self-similar model
K	storage constant
N	length of record
P	absolute value of root
R	range of cumulative flows
R_s	rescaled range
S	storage
SD	standard deviation
SS	self-similar
W(t)	error; difference between observed and predicted value
X(t)	input process
Y(t)	output process
Z	transform operator
Γ_{xx}	autocovariance function of X(t)
Γ_{xy}	cross covariance function of Y(t)
δ	length of side opposite given angle in cosine law
θ	argument in complex root
λ_i	ith root of characteristic equation
ρ	first autocorrelation coefficient
τ	lag
Φ_L	linear operator
ψ	argument of complex root

8 .12

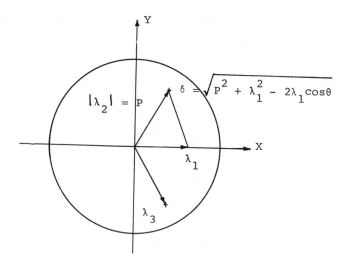

Fig. 1   Roots of Characteristic Equation Defining
Kernel of Third Order A.R. Model

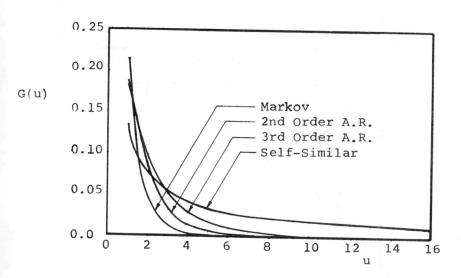

Fig. 2   Kernel Functions of Different Models

8 .13

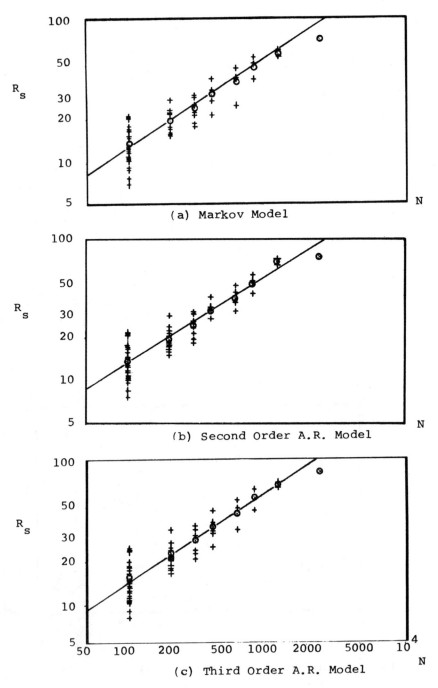

(a) Markov Model

(b) Second Order A.R. Model

(c) Third Order A.R. Model

Fig. 3 R_s vs. N Plots for Markov and A.R. Models

8.14

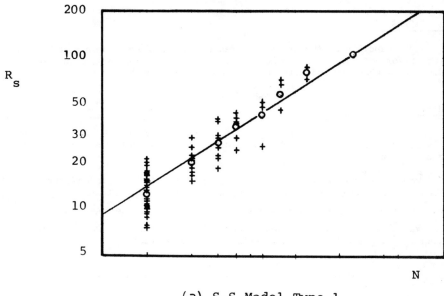

(a) S-S Model Type 1

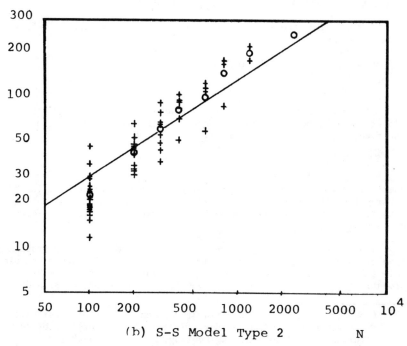

(b) S-S Model Type 2

Fig. 4 R_s vs. N Plots for Self-Similar Models

8 .15

DISCUSSION

P. S. EAGLESON

Is reproduction of the property, "range", a necessary and/or a sufficient criterion for adequacy of a streamflow simulation model to be used in storage studies? How about reproduction of the behavior of runs?

M. HINO

The author's method of simulation of runoff data discards the information available from record of runoff. As a result, for instance, the periodicity of long cycle cannot be realized.

I would like to intorduce a simulation technique*) which I have successfully applied to the simulation of random wave with Neumann type of spectrum. Let $\Phi_{YY}(\omega)$ be the spectrum of output to be simulated, and $\Phi_{XX}(\omega)$ be the spectrum of arbitrary random variable X(t), which is not necessarily the rainfall. Then, the relationsh: between Φ_{YY}, Φ_{XX} and the system function H(ω), is written as

$$\Phi_{YY}(\omega) = H(\omega)H^*(\omega)\Phi_{XX}(\omega) \tag{1}$$

One of the simplest case of runoff simulation by the above equation is to assume $\Phi_{XX}(\omega)$ to be a white noise; i.e. $\Phi_{XX}(\omega)$ = const. $\tag{2}$

On the other hand, the spectrum of runoff $\Phi_{YY}(\omega)$ is factorized as a product of two terms,

$$\Phi_{YY}(\omega) = \Phi_{YY}^{+}(\omega) \cdot \Phi_{YY}^{-}(\omega) \quad , \tag{3}$$

where the complex function Φ_{YY}^{+} (Φ_{YY}^{-}) contains only poles and zeros in the upper (lower) half-plane of ω-domain. Then, from a comparison of equations (1) and (3), the frequency response function H(ω) is given as

$$H(\omega) = \text{const } \Phi_{YY}^{+}(\omega) \quad . \tag{4}$$

The inverse Fourier transform of H(ω) yields the response function h(t). Of cours the function thus derived is not hydrograph. I am now investigating the runoff data simulation by this method collaborating with Mr. Kim from Korea who stayed in my laboratory last year.

The second point of my comments is the importance of the probability distribu tion of random variable. The synthesized data of a time series should simulate no only the second order moments such as correlation and spectrum but also the probability distribution which is sometimes skew to the Gaussian distribution.

---

*) Hino, J.: Prediction - and transformation filters of water waves. - (1), Proc. 14th Conf. on Coastal Eng. (Japan), JSCE (1967); Also included in Lecture Note on Hydraulic Engineering, Section A, JSCE (1970)

T. KISHI

1) In the comparison of several stochastic models the author introduces the concept of "equivalent models".

The author's explanation is that "equivalence" is determined by a least-square fitting technique based on the Kernel of the basic s-s model.

The writer would like to know the meaning and mathematical procedures of "equivalence" in more detail.

2) The writer points out the following relationship between the self-similar process (fractional gaussian noise) and the auto-regressive process.

a) Variance of secular average

$$E[N^{-1} \sum_{s=1}^{N} Y(t+s)]^2 = (EY^2)N^{2H-2} \qquad \text{for s-s process} \qquad (1)$$

$$= (EY^2)L_N(\rho)N^{-1} \qquad \text{for a-r process} \qquad (2)$$

where

$$L_N(\rho) = 1 + 2\{ \left(\frac{N-1}{N}\right)\rho_1 + \left(\frac{N-2}{N}\right)\rho_2 + \cdots \frac{1}{N}\rho_{N-1} \} \qquad (3)$$

ρ_k : serial correlation coefficient for lag k
H : parameter of fractional noise. $0 < H < 1$

b) Sequential variance

$$E[s^2(N)] = EY^2 - E[N^{-1}\Sigma Y]^2$$

$$= EY^2[1 - N^{2H-2}] \qquad \text{for s-s process} \qquad (4)$$

$$= EY^2[1 - L_N(\rho)N^{-1}] \qquad \text{for a-r process} \qquad (5)$$

Equation (3) approaches to equation (6) as the sampling interval becomes small.

$$L_N(\rho) \approx 2 \int_0^N (1 - \frac{k}{N}) R(k)dk \qquad (6)$$

$$\lim N \to \infty \quad L_N(\rho) = 2 \int_0^\infty R(k)dk = 2 N_E \qquad (7)$$

N_E is the Eulerian Time scale or the relaxation time in fluid mechanics. For gaussion noise

$$L_N(\rho) = 2 \int_0^\infty \delta(k)dk = 1 \qquad (8)$$

From equations (1), (2) and (7) one has

$$N^{2H-1} = 2N_E \qquad (9)$$

For the case of Markov process

$$N^{2H-1} = -2/\log_e \rho \qquad (10$$

Equation (9) or (10) would give an approximate estimate of H. It is also found that the parameter H which satisfies equation (9) or (10) is not a constant but a function of N. As an example, let us consider the case of $\rho = 0.3$ in equation (10). H = 0.61 for N = 10; H = 0.56 for N = 100; H = 0.54 for N = 1,000 are obtained.

3) Looking at Figs. 3 and 4 one can find that the variance of R_s increases as N decreases. In the statics of hydrologic variables the variance is also very important not only the mean, especially for the practical application.

I would like to know the expression for the probability distribution functio of R_s as a function of N. Your comment of this point is much appreciated.

4) What do you think of the present practice in the design of reservoir capacity? What is the reliability of the conventional design method which is based on the relatively short records.

C. KISIEL

What are the necessary and sufficient conditions for fitting a stochastic model to an observed time series? Are there errors in Eq. (30)? No bounds plac on relation of N to M. Why?

T. STEELE AND C. KISIEL

This is an interesting paper on a topic of great importance in stochastic hydrology today. The study of the Hurst phenomenon, its significance, and metho for modeling it are of concern to all modern hydrologists. Some of the results reported in this paper have been previously presented by one of the discussers.[*]

The paper attempts to compare "equivalent" autoregressive and self-similar models. From figure 2 it appears that these "equivalent" models are equivalent only by Professor Quimpo's definition. This aspect of the paper is crucial to the acceptance of its conclusions. It merits a rational explanation rather than an appeal to subjectivity. The shapes of the kernels are radically different. The physical parameters (like the time constant) implied in each kernel function arise from different model representations. Comparisons must in the final analy be made on the basis of model assumptions and parameters.

In particular, the first order serial correlation coefficient for the auto-regressive schemes are greatly inflated in relation to that for the equivalent self-similar process. If a sample estimate of ρ_1 is 0.3, which is usual for ann streamflow data, what value of ρ_1 should be used in simulation other than 0.3, a how should that value be estimated from the sample? It can be shown that self-similar processes can preserve both ρ_1 and a Hurst coefficient. Does Professor Quimpo know whether this is possible for autoregressive schemes?

---

[*] C. C. Kisiel, "Transformation of deterministic and stochastic processes in hydrology," *Proc.*, International Hydrology Symposium, Vol. 1, Sept. 1967, Fort Collins, Colorado, pp. 600-607.

The self-similar processes modeled by Professor Quimpo are for H= 0.633 and M=50, and "the value of 50 for M was chosen arbitrarily as comparable in length to streamflow data currently available." Is not M a memory parameter, and therefore not related to sample length? True, memory cannot be estimated prior to the sample, but is this to be interpreted as implying that the process is nonstationary, with one parameter growing with time? By analogy with the uncited reference by Fiering concerning autoregressive schemes, the preservation of Hurst phenomenon should not extend much beyond 3 or 4 times the order of the process, say N = 200. However, the self-similar processes, as shown in Figure 4, seem to preserve H > 0.633 for up to about N = 1000 before tending asymptotically to the expected value of H = 0.5.

For the autoregressive schemes shown in figure 3, the lines shown for the relation of R_s to N are perhaps misleading. They seem to be drawn arbitrarily at a slope of 0.633 and therefore the eye leads the mind to the conclusion that the lines fit the points. For instance, figure 3 shows the same data, with lines drawn arbitrarily with the expected slope of 0.5, and these seem to fit the data much better than those shown on figure 3. What are the least squares fitted slopes for the open circles shown in figures 3 and 4? Apparently in order to emphasize rather than disguise sampling variability, Mandelbrot and Wallis* drew the line with population slope through the point for N = 20. Note that the trend lines of slope 0.5 in figure 3 are pivoted about N = 100, the lowest value of N shown. Is there a particular reason for not using similar methods of comparison for figures 3 and 4? Does Professor Quimpo have any information concerning the sampling properties of a self-similar process with H = 0.633 and M = 50? Were more traces run than just the single traces shown in figures 4a and 4b? If not, would other simulations give the same results (refer to Wallis and Matalas*)? What are the expected trend lines, and at what point do they break over to a slope of 0.5?

---

*Mandelbrot, B. B. and James R. Wallis, Some long-run properties of geophysical records, Water Resources Res., 5(2), 321-340, 1969.
*Wallis, J.R. and N.C. Matalas, Small sample properties of H and K -- Estimators of the Hurst coefficient h, Water Resources Res., 6(6).

V. YEVJEVICH

This paper seems to imply that self-similar models are linear models. The question arises whether they are stationary or nonstationary processes.

The use of the so-called Hurst law becomes equivalent to fitting of a power function to the relation of the mean range to the subsample size, with the estimate of the exponent H . It is easy to show that the exact relations of mean range to the subsample size are not power functions for any linear model. As a result, the population parameter in the Hurst law is obtained from an arbitrarily fit of straight lines to the sample relations by using the log-log scales.

The self-similar models seem to especially stress the interval of low frequencies of spectra of hydrologic variables. However, the accuracy of spectral densities of these intervals of frequencies cannot be checked by sample data because of the short time series usually available. The arbitrary assumptions underlying the self-similar models cannot be thus either proven or disproven easily.

RESPONSE BY R. G. QUIMPO

The response to questions and comments made by P. S. Eagleson are as follows.

I really do not know the answer to this question. Only time will tell whether the reproduction of range is indeed necessary and/or sufficient. The behavior of runs definitely affects the range since the latter is determined by a particular combination of runs of surpluses and deficits. The predominant interest in the range is probably historical initiated by Hurst's studies. It may also be due to the fact that the range is explicitly related to storage for a constant demand function. As we investigate more complex demand functions, we might find the range by itself inadequate and thus we might want to supplement (or supplant) the range with runs. This would require development of new methodology or at least the quantification of the effect of run length on storage. I understand some work on this is in progress at CSU.

In addition to the above two measures, we might want to preserve the autocorrelation properties. Presently, we try to preserve the first autocorrelation coefficient. This is adequate only for certain models. One might later want to preserve autocorrelation at higher lags.

The response to discussion by M. Hino is as follows.

The techniques used in my paper are based on the assumption that the process considered are all stochastic. If there are cycles in the record and the lineari assumption is valid, they could be identified and isolated as deterministic components, leaving the stochastic component to be modeled. Once the stochastic model is found, the effect of cycles, if they exist, may be incorporated in the final synthesis. A method of doing this was outlined in Reference 7.

The technique which Professor Hino suggests has its merits. It might be pointed out that essentially, it belongs to the technique of analyzing systems in the transformed domain just like Professor Delleur's approach. There are advantages and disadvantages in working in the frequency - as well as in the time domain. The choice, of course, depends on the problem as well as the preferences of the investigator.

Regarding the second point raised, in all the series simulated, the variable x_t was Gaussian mainly because the reference publications used the normal distribution for the underlying variable. In these cases, preserving the mean and second order moments is sufficient because the mean and covariance properties completely determine Gaussian processes. If x_t is not Gaussian, and this possibility was allowed for in my paper, one approach is to use a normalizing transformation. Alternatively, the input may be "pre-whitened" as Professor Hino suggests in his paper. In any case, the system function does not change as it is just the input which in modified.

The response to questions and comments made by T. Kishi are as follows.

1. In obtaining the "equivalent" models corresponding to the self-similar model, the equivalence was based on finding the value of the parameter(s) such that the sum of the squares of the differences between the two kernal functions : minimized. For example, for the Markov model, the parameter ρ was estimated by minimizing

$$\varepsilon^2 = \sum_{u=0}^{M} [G(u) - \rho^u]^2$$

where $G(u)$ is the self-similar kernal with H=0.633

2. The approach which Professor Kishi proposes to determine equivalent models seems to be promising. However, in computing $E[N^{-1} \Sigma Y(t+s)]^2$, he

seems to have neglected the covariance terms. If covariance terms are included in Eq. (1) of his discussion and if the resulting expression can be simplified to be manageable, it seems to be a better way of obtaining equivalent models. I will look further into this approach.

3. As stated in the paper, R_s varies with N. The distribution of R_s as a function of N has been studied previously. As far as I know, results for the case where the basic variables (i.e. Y) are independently and normally distributed are available. Some asymptotic results are also reported in the literature (See for example Fiering's "Streamflow Synthesis").

4. The determination of reservoir capacity using mass curve analysis has been subjected to criticism for some time now. Among the suggestions to alleviate the effect of short records is the use of simulated flows. But simulation is still based on models whose parameters are obtained from short records so that while it gives some indication of the variability, it does not necessarily elimi- nate the problem. One other alternative is to couple the streamflow simulation with an optimization model making use of some payoff function to determine optimum reservoir size as well as operating strategy. Some work is being done using this approach.

The response to questions and comments made by C. Kisiel are as follows.

If Professor Kisiel is asking for mathematically rigorous conditions of necessity and sufficiency, I am afraid he is asking the wrong person. However, if I may venture a pragmatic approach and focus on some specific hydrologic time series, one may look at some of the assumptions made in time series modeling to determine what is necessary. The most common of these assumptions is that the time series representing the process being modeled is stationary. An evolutionary model presents the additional problem deducing another a priori model for non- stationarity. This difficulty is outlined in Ref. 14. The model in my paper was very restrictive, it being linear and spatially lumped. Other investigators might want to look at non-linear as well as distributed models. These are some of the assumptions that are necessary. Under these assumptions, the models which result are also sufficient.

There is another meaning of "sufficient" which we might want to examine. Taken in the context of Professor Eagleson's discussion, a model may be sufficient for a specific purpose (e.g., 6-hour unit hydrograph for runoff prediction). Thus, one might legitimately raise the question of whether a model which reproduces the first autocorrelation coefficient of historical data is sufficient in storage studies. As in my reply to Professor Eagleson, only experiment can answer this question on sufficiency. Needless to say, the outcomes could be quite expensive.

On the question of a relation between N and M in Eq. 30, one must differenti- ate between specifying a model and modifying it in the light of sampling theory. To quote Dr. Kisiel's previous discussion, M is a memory parameter and initially should not be tied to sample length. Thus, it is a question of which comes first. Eq. 30 is a model expressed in its general form and therefore M was not related to N.

The response to questions and comments made by Drs. Kisiel and Steele are as follows.

Firstly, I would like to apologize for failing to cite Prof. Kisiel's work on the subject. As acknowledged in the synopsis, the techniques used in my paper have been abstracted from methods of operational mathematics, which if I recall correctly, dates back to Heaviside. Thus, there is no claim to originality in the mathematical development as evidenced by the citations which obviously could only be representative. I must, however, confess that my sampling technique could be improved. In the case of Eq. 25b which to my knowledge has not been published before, my only claim is for having worked out the trigonometry. I have even left the geometric significance of the kernel function for others to explain.

The question of "equivalence" of the models was a motivation for carrying out the simulation. If they were indeed "equivalent" in some sense, they must exhibit some common characteristic. The slope of Hurst's plot was chosen as the characteristic to be compared. In fact, in the discussion of results, the paper was quite specific on the limitation of the study and explicitly recognized the possibility of a different conclusion if some statistic other than the range were used.

This writer is not convinced that the preservation of autocorrelation properties must be tied to a simultaneous preservation of a Hurst coefficient (which value is difficult to reliably estimate in the first place) and hence he has not exerted efforts towards this objective. The importance of preserving Hurst's coefficient may be examined in a practical problem: The range of deviations from the mean has historically been recognized as an indicator of required reservoir capacity. Although it has not yet found general acceptance, it is gradually being recognized that reservoir sizing should be coupled to some optimum operating strategy, optimization being made with respect to some economic measure. In these operation studies, it is the rule rather than the exception that the demand curves are curvilinear. In this case, while the range is still important, the range that one obtains is no longer the same range that Hurst used in his study since the latter is that for deviations from the mean and the former is that for deviations from demand (which is no longer equal to the mean nor constant.) So one might ask, why worry about Hurst's H?

Regarding the asymptotic behavior of the R_s plot, there seems to be some misunderstanding regarding the value of H. The original self-similar model used in the study had an H-value equal to 0.633. Using this model, according to the theory of self-similar processes, the slope of the R_s vs N plot should tend toward the original H and not 0.5. In fact, this is the reason for the solid lines in Figs. 3 and 4. The line in each figure was intended to show how the self-similar and derived models vary from expected plots when simulated. It might be pointed out that the S-S model's inability to reproduce its own H-value has been reported in an independent study by Hamlin at the University of Birmingham*.

The discussers ask about the sampling properties of the self-similar process. One difficulty with this new model is that no sampling theory for the parameter H has yet been developed. If the discussers mean the scatter of points in the R_s vs N plot, historical records of annual flows of sufficient length are not available to determine this scatter. Figs. 3 and 4 show scatter from simulated series, as are those which the discussers cite.

---

* Personal Communication.

The response to questions and comments made by V. Yevjevich are as follows.

Regarding the first comment, the self-similar model is indeed linear. This was acceded to by one of the proponents of the model. On the question of stationarity, Mandelbrot* claims that theoretically $\sum_{u=0}^{\infty} G(u)$ may equal infinity as long as $\Sigma \ G^2(u)$ remains finite. This condition goes beyond the assumption by Wold, namely that $\Sigma \ G(u)$ must be finite and thus, raises the question as to whether Wold's results are still applicable.

I concur with your observations regarding the difficulty with self-similar models from the point of view of short record lengths currently available to hydrologists.

---

* Bulletin, International Association of Scientific Hydrology, Vol. 14, No. 1, March 1969, p. 58-59.

UNITED STATES-JAPAN BI-LATERAL SEMINAR IN HYDROLOGY

Honolulu, Hawaii
January 1971

"HYDROLOGIC SYSTEMS IN HAWAII"

by

Paul C. Ekern
Professor of Agronomy & Soil Science
University of Hawaii
Honolulu, Hawaii

L. Stephen Lau
Professor of Civil Engineering
University of Hawaii
Honolulu, Hawaii

Frank L. Peterson
Assistant Professor of Geosciences
University of Hawaii
Honolulu, Hawaii

Saul Price
Regional Climatologist
U.S. National Weather Service
Pacific Region
Honolulu, Hawaii

Ronald Pulfrey
Assistant Chief, Engineering Division
for Flood Plain Management Services
U.S. Corps of Engineers
Pacific Ocean Division
Honolulu, Hawaii

SYNOPSIS

Geologic history, rainfall climate, evaporation and transpiration, flood hydrology, and geology and groundwater under Hawaiian conditions are each briefly presented.

9 .1

GEOLOGIC HISTORY[1]

The Hawaiian Archipelago is a group of islands, reefs, and shoals, strung out for 1600 miles from the southeast (Midway Islands) to the northwest of Midway Islands to the island of Hawaii which is the largest island and has the only active volcanoes (Fig. 1). Important statistics regarding the major islands are given below[2]:

Island	Area (Square Miles)	Highest Altitude (Feet)	Maximum Distance (Miles)		Population (1970)
			North-south	East west	
Hawaii	4,030	13,784	87.3	75.3	63,468
Maui	728	10,025	25.0	38.4	38,863
Oahu	604	4,025	40.0	26.0	629,176
Kauai	555	5,170	24.5	29.9	29,524
Molokai	260	4,970	10.1	37.0	5,089
Lanai	141	3,370	13.3	13.0	2,204
Niihau	72	1,281	9.7	9.0	237
Kahoolawe	45	1,477	6.4	10.9	0

According to Stearns, the major Hawaiian islands were built *above* sea level in tertiary time, possibly as late as the end of the Pliocene epoch, several million years ago. In the 1960's, the geologic ages previously assigned to the volcanic rocks on the basis depth of weathering and erosion were checked by the potassium-argon dating method. The K-A ages are essentially consistent with the geologic age:

Island	Volcano	Volcanic series or formation	K-A age (millions of years)	Geologic Age presently assigned
Hawaii	Mauna Loa	Ninole	0.1 - 0.5	Pleistocene
	Kahala	Pololu	0.8	Pleistocene

[1]This section authored by L. Stephen Lau.

[2]Stearns, H. T. *Geology of the Hawaiian Islands,* Territory of Hawaii, Division of Hydrography, Bulletin 8, supplemented 1967.

9 .2

(Continued)

Island	Volcano	Volcanic series or formation	K-A age (millions of years)	Geologic Age presently assigned
Maui	Haleakala	Kula	0.4 - 0.8	Pleistocene
	West Maui	Honolua	1.15 - 1.17	Pleistocene
	West Maui	Wailuku	1.27 - 1.30	Pleistocene
Molokai	East Molokai	Upper member	1.3 - 1.5	Pleistocene
	East Molokai	Lower member	1.5	Pleistocene
	West Molokai	---	1.8	Pleistocene
Oahu	Koolau	---	2.2 - 2.6	Pliocene
	Waianae	Upper member	2.7 - 2.8	Pliocene
	Waianae	Middle member	2.5 - 3.0	Pliocene
	Waianae	Lower member	2.9 - 3.3	Pliocene
Kauai		Koloa	0.6 - 1.4	Pleistocene
		Makaweli	3.3 - 4.0	Pliocene
		Napali	4.5 - 5.6	Pliocene

The Hawaiian islands are a chain of shield-shaped basaltic domes built over a 1,600 mile fissure of the ocean floor which has existed probably since at least Middle Tertiary (about 30 million years). The usual eruption, preceded by a few slight earthquakes, occurs through fissures which are a few inches to a few feet wide. Eruptions often begin with a lava foundation and later produce spatter cones or cinder cones. Rivers of Pahoehoe pour from the fissure, but as it flows down the mountain side, the lava usually changes to aa and sometimes reaches the sea.

The Hawaiian islands were formed in the following manner. Once an aa lava core was above sea level, lava poured out, usually from one minor and two major rifts as well as from a small crater at their intersections, and eventually a shield-shaped dome was built. Stream erosion is non-existent at this young stage. The youthful stage was followed by formation of a caldera and shallow grabens along the major rifts. Lavas ponded in closed fault basins tend to be massive and when eroded they form sheer cliffs showing columnar structure. Thick sheets of aa may flow laying down trachyte. At the same time high lava fountains may build cinder cones.

Excluding secondary activities, the Hawaiian volcanoes became extinct from northwest to southeast. During the long marine and stream erosional period, high cliffs and deep canyons were cut and destroyed the volcanic dome. This period was followed by a great submergance which partly drowned the islands and to develop extensive reefs. On Lanai, fossiliferous marine sediments 1,070 feet above present

9.3

sea level and excellent beach deposits at 560 feet are considered to be demonstrable proof of large emergence. Barrier reefs may be developed or the growth of coral may be interrupted by secondary volcanic eruptions.

The next stage was the rejuvenation of volcanism in late Pleistocene epoch, several hundred thousand years ago, and Recent times, twenty thousand years ago, on all major islands except Lanai which was followed by a short and complex series of emergences and submergences. Very little reef or cliff-forming took place during this period.

Historic eruptions, such as at Mauna Loa, Kilauea and Hualalai on the island of Hawaii, have been recorded. The last reported eruption of Haleakala on the island of Maui was in 1750. On the island of Oahu, the last of the Honolulu volcanic series took place in Recent times creating such landmarks in Honolulu as Diamond Head, Salt Lake Crater, Koko Head, and Hanauma Bay.

My fellow speakers will give you some pertinent information on the hydrologic systems in Hawaii.

SOME ASPECTS OF THE RAINFALL CLIMATE OF THE HAWAIIAN ISLANDS[1]

The following is a brief summary of some aspects of the rainfall climatology of the Hawaiian Islands, and is intended as an aid in understanding flood hydrology in Hawaii, as well as ground water and evapotranspiration problems.

The major climatic controls in Hawaii are exercised by the tropical locale, the surrounding ocean, the Pacific anticyclone and topography.

Hawaii lies within the oceanic subtropics and extends from Kilauea Point, Kauai, at 22° 15' N, to South Point, Hawaii, at about 19° N.

The atmospheric circulation is dominated by the extensive high pressure area known as the North Pacific high or anticyclone. This anticyclone is the source of the east northeasterly trade winds which are Hawaii's prevailing winds throughout the year, although their frequency varies from about 90 percent in July to only 50 percent in January, and they may be absent entirely for days or occasionally even for weeks at a time, particularly during the winter half-year. The seasonal variation in the frequency of the trade winds reflects the seasonal change in intensity of the Pacific high, and its north-south migration with the sun. This variation, in turn, is shown in the seasonality of rainfall.

Fifty percent of the land area of Hawaii lies above 2,000 feet in elevation. The ascent of the trade winds up and over the topographic barriers of the various islands is the chief source of what might be called "pure orographic rainfall," rainfall in excess of that which might otherwise be expected to occur in the absence of the mountains.

The trade winds that reach Hawaii are usually unstable in their lower levels, since they consist of cooler air moving over warmer waters. Although they have picked up heat and water vapor over the ocean, they remain cooler and less humid than the maritime tropical air to the south of the islands.

Usually the trade winds are capped by a temperature inversion produced by the large-scale subsidence or sinking of air characteristic of the Pacific high pressure area, from which they come, and of similar anticyclones. In the Hawaiian area, the height of this inversion above sealevel ranges from about 5,000 to 10,000 feet, with an average of about 6,500 feet. This, by the way, is the same inversion whose height along the coast of California is often only 1,000 feet or less.

The condensation level of the trade wind air in Hawaii is usually about 1,800

[1]This section authored by Saul Price.

or 2,000 feet.

The significance of the trade wind inversion for Hawaii's rainfall is that it restricts the buoyant ascent of the air -- hence controlling the height to which the orographic clouds may grow and the intensity, amount, and geographical distribution of the rain that occurs under trade wind conditions. It also affects, for the higher mountains, the degree to which the air will flow around rather than over them.

During storms and perturbations in the trade winds, the inversion vanishes, permitting clouds to grow to much greater heights and rainfall to be correspondingly more intense.

Rainfall occurs in Hawaii not only because of the orographic ascent of the trade winds, but also under the other meteorological circumstances discussed later in this paper. However, the mean isohyetal pattern is dominated by the trade wind rainfall distribution in which topography plays a more consistent and clearly defined role than it ordinarily does in storm rainfall. The effect of topography is to make the horizontal and vertical air motions, and the resulting rainfall distribution, much more complex than they might otherwise be if these were flat islands of the same size.

Each of the major islands has its distinctive terrain, but their mean rainfall distributions have certain features in common. For one thing, great variations of rainfall occur within small distances and with elevation. In some areas, mean annual rainfall increases by 75 inches for each 1,000 feet of elevation and 2 or 3 miles of distance. On all the major islands, localities with over 300 inches of rain a year and others with less than 20 inches a year may be 20 miles or less apart.

Mean rainfall tends to be greater along coasts and slopes that face the trade winds, because the air is ascending there, and to be less in leeward areas, where the air is descending. Hence, windward and mountain areas get much of their rainfall, on the average, from trade wind showers; while leeward areas must depend on a relatively small number of winter season storms for most of their rainfall.

The mean isohyetal patterns of the four major islands, and their relation to topography, are described briefly below:

Kauai. The island is a single deeply dissected volcanic cone approximately 5,000 feet high, whose summit contains Mt. Waialeale, the "world's wettest spot," with a mean annual rainfall of 486 inches. Barking Sands, less than 20 miles distant, has under 20 inches a year. Near Mt. Waialeale, the gradient of average annual rainfall is 118 inches in 2-1/2 miles.

Oahu. The island consists of two long mountain ranges 2,000 to 3,000 feet in height lying approximately perpendicular to the trade winds. The greatest mean rainfall, 200 inches to more than 300 inches, occurs just leeward of the crests of the Koolau Range. A lesser maximum of about 100 inches a year occurs over the Waianae Mountains. Leeward coasts receive 20 inches or less a year.

Maui. Haleakala Mountain, in East Maui, is broad and high with a summit of about 10,000 feet, so that air flows around instead of over the mountain. The maximum rainfall, 300 to 400 inches occurs not at the summit, but at relatively moderate elevations of 2,500 to 3,000 feet along the slopes. Rainfall decreases with further elevation, dropping to about 45 inches at the summit. West Maui is very much like Kauai with a single eroded cone reaching an elevation of about 5,800 feet. The maximum rainfall at the summit is about 400 inches a year.

Hawaii. Mauna Loa and Mauna Kea are broad, high mountains, approximately 13,750 feet in elevation, which deflect the trades around them. The maximum rainfall of more than 300 inches a year occurs at 2,500 to 3,000 feet along the windward (eastern) slopes. The summits are very dry, with less than 15 inches a year. One of the most interesting features is that the rainfall maximum of the leeward (Kona) area, which is completely sheltered from the trade winds, also occurs at about the same elevation as on the windward side, yet is produced, not by the trade winds, but by the ascent of onshore sea breezes during the day.

If these were flat islands of the same size, the geographical distribution both of storm and trade wind rainfall would be much more uniform than it is. Even in the absence of mountains, however, we would expect to find differences in average rainfall from place to place owing to the cellular nature of rainfall and to the effect of solar heating of the islands on the flow of air over and around them. But topography undoubtedly makes these differences much greater than they would otherwise be.

Over the open ocean in the Hawaiian area the average rainfall is estimated to be about 25 inches a year. But some parts of Hawaii get much more than this and others less.

Over the state as a whole, the average annual rainfall is approximately 75 inches, about 3 times that over the nearby open sea. This represents 5,000 billion gallons of water a year in addition to what would be expected to fall over the surrounding ocean.

While the wetter areas get most of their annual rainfall from the year-round trade wind showers, the drier areas obtain relatively little of their rainfall from that source but are dependent instead on a few winter-season storms. Hence, rainfall is more strongly seasonal in the drier than in the wetter areas. It is not at all uncommon for a dry leeward station to get half its mean annual rainfall of about 23 inches, has had 18 inches in a single day, and most of that within about 8 hours.

There are also great differences from year to year, especially in the winter season. For example, Hilo, a wet station, with 140 inches a year, has had more than 50 inches of rain in January, but also less than 0.2 inches. Honolulu, a relatively dry station, with 24 inches a year, has received as much as 18 inches in January, and as little as .12 inches.

Hawaii's most serious hydrologic problem, other than long-range water resources management and planning, is flash flooding. The rapid growth in population and the development of previously sparsely settled areas, especially on coastal flood plains and often without adequate flood protection, is increasing the frequency and severity of damage from intense rains and flash floods.

Although the subject of this paper is rainfall, rather than what happens once the rain water reaches the ground, it should for the sake of completeness, say a few words about Hawaii's watersheds, whose characteristics are as responsible for the flash flooding as are the rains themselves.

Most of Hawaii's drainage basins are very small in comparison with those elsewhere. Of 58 gaged Oahu watersheds studied by I-pai Wu, 44 were less than 5 square miles in area and some only a few acres. The watersheds are heterogeneous, each one unique. They are steep sloped and have little channel storage. They vary from one part of an island to another, so that, for example, rainfall-runoff relationships can not be generalized.

Flood hydrographs on Oahu, where much work has been done by I-pai Wu, are steeply triangular with very sharp rise and recession. Concentration times range from a few minutes to a very few hours. Time to peak is usually less than one hour. Most soils are highly permeable, with infiltration capacities ranging from one-half inch to more than 10 inches an hour.

Most flash floods in Hawaii occur during the winter half-year from approximately October to April. However, several severe floods have occurred as late as May and even in the summer, since the area is also vulnerable to hurricanes and other tropical storms.

Flooding rains in Hawaii occur under a number of different meteorological circumstances: slowly moving or nearly stationary cold fronts, the subtropical cyclones, known as Kona storms, which form in or move into the Hawaiian area, tropical storms and hurricanes, isolated thunderstorms that build up over mountain slopes or island interiors on warm afternoons, and low pressure systems in the upper atmosphere. Trade wind showers in Hawaii are not ordinarily heavy enough to cause flash flooding, except when an upper-level low pressure area has eliminate the inversion and permitted the orographic clouds to grow to great heights.

All of these flood producing situations, and others that are less clearly defined, are capable of serving as the probable maximum precipitation (PMP) type o storm: a stationary or nearly-stationary zone of converging winds, associated wit an inflow of moist air and strong upward motion, and leading to the formation of a so-called thunderstorm-infested-fixed-convergence-area (TIFCA). The PMP type of storms all have efficient convergence mechanisms capable of producing intense rainfall over the open sea without augmentation by orographic uplift of the moist airflow.

How intense are Hawaii's flood-producing rains? We can not be certain. Even our large number of rain gages is not adequate for a detailed analysis of storm -- or even trade wind -- rainfall in the small Hawaiian drainage basins. However, past records show several hundred instances of one-half inch or more in 10 minutes at various locations in the Hawaiian islands.

Every station in Hawaii with 50 years or more of record has had 24-hour rains of 8 inches or more, and most of them of 12 inches or more. Some readings from 23 flash floods in the 6 years since January 1965 are listed below:

> 1 inch in 10 minutes
> 2 inches in 15 minutes
> 3.65 inches in an hour
> 4 inches in an hour
> 4.25 inches in an hour
> 4.6 inches in an hour
> 5.2 inches in an hour

The 100-year recurrence interval amounts for various durations are frequently exceeded.

Hawaii's most intense rain appears to have occurred at Kilauea Plantation on the Island of Kauai in January 1956. Out of a storm total of 43.5 inches, over 3 inches fell within 24 hours, nearly 11 inches in 1 hour and 6 inches in a single half-hour. The 24-hour rainfall of 38 inches at Kilauea Plantation compares with the 100-year storm of about 19 inches and the probable maximum precipitation of about 47 inches.

The influence of topography in Hawaii is much less pronounced in storm rainfall than in trade wind rainfall. In fact, orographic augmentation in Hawaii is estimated to average only about 15 percent, although it may be different in individual instances. For example, several of Oahu's most intense flooding rains have occurred in a single relatively small area along the windward slopes and coasts, and may have been caused by the orographic ascent of surface trade winds over the Koolau mountains at a time when low pressure aloft had eliminated the inversion and permitted clouds to build to great heights.

In the Kilauea rainfall, the highly localized downpours appear to have occurred when a current of moist unstable air, converging as it moved up a narrow valley, was at the same time forced to rise abruptly over steep mountains nearby. But such special topographic circumstances are not essential to the occurrence of torrential rains. For example, in November 1931, Moanalua, Oahu, a flat area several miles from the Koolau mountains, received 5 inches of rain in each of three successive hours and there are many other such cases.

Maps of probable maximum precipitation in Hawaii were derived by the Weather Bureau in the usual manner -- that is, by first estimating a non-orographic PMP an then adjusting it to island topography. A 24-hour rainfall value of 40 inches was assigned to coastal areas and other locations relatively free from orographic influence, and the effect of orography was obtained by considering the depletion of the moisture column by elevation or mountain barriers, which would tend to reduce

rainfall, and the slope effect, which would tend to increase it. Additional subjective adjustments were then made. The PMP values for Oahu very closely approach
the world's greatest observed rains.

EVAPORATION AND TRANSPIRATION UNDER HAWAIIAN CONDITIONS[1]

Definition

Evaporation is the direct transformation of liquid water into the vapor phase
without the living plant as an intermediate. Interposition of the plant so that
evaporation occurs from within the plant leaf is called transpiration. The combined
evapotranspiration from different surfaces depends upon four factors:
1. the amount of energy available for vapor formation
2. the confrontation of the energy and the liquid water
3. the escape of the vapor from the immediate site of formation
4. the removal of the escaped vapor.

Fraction of Sunlight Retained as Net Radiation in Hawaii

The net radiation supplies the bulk of the energy used in evapotranspiration.
The net short-wave solar radiation is generally high, since the reflectance is
small, a consequence of the high elevation of the sun and the mineralogic nature of
the latosol. The net long-wave infrared radiation is surprisingly conservative and,
near sea level, averages 250 ly/day for clear skies and 100 ly/day for cloudy skies.
For example, the fraction of sunlight converted into total net radiation over sugar
cane in the summer, with 600 ly/day sunlight, is 0.55, but in winter, with 300 ly/
day sunlight, is only 0.30.

Disposition of Net Radiation by Pan Evaporation

Class A pan evaporation can be approximated by the Penman and Dalton-type
expressions, but constants appropriate to the tropics must be used. Air temperature alone is not a useful index, since it is not controlled by sunlight in the
marine climate. During the summer months, positive advection of heat to the pan,
makes evaporation equal or greater than the net radiation. The net radiation over
the pan is larger than that over sugar cane, since the reflectance of the pan is
only 0.08. Pan evaporation rates range from 0.3"/day in summer to 0.15"/day in
winter for the high sunlight areas.

Disposition of Net Radiation over Latosol

The net radiation over Latosol is high, since the reflectance is about the
same as water because of the dark red and black colors of the soils. However, the
heavy clay soils are generally so well aggregated that they have water properties

---

[1]This section authored by Paul C. Ekern.

similar to those of coarse sand or gravel. The soil drains almost immediately to the point where the falling rate phase of evaporation occurs. This self-mulching action of the soil allows evaporation rates only one-third that of pan evaporation. The mineralogic composition and thorough aggregation makes extremely important the vapor phase transfer of water and heat within the soil.

Disposition of Net Radiation over Sugar Cane and Grass Sod

The reflectance of sugar cane and sod is about 0.2, hence the net radiation is less than that for the pan or for the Latosol. When the soil moisture is readily available, both sugar cane and bermuda grass sod use water at the same rate as pan evaporation, hence use full net radiation for evaporation. As the soil dries, soil water is less readily available to the plant, the water use of grass falls progressively below that for a pan and approaches that for the Latosol. A specific example of water use by full cane canopy at the Kunia substation is 65"/year.

Disposition of Net Radiation over Pineapple

Pineapple is a succulent, with very greatly restricted transpiration as a result of stomatal design and stomatal closure by day. The summertime consumptive use of water by pineapple is about 0.1 that for sugar cane, or 0.03"/day rather than 0.3"/day. Consumptive use of water by pineapple culture with plastic mulch is 18"/year and with trash mulch is 12"/year.

FLOOD HYDROLOGY IN HAWAII - PROBLEMS ENCOUNTERED[1]

Flood flow frequency analysis, always a significant part of flood hydrology, has taken an added importance with the greatly increased activity in flood plain regulation and flood insurance to the point where it now constitutes the preponderance of flood hydrology work in Hawaii. Of the total of four local governments in the state, one has a flood plain regulation in its zoning code and three have been granted eligibility for federally subsidized flood insurance. It is anticipated that within a year all will have adopted flood plain regulation laws and will have been granted flood insurance eligibility. This means that frequency curves of annual flood flow will be needed for each of a great number of streams to provide a basis for delineating flood hazard areas of specific probabilities and for computing flood insurance premium rates. This discussion presents some of the problems encountered in the determination of flood frequency curve.

It should be explained that the statistical procedure now in general practice in Hawaii is the Log Pearson Type III method. Also, problems encountered in the Islands in flood hydrology work may be better understood if it is known that current meter measurements of even moderate floods are rarely possible. This is because of the quickness of response of our streams to rainfall, their short duration of peak flow, and their high debris load. Methods of direct measurements other than by current meters are now being studied and hydraulic models have been made for gauging stations, but current practice is to estimate peak flows using high water marks and a flow-energy formula. In spite of a high degree of expertise errors inherent in the procedure itself must be recognized, and, unfortunately, this error may be expected to increase with the magnitude of discharge.

[1]This section authored by Ronald Pulfrey.

A typical flood frequency study will require the development of frequency curves for maximum annual flood discharge extended to a 100-year event for one or more ungauged drainage areas. There probably will exist a number of records for streams with apparently similar exposure and runoff characteristics, frequency data for these streams will probably be adopted as basic data for the study. However, since it is considered unwise to rely on a single stream-flow record for a frequency derivation at any specific location, the hydrologist will probably use as many records as is practicable. Then, by some procedure of ratios, averaging, or other method of his choice, he will adapt frequency data from known areas to the areas under study. He may wish to adjust "regionalized" values of mean annual flood, standard deviation, and skew to his study area or he may decide to determine only one or two values, perhaps the 100-year and 10-year floods. In any case, his first task is to determine the best possible frequency curve for each individual record. As a first step, frequency curves are computed and drawn on log probability paper; then, annual events are plotted graphically and an examination is made to detect errors, outliers, and questionable data. Often adjustments are in order.

In the example on Figure 2, the data shown is for a key station on leeward Molokai. It is obvious that the trouble here lies with the maximum annual discharge value of 7 c.f.s. An examination of regional historic data revealed only that is was a year of low -- but not record low -- maximum discharges and storm rainfall. In this case, the hydrologist may reason that this unrealistic figure has resulted from a cause, such as the recharge of bank storage, which may have negligible effect on the maximum flow of a more normal year and that to constitute relevant data, it should be given a much higher value, he may simply consider it erroneous data, or he may decide that it is truly an event of extremely rare cause. In any case, there are a number of solutions to the problem, one of which is shown in the example. Finally, his choice will no doubt be strongly influenced by what he considers to be reasonable for values of standard deviation, skew, and the 100-year flood.

An example of the problem of a suspiciously high point is shown on Figure 3. Factors in favor of altering this point are the apparently high positive skew factor of plus 1.1 in an area where skew factors are generally zero to a low negative value and the desirable alignment of the other points in the array. On the other hand, the standard deviation of 0.200 is relatively low. Subsequent to this computation, however, the greatest stage of record, a preliminary estimate of the discharge of which is 10,000 c.f.s., occurred, indicating that the tempting adjustment shown on the figure may have been unwise. It is of interest that the two highest discharge values occurred during the last two years of record.

In dealing with unrealistic values of skew, the hydrologist is always conscious that the curvature of the frequency curve is closely related to the curvature of the station-rating curve and since these rating curves are extended to higher flows on the basis of estimates, he may abandon the use of the skew coefficient, giving it the value of zero in his computation. He will, at most, use a regionalized value.

Using a zero skew coefficient indiscriminately may lead to unrealistic results, as shown in the example of Figure 4. Here, two low values result in an unusual negative skew. However, values for higher floods taken from the curve appear typical, while those for a curve computed with zero skew would obviously produce values outside of reason.

The curve shown on Figure 5 tends to instill confidence in using a single record as the total of basic data for a frequency determination, even though the skewness here is somewhat greater than is considered typical. Decisions regarding the treatment of such a frequency curve depend on the hydrologist's confidence in the recorded data, but experience has shown that the use of a single record may prove to be a mistake.

Finally, in an effort to use every means possible to estimate reliable and dependable frequency curves, the hydrologist may, in addition to the regional studies derive discharge values for rainfall of certain probabilities by using unit hydrograph procedures. Rainfall records are of longer duration and higher accuracy than stream-flow records and comprehensive rainfall frequency data for Hawaii is readily available from National Weather Service publications. On the other hand, unit hydrograph derivation is expensive in time and funds and unless the study is in connection with flood control requiring unit hydrograph procedure for design flood computations, it is not usually considered feasible from an economic standpoint. There is also the question of other variable conditions which contribute to the magnitude of a flood, along with a number of problems common to unit hydrograph procedure.

GROUND WATER[1]

Despite rainfalls which commonly exceed 200 inches per year in the mountainous portions of many of the islands in the Hawaiian chain, most streams in the islands are very flashy and only a very few carry water throughout the year. This is in part due to the generally small size of the watersheds, but primarily it is owing to the extremely high permeability of the volcanic rocks and soils which make up the Hawaiian islands. In particular, the permeability of some of the younger volcanic rocks is so great that virtually no runoff occurs and few, if any, well-defined stream channels exist even in areas where the annual rainfall may approach 200 inches. Consequently, because of the very high infiltration capacities of the rock and soil cover, ground water plays an extremely important role in the Hawaiian hydrologic cycle.

The high permeability of the rock and soils in Hawaii and, indeed, the entire mode of ground water occurrence can best be understood by consideration of the geology. All of the major islands in the Hawaiian chain consist essentially of one or more shield volcanoes which are composed primarily of thin basaltic lava flows which gently dip away from axial rift zones. Ordinarily, basalts are among the most permeable rocks on earth and the basalts, which comprise the Hawaiian islands are especially permeable owing to their very young age and, probably even more important, to the small thickness of individual lava flows. The lavas, which stand above sea level, are thought to range in age from three to five million years to only a few tens of years and, in fact, on the island of Hawaii new lava flows are being formed almost daily. The flows range in thickness from a few inches to several hundred feet, but most are 20 feet or less. This is especially important as many of the water-bearing structures in lava flows are associated with the surface and near-surface portions of flows. Depending on their physical state and the environment in which they cooled, the flows solidified into either pahoehoe, which is a very liquid, smooth-flowing lava, or aa, which is a very viscous, blocky, slow-flowing lava. Pahoehoe flows often grade into aa flows. The chemical composition of these flows is remarkably uniform. However, their physical characteristics, including the water-bearing properties, are quite variable on a coarse scale. The high permeability of Hawaiian lavas results primarily from major flow structures, such as clinker zones in aa, lava tubes and gas vesicles in pahoehoe, vertical contraction joints formed by the cooling of the lavas, and irregular openings associated with the surface between flows. The horizontal component of permeability of lava flows probably exceeds the vertical, however, permeability in both directions is so great and so subject to local deviations that any difference between them is difficult to assess.

---

[1]This section authored by Frank L. Peterson.

9 .11

The rift zones of Hawaiian volcanoes contain many vertical or steeply dipping dikes which cut through the lava flows. In the central portions of the rifts, the dikes are closely spaced and almost completely replace the lava flows. Toward the outer edges of the rift zones, the dikes are more widely spaced and form large compartments which enclose permeable lavas. Because the dikes are dense and have low permeabilities, ground water may be impounded within these compartments.

On most of the Hawaiian islands, especially the older ones like Kauai and Oahu, the margins of the volcanic mountains are overlapped by coastal plain sediments of alluvial and marine origin which were deposited during periods of volcanic quiescence. The greatest thickness of coastal plain sediments occurs on southern Oahu beneath the Honolulu and Pearl Harbor areas, where the sediments have a maximum thickness of over 1000 feet. Although the permeability of the sediments varies widely, the overall effect is one of low permeability compared to the basalts. The coastal sediments contain large quantities of water, varying from fresh to sea water. Compared to the basalt aquifers, however, the capacity of the sediments to store and transmit water is small. Consequently, the sediments act as a caprock retarding the seaward movement of fresh ground water from the more permeable underlying basaltic aquifers.

Two general modes of ground water occurrence are present in the Hawaiian islands: high-level ground water and basal ground water. Dikes in and near the rift zones of the volcanoes impound large volumes of fresh water. The compartments formed by the dikes are commonly saturated to levels several hundred feet above sea level and natural discharge often occurs in the form of high-level springs. Other high-level water is perched on beds of weathered ash, tuff, soil, and thick sills or flows. Perched water makes up only a very small part of all high-level water.

The principal source of fresh ground water in the Hawaiian islands is the lens-shaped basal water body, commonly called the Ghyben-Herzberg lens, floating on denser salt water. The basal water body is largely unconfined. However, where the basaltic aquifer is directly overlain by the sedimentary caprock along some of the coastal margins, artesian heads of a few feet to over 20 feet above sea level may occur. When steady-state conditions exist, the location of the bottom of the fresh-water lens floating on sea water is dependent on the relative densities of the two liquids, and a sharp interface may exist, however, in most natural situations steady-state conditions are not achieved. Because of constant movement of the interface between fresh and salt water owing to tidal fluctuations, seasonal fluctuations in recharge and discharge, and discharge cause by pumping, mixing of the salt and fresh water takes place and the salt water grades upward into fresh water forming a zone of transition. In Hawaii, the depth to the bottom of fresh water is normally a few tens to many hundreds of feet and the thickness of the transition zone varies from only a few tens of feet in relatively undisturbed areas to as great as 1000 feet in parts of southern Oahu. The accompanying diagram (Fig. 6) shows the generalized ground-water occurrence through a cross-section of Oahu from Honolulu to Kaneohe.

198

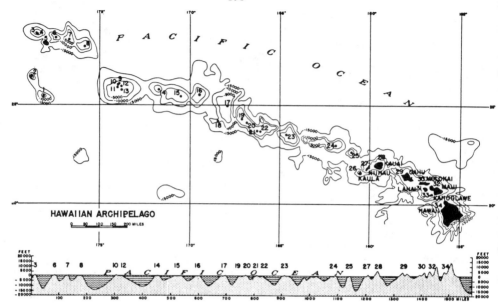

FIGURE I. MAP AND PROFILE OF THE HAWAIIAN ARCHIPELAGO SHOWING SUBMARINE
CONTOURS IN FEET. (AFTER STEARNS, 1946.)

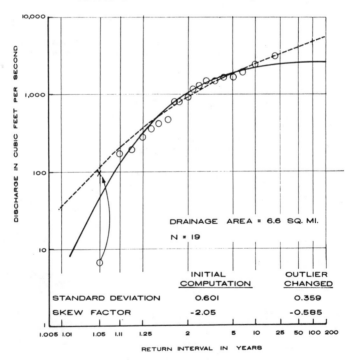

FIGURE 2. KAUNAKAKAI GULCH AT KAUNAKAKAI.

9 .13

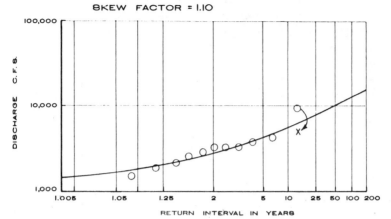

DRAINAGE AREA = 13.5 SQ. MI.

N = 11

STANDARD DEVIATION = 0.200

SKEW FACTOR = 1.10

FIGURE 3. ANAHULU RIVER NEAR HALEIWA.

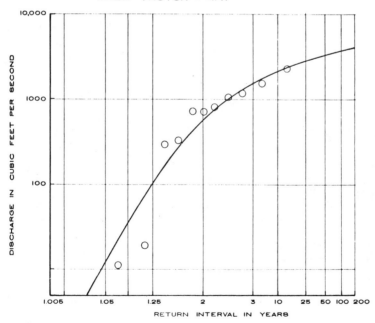

DRAINAGE AREA = 1.51 SQ. MI.

N = 11

STANDARD DEVIATION = 0.748

SKEW FACTOR = -1.41

FIGURE 4. MAILIILII STREAM NEAR WAIANAE.

9.14

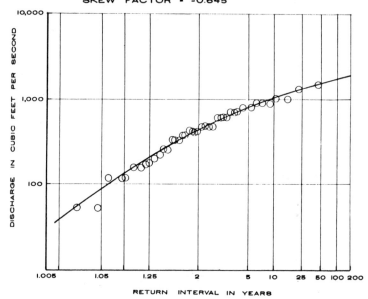

DRAINAGE AREA = 1.04 SQ. MI.

N = 43

STANDARD DEVIATION = 0.357

SKEW FACTOR = -0.645

FIGURE 5. WAIOMAO STREAM NEAR HONOLULU.

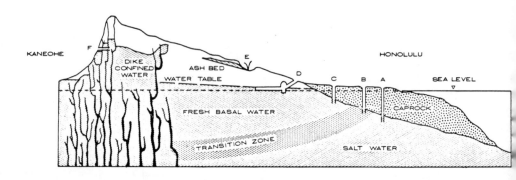

A ARTESIAN WELL PRODUCING SALT WATER

B ARTESIAN WELL PRODUCING BRACKISH WATER

C ARTESIAN WELL PRODUCING FRESH WATER

D MAUI SHAFT

E PERCHED WATER SPRING

F HIGH LEVEL TUNNEL TAPPING DIKE WATER

FIGURE 6. GENERALIZED GROUND WATER OCCURRENCE IN THE HONOLULU AREA

9.15

DISCUSSION   J. PAUL RILEY

Your precipitation records seem much more complete in a time and spatial sense than do the available runoff records. I realize that there are many problems involved but it would seem that it would be worth while to consider techniques for estimating runoff flows from precipitation records. In a large measure that is what hydrology is all about.

The techniques and concepts apparently being applied by the Corps of Engineers office in Hawaii well illustrate the gap which often exists between scientific and applied hydrology.

RESPONSE BY THE AUTHORS OF PAPER "HYDROLOGIC SYSTEMS IN HAWAII"

With reference to the US-Japan Bilateral Seminar in Hydrology, the following comments are in response to Professor J. Paul Riley's discussion on the paper "Hydrologic Systems in Hawaii."

While it is true that there are more years of rain gage record than of stream gage record in Hawaii, and certainly rain gages should give a more accurate accounting of rainfall than stream gages of runoff (runoff is derived from recorded stage), only in very special cases is areal coverage of rainfall record adequate for the reconstruction of historic flood flows. Areal variations of rainfall are especially great in Hawaii and significant differences are often observed between adjacent rain gages even during great storms.

Also rain gages are not always ideally located for use in flood hydrology. Until recently, most rain gaging stations were established in the interest of agriculture and located in areas of water use rather than in areas of greatest runoff generation. In addition, much of the watershed areas are in nearly inaccessible mountainous terrain, not suitable for the installation of gages.

A rain gaging station designed for surface-water supply studies may be of limited use in flood hydrology studies. Most gages are non-recording, usually being read daily but sometimes only weekly, or "after rain," while on most streams, the time between flood-producing rainfall and the corresponding discharge at the mouth of the stream is less than one hour.

Since actual basin storm rainfall cannot be determined to the accuracy necessary to reconstruct the flood hydrograph, unit hydrograph derivation is more arbitrary than desirable, and storm losses can only be roughly estimated in unit hydrograph application. To better understand the relationship of runoff to rainfall in Hawaii, and particularly the unit hydrograph procedure, the Corps of Engineers in 1962 initiated a study which installed a network of recording rain gages on three stream-gaged drainage basins on three separate islands. The three basins were considered typical for their respective areas, and it was hoped that rainfall-runoff relationships could be established which, with appropriate adjustments, could be applied to all areas in the islands. This study is still underway.

While rainfall records may not be suitable for reconstructing historic flood hydrographs, certainly they are adequate for deriving theoretical design storms, such as the standard project storm, or storm intensities for various probabilities of occurrence. Employing unit hydrograph procedure, these design storms have been used with a certain amount of confidence to compute maximum probable and standard project floods, but attempts to derive frequency curves in this way have not produced results which are within reason. There are a number of explanations for this. Errors in estimated loss rates, which may be negligible for greater storms, may become appreciable for the smaller ones. Also there are questions of how to distribute increments of rainfall, probable areal coverage of the basin by rainfall, and unit hydrograph shape adjustment for smaller flows, all of which may be handled in different ways with varying results.

For the present, the most satisfactory procedure for deriving frequency curves of maximum annual stream flow appears to be one of regionalized frequency studies with judicatory adjustments of questionable individual data.

United States - Japan Bi-Lateral Seminar in
Hydrology, Honolulu
January 1971

THE STOCHASTIC KINEMATIC WAVE

by Peter S. Eagleson
Head of the Department of Civil Engineering
Massachusetts Institute of Technology
Cambridge, Massachusetts, USA

Synopsis

The kinematic wave method of hydrograph forecasting is generalized through the incorporation of random variations in the temporal and areal distribution of the storm rainfall excess. Expressions are derived for the peak direct runoff and streamflow in terms of the statistics of these random variables.

Generalized probability density functions of storm duration and storm rainfall depth given duration, an assumed loss function and an assumed probability density function for runoff-producing area are used, with the stochastic equations for maximum direct storm runoff, to derive the probability density function of peak streamflow. The latter is used to obtain the classical flood-frequency curve as an explicit function of parameters defining the rainfall distributions and the catchment-stream physiography.

The flood-frequency relation is used to derive the mean annual flood as a function of catchment area and this compares well with observations from 44 Connecticut rivers. Agreement of the predicted flood-frequency curve with observation on particular catchments is also good but is apparently sensitive to the particular value of the direct runoff fraction and to the fraction of the catchment area contributing direct runoff.

THE STOCHASTIC KINEMATIC WAVE

Introduction

The classical hydrologic problem involves the synthesis of streamflow given only the rainfall and the structure of the drainage basin. Interest in this problem was originated by the need for flood forecasting and for engineering decisions concerning river basin planning in the absence of streamflow data. Concern has since expanded to encompass questions of water yield, water quality and the effect of man's activities within the watershed. Most of these objectives are being met today through numerical simulations such as the Stanford Watershed Model[1] although, as the complexity of these models increases, so does the need for field data with which to evaluate their "invisible" parameters.

---

[1] Linsley, R.K. and N.H. Crawford, "Digital Simulation in Hydrology: Stanford Watershed Model IV," Tech. Rep. 39, Dept. of Civil Eng., Stanford University, July, 1966.

The hydrologist still needs in his kit of tools a general analytical (as opposed to numerical) synthesis which combines a high degree of physical validity with sufficient simplicity to allow explicit solution for important hydrograph properties (such as peak flow and time to peak) in terms of rainfall and watershed parameters. Such a synthesis contributes significantly to decision-making at levels not warranting the time and expense of a general numerical simulation and helps the student of hydrology to better understand the complex relation between rainfall and runoff. The kinematic wave method provides this tool.

Iwagaki[1] was the first to use the kinematic wave method of flood routing[2] for hydrograph forecasting while Henderson and Wooding[3], and Wooding[4,5] demonstrated the power of the method for defining the basic categories of overland flow and streamflow. Wooding[6] has applied the kinematic wave to natural catchments having areas of from 0.84 to 3,383 mi^2 by using the simplified geometry shown in Figure 1. His efforts, along with those of most other investigators, have concentrated on forecasting the runoff from individual storms, and while they are qualitatively correct, there are large errors resulting in part at least from the unknown and/or unaccounted for heterogeneities in the rainfall and in the watershed properties. These errors are largely random however and should be unimportant when synthesizing that most useful measure of long-term behavior, the flood-frequency relation.

It is the aim of this paper therefore to modify the kinematic wave method so that it can deal conveniently with certain classes of parameter and input variability and to apply the result to forecasting the statistics of peak direct runoff given the statistics of the rainfall and the watershed parameters.

Overland Flow[7]

The equations governing the kinematic wave are

$$\frac{dq}{dt} = i_e c_c, \quad \frac{dy}{dt} = i_e, \quad \frac{dq}{dx_c} = i_e, \quad \frac{dy}{dx_c} = i_e/c_c \qquad [1]$$

---

[1] Iwagski, Y., "Fundamental Studies on the Runoff Analysis by Characteristics," Disaster Prevention Res. Inst. Bull. 10, Kyoto, Univ., December, 1955.

[2] Lighthill, M.H., and G.B. Whitham, "On Kinematic Waves, I. Flood Movement in Long Rivers," Proc.Roy.Soc., ser. A., vol. 229, pp. 281-316, 1955.

[3] Henderson, F.M. and R.A. Wooding, "Overland Flow and Groundwater Flow from a Steady Rainfall of Finite Duration, J.G.R., vol. 69, no. 8, pp. 1531-1540, April, 1964.

[4] Wooding. R.A., "A Hydraulic Model for the Catchment-Stream Problem. I. Kinematic Wave Theory," Journ.Hydrol., vol. 3, now 3/4, pp. 254-267, 1965.

[5] Wooding, R.A., "A Hydraulic Model for the Catchment-Stream Problem. II. Numerical Solutions," Journ.Hydrol., vol. 3, nos. 3/4, pp. 268-282, 1965.

[6] Wooding R.A., "A Hydraulic Model for the Catchment-Stream Problem. III. Comparison with Runoff Observations," Journ.Hydrology, vol. 4, pp. 21-37, 1966.

[7] Variables used to define flow over the catchment surface (as distinguished from streamflow) will be distinguished by the subscript c.

which apply along the characteristics

$$\frac{dx_c}{dt} = c_c = \alpha_c \, m_c \, y^{m_c-1} \qquad [2]$$

In addition, the dynamic equation to be satisfied is

$$q = \alpha_c \, y^{m_c} \qquad [3]$$

where α_c reflects the local average properties of the surface. We will now introduce variability in the rainfall excess i_e by assuming

$$i_e(x_c,t) = \bar{i}_e + I(x_c,t) \qquad [4]$$

where the fluctuating term, $I(x_c,t)$, has zero mean. This particular form of rainfall variability is most applicable for convective storms and for the central portion of cyclonic events where the storm mean point rainfall is areally uniform.[1]

Two factors operate to cause the area producing direct runoff to be less than the full basin area in a given situation. We will call this the "runoff area". The first of these factors is the finite storm area. This is particularly important for large watersheds where the storm may occur over only a portion of the basin. Since the kinematic wave routs a flood without change in the peak discharge,[2] the storm location within the watershed is of only second order importance in this development. Thus, for computational convenience we will always center it about the stream and place it tangent to the stream mouth. The second factor results from the observation of Betson[3] that the catchment area contributing to direct runoff is usually only a fraction of the area wetted by a storm. This percentage was observed to be as low as 5% in some cases and occurs in the low portions of the catchment, near the streams, where the initial soil moisture is highest.

Accordingly, in this analysis the area contributing to direct runoff will be symmetrical about the stream, will contain the stream mouth, and will have catchment and stream dimensions R_c and R_s respectively as shown in Fig. 1.

Letting $t = 0$ at the first appearance of rainfall excess anywhere on the watershed and following a characteristic which begins then at $x_c = 0$ with $y = 0$ we can use the second of Eqs. [1] to write

$$y = \int_o^t [\bar{i}_e + I(x_c,\sigma)] \, d\sigma \;, \quad t \leq t^*_{re} \qquad [5]$$

---

[1] Eagleson, P.S. Dynamic Hydrology, McGraw-Hill Book Co., 1970, pg. 198.

[2] ibid, p. 362.

[3] Betson, R.P., "What is Watershed Runoff," J.Geophys. Res., vol. 69, no. 8, pp. 1541-1552, April 1964.

where t^*_{re} is the duration of rainfall excess and is a random variable over the runoff area. Assuming the statistics of the temporal fluctuations to be independent of location, we can integrate Eq. [5] to obtain

$$y = t(\bar{i}_e + \bar{I}^t) \quad , \quad t \leq t^*_{re} \qquad [6]$$

where $\bar{I}^t$ signifies $I(x_c,t)$ averaged over the time t. $\bar{I}^t$ is a random variable. Next, using Eqs. [2] and [6] along the same characteristic as earlier and neglecting variability in the local average surface slope and roughness

$$R_c = \int_0^{R_c} dx_c = \alpha_c m_c \int_0^{t_c} [t(\bar{i}_e + \bar{I}^t)]^{m_c-1} dt \qquad [7]$$

where t_c is the so-called "time of concentration" of the catchment.

Assuming[1] $m_c = 2$ we can integrate the right hand side to get

$$R_c/\alpha_c = \bar{i}_e t_c^2 + 2 \int_0^{t_c} \bar{I}^t t\, dt \qquad [8]$$

Multiplying both sides by $f(\bar{I}^t)$, the probability density function for the sample mean $\bar{I}^t$, assuming independence of $\bar{i}_e$ and $\bar{I}^t$, and integrating for a given t over all values of $\bar{I}^t$

$$R_c/\alpha_c = \bar{i}_e t_c^2 + 2 \int_0^{t_c} t \int_{\bar{I}^t} \bar{I}^t f(\bar{I}^t)\, d\bar{I}^t\, dt = \bar{i}_e t_c^2 \qquad [9]$$

where the integral vanishes due to the sample mean of size t having zero mean. From this the concentration time is

$$t_c = \left| \frac{R_c}{\bar{i}_e \alpha_c} \right|^{\frac{1}{2}} \quad , \quad t_c \leq t_{re} = E[t^*_{re}] \qquad [10]$$

As presented in Eq. [10] the concentration time is for a storm which produces uniform $\bar{i}_e$ over a given surface of length R_c. When considering the population of storms and catchments for a surface of given α_c, t_c becomes a random variable dependent upon the distributions of the areal and time averaged storm rainfall excess intensity $\bar{i}_e$, and of the surface length R_c over which direct runoff occurs.

Since we ultimately wish to find the distribution of peak flows as a function of catchment properties we must consider the conditions producing peak depth at $x_c = R_c$. To the first order, with $y(x_c = 0) = 0$ and $t_o = 0$, Eq. [6] gives

[1]Wooding, R.A., 1967-1966, op.cit.

10.4

$$y_{max} = y_{max}(R_c) = (\bar{i}_e + \overline{I}^{t_c}) t_c \quad , \quad t_{re} \geq t_c \qquad [11]$$

and, since $\overline{I}^{t_{re}} \equiv 0$

$$y_{max} = y_{max}(R_c) = \bar{i}_e t_{re} \quad , \quad t_{re} < t_c \qquad [12]$$

From Eq. [3], with $m_c = 2$, and using Eqs. [10] to [12]

$$q_{max} = q_{max}(R_c) = R_c (1 + \frac{\overline{I}^{t_c}}{\bar{i}_e})^2 \bar{i}_e \quad , \quad t_{re} \geq t_c \qquad [13]$$

and

$$q_{max} = q_{max}(R_c) = \alpha_c [\bar{i}_e t_{re}]^2 \quad , \quad t_{re} < t_c \qquad [14]$$

Streamflow[1]

When considering the formation of peak streamflow, we must compare the duration of rainfall excess with the concentration time t_* of the combined catchment-stream runoff area. For $t_{re} \geq t_*$ the entire runoff area will contribute to peak streamflow and

$$Q_{max} = Q_{max}(R_s) = 2 \int_0^{R_s} q_{max} dx_s \quad , \quad t_{re} \geq t_* \qquad [15]$$

Assuming $\overline{I}^{t_c} / \bar{i}_e \ll 1$, Eq. [13] can be used to write Eq. [15]

$$Q_{max} = 2 R_c R_s \bar{i}_e = A_r \bar{i}_e \quad , \quad t_{re} \geq t_* \qquad [16]$$

where A_r is the area producing direct runoff.

For $t_{re} < t_*$ only part of the area A_r contributes. For $m_s = 3/2$ and letting the cross-sectional area of streamflow be A_s, we can write

$$Q_{max} = \alpha_s A_{s_{max}}^{3/2} = \alpha_s \left[\int_0^{t_{re}} 2 q \, dt \right]^{3/2} \quad , \quad t_{re} < t_* \qquad$$

or, using Eqs. [3] and [6]

$$Q_{max} = \alpha_s \left[\int_0^{t_{re}} 2\alpha_c (\bar{i}_e + \overline{I} t)^2 t^2 dt \right]^{3/2} , \quad t_{re} < t_* \qquad [17]$$

Integrating as for Eq. [9] gives

---

[1] Eagleson, P.S., op. cit. pg. 352.

$$Q_{max} = \alpha_s \ (2\alpha_c/3)^{3/2} \ \bar{i}_e^{\ 3} \ t_{re}^{\ 9/2} \quad , \quad t_{re} < t_* \quad [18]$$

The next step is to obtain the probability density functions for the independent variables appearing in Eqs. [16] and [18].

Point Storm Rainfall

It is well known that the probability density function of point rainstorm duration, t_r, may be fitted closely by the exponential

$$f(t_r) = \lambda e^{-\lambda t_r} \quad , \quad t_r \geq 0 \quad [19]$$

An example of this fit is shown in Fig. 2 through comparison with 5 years of hourly rainfall data (546 storms) at Boston, Massachusetts.[1] For this locality $\lambda = 0.13$ when t_r is in hours.

Using data from the same storms, the (marginal) distribution of point rainstorm depth, d, may be approximated over the range of observations by the function

$$f(d) = \frac{k}{d^{3/2}}$$

as is shown in Fig. 3. For this to be a legitimate probability density function it must have both lower and upper bounds to its applicability, the former to insure unit area and the latter to provide (the proper) finite expected value. Applying these conditions gives

$$f(d) = \frac{k}{d^{3/2}} \quad , \quad \left[\frac{2kP}{P+4k^2\Theta} \right]^2 \leq d \leq \left[\frac{P}{2k\Theta} \right]^2 \quad [20]$$

where

P = average annual point rainfall (inches)

Θ = average annual number of independent rainfall events

With all depths in inches, $k = 0.10$ for Boston, Massachusetts.

The conditional probability density function of point rainstorm depth given the storm duration is not described so simply. Observations at Boston, Massachusetts are presented in Fig. 4 for three class intervals of storm duration. Grayman and Eagleson[2] have fitted these distributions with the gamma function

---

[1] Grayman, W.M. and P.S. Eagleson, "Streamflow Record Length for Modelling Catchment Dynamics," M.I.T. Dept. of Civil Engineering, Hydrodynamics Laboratory, Report No. 114, February 1969.

[2] Grayman, W.M. and P.S. Eagleson, op.cit. pg. 31.

$$f(d|t_r) = \frac{d^{at_r} e^{-d/b}}{\Gamma(at_r + 1) b^{at_r+1}}$$ [21]

where a and b are parameters of the distribution. Manipulation of this function in order to derive the distribution of storm intensity presents great difficulties however. To proceed with an analytical (as opposed to numerical) solution of our problem we will use the exponential

$$f(d|t_r) = \frac{\beta}{t_r} e^{-\beta d/t_r} , \quad t_r \geq 0, d \geq 0$$ [22]

which is a reasonable representation at large depths, where our present interest is centered. For Boston, Massachusetts with d in inches and t_r in hours, $\beta = 30$. Eq. [22] is compared with the observations in Fig. 4.

Areal Storm Rainfall

Working toward areal average rainfall excess we will next apply a correction to Eq. [22] to account for the fact that for an event of given probability, the areal average storm depth d_A is less than the amount, d, measured at some arbitrary point within the storm isohyetal pattern. The U.S. Weather Bureau[1] has developed just such a relationship by using data from 20 dense raingage networks in various climatic regions of the United States. This is presented in Fig. 5 along with the fitted function

$$\frac{d_A}{d} = 1 - e^{-1.1 t_r^{\frac{1}{4}}} + e^{-1.1 t_r^{\frac{1}{4}} - 0.01A}$$ [23]

where the durations are in hours and the area A is in square miles. This function applies only for constant event probabilities.

By definition, the time average point storm rainfall intensity is

$$i_o = \frac{d}{t_r}$$ [24]

and we will represent the areal average of i_o by

$$\bar{i}_o = \frac{d_A}{t_r}$$ [25]

Thus

$$\bar{i}_o = \frac{d_A}{d} i_o$$ [26]

---

[1]U.S. Weather Bureau, "Rainfall Intensity-Frequency Regime" Tech. Paper 29, pts. 1-5, Washington, 1957-60.

Using Eqs. [19 and [22]

$$\tilde{\imath}(d,t_r) = f(d|t_r)\ f(t_r) = \frac{\beta\lambda}{t_r}\ e^{-\frac{\beta d}{t_r} - \lambda t_r} \tag{27}$$

and then since

$$f(i_o) = \frac{\partial F}{\partial i_o}(i_0) = \frac{\partial}{\partial i_o}\left[\int_0^\infty dt_r \int_0^{i_o t_r} f(d,t_r)dd\right] \tag{28}$$

we have

$$f(i_o) = \beta e^{-\beta i_o}\ , \qquad i_o \ge 0 \tag{29}$$

To derive the distribution for i_o we will assume independence of d_A and t_r and then use Eqs. [24], [25] and [27] to derive

$$f(d_A,t_r) = \frac{\beta\lambda}{d_A t_r/d}\ \exp\ [-\frac{\beta d_A}{d_A t_r/d} - \lambda t_r] \tag{30}$$

The integration necessary to arrive at $f(\bar{i}_o)$ is analogous to that of Eq. [28] and is very difficult due to the dependence of d_A/d upon t_r (see Eq. [23]). As a further approximation therefore we will replace t_r by its average value in d_A/d to write

$$\frac{d_{A_c}}{d} = K = 1 - \exp\ [-\lambda^{-\frac{1}{4}}] + \exp\ [-\lambda^{-\frac{1}{4}} - 0.01A_c] \tag{31}$$

We can now use Eqs. [26], [29] and [31] to derive

$$f(\bar{i}_o) = \frac{\beta}{K}\ e^{-\beta\bar{i}_o/K}\ , \qquad \bar{i}_o \ge 0 \tag{32}$$

Rainfall Excess

We will separate the areal average storm rainfall excess from the total storm rainfall by applying a potential "loss" rate ϕ to each storm period.

That is, we are assuming

$$\bar{i}_e = \bar{i}_o - \phi\ , \qquad \bar{i}_o > \phi$$
$$\bar{i}_e = 0 \qquad \bar{i}_o \le \phi \tag{33}$$

In actuality, of course, ϕ should vary probabilistically but this leads to very complicated mathematics. For simplicity we will assume ϕ to be a constant for a given catchment which allows us to derive the distribution of areal average rainfall excess as

$$f(\bar{i}_e) = \frac{\beta}{K}\ e^{-\beta\bar{i}_e/K}\ , \qquad \bar{i}_e \ge 0 \tag{34}$$

10.8

We should note however that this "loss" rate eliminates from consideration as rainfall excess events all of the storms with average intensity $\bar{i}_o \leq \phi$. Calling

$$n = \text{average annual number of rainfall excess events}$$

we can write

$$\frac{n}{\Theta} = \int_\phi^\infty f(\bar{i}_o) \, d\bar{i}_o = e^{-\beta\phi/K} \qquad [35]$$

If we define

$$\Phi_1 = \frac{\text{average annual runoff}}{\text{average annual rainfall}} \qquad [36]$$

and

$$\Phi_2 = \frac{\text{average annual direct runoff}}{\text{average annual runoff}} \qquad [37]$$

we can write

$$P \, \Phi_1 \, \Phi_2 = nE[\bar{i}_e t_{re}] \qquad [38]$$

where t_{re} is the duration of rainfall excess. It can be shown using Eq. [27] that

$$f(t_{re}) = f(t_r) \qquad [39]$$

In approximation

$$E(\bar{i}_e t_{re}) \simeq E(i_o t_r) = \frac{P}{\Theta} \qquad [40]$$

which, using Eq. [38], gives

$$n = \Phi_1 \, \Phi_2 \, \Theta \qquad [41]$$

Some typical values of Φ_1 and Φ_2 are given in Table I.

Area of Direct Runoff

For a catchment of given area, the area producing direct runoff will vary probabilistically due first to geomorphology, second to the variability of storm size and third to the antecedent conditions accompanying a given storm. Clearly, the probability density function for A_r must be joint with those variables describing the geomorphology, the rainfall excess and the antecedent moisture conditions. It is not clear however what the form of this joint density function should be. We will therefore assume a marginal distribution for A_r. The simple assumption which allows for a distribution of values and yet provides the observed bias[1] toward small fractions of the catchment area is the triangular distribution

1 Betson, R.P., op. cit.

10.9

$$f(A_r) = \frac{2}{A_c} [1 - \frac{A_r}{A_c}], \quad 0 \le A_r \le A_c \qquad [42]$$

Table I
Typical Values of the Loss Parameters[*]

Basin	P (inches)	Φ_1	Φ_2
Red River above Grand Forks, N. Dakota	18.5	0.03	0.59
Mississippi River above Keokuk, Iowa	28.6	0.21	0.56
Neosho River above Iola, Kans.	33.1	0.15	0.83
Merrimac River above Lawrence, Mass.	40.7	0.48	0.51
James River above Cartersville, Va.	38.0	0.35	0.54
Tennessee River above Chattanooga, Tenn.	49.8	0.48	0.64
Chattahoochee River above West Point, Ga.	59.7	0.39	0.50
Miami River above Dayton, Ohio	37.1	0.32	0.66
Pomeraug River above Bennetts Bridge, Conn.	44.5	0.47	0.58

[*] From Hoyt, W.G. and others, "Studies of Relations of Rainfall and Run-Off in the United States", U.S.G.S. Water Supply Paper No. 772, Washington, 1936.

Flood Peaks

Having found or assumed distributions for the independent storm and catchment variables, we can now derive the cumulative distributions $F_1(Q_{max})$ from Eq. [16] and $F_2(Q_{max})$ from Eq. [18]. In order to find the desired composite cumulative distribution $F(Q_{max})$ we need to weight $F_1(Q_{max})$ and $F_2(Q_{max})$ according to their respective probabilities of occurrence. That is

$$F(Q_{max}) = F_1(Q_{max}) F(t_{re} \ge t_*) + F_2(Q_{max}) F(t_{re} < t_*) \qquad [43]$$

The concentration time t_* is a random variable. It depends critically on not only the size of the direct runoff area but also upon its shape since the propagation velocities of overland flow and streamflow differ by an order of magnitude. Writing

$$t_* = t_c + t_s \qquad [44]$$

we have

10.10

$$\frac{t_*}{t_c} = 1 + \frac{t_s}{t_c} \qquad [45]$$

In tests of natural catchments with areas of from 0.84 to 3,383 sq. mi. Wooding[1] has found t_s/t_c to be less than 0.5. To the first approximation then $t_* = t_c$. If the area of direct runoff is a relatively narrow band along the main stream, R_c and hence t_c will be small. For such events we will assume

$$F(t_{re} \geq t_*) = 1 \qquad [46]$$

and hence

$$F(t_{re} < t_*) = 1 - F(t_{re} \geq t_*) = 0 \qquad [47]$$

Thus, from Eq. [43]

$$F(Q_{max}) = F_1(Q_{max}) \qquad [48]$$

and we need worry only about deriving $F(Q_{max})$ from Eq. [16] using Eqs. [34] and [42]. We will first rewrite Eq. [16] so that $\bar{i}_e$ is in inches per hour and A_r is in square miles. This yields

$$Q_{max} = \frac{(5,280)^2}{(12)(3600)} A_r \bar{i}_e = 645 A_r \bar{i}_e , \quad t_{re} \geq t_* \qquad [49]$$

To continue we need to think further about the interdependence of A_r and $\bar{i}_e$. It is consistent with our earlier assumption (that A_r is a narrow band along the main stream) to further assume the variability of A_r to be primarily a result of geomorphology. (Clearly for rare events the area A_r will approach A_c and both of these assumptions will fail). Under these conditions A_r does not vary in time and we may average Q_{max} over the population of runoff areas for given catchment size according to

$$\bar{Q}_{max} = \int_{A_r} Q_{max} f(A_r) dA_r = 645 \bar{A}_r \bar{i}_e , \quad t_{re} \geq \bar{t}_* \qquad [50]$$

where, from Eq. [42]

$$\bar{A}_r = E[A_r] = A_c/3 \qquad [51]$$

and where $\bar{t}_*$ represents a similar averaging of t_*.

---

[1]Wooding, R.A., op. cit. 1966.

The probability $F(\bar{Q}_{max})$ that any peak of direct runoff exceeds the value $\bar{Q}_{max}$ can now be derived from Eq. [50] and is

$$F(\bar{Q}_{max}) = \exp\left[\frac{-\beta \bar{Q}_{max}}{645 \, K \, \bar{A}_r}\right] \tag{52}$$

To convert to total streamflow we will add the average "base flow" $\bar{Q}_b$ which can be written

$$\bar{Q}_b = \frac{\cdot (5,280)^2 (1-\Phi_2)\Phi_1 \, P \, A_c}{(365)(24)(3600)(12)} = 0.074(1-\Phi_2)\Phi_1 P \, A_c \tag{53}$$

The peak total streamflow $\bar{Q}_p$ is then

$$\bar{Q}_p = \bar{Q}_{max} + \bar{Q}_b = 645 \, \bar{A}_r \, \bar{i}_e + \bar{Q}_b \tag{54}$$

whereupon, using Eq. [48]

$$F(\bar{Q}_p) = F_1(\bar{Q}_p - \bar{Q}_b) \tag{55}$$

or, from Eqs. [51] and [52]

$$F(\bar{Q}_p) = \exp\left[\frac{-\beta(\bar{Q}_p-Q_b)}{215 \, K \, A_c}\right] , \quad \bar{Q}_p \geq \bar{Q}_b \tag{56}$$

from which the probability density function of $\bar{Q}_p$ is

$$f(\bar{Q}_p) = \frac{\beta}{215 \, K \, A_c} \exp\left[\frac{-\beta(\bar{Q}_p-\bar{Q}_b)}{215 \, K \, A_c}\right] , \quad \bar{Q}_p \geq \bar{Q}_b \tag{57}$$

The mean and variance of this distribution are, respectively

$$E[\bar{Q}_p] = \mu_Q = \frac{215 \, K \, A_c}{\beta}[1 + 3.44\times10^{-4}(1-\Phi_2)\Phi_1\beta P/K] \tag{58}$$

and

$$VAR[\bar{Q}_p] = \sigma_Q^2 = 2\left[\frac{215 \, K \, A_c}{\beta}\right] - \mu^2 \tag{59}$$

Comparison with Observations

We wish to compare the flood frequency curve, as defined by this analysis, with field observations. However, most available flood frequency data are in the form of annual maximum flood series or annual exceedance flood series while our series is an exceedance series comprised of all flood events.

Consider a record of stream discharge which is N years long. It will contain nN flood peaks which are samples from a population distributed according to Eq. [56]. The rth most severe event $\bar{Q}_{pr}$ in the sample will have an exceedance probability which is generally approximated by

$$F(\bar{Q}_{pr}) = \frac{r}{nN+1} \qquad [60]$$

The annual exceedance series selected from this same N year record will contain only N flood peaks which are the worst N events in the set of nN. The exceedance probability of $\bar{Q}_{pr}$ as determined from the annual exceedance series is written

$$\text{Prob } (\bar{Q}_p \geq \bar{Q}_{pr}) = \frac{r}{N+1} = \frac{1}{T_E} \qquad [61]$$

where T_E is the recurrence interval in years on an annual exceedance basis.

The rth event in both of these sets is identical $(r \leq N)$ and we can write

$$\frac{\text{Prob}(\bar{Q}_p \geq Q_{pr})}{F(Q_{pr})} = \frac{nN+1}{N+1} \qquad [62]$$

for N >> 1, this becomes, using Eq. [56]

$$\frac{1}{T_E} = n \, F(\bar{Q}_p) = n \, \exp \left[\frac{-\beta(\bar{Q}_p - \bar{Q}_b)}{215 \, K \, A_c} \right] \qquad [63]$$

The flood event $\bar{Q}_p$ having recurrence interval T_E on an annual exceedance basis will have a different recurrence interval T_M when considered on an annual maximum basis. These are related according to[1]

$$T_E = \frac{1}{\ln T_M - \ln (T_M - 1)} \qquad [64]$$

One statistic which has received much attention as an index of catchment behavior is the so-called "mean annual flood," $\bar{Q}$. The definition of this even is usually based upon the assumption that the annual maximum floods are distributed according to the Type I extreme Value Distribution of Gumbel[2]. The expected value of this distribution has a recurrence interval T_M = 2.33 years which, according to Eq. [64] is equivalent to T_E = 1.79 years. To compare observed mean annual floods with the distribution derived here we must use Eq. [63] to write

$$\frac{1}{1.79} = n \, \exp \left[\frac{-\beta(\bar{Q} - \bar{Q}_b)}{215 \, K \, A_c} \right] \qquad [65]$$

or

[1]Chow, V.T., (Editor), Handbook of Applied Hydrology, McGraw-Hill Book Co., N.Y 1964, pp. 8-19 to 8-22.

[2]Gumbel, E.J., "The Return Period of Flood Flows," Ann. Math. Stat., vol. 12, no. 2, pp. 163-190, June, 1941.

$$\bar{Q} \; = \; \frac{215KA_c}{\beta} \; \ell n \; (1.79 \; n) + \bar{Q}_b \qquad\qquad [66]$$

Bigwood and Thomas[1] have tabulated observed mean annual floods for 44 catchments in Connecticut having areas A_c of from 4.1 to 1,545 square miles. Eq. [66] is compared with these observations in Fig. 6 with K, n and $\bar{Q}_b$ defined by Eqs. [31], [41] and [53] respectively and using:

Φ_1 = 0.47   (see Table I)

Φ_2 = 0.58   (see Table I)

β = 30   (valid for Boston, see Fig. 4)

P   = 44   (see Table I)

λ = 0.13   (valid for Boston, see Fig. 2)

θ = 109   (valid for Boston)

The observations show the expected scatter about Eq. [66] due to the variability in A_r for a given A_c. To compare the derived distribution with observations for a given catchment but across a wide range of frequencies we can write Eq. [63]

$$\bar{Q}_p \; = \; \frac{215KA_c}{\beta} \; \ell n \; (nT_E) + \bar{Q}_b \qquad\qquad [67]$$

This relationship is compared with observations on two of the Connecticut catchments in Fig. 7. Since the average value of A_r was used in deriving Eq. [67] we will select for this comparison catchments having A_r close to $\bar{A}_r = A_c/3$ as is indicated by close agreement with Eq. [66] in Fig. 6. Other criteria used in this selection are:

1. Widely different A_c in order to test a range of this variable

2. As long a period of observation as possible in order to minimize errors in estimating recurrence interval.

The chosen catchments are identified on the plot of mean annual floods (Fig. 6) by the solid, numbered symbols.

From an examination of Figs. 6 and 7 there can be little doubt that the essentials of the flood-frequency relationship are incorporated in Eq. [67] at least in the recurrence interval range $1 \le T_E \le 10$ years. For larger values of the recurrence interval it is apparent that the observations in Fig. 7 turn upward. This is probably a result of an expansion of R_c for these rarer events, causing $t_{re} < \bar{t}_*$ and thus invoking Eq. [18]. We also notice that a least squares fit to the observations in Fig. 6 would present a somewhat flatter slope than is given by Eq. [66]. That is, the mean annual flood should be

---

[1] Bigwood, B.L., and M.P. Thomas, "A Flood-Flow Formula for Connecticut", U.S. Geological Survey Circular 365, Washington, 1955.

smaller than Eq. [66] for large catchments and vice-versa. Notice also that the slope of the flood-frequency curves in Fig. 7 is given well by Eq. [67] but that the predicted curve is shifted from the data according to the amount by which the observed mean annual flood departs from Eq. [66]. In other words, reduction of the standard deviation in Fig. 6 will improve the flood-frequency prediction for individual catchments, on the average. The primary sensitivity of Eq. [66] and [67] resides in the assumed distribution for A_r. It would thus appear both helpful and logical to use a distribution for which the ratio $\bar{A}_r/A_c$ varied inversely with A_c.

Summary

The flood-frequency relation for natural catchments has been derived theoretically beginning with observed distributions of rainfall parameters and expressing catchment dynamics in terms of the kinematic wave. The resulting relationship between flood peak $\bar{Q}_p$ and annual exceedance recurrence interval T_E agrees well with observation for events of modest frequency and has the form

$$\bar{Q}_p = \frac{215KA_c}{\beta}\, \ell n\ (\Phi_1\Phi_2\Theta T_E) + 0.074(1-\Phi_2)\Phi_1 PA_c \qquad [68]$$

where

1. A_c = catchment area (square miles)
2. Φ_2 = fraction of runoff occurring as direct runoff
3. Φ_1 = fraction of rainfall occurring as runoff
4. K = fraction of point rainfall occurring as areal rainfall
5. P = average annual rainfall (inches)
6. λ = parameter of rainstorm duration distribution (hours)
7. β = parameter of conditional distribution of rainstorm depth given duration (hours/inch)
8. Θ = average annual number of independent rainfall events

The principal assumptions involved are:

1. Applicability of the Kinematic Wave Method to the forecasting of peak streamflows. This method is known to omit the diffusive attenuation of peak flows which accompanies flood wave movement in natural streams. Consequently it predicts peaks which are too high. However, it does contain the essential relative behavior of stream and catchment in a simple form which clarifies the critical relationship between storm duration and the properties of the runoff-producing surface.

2. The marginal probability density function for the direct runoff-producing area, A_r. This appears to be a critical assumption and will have to be elaborated to reveal the interdependence of A_r and the storm and catchment variables of significant improvements and extensions of the method are to be realized.

3. A_r is a narrow strip along the stream and hence the probability that $t_{re} \geq \bar{t}_*$ equals unity. This definitely restricts the applicability of

10.15

the results to runoff events of moderate recurrence interval. For rare
events, the whole catchment is likely to come into play and the
probability that $t_{re} \geq \bar{t}_*$ approaches zero.

The unexplained variance in the observations of mean annual floods (Fig. 6) is
very likely due to variability of A_r and Φ_2 from catchment to catchment within
the same climatic region. The fact that the observations for a given catchment
(Fig. 7) do not scatter but follow a smooth curve parallel to Eq. [67] for
moderate recurrence intervals indicates that A_r and Φ_2 are fairly stable from
storm to storm within this range.

The obvious validity of Eq. [68] lends additional support to the use of the
kinematic wave theory for describing the gross (if not the detailed) dynamics of
the runoff process.

LIST OF SYMBOLS

A = area (square miles)
A_c = catchment area (square miles)
A_r = direct runoff producing area (ft^2 or square miles)
$\bar{A}_r$ = expected value of direct runoff area for a given A_c
a = parameter of distribution of rainstorm depth given duration (hours^{-1})
b = parameter of distribution of rainstorm depth given duration (inches)
c = propagation velocity of surface disturbance in overland flow (ft/sec)
d^c = point rainstorm depth (inches)
d_A = rainstorm depth averaged over area A (inches)
$E[\ ]$ = expected value of [ ], (units of [ ])
e = base of natural logarithms, $2.718\cdots$
$F(\ )$ = cumulative probability distribution function of ( )
$f(\ )$ = probability density function of ( )
I = fluctuating component of rainfall excess
$\bar{I}^t$ = I averaged over time t (inches per hour or ft/sec)
i_e = local intensity of rainfall excess (inches/hour or ft/sec)
i_o = time averaged intensity of point storm rainfall (inches/hour)
$\bar{i}_e^o$ = temporal and spatial average rainfall excess intensity (inches/hour of ft/sec)
$\bar{i}^o$ = areal and temporal average storm rainfall intensity (inches/hour)
K = factor reducing point rainstorm depth to catchment average for events of common probability (dimensionless)
k = parameter of distribution of rainstorm depth (inches$^{3/2}$)
ℓn = natural logarithm
m_c = parameter of overland flow (dimensionless)
m_s = parameter of streamflow (dimensionless)
N = number of years in record
n = average annual number of rainfall excess events
P = average annual point rainfall (inches)
Q_{max} = peak of direct streamflow (cfs)
$\bar{Q}$ = mean annual flood (cfs)
Q_b = annual average base streamflow (cfs)
$\bar{Q}_{max}$ = peak direct streamflow averaged over population of direct runoff areas for given A_c (cfs)
Q_p = peak of total streamflow (cfs)
Q_{pr} = r th peak total streamflow (cfs)
q = overland flow (cfs/foot)
q_{max} = peak of overland flow (cfs/ft)

R_c = dimension, perpendicular to stream, of area producing direct runoff (ft. or miles)

R_s = dimension, along stream, of area producing direct runoff (ft. or miles)

r = rank, beginning with most severe, of given event in an ordered array of observations

T_E = recurrence interval on annual exceedance basis (years)

T_M = recurrence interval on annual maximum basis (years)

t = time (seconds or hours)

t_c = time of concentration of catchment direct runoff area (seconds or hours)

t_o = origin of time (seconds or hours)

t_r = duration of point storm rainfall (hours)

t_{re} = areally averaged storm rainfall excess duration (seconds or hours)

t_s = time of concentration of stream segment within direct runoff area (seconds of hours)

t_* = areally variable duration of storm rainfall excess (seconds or hours)

t_*^{re} = time of concentration of the combined catchment-stream direct runoff are (seconds or hours)

$\bar{t}_*$ = time of concentration of direct runoff area averaged over population of direct runoff

VAR[] = variance of [ ], (units of [ ]^2)

x_c = coordinate of distance in direction of overland flow (ft)

y = local depth of overland flow (ft)

y_{max} = maximum overland flow depth (ft)

α_c = parameter of overland flow (ft^{2-m}c/sec)

α_s = parameter of streamflow (ft^{3-2m}s/sec)

β = parameter of distribution of rainstorm depth given duration (hours/inch)

$\Gamma( )$ = gamma function

Θ = average annual number of independent rainfall events

λ = parameter of distribution of storm duration (hours^{-1})

μ_{Q_2} = $E[\bar{Q}_p]$, (cfs)

σ_Q = VAR $[\bar{Q}_p]$ (ft^6/sec^2)

Φ_1 = average fraction of average annual rainfall becoming annual runoff (dimensionless)

Φ_2 = average fraction of average annual runoff becoming annual direct runoff

ϕ = potential storm rainfall loss rate (inches/hour)

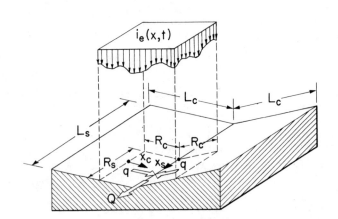

Fig. I Idealized Catchment - Stream Element

10.17

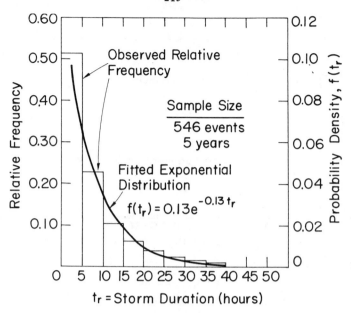

Fig. 2 Distribution of Storm Durations at
Boston, Massachusetts

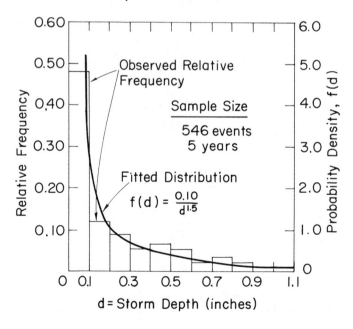

Fig. 3 Distribution of Storm Depths at
Boston, Massachusetts

10.18

220

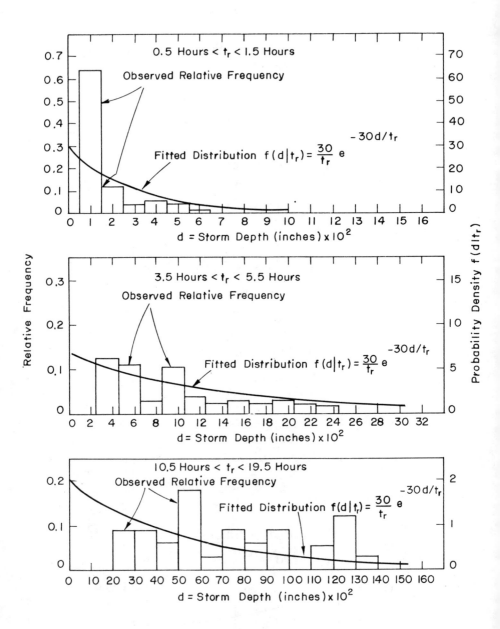

Fig. 4 Conditional Distribution of Storm Depths Given Duration, Boston, Massachusetts

10.19

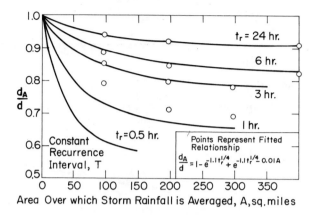

Fig. 5 Areal Reduction of Point Storm Rainfall

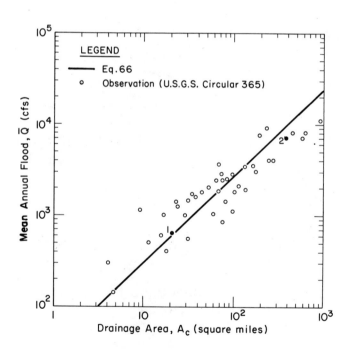

Fig.6 Mean Annual Flood on Connecticut Rivers

10.20

222

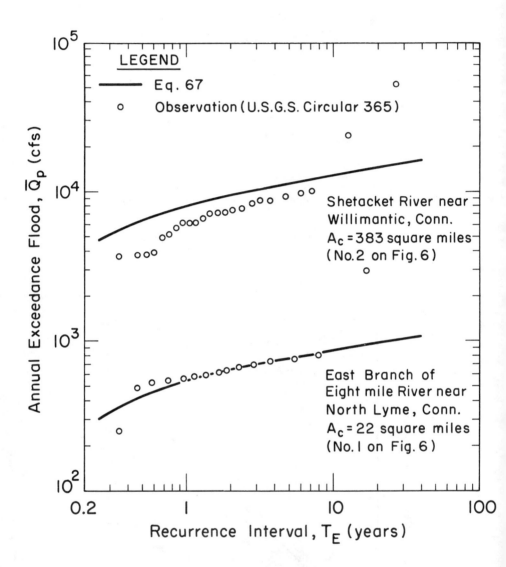

Fig. 7 Annual Exceedance Flood Series on Two
Connecticut Rivers

10.21

DISCUSSION

C. KISIEL

The effort to predict flood frequencies based on watershed mechanics is an important contribution and direction for future research.

1. It would be useful to have a summary of the assumptions and their implications for judging the reliability of the results.

2. Our research with rainfall and streamflow probability models leads us to the conclusion that generating functions or Z-transforms of the discrete analog of continuous probability distributions have definite advantages in the convolution of random variables. Of course, the problem of finding the inverse transform remains.

3. The Gumbel distribution is invoked to relate mean annual flood to drainage area. However, given the assumed distributions for the rainfall and the assumed watershed model, would not another extreme value distribution perhaps be fixed by the model structure?

4. Concerning Betson's results, how large a sample did he analyze? Was his analysis confined to the TVA area?

5. There is evidence that annual flood peaks are correlated in some river basins. Reference: P. Carrigan and C. Huzzen, "Serial correlation of annual floods," Proc. International Hydrology Symposium, 1967.

6. An alternate approach to estimation of flood frequencies would be to simulate the distributed properties of the watershed.

7. Given nonstationary environments induced by man's activities how might the profession gain confidence in the simulated flood frequencies? Historical records may have less meaning in such contexts.

8. The fitted flood frequencies in Figure 7 are best for floods with return periods less than 10 years. The lumping and averaging induced by many of the assumptions probably reduces the model's capability to generate meaningful extreme values beyond T_m = 10 years. Pertinent here is the fact that Gumbel's model is based on a complete duration series and not on a partial duration series.

J. PAUL RILEY

The paper raises the question of introducing stochasticity into deterministic models. Problems are encountered in assigning adequate density distribution functions to observed phenomena, such as precipitation and runoff. Much more complicated is the problem of objectively determining probability distribution functions for model parameters, the values of which are not directly measured. This situation reflects, of course, our lack of understanding of the physical processes, and for the present, at least, perhaps it will be necessary to assign density functions to some model parameters on only a subjective basis.

T. D. STEELE

I have two questions:

(1) I would like some clarification on the terminology used in figures 6 and 7. Is the y-axis the average of the annual maximum floods as shown in the examples in figure 7? Hence, the open circles then represent the instantaneous annual flood peaks for the available period of record?

10.22

(2) Given the objective in your approach as a general planning tool, do you foresee any utility of your approach in regionalizing information on annual flood peaks, particularly for ungaged drainage basins?

You undoubtedly will need some more geographical spread for experience before fully realizing the potential of this technique.

V. YEVJEVICH

The marginal and conditional probability distributions of rainfall intensity and duration are used to describe the point and areal storm rainfall. An ideal approach would be to obtain a trivariate (average intensity-duration-area) probability distribution function, from which all marginal and conditional distributions may be derived.

The use of Φ_1 and Φ_2, the runoff and direct runoff coefficients, as defin in the paper, take care of the continuity (conservation of mass) condition; however, these coefficients are also random variables when estimated from sample data.

It is not evident how the antecedent moisture conditions can be taken into account to obtain the flood peak distributions from the rainfall inputs as the method is applied.

RESPONSE BY P. S. EAGLESON

The response to discussion by C. Kisiel is as follows.

The following numbered responses refer to the corresponding number of Dr. Kisiel's comments. Many of the latter are merely observations which require no reply and hence are not addressed here.

1. In revising the paper for publication I have incorporated, in the summary section, a list of the principal assumptions and their effect upon the results obtained.

3. The Gumbel distribution is not invoked in this paper. The Gumbel distribution was assumed by the investigators who complied the data plotted in Figure 6 when they selected as the "mean annual flood" that event from their observed series having a 2.33 year recurrence interval. All I did was to calculat the Q vs A_c relationship according to the theory developed for the event having T_M = 2.33 years.

4. Betson observed 6 catchments, all within the TVA area.

7. Confidence may be gained in the simulated frequencies only by an array of (successful) comparisons of the theory with observations from catchments which have had fairly constant environments. To apply the method in the face of environ mental change we need to be able to estimate the parameter changes which this environmental alteration will produce.

There is no provision in the single element catchment-stream kinematic model to incorporate in a physically realistic way any nonhomogeneous activity of man such as construction of a reservoir.

General changes in land use can be reflected however through predictable changes in α_c, m_c, Φ_1, Φ_2, and in the assumed distribution for A_r. Indeed, this is one of the chief arguments for using a physically valid model of catchment dynamics. Representation of local changes in stream properties would have to be

10.23

done through after-the-fact fitting of α_s and m_s although the nature of the required change to these parameters could probably be foreseen.

8. In the published version of the paper I explain that the divergence of theory and observation for $T_E > 10$ years is almost surely due to the assumption regarding the shape of A_r and hence that $t_{re} > \bar{t}_*$. For rare events it is likely that $t_{re} < \bar{t}_*$ and the flood frequency forecast must be based upon Eq. [18]. This is the subject of further study which is currently nearing completion.

The response to discussion by J. P. Riley is as follows.

Dr. Riley is quite right in this comment. The two variables in this study for which distributions were assumed without benefit of observation were the storm loss rate, ϕ, and the area A_r producing direct runoff. In the former case ϕ was assumed constant in order to obtain an analytically manageable form for the distribution $f(\bar{i}_e)$. In the latter case the general shape of the distribution of A_r could be inferred from the work of others. It is not clear how sensitive the final results are to the assumed distribution of ϕ but the distribution of A_r and its dependence upon the rainfall parameters seems critical to improvement and extension of this work.

The response to discussion by T. D. Steele is as follows.

1. In Figure 6 the ordinate represents the flood peak which, in a series of annual maximum floods, has the recurrence interval $T_M = 2.33$ years. In the Gumbel distribution, the expected value of the annual maximum floods is an event with recurrence interval $T_M = 2.33$ years hence the term "mean annual flood". The circles represent values picked off flood frequency curves at the frequency $T_M = 2.33$ years.

In Figure 7 the ordinate represents observed flood peaks from a series of annual maximum events which have had their plotting position converted (to facilitate comparison with an exceedance theory) to an annual exceedance basis.

2. Yes, regionalization of ungaged watersheds is perhaps the greatest potential of this method but as you observe, verification is needed over a wider range of parameter values.

The response to discussion by V. Yevjevich is as follows.

Dr. Yevjevich is indeed correct that the proper approach would be to develop a trivariate density function containing the joint variability of $\bar{i}_e$, t_{re} and A_r. This is a goal toward which we must continue to work but at the moment a manageable form of this relationship has eluded me.

He is also correct in noting the true probabilistic nature of Φ_1 and Φ_2 (P and ϕ also, I might add). What is needed however is an estimate of the mean of these parameters and this does not require a very long record at least in climates where the annual variability is low.

There is no way in which antecedent moisture conditions can be incorporated explicitly. They are included implicitly now in the recognized variability of A_r and could be further introduced through allowing probabilistic variations in the loss potential ϕ .

United States-Japan Bi-Lateral Seminar in Hydrology

Honolulu, January 1971

SYSTEMS SIMULATION OF STREAMFLOWS

by   Yoshiaki Iwasa
Professor of Civil Engineering

Kazuya Inoue
Lecturer of Civil Engineering

and   Yoshiaki Tsunematsu
Graduate Student in Civil Engineering

Department of Civil Engineering
Faculty of Engineering
Kyoto University, Kyoto, Japan

Synopsis

Basin runoff hydrology may be modeled by mathematical simulation of the overland and streamflows. The present paper deals with the mathematical formulation of streamflow behavior by means of the one-dimensional method of hydraulic analysis and with its use in the streamflow simulation.

The simulation technique described herein consists of building an imitating structure composed of a series of channel reaches in which the flood routing procedure will be applied. A classification of the model-approximations in the system structure and their hydraulic role in mathematical expressions will be described.

Evaluation of simulated models made under some idealized conditions will give a physical significance to the channel storage as a result of flood routing. Through numerical computations, the qualitative characteristics of channel storage will be shown in terms of the channel geometry.

1. Recognition of Present Aim

There are a large variety of techniques for simulating streamflow. Consider the following contrast of, black box and structure-imitating, hydrologic and hydraulic models, mathematical formulation and physical analysis, actual and idealized lumped systems, and so on. Each technique

possesses its particular characteristic in the streamflow simulation,
as seen in many references.

The present aim is to describe the physics of streamflow in a
lumped structure-imitating system and to understand the hydraulics
of the structures themselves. So, first we will be concerned with the
mathematical simulation of streamflows. Problems involved in the
structure-imitating simulation are the following:

1. What type of mathematical equations should be used to simulate
the physical behavior of flow? The solution is evidently the structure-
imitating system itself.

2. How will the model structure be simplified? The mathematical
model is so complicated in its expressions that much simplification
must be made to warrant a realistic methodology.

3. What is an appropriate length of channel reach in a series of
lumped systems? How should the neighbouring reaches be connected?
The first question will introduce how to choose the reach and time
increments in finite difference schemes. The second one introduces the
additional question of flood routing method and provides a technical
limit of the simulation.

The paper will discuss these questions in sequence. As a result of
numerical computations, some qualitative characteristics of channel
storage will also be shown.

Problems concerning the accuracy and stability of finite difference
schemes will arise from numerical analysis. These, however, will not
be discussed.

2. Mathematical Models to Simulate Streamflows in Structure-Imitating
    Systems

The movement of streamflow in an open channel will be exclusively
expressed by the one-dimensional method of hydraulic analysis. A very
common technique is the storage equation simulation, as seen in the
Muskingum method. The desire to know more detailed information will
replace this simulation by the kinematic wave simulation, which is
constructed using the unsteady continuity equation and a discharge
formula, or similar equation. In a more comprehensive analysis, the
dynamic wave simulation derived from the method of characteristics and
the Lax-Wendroff scheme will be used. In any case, as flood routing
will be involved in the model structure, the simulation technique will
start from a system of one-dimensional equations for open channel flows.
The problem concerned is the mathematical expression of the original
streamflow because the streamflow must be heavily influenced by channel
irregularities in shape, width, bottom slope, roughness, and other factors.

(1) Generalized Expressions of One-Dimensional Equations in Open
       Channel Hydraulics

Usual forms of the one-dimensional equations for open channel flows
are only valid in an idealized channel, in which the shape is wide and
rectangular and the bottom slope is constant throughout the whole reach.
Actual channels are quite irregular in direction. shape, bottom slope,

roughness and all other geometric factors. Hayami [1] introduced the irregularity effect in the continuity equation and presented a modified equation of continuity with longitudinal and transverse mixing. The present discussion, however, will start from the use of generalized expressions for the system of one-dimensional equations of flow [2], which are reduced from hydrodynamic equations in curvilinear orthogonal coordinates.

Equation of continuity:

$$\int h_{1s}h_{3s}\frac{\partial h}{\partial t}\,dx_{3s} + \frac{\partial}{\partial x_1}\int \bar{u}\,dS_{x1} + \int h_{1b}u_{nb}\,ds = 0 \qquad (1)$$

Equation of energy:

$$\frac{\partial}{\partial t}\int h_1 \frac{\bar{q}^2}{2g}\,dS_{x_1} - h_{1s}\frac{\bar{q}_s^2}{2g}\frac{\partial S_{x_1}}{\partial t} + \frac{\partial}{\partial x_1}\int(\frac{\bar{q}^2}{2g} +$$

$$\frac{\bar{\Omega}}{g} + \frac{\bar{p}}{\rho g})\,u_1 dS_{x_1} + \int h_{1s}h_{3g}(\frac{\bar{q}_s^2}{2g} + \frac{\bar{\Omega}_s}{g})\frac{\partial h}{\partial t}\,dx_{3s}$$

$$+ \int h_{1b}(\frac{\bar{q}_b^2}{2g} + \frac{\bar{\Omega}_b}{g} + \frac{\bar{p}_b}{\rho g})\,\bar{u}_{nb}\,ds =$$

$$-\int \frac{h_{1b}}{\rho g}(\,\bar{\tau}_{x_{1b}}\bar{u}_{1b} + \bar{\tau}_{x_{2b}}\bar{u}_{2b} + \bar{\tau}_{x_{3b}}u_{3b})\,ds$$

$$(2)$$

where
$h_1 dx_1$, $h_2 dx_2$, $h_3 dx_3$; distance elements in the curvilinear orthogonal coordinate system x_1-x_2-x_3.

t: time
$\bar{u}$: local velocity component in the x_1 direction
q: magnitude of velocity
$\bar{u}_n$: outward normal velocity from the channel boundary

h: flow depth
p: fluid pressure
S: flow area
τ: shear
Ω: force potential
ρ: fluid density
g: acceleration of gravity
subscripts b and s: values at the channel boundary and free surface

1. Shoitiro Hayami: On the propagation of flood waves, Bulletin No. 1, Disaster Prevention Research Institute, Kyoto University, Kyoto (1951)

2. Yoshiaki Iwasa: Lecture note on hydrodynamic aspects of one-dimensional method in hydraulic analysis, Advanced Courses in Fluid Mechanics and Hydraulics -1, Hydraulics Laboratory, Department of Civil Engineering, Kyoto University, Kyoto (1967)

The mathematical derivations of (1) and (2) from the set of original hydrodynamic equations of continuity and motion can be made under the following premises and assumptions:

1. The mean flow pattern will be assumed to be consistent with the channel boundary.

2. The flow may be a turbulent mean motion.

3. In the mechanical energy and work relationship, the triple correlation among velocity fluctuations will be ignored.

4. The primary characteristic in turbulence will be isotropy.

5. The viscous shear resulting from the fluid motion may be neglected.

More detailed treatment concerning the derivation of one-dimensional equations for open channel flows will be seen in the reference [2].

(2) Derivation of Basic System of One-Dimensional Equations for Open Channel Flows

The mathematical expressions of (1) and (2) are so complicated in their formulation that more simplifications warranted by the technical information concerning the real flow behaviors and the channel boundary will be required.

For obtaining the bulk streamflow behavior, the following assumptions will be added:

1. The channel geometry will be gradually varying. $h_1 = 1 + kx_2 = 1$ and $h_3 = 1$, where k: local curvature of channel bottom and x_2: upward distance measured from the channel bottom.

2. The flow will be uni-directional so that $\bar{q}$ may be replaced by $\bar{u}$ i.e. $\bar{u} \gg \bar{v}, \bar{w}$.

3. The fluid pressure may be assumed to be hydrostatic and therefore the flow is gradually varied.

4. The transverse profile of surface velocity will be uniform.

Replacing x_1, S_{x_1}, and τ_{x_1} by x, A and τ, the above assumptions simplify Eqs. (1) and (2) to the following:

$$\frac{\partial A}{\partial t} + \frac{\partial Q}{\partial x} + q = 0 \qquad (3)$$

$$\frac{\partial}{\partial t}\left(\frac{\beta v Q}{2g}\right) - \frac{v_s^2}{2g}\frac{\partial A}{\partial t} + \frac{\partial}{\partial x}\left(\frac{\alpha v^2 Q}{2g} + zQ + hQ\right) +$$

$$\frac{\partial A}{\partial t}\left(\frac{v_s^2}{2g} + z + h\right) + q\left(\frac{v_b^2}{2g} + z + h\right) + \frac{\tau u_b}{\rho g} s = 0 \qquad (4)$$

in which

$$\int \bar{u}_{nb} ds = q, \qquad \int \frac{\partial h}{\partial t} dx_{3s} = \frac{\partial A}{\partial t}, \qquad \int \frac{\bar{u}^2}{2g} dS_{x_1} = \frac{\beta v Q}{2g},$$

$$\int \frac{\bar{u}^3}{2g} dS_{x_1} = \frac{\alpha v^2 Q}{2g}, \qquad \int \frac{\bar{\tau}_{x_{1b}} \bar{u}_{1b}}{\rho g} ds = \frac{\tau u_b}{\rho g} s$$

α: energy correction coefficient of Coriolis, and
β: momentum correction coefficient of Boussinesq

Eq. (4) may be transformed into, under constant α and β,

$$\frac{\beta}{g} \frac{\partial v}{\partial t} + \frac{\alpha v}{g} \frac{\partial v}{\partial x} + \frac{\partial h}{\partial x} + \frac{\alpha v}{2gA} (\frac{\beta}{\alpha} \frac{\partial A}{\partial t} +$$

$$\frac{\partial Q}{\partial x} + \frac{u_b^2}{\alpha v^2} q) = i - \frac{\tau}{\rho g R} \frac{u_b}{v} \qquad (5)$$

where i: channel slope.

(3) Usual Form for System of One-Dimensional Equations in Open Channel Hydraulics

we will further assume that

$$\frac{\beta}{\alpha} \frac{\partial A}{\partial t} + \frac{\partial Q}{\partial x} + \frac{u_b^2}{\alpha v^2} q = 0,$$

which will be valid in engineering approximations.

The basic system of one-dimensional equations in open channel hydraulics is then

$$\frac{\partial A}{\partial t} + \frac{\partial Q}{\partial x} = - q \qquad (6)$$

$$\frac{\partial}{\partial t} (\frac{Q}{gA}) + \frac{\partial}{\partial x} (h + \frac{Q^2}{2gA^2}) = i - i_f \qquad (7)$$

under the assumption that α and β are unity. i_f represents the friction slope expressed by the Chezy or Manning formula. The two partial differential equations (6) and (7) comprise the basic system for the streamflow simulation.

11.5

3. Mathematical Approximations in Imitating Structure

Before applying the system of Eqs, (6) and (7) to flood routing in the streamflow simulation, further approximations in the system will be made. Existing methods of flood routing by means of one-dimensional open channel hydraulics can be classified as is shown in Table 1.

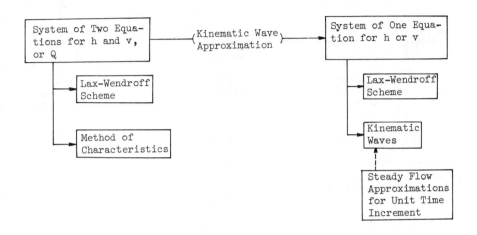

Table 1 Classification of Flood Routing
Methods by Means of One-
Dimensional Hydraulic Equations

The scheme of Lax-Wendroff is a mathematical tool in numerical analysis. The method of characteristics for two equations and the kinematic wave theory have their particular significance in open channel hydraulics.

(1) Kinematic Wave Approximation

The kinematic wave approximation is frequently used in basin runoff hydrology and especially in overland flow simulation. The discharge formula, which expresses that the discharge is proportional to the pth power of the flow depth, $Q \propto h^p$, is used as an approximate solution of the dynamic equation (7).

Qualitative comparison of both the dynamic and kinematic wave theories have been discussed by Hayashi [3]. Although he treated only flow in a wide and rectangular channel, the essential characteristics in his discussion will remain same. Treating a small disturbance travelling on the free surface of uniform flow, and making an order of magnitude analysis of the approximate equation thus obtained, he concluded the following:

---

3. Taizo Hayashi; Unsteady flows in rivers, Lecture Series in
    Advanced Hydraulic Engineering, A. Dam and River Hydraulics,
    Hydraulics Committee. JSCE (1966) (in Japanese)

1. In the case of horizontal bottom and short waves, where $h_o \gg iL$, the unsteady fluid motion in open channels will be of translation wave type. h_o is the uniform flow depth and L is the assumed wave length.

2. On the contrary, in the case of $h_o \ll iL$, the kinematic wave approximation will become possible. Actual floods possess a length of from 100 km to 1000 km and a channel slope of from 1/1000 to 1/10000. The uniform flow depth will be on the order of 10 m. The kinematic wave approximation will thus be useful practice in the flood routing analysis.

3. Between the two extreme cases just described, no simplification will be possible. All the terms involved in the basic system of Eqs. (6) and (7) must be considered. The dynamic wave theory must then be used.

Experimental observations made in a very long flume at the Disaster Prevention Research Institute, Kyoto University [4] support this conclusion at least in a qualitative aspect, though the original purpose of the study was not directed to understanding the kinematic wave theory.

(2) Defects in Kinematic Wave Theory

The kinematic wave theory may be essentially characterized by the relationship of $Q = Q(A)$ of $Q = Q(h)$. Then, the equation of continuity (6) indicates that wave motion will be possible. The velocity of propagation is known as the Kleitz-Seddon law, $c = dQ/dA$.

Actually, the first approximation in the kinematic wave theory consists of the continuity equation (6) and $i = i_f$ in Eq. (7). Replacing i_f by the Chezy formula, the mathematical expression in

$$\frac{dt}{1} = \frac{dx}{\frac{Q}{A} \left[1 + \frac{A}{C} \left(\frac{\partial C}{\partial A} \right)_x + \frac{s}{2} \left(\frac{\partial R}{\partial A} \right)_x \right]} =$$

$$\frac{dQ}{- q \frac{Q}{A} \left[1 + \frac{A}{C} \left(\frac{\partial C}{\partial A} \right)_x + \frac{s}{2} \left(\frac{\partial R}{\partial A} \right)_x \right]} \qquad (8)$$

where the subscript x means that partial differentiation will be made under constant x. If the streamflow possesses no lateral inflow, $dQ = 0$, which indicates that no attenuation of flood will occur. This is an inaccuracy in the first approximation.

The first approximation ignored all the terms concerning the local and convective derivatives on the left side of Eq. (7). The second approximation will be provided by the introduction of these terms. Denoting the left side by iL, it becomes

$$iL = \frac{1}{g} \frac{\partial v}{\partial t} + \frac{v}{g} \frac{\partial v}{\partial x} + \frac{\partial h}{\partial x}$$

---

4. K. Yano, K. Asida and T. Takahashi; Studies on deformation of flood caused by change in channel geometry, Paper Presented to 9th Hydraulics Meeting, Hydraulics Committee, JSCE (1965) (in Japanese)

With use of iL in Eq. (6), the second approximation will be given by

$$\frac{dt}{1} = \frac{dx}{\frac{Q}{A}[1 + \frac{A}{C}(-\frac{\partial C}{\partial A})_x + \frac{s}{2}(-\frac{\partial R}{\partial A})_x]} =$$

(9)

$$\frac{dQ}{-\frac{Q}{A}[1 + \frac{A}{C}(-\frac{\partial C}{\partial A})_x + \frac{s}{2}(-\frac{\partial R}{\partial A})_x][q + \frac{A}{2(1-L)}\frac{\partial L}{\partial t}]}$$

The attenuation of flood and the channel storage will be verified in the second approximation. Hayami [1] used the assumption of iL = ∂h/∂x in his theory. The basic mathematical simulation is then a non-linear partial differential equation of 2nd order. Expanding the solution in a power series, he solved the problem.

If dQ = 0 and thus the channel storage is of extremely small order, the first approximation may be replaced by the steady flow approximation for a unit time increment. A channel reach will be divided into a series of sub-reaches, each being a lumped system. This method consists of the following procedures:

1. Assume the downstream stage-discharge relationship at a particular time.

2. Trace the subcritical branch of the free surface profile in the upstream direction (The present discussion deals only with the subcritical branch of profile).

3. Compare the result with the initial upstream stage hydrograph.

The computation is very simple, compared with other existing methods. However, the essential defect in channel storage is involved in this method.

4. Numerical Analysis of Lumped System

The previous section described existing methods of flood routing by means of the one-dimensional hydraulic equations and some approximate procedures. Actual numerical computations will require each reach increment to be appropriately chosen according to the Courant-Friedlichs-Lewy criteria. The whole channel reach will be represented by a series of these lumped systems.

(1) Lax-Wendroff Scheme in Flood Routing [5]

The vector expression for the basic system of Eqs. (6) and (7) is

$$\frac{\partial U}{\partial t} + \frac{\partial F}{\partial x} = \hat{1}$$

5. R.D. Richtmyer and K.W. Morton; Difference methods for initial value problems, 2nd edition, John Wiley & Sons, New York (1967)

in which

$$U = \begin{bmatrix} \dfrac{Q}{gA} \\ A \end{bmatrix} \qquad F = \begin{bmatrix} h + \dfrac{Q^2}{2gA^2} \\ Q \end{bmatrix} \qquad i = \begin{bmatrix} i - i_f \\ -q \end{bmatrix}$$

F may be transformed into

$$F = \begin{bmatrix} \dfrac{A}{B} + \dfrac{g}{2}(-\dfrac{Q}{gA})^2 \\ g(-\dfrac{Q}{gA})A \end{bmatrix} = F(U) \tag{10}$$

under the assumption that

$$A = \int h\, dx_3 = Bh$$

where B: top width.

Referring to Fig. 1, Eq. (10) can be formulated in a 2nd-step finite difference scheme of Lax-Wendroff.

1st step:

$$U_{j+(1/2)}^{n+(1/2)} = \frac{1}{2}(U_{j+1}^{n} + U_{j}^{n}) - \frac{\Delta T}{2\Delta x}(F_{j+1}^{n} - F_{j}^{n}) +$$

$$\frac{\Delta T}{4}(i_{j+1}^{n} + i_{j}^{n}) \tag{11}$$

2nd step:

$$U_{j}^{n+1} = U_{j}^{n} - \frac{\Delta T}{\Delta x}(F_{j+(1/2)}^{n+(1/2)} - F_{j-(1/2)}^{n+(1/2)}) +$$

$$\frac{\Delta T}{2}(i_{j+(1/2)}^{n+(1/2)} + i_{j-(1/2)}^{n+(1/2)}) \tag{12}$$

in which

$$F_{j}^{n} = F(U_{j}^{n}) \text{ and } i_{j}^{n} = i(U_{j}^{n})$$

At the upstream section, the discharge hydrograph will be given. Under this condition, the flow area A_{1}^{n+1} will be determined by the continuity principle as follows:

$$A_{1}^{n+1} = \frac{\Delta T}{\Delta x}(Q_{1}^{n+1} + Q_{1}^{n} - Q_{2}^{n+1} - Q_{2}^{n}) + A_{1}^{n} + A_{2}^{n} - A_{2}^{n+1}$$

where the subscripts 1 and 2 denote the upstream and next sections,

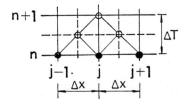

Fig. 1   Solution by L-W Method

(2) Method of Characteristics for Two Equation System

Flood routing by the method of characteristics has been very popular among hydraulic engineers. Mathematics involved in this method is significant, but the computational formulation is extremely complicated. In reality, the present system may be expressed by

$$\frac{dx}{dt} = \frac{Q}{A} \pm \sqrt{(\frac{Q}{A})^2 [1 - \frac{(\frac{\partial A}{\partial h})_t}{(\frac{\partial A}{\partial h})_x}] + \frac{gA}{(\frac{\partial A}{\partial h})_x}} \qquad (13)$$

$$\frac{1}{gA} dQ - \frac{1}{gA} (\frac{\partial A}{\partial h})_x \left\{ \frac{Q}{A} \mp \sqrt{(\frac{Q}{A})^2 [1 - \frac{(\frac{\partial A}{\partial h})_t}{(\frac{\partial A}{\partial h})_x}]} + \right.$$

$$\left. \frac{gA}{(\frac{\partial A}{\partial h})_x} \right\} dh = \left\{ i - i_f \pm \frac{q}{gA} \sqrt{(\frac{Q}{A})^2 [1 - \frac{(\frac{\partial A}{\partial h})_t}{(\frac{\partial A}{\partial h})_x}]} + \right.$$

$$\left. \frac{gA}{(\frac{\partial A}{\partial h})_x} \right\} dt \qquad (14)$$

and no actual solution will be obtained.

In practice, an approximation will be used: i. e, flood routing in a wide retangular channel. This approximation gives the popular system of equations

$$\frac{dx}{dt} = v \pm \sqrt{gh} \qquad (15)$$

$$\frac{1}{gA} dQ - \frac{v \mp \sqrt{gh}}{gh} dh = [i - i_f \mp \frac{q}{gA} \sqrt{gh}] dt \qquad (16)$$

Among many procedures existing in numerical analysis, the second approximation of fixed grid method [6] will be a useful tool. Referring to Fig. 2, the computation procedure will be described.

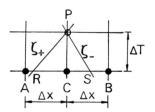

Fig. 2 Solution by Characteristics

1. Assume Q and h at P, and obtain v and i_f.

2. Compute $\zeta_{\pm p} = v \pm \sqrt{gh}$ and determine two points, R and S, through

$x_p - x_R = \Delta T/\zeta_{+p}$ and $x_p - x_S = \Delta T/\zeta_{-p}$.

3. Obtain v and h at R and S from known values at A, B, and C through the interpolation.

4. Obtain Q, i_f, ζ_+ and ζ_- at R and S.

5. Compute Q_p and h_p through Eq. (16).

6. Repeat the steps 1 - 5, until the initial assumption for Q and h will become equal to Q_p and h_p.

Being different from the characteristics net method, the fixed grid method possesses the advantage of obtaining desired hydrographs at desired locations.

Real channels except man-made waterways have many irregularities in geometry. In order to justify using the approximate system of Eqs. (15) and (16), the whole reach must be divided into sub-reaches, where the channel geometry and the roughness will be uniform. At the junction of two sub-reaches, there will be a discontinuity in hydraulic variables. Koreeda, Akimoto and Maruoka [7] applied this simulation to the flow at sudden expansions and contractions. Two principles of mass and momentum

6. J.J. Zovne ; The numerical solution of transient supercritical flow by the method of characteristics with a technique for simulating bore propagation, ERC-0370, School of Civil Engineering, Georgia Institute of Technology, Atlanta (1970)

7. S. Koreeda, T. Akimoto and H. Maruoka; Simulation of flood propagation in natural rivers, Paper Presented to 13th Hydraulics Meeting, Hydraulics Committee, JSCE (1969) (in Japanese)

conservations are applied. The discontinuity at the junction will then
be solved by a suitable combination of expansions, contractions, abrupt
rises and abrupt drops. A typical model for the flow at the channel expansion
is of Jaeger type, which has demonstrated its validity to the subcritical
transition through much experimentations at various laboratories. However,
the flow near critical state will be simulated by another model [8]. Many
models for the flow at channel contractions have also been presented.
The abrupt rise models are of the Jaeger and Forster-Skrinde types and
those at the abrupt drop of the Jaeger and Hsu-Moore-Morgan. Further
investigations concerning the validity of mathematical models to original
physical phenomena must be made.

(3)   Advantages of Two Methods

The Lax-Wendroff scheme possesses the primary characteristic of easy
programming. Another significance is short running time. The latter
characteristic will be very important in practice.

When the supercritical branch of flow is traced, some modification in
programming are needed. The method of characteristics is then a convenient
procedure. On the other hand, the method of Lax-Wendroff shows many
complexities.

5. Flood Routing and Channel Storage

Hydraulic characteristics of the system structures described in the
foregoing will be shown by making flood routing computations.
Computations have been made only for two floods in a man-made rectangular
channel, and better understanding of the original systems must be obtained
by the routing of floods in natural rivers. Throughout the whole computation,
FACOM 230-60 at the Data Processing Center, Kyoto University, was used.

Main dimensions used in computations are the following.

1. Upstream hydrographs:

Two types of floods are assumed. Both floods are characterized by
the base flow discharge 300 m^3/sec, the peak discharge 800 m^3/sec and
no lateral supply. The duration of the type (a) flood is assumed to be
12 hrs and that of (b) flood 9 hrs.

2. Whole reach:

L = 32, 16, 8 and 4 km

3. Rectangular channel characteristics:

i = 0.001

Manning roughness n = 0.025 (m-sec unit)

4. System structure:

(1) Steady uniform flow approximation

(2) Steady non-uniform approximation

8.   T. Shikata; Hydraulic behaviors of flows at sudden expansions and
     contractions, Ph.D. thesis, Kyoto University, (1968) (in Japanese)

(3) Kinematic wave approximation (first approximation)

(4) Dynamic wave approximation by characteristics

(5) Dynamic wave approximation by Lax-Wendroff scheme

5. Reach and time increments:

$\Delta x = 400$ m

$\Delta T = 50$ sec.

Figs. 3 (a) and (b) show the discharge hydrographs at various sections. Fig. 3 (a) is for flood (a) and Fig. 3 (b) for flood (b). Some conclusions obtained from the numerical computations are as follows:

1. The steady flow approximations give the same downstream hydrographs as the upstream ones. No availability of the approximations to the flood routing method is shown. It will, however, be useful only when the local change in hydrographs is requested.

2. No attenuation of the peak discharge will result through the kinematic wave approximation, as predicted by the theory. The dynamic wave approximation will explain the attenuation phenomenon.

3. Rare distinction in qualitative and quantitative results between the method of characteristics and the Lax-Wendroff scheme will be seen.

4. The same computation has been followed in the case of L = 4 km, but no practical distinction of the kinematic wave approximation to the dynamic approximation results.

The channel storage obtained during the flood routing procedure will describe qualitative and quantitative characteristics of the system structure.

Fig. 4 illustrates the channel storage throughout the whole reach of 8 km during flood (a). In the figure, the storage is defined by the height S, which is

$$S = \frac{1}{BL} \int_o^L A \, dx$$

Figs. 5 (a) and (b) are modified indications of channel storages. Better understanding of hydraulic characteristics resulting from various methods of computation and system structure are obtained.

The following conclusions are reached:

1. Wedge storage will be of primary significance in the dynamic wave approximation. However, its effect will not be evident in the present computations because of shortness in the reaches.

2. Solutions obtained by the steady flow approximations S_1 and S_2 deviate from those by the dynamic wave approximation S_4, when the discharge increment for a unit time is large.

3. Solutions by the kinematic wave approximation S_3 become inexact for longer reaches. Their deviations from solutions by the dynamic wave approximations S_4 are large for the rising limb of hydrograph and small for the descending limb.

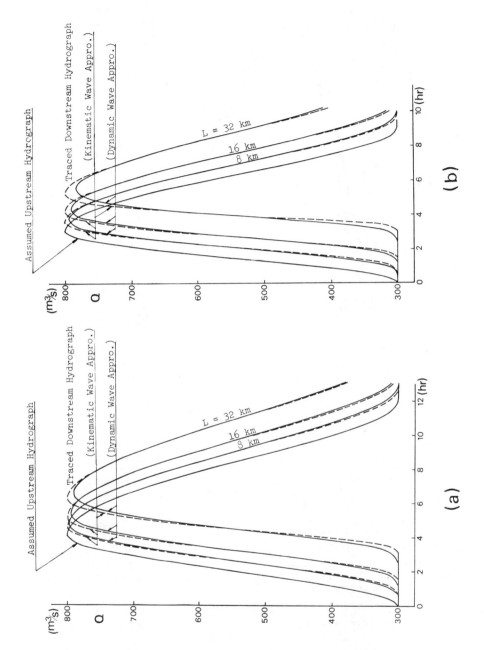

Fig. 3 Comparison of Discharge Hydrographs at Various
        Downstream Sections ((a) and (b) indicate
        flood types)

11.14

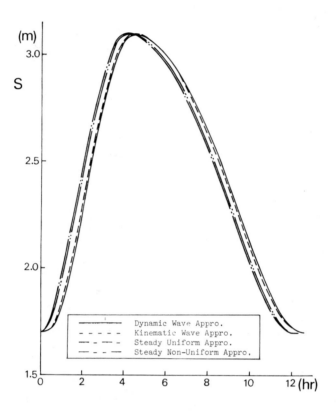

Fig. 4   Change in Channel Storage When Flood
(a) Passes a Reach of 8 km

6. Further Problems to Be Solved

The present paper gives a short description of the hydraulic
characteristics of system structure for streamflow simulation. Nevertheless,
many problems remain unsolved.

1. The basic models used for structure-imitating in streamflow
simulation must be better known in their qualitative and quantitative
characteristics through making more computations for various flow conditions.

2. Simplified techniques for routing actual streamflow using a series of
sub-reaches will be further refined. These will address computation errors
and the routing method itself.

3. The search for a simple simulation technique will be continued.

4. Real benefits from the present streamflow simulation will be a
substantial change of hydraulic model tests.

5. Empirical methods of flood routing by means of storage equations will
be verified after the present research program is completed.

6. Representative parameters to express the channel irregularity and
the channel storage must be obtained.

11.15

241

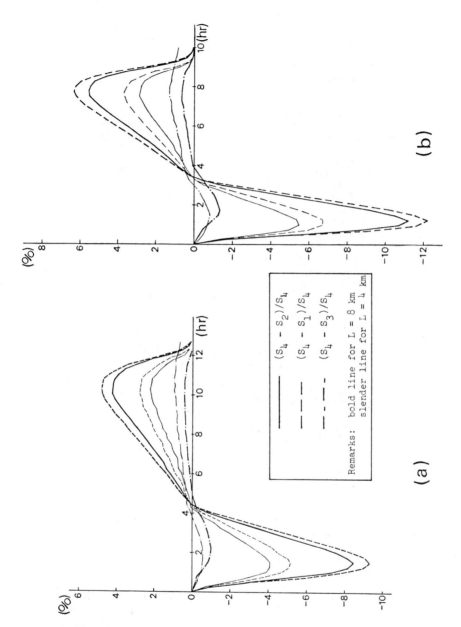

Fig. 5 Variations of Channel Storage Resulting from
Various Methods of Approximations

11.16

LIST OF SYMBOLS

A : Flow area used in one-dimensional analysis
B : Top width
C : Chezy coefficient
F : Vector used in Lax-Wendroff scheme
g : Acceleration of gravity
h : Flow depth
h_1: Function associated with length element in x_1-direction
h_2: Function associated with length element in x_2-direction
h_3: Function associated with length element in x_3-direction
h^o: Uniform flow depth
i^o: Bottom slope
i_f: Friction slope
k : Local curvature of channel bottom
L : Wave length
  Reach distance
  Mathematical expression used in one-dimensional analysis
n : Manning roughness
p : Fluid pressure
q : Magnitude of velocity
  Out- or inflow rate per unit distance
Q : Discharge
R : Hydraulic radius
s : Wetted perimeter
S : Flow area used in orthogonal curvilinear coordinates
  Channel storage height
t : Time
T: Time increment in numerical analysis
u : Velocity component in x- or x_1-direction
U : Vector used in Lax-Wendroff scheme
v : Velocity component in x_2-direction
  Mean velocity in one-dimensional analysis
w : Velocity component in x_3-direction
x : Distance in one-dimensional analysis
x_1: Distance in x_1-direction
x_2: Distance in x_2-direction
x_3: Distance in x_3-direction
X: Distance increment in numerical analysis
z : Elevation of bottom from reference datum
α : Coriolis energy correction coefficient
β : Boussinesq momentum correction coefficient
ξ : Propagation velocity of disturbance in characteristics method
ρ : Fluid density
τ : Local shear

11.17

DISCUSSION

J. W. DELLEUR

The speaker, during a recent sabbatical leave in France, had the opportunity to observe that Hayami's flood routing method is popular among French hydrologists. The Hayami method has been brought to the attention of American hydrologists by Ven Te Chow[1,2] who gave a summary of theory and references to electronic analog non-linear flood routing procedures based on Hayami's work. The speaker observes that this method was only briefly mentioned in References 1 but not treated or compared with the other methods. It would be of interest to know if the Hayami method is still used in Japan and if further work has been done on this approach.

[1] Chow, Ven Te, "Open Channel Hydraulics," p. 601-603, McGraw-Hill, 1959.

[2] Chow, Ven Te, ed.: "Handbook of Applied Hydrology," p. 29-7, McGraw-Hill, 1964.

[3] Larinier, M. & Saucerotte, H. "La propagation des crues à partir des hypothèses d'Hayami" Laboratoire National d'Hydraulique - Groupe Hydrologie, Faculté des Sciences, Montpellier, France, Note HYD 16/70, May 1970

T. KISHI

(1) In performing the dynamic wave approximation, what do you think of the theoretical difficulty in applying the boundary conditions? I mean, for example, the inpreciseness of the Stoker's method of approximation. Especially, the condition at the downstream end is difficult to introduce in the practical application. This kind of difficulty is not accompanied by the kinematic wave method because the number of characteristic curve is one.

(2) In the Hayami's method, the coefficient of eddy diffusivity includes the integrated effects of channel irregularities, effects of river confluent, and so on. The discusser thinks Hayami's method would be applied favorably to the more complicated systems of flow.

C. KISIEL

1. Systems simulation, in part, makes use of the unit impulse response functions (kernel function) as it is imbedded in the convolution integral. At the 1967 International Hydrology Symposium J.C.I. Dooge and B. Harley presented a linearized version of the complete equation for one-dimensional streamflow and, in turn, found the response of the model river system to a unit impulse. I wish to suggest that this approach complements the hydraulic analysis presented in the paper.

V. YEVJEVICH

In general it is not necessary to assume idealized channel shapes to link Eqs. 3 and 4 or Eqs. 6 and 7 together, provided that the relations between the changing geometry parameters, both with distance and elevation, can be expressed in approximate functional forms.

Equations 6 and 7 are the classical equations of the free-surface gradually-varied unsteady flow, given in 1871 by Barre de Saint-Venant. It is appropriate to underline at this place the centennial of these equations and the importance these equations have played in the solution of hydrologic and hydraulic problems during the last hundred years.

Using area, A , and discharge, Q , as the two dependent variables in Eqs. 6 and 7 instead of using depth, y , and mean velocity, V , usually results in a more complex computational finite-differences method, while requiring more computer time.

It should be also stressed that the velocity of propagation of a wave, or the celerity of the wave, often called the Kleitz-Seddon law, was first derived by Graeff in 1875, with Kleitz presenting it two years later in 1877, and Seddon reinventing it in 1900.

A recently completed study on flood-routing through storm drains (Colorado State University Hydrology Papers Nos. 43-46, and particularly No. 46) has shown that the method of characteristics using the specified intervals in the (x, t)-plane has some advantages in comparison with the Lax-Wendroff scheme in flood routing, both from the points of view of numerical computations and the computer time savings.

RESPONSE BY Y. IWASA

The response to discussion by J. W. Delleur is as follows.

One of the writers assisted in developing the Hayami's mathematical theory more than 20 years ago when he was preparing his graduation thesis under the supervision of Professor Hayami at Kyoto University. During the 50's, Hayami's theory was applied to construct analog computers [1] and it stimulated the modern development in flood hydrology. However, the present-day trend in Japan shows that his theory would only be used in qualitative analysis of floods as the use of digital computers becomes popular. Because the diffusivity in his basic equation gives only macroscaled patterns of channel geometry, a precise estimation to provide technical understanding is not possible.

---

1. T. Ishihara, S. Hayami and S. Hayashi: On the electronic analog computer for flood routing, Proc. of the Japan Academy, Vol. 30, No. 9, Tokyo, 1954

The response to discussion by T. Kishi is as follows.

(1) Mathematical solutions of partial differential equations consist basically of a combined system of the equations themselves and the boundary conditions. In view of this mathematical theory, the authors agree with the discusser. Actually, the numerical computation is a trial-and-error method.

In the present numerical programming, the authors treat the problem with a second-order approximation, whereas the Stoker's method is a first-order approximation. So, the writers in view of accuracy do not agree with the discusser. Obviously, the kinematic wave method possesses one characteristic, but it involves an essential defect in the basic theory. Furthermore, they are different from each other in mathematical theory.

(2) The second statement by T. Kishi is correct. However, the diffusivity in the Hayami's theory is rather qualitative and actually no evident distinction will result from a large variety of channel elements and flow conditions. Therefore, it may be said that a quantitative evaluation of flood behavior in connection with technical applications is impossible.

The response to discussion by C. Kisiel is as follows.

The authors appreciate very much for a kind comment of the discusser. It
looks superfluous to complement the work of Dooge and Harley in the present paper.
However, the original purpose of the paper is only to search for the non-linear
behavior of flood flows and, therefore, the paper by these writers is quite
different in qualitative and quantitative character from the paper by Dooge and
Harley. Past experiences of these writers on open channel hydraulics show that
the linearized solutions would only relate well to the movement of intumescences.

The response to discussion by V. Yevjevich is as follows.

The original purpose to show such a complicated system of equations is to
notify the underlying assumptions and premises in establishing the structure which
is being reproduced. In practice, the writers agree completely with the discusser.
However, the assumptions have to be disclosed. Furthermore, if the assumptions
are not recognized, large calculations made by the use of the model will become
less significant, because the recognition of assumptions in the basic theory
gives mathematical limitations.

As pointed out by the discusser, the mean velocity v and the flow depth y
are usually denoted in place of A and Q. The present paper uses A and Q only
for a refinement in description.

The writers as well as other Japanese participants hear the name of Graeff
for the first time. The writers appreciate very much for kind cooperation of the
discusser.

Concerning advantages in numerical analysis between the method of characteristics and the Lax-Wendroff scheme, computation in numerical analysis, the saving
time and the cost must be considered. In the present case, FACOM 230-60, a
computer at the Data Processing Center of the Kyoto University is used and the
cost is very low, i.e. one cent per second. The last restraint will therefore be
excluded from consideration. The Lax-Wendroff scheme becomes very effective in
flood routing computation.

United States-Japan Bi-Lateral Seminar in Hydrology
Honolulu, January 1971

EFFICIENCY OF PARAMETER AND STATE ESTIMATION METHODS
IN RELATION TO MODELS OF LUMPED AND DISTRIBUTED
HYDROLOGIC SYSTEMS

by Chester C. Kisiel
Professor of Hydrology and Water Resources
University of Arizona
Tucson, Arizona 85721 USA

SYNOPSIS

A review of the important philosophical and practical issues inherent in
modeling and parameter estimation errors is given. Included is a discussion
of the identification problem and its relation to optimization theory and stat
istical estimation theory. System determinacy and indeterminacy is defined
in terms of the number of variables, data points, and equations and then further elaborated in terms of design, identification and parameter estimation
problems.

In view of the proliferation of hydrologic models and an apparent polar-
ization of viewpoints on modeling, some issues involved in choosing among
models are presented. These include model validation, apparent and inherent
randomness, and lumped and distributed parameter models. The latter models
are interpreted by a frequency domain method; a heat flow problem is modeled
by both methods and interpreted in terms of autocorrelation and spectrum
functions for the lumped model. Objective and subjective criteria are presented for validation of hydrologic models.

Finally, an outline of Bayesian decision theory is presented and then
applied to evaluating the cost of uncertainty in the design of bridge piers.
The uncertainty exists in the mean and variance of the log-normal distribution
used to describe the annual peak flows on Rillito Creek in Tucson, Arizona.
A model for evaluating the worth of additional hydrologic data is also presented.

1.0 Introduction

The more efficient extraction of information content of data on hydrologic processes is growing in importance as hydrologists endeavor to make
greater use of computers. Recognized increasingly is the need to integrate
computer use with observation systems and man's intelligence, experience and
values. Interest in real-time control of hydrologic systems is growing
(Lindahl and Hamrick, 1970). Imbedded in the above trend are the problems
of model-building, parameter estimation, sampling in space-time, approximation and computation. Consideration of these problems naturally leads to recognition of the following four classes of errors (Deutsch, 1969, p. 319):

(a) System representation
(b) Parameter estimation
(c) Truncation (in the approximation of model equations)
(d) Roundoff (in the use of computers).

12.1

Of prime concern in this paper is a review of the important philosophical and practical issues inherent in the first two classes of error. But the rather broad scope of the subject, suggested by the title, must be constrained. Included are some recent results on the role of decision theory in evaluating the first two errors and on the accuracy of parameter and state estimates. The definition of efficiency is taken to include not only the standard statistical concept of relative variance of one estimator in relation to the variance of a second estimator but also the broader decision framework in hydrologic science and water management. The ultimate test of any model is its ability to predict, within economic and socially-acceptable error bounds, future states of the system being managed.

A unified theory for error analysis of hydrologic measurements, system identification, modeling, parameter estimation, truncation and computation seems to be a desirable goal from the standpoint of budgetary constraints, cost effectiveness in design of hydrologic data collection systems, future computer use and growing importance of environmental management. Pointing in this direction is the recent comparison by James, Bower and Matalas (1969) of the relative importance of hydrologic, physical, economic and political variables in managing the water quality of the Potomac Estuary. Similar concern has been expressed in meteorology (Gandin and Kagan, 1967) and in the general problem of process control (Eykhoff, 1968; Astrom and Eykhoff, 1970). It is hoped that this paper stimulates serious discussion about some of these issues.

1.1 Classes of problems

Problems inherent in the first two classes of error include

(a) Representation problem
(b) Identification problem (Eykhoff, 1968; Astrom and Eykhoff, 1970).
    (1) Optimization problem
    (2) Process parameter estimation problem
    (3) Unscrambling problem (Bellman, Kagiwada and Kalaba, 1965) - basically this includes time series analysis, quasilinearization and differential approximation.

The representation problem focuses on the guidelines for choosing among the various possible descriptions of a phenomenon: molecular, microscopic, macroscopic. It also leads to the following alternate classification, focusing more so on the solution aspects of the problem: linear or nonlinear, lumped or distributed, time-invariant or time-variable, space-invariant or space-variant, state-variable or frequency domain, deterministic or stochastic, discrete or continuous.

System Identification is the determination, on the basis of an input signal x in {x} and output signal y in {y}, of a system s in S to which the system under investigation is equivalent. The class of models S may be

(a) Non parametric representations such as impulse responses, transfer functions, covariance functions, spectral densities, Volterra series, orthogonal functions such as Fourier series and Laguerre functions.

(b) Parametric models such as state models

$$z(t) = f(z, x, b) \tag{1}$$

and the measurement equation

$$y(t) = g(a, x, b) \tag{2}$$

in which z(t) is the state vector, x(t) the input, y(t) the output and b a true parameter vector.

In the parametric case the order of the model must be explicitly specified before identification of parameters β as estimates of b. Experience has shown that large errors arise if the order of the model does not agree with the order of the actual process. On the other hand, the nonparametric model is inherently infinite dimensional so that in principle very good matches are obtainable between model and process output at least if the system is initially at rest. However, as pointed out by Jenkins and Watts (1968) the parametric representation in terms of physically-motivated lumped-parameter models such as moving-average and linear autoregressive schemes greatly simplifies the estimation problem. The coefficients of these models are related to physically-meaningful parameters such as time constants and damping ratios. The order of the stochastic linear difference equation is likewise estimated and statistical tests such as the F-test can be applied to check the hypothesis concerning order of the system. Rather interesting applications of this approach to annual streamflows have been presented by Carlson, MacCormick and Watts (1970). For the class of problems involving forecasting and control of hydrologic water quality systems, the parametric models outlined by Jenkins and Watts seem to have economic advantages in that they embody the principle of conservation of effort (Occam's Razor). See section 3 on model validation.

Frequently, equivalence is defined in terms of a loss function[1] that is a functional of the process y and the model output y_M. In both the parametric and nonparametric models of the system, the identification problem is transformed to an optimization problem. A well known loss function that assumes very little prior knowledge is the quadratic error or least squares criterion

$$V(y, y_M) = \sum_{k=0}^{K} e^2(k) \tag{3}$$

in which $e = y - y_M$ and k is the discrete time integer in $t = k\Delta t$. The optimization problem is to find a model s in S such that $V(y, y_M)$ is a minimum. The set of models S is identifiable if the optimization problem has a unique solution to the chosen loss function (Astrom and Eykhoff, 1970). Least squares estimation of unit hydrograph ordinates falls into the above formalism. The ordinates of the identified kernel function are the desired "parameters." Theoretically, such ordinates are infinite in number. Barrera and Perkins (1967) give excellent hydrologic examples of identification in the least squares sense for nonparametric models. They address themselves to the problem of estimating, from a sample of L input-output pairs $\{x^\ell(k), y^\ell(k)\}$, ($\ell=1, 2, ..., L$), the parameters associated with initial conditions and a linear time-variable kernel function subject to physical realizatility, stability and continuity constraints. The approach overcomes some of the problems with Wiener-Hopf convolution relations for identification of the optimum kernel.

---

[1]The loss function has various names: error, penalty, criterion, objective, cost or ranking function. It may be based on economic or scientific criteria.

Consider the process S with true parameters b' = $(b_1, \ldots, b_m)$ and the process model M with parameters $\beta' = (\beta_1, \ldots, \beta_m)$. The measurements y' = (y(0), y (1), $\ldots$, y(K)) are defined in terms of additive noise n superposed on the true state vector z = z(b,k) such that

$$y(k) = z(b, k) + n (k) \qquad (4)$$

The model response to input x' = (x(0), x(1), $\ldots$, x(K)) is y_M. When S = S(b) is defined now as being in the parametric class of system representation, the identification problem reduces to a process parameter estimation problem. The task is to find the "best" estimate of β of the true process parameters b based on observations y. Because of the probabilistic framework induced by Equation (4), one can exploit the tools of estimation and decision theory, such as Bayes' method, the maximum likelihood method or the min-max method. Least squares estimation is a rather special case of these methods. Advantages of these approaches include the opportunity to make fuller use of prior knowledge, to assign accuracies or variances to the various parameter estimates, and to test various hypotheses concerning models and parameters. Astrom and Eykhoff (1970) also point out that the loss function V(y, y_M) can now be given a probabilistic interpretation and that a system is identifiable if the parameter estimate is consistent, that is, the probability P of parameter error has the limiting condition:

$$\lim_{K \to \infty} P \{ (\beta(K) - b) = 0\} = 1 \qquad (5)$$

Consistency, efficiency and unbiasedness are pertinent to the question of how many input-output pairs should be used. The above approach leads naturally into questions of required sample size for a pre-specified level of accuracy (perhaps set by budgetary and social constraints).

The unscrambling problem concerns itself with identifying what source provided what stimulus. This may be a preliminary to model-building where little prior knowledge exists about the system. In many geophysical problems the inputs generating the observed sequences at one or more points are not known. Univariate and multivariate time series methods are of major importance in helping to unscramble the data (Jenkins and Watts, 1968).

Most issues concerning system identification remain unresolved. Of importance is the choice of measure of accuracy, choice of loss function, choice of system order and structure, evaluation of the a priori assumptions of the identification procedure, and role of errors in the input.

The major point of this paper is that the accuracy assignable to an identification procedure depends on the ultimate use of the results. For linear systems, accuracy may be defined in terms of deviations in the weighting function, in the impulse response or in the parameters of a parametric model (such as time constants, time to peak flow, peak discharge, total volume, etc.).

Choice of loss functions is ad hoc when the identification problem is transferred into an optimization problem, but in the case of parameter estimation the choice depends on use of the model, amount of prior knowledge and bias of the analyst. Loss functions may be symmetric or asymmetric, depending on the relative importance assigned to negative e(k) and positive e(k), that is, over- and under-estimation.

In order to place economic criteria for parameter estimation in proper perspective, it is constructive to review criteria used in recent years by hydrologists. Symmetric loss functions are exemplified by the integral square error, mean square error, and integral of the absolute value of error, respectively, given below:

$$V_{ise}(y, y_M, \beta) = \sum_{k=0}^{K} (y(k) - y_M(k, \beta))^2 \qquad (5)$$

$$V_{mse}(y, y_M, \beta) = \frac{1}{K} \sum_{k=0}^{K} (y(k) - y_M(k, \beta))^2 \qquad (6)$$

$$V_{iae}(y, y_M, \beta) = \sum |y(k) - y_M(k, \beta)| \qquad (7)$$

All three criteria assign equal weight to $-e(k)$ and $e(k)$. Equation (5) has been applied to both single and multiple input-output pairs (Dawdy, 1968). Equation (6) is applicable when large enough samples are available to obtain consistent estimates of parameters. Equations (5) and (6) assign larger weights to large errors whereas Equation (7), a linear loss function, assigns greater weight to small errors than does Equation (5). To reduce the effect of squared error, Dawdy (1969) takes logarithms of the streamflow and then proceeds with parameter optimization according to Equation (5). Even, in this case, the optimal parameter set is valid only in the log-space. This point emphasizes the lack of an absolute or universal criterion or loss function.

Some hydrologists choose to optimize with respect to deviations at one time point of the hydrograph, for example

$$V_i(y, y(k), y_M(\beta, k)) = (y(k) - y_M(\beta, k))^2 \qquad (8)$$

which is a criterion function at instantaneous time k and results in a static optimization problem. On the other hand, the minimax error criterion

$$V_{min-max}(y, y_M) = \min_{y_M(\beta, k)} \max_{y(k)} |y(k) - y_M(\beta, k)| \qquad (9)$$

takes a pessimistic or conservative view in an economic context by treating all occurrences alike.

A comparative evaluation of the above loss functions for a variety of hydrologic problems is needed but in an economic framework. A negative view about parameter optimization in chemical process control is taken by Gould (1969, p. 90) who states

> ...detailed analysis to optimize this or any other criterion is rarely worth the effort. Not only is the plant model usually inaccurate but also the criterion is rarely worth the effort. One also finds that the different values of the optimum parameters found by using a variety of different criteria usually do not dif-

fer enough to be significant. In other words one criterion is
about as meaningful as another and one might as well work with
methods that are simple to apply....the commonly-used criteria
produce flat minima (or maxima) and therefore exhibit very little
selectivity or sensitivity to parameter changes.

While these comments are food for thought, the above judgments about criterion
functions change rapidly if an economic interpretation is given to the loss
function (Folayan, et al, 1970) and if there is interest in evaluating the worth
of additional hydrologic data (Davis and Dvoranchik, 1970).

2.0   Strategy for modeling of hydrologic processes

The past ten years have witnessed substantial progress in hydrologic
model-building. There is a gradual convergence of diverse viewpoints in this
activity. Representative reviews of this progress have been given by
Amorocho and Hart (1964) who contrast the "systems" and physically-based
viewpoints; Kraijenhoff and O'Donnell (1966) and Dooge (1967) who consider
the classes of system problems; Chow)1964); Eagleson (1969) who outlines
modeling of urban watersheds; Dawdy (1969) who outlines watershed modeling
in terms of parameter optimization; Freeze and Harlan (1969) who present a
"blue-print" for a physically-based digital computer model of a watershed in
terms of partial differential equations for subsystems; participants at the
International Seminar for Hydrology Professors (edited by Chow, 1969) who
review the deterministic and stochastic approaches to modeling, system identification and parameter estimation; and V. Vemuri and N. Vemuri (1970) who
augment the above with a review of recent applications of control theory. In
all of this, one recognizes a groping for solutions to:

(a) problems of representing hydrologic systems by basic mechanisms
     as derived from physical, chemical and biological knowledge, and
(b) the complementary problems of system identification and process
     parameter estimation.

Frequently, the model-building activity is inextricably tied to system identification and process parameter estimation because of incomplete understanding of natural phenomena and incomplete data in space-time.

Generally speaking, only under highly controlled experiments, where a
one-to-one correspondence exists between the model assumptions and experimental conditions, is the parameter estimation problem separable from model-
building. To estimate parameters from independent sets of data or independent
equations based on physical properties of the system is a continuing challenge.

2.1   Model Calibration

All of this suggests that a distinction should be made between model
validation and model calibration. Note that calibration of instruments and
models in nature are not necessarily identical. A calibration equation is
derived under controlled experimental conditions so that easily measured
variables can be observed in the field rather than observing another variable
of greater interest. A rating curve and tracer-fluorescence curves are examples. On the other hand, the calibration problem in nature is illustrated
by two examples:

(a) Use of streamflow records x of length v years on stream A to augment the information content of streamflow records y of length $v_1 < v$ on stream B of similar hydrologic properties (Matalas and Jacobs, 1964).

(b) Use of tree ring sequences (in a climax zone) or mud varves to augment information content of precipitation and streamflow records about extreme droughts in the past (Fritts, 1966; Tschannerl, 1970).

In each instance a linear regression model is proposed as a first approximation and parameters are estimated in a least squares sense over concurrent periods of record on each variable. Dunsmore (1968) has formulated the above problem in the framework of Bayesian decision theory. The net effect of model calibration is to substitute a proxy variable for the hydrologic variable of real interest. In both of the above examples, common causal factors are assumed to influence both variables so as to justify the noncausal regression models. In both cases, the reciprocal of the variance of each moment parameter of the Gaussian time series in original or transformed space is taken as a measure of information content. Adequacy of the model and information criterion motivate part of a current study by Davis (1971) of this problem in the manner proposed by Dunsmore.

Parameter estimation is sometimes confused by hydrologists as being the same as model calibration. Given one or more pairs of input-output sequences and a connecting model, the problem is to find the parameters, as in the above regression model for "proxy" variables, of the process model. There is a resemblance between the parameter estimation and calibration problems in the sense that in both cases the resulting models are used subsequently to estimate a variable not so readily measured. The major difference is in their causal descriptions; these are present in watershed models (Dawdy, 1969; Crawford and Linsley, 1966) but are absent in the calibration models as pursued in the spirit of regression theory. In either case model validation questions arise.

2.2 Model validation

In order to give insight into the model validation problem, it seems worthwhile to review how models are derived in general. Wold (1967) sets up two dichotomies in order to arrive at four categories of forecast models: the aim may be to build either a descriptive or explanatory model whereas the means to do this are in terms of experimental data. Four combinations of aims and means arise: descriptive-experimental, descriptive-nonexperimental, explanatory-experimental, explanatory-non-experimental. Explanatory models are based on detailed physical reasoning whereas descriptive models may be purely statistical or conceptual models. Generally, hydrologists deal with historical or nonexperimental data; only one opportunity exists to make a measurement in the real world except under steady-state circumstances where small localized field experiments may be constructed: alternate shading to control solar radiation input to a soil, sand or snow system; field rainfall simulators; or well pumping tests. Laboratory experiments, on the other hand, may strengthen our understanding of physical processes and thus descriptive specification of the dynamic equations (as partial differential equations), but these results are for highly idealized conditions and may only after considerable field experience constructively influence our subjective or psychophysical interpretation of field data. This fact is crucial to appreciating the potential utility of descriptive-nonexperimental models.

12.7

The non-replicative character of the data coupled with imperfectly sampled initial conditions conspire to make the process stochastic irrespective of its subsequent deterministic evolution (Papoulis, 1965, p. 280; Gleeson, 1970). Even if the model perfectly represents the real system, the aforementioned uncertainties in initial conditions lead to error propagation as predictions into the future are made. Of later concern in this paper is the problem of parameter estimation in the face of an imperfect model, undersampling in space-time and noisy measurements of inputs, outputs and system parameters. These issues are central to a more constructive link between models based on retrospective conditions and their subsequent use for prediction of future response to, perhaps, a different set of conditions (Wold, 1967).

Frequently, validation and parameter estimation go hand in hand. Consider the study of overland flow or moisture flow through soil columns. Steps in building and validation of models for these processes might include:

(a) Representation of the process by means of differential and integral equations based on the physics of each phenomenon,
(b) Laboratory set up that is one-one in correspondence to model assumptions,
(c) Acquisition of experimental data on response to controlled inputs,
(d) Estimation of model parameters either by a subjective trial and error process or by parameter optimization (Schreiber, 1970),
(e) Use of independent sets of laboratory data obtained under similar controlled conditions,
(f) Use of independent sets of field data.

Application of the model to larger natural areas is the supreme test but probably entails considerable data and increased violation of assumptions. The choice varies between the use of input-output relations with minimum assumptions about the transfer mechanism and an insistance on detailed understanding irrespective of the marginal return on the research dollar as judged by accuracy of predictions.

In the above example, only one subsystem of a watershed is evaluated. For obvious reasons the hydrologist like other geophysicists, cannot dynamically simulate in the laboratory or computer all of the intricate patterns of flow in nature. Even if he conceives ingenious experiments to better understand the processes, transferability of these laboratory findings to the field is largely a qualitative effort. This fact is a reason for the diverse approaches to modeling that have arisen in recent years. The problem of choosing among models has gradually emerged. Is the choice to be made strictly in terms of scientific criteria, in terms of engineering or managerial criteria, or in terms of both kinds of criteria? For example, Mandelbrot and Wallis (1969) explicitly invoke a subjective criterion; that is, they appeal to the analyst's "psychology of perception" subsequent to a careful inspection of their simulated sequences based on a model of the self-similar process. This is akin to a Turing test. Maddaus and Eagleson (1969) propose the following criteria for evaluating the performance of one mathematical model as against another:

(a) accuracy
(b) computational efficiency (speed)
(c) simplicity
(d) flexibility

Hammer (1968) suggests similar criteria (where p is the real world and q the model):

(a) "q must contain the <u>essential information</u> in p, that is, q must <u>adequately</u> preserve the pattern of p."
(b) "q must be within reach economically."
(c) "q must be <u>better</u> than p for the purposes in hand."

The underlined words imply criteria of preference, an aspect of model validation requiring more formal study. Establishment of a precise preference relation is difficult. The first criterion given by Hammer implies a measure
of closeness in terms of information content; information is not necessarily
measured in terms of accuracy or variance as suggested by the maximum likelihood principle. The second is self-evident but leads into the difficult
problem of identifying economic loss functions associated with the use of a
particular model. The third specifies that the model q must be better than
the observed system p; an initial reaction to this criterion may be one of
skepticism but if one realizes the abstract character of our <u>conceptualiza-
tion</u> of p, the idea begins to make sense. Knowledge of p is <u>derived only</u>
through our senses and field sensors. A classical example is the forecast
model for eclipses in the solar system. Reinforcing this point is a recent
seminar by M. Diskin (personal communication, 1970) where he nicely outlined
the many conceptual flow charts put forth by hydrologists. Hence, the
approximation space contains a set of possible models q for p. But how to
choose the best model is open to debate. Obviously, those in positions of
responsibility for day-day decisions about hydrologic problems have considerable empirical knowledge about such choices. However, if such intuition,
experience, judgment, and so on, remain unanalyzed, they have little operational meaning. According to Morgenstern (1964), "if a rigorous theory is
rejected as inadequate for analyzing a problem, <u>a less rigorous procedure</u>
<u>can lead to better or equivalent results only by accident.</u>" Should the
potential value of raw judgment and intuition be so summarily dismissed
in the representation and estimation problems? No, it should not.

The ultimate test of any model is its ability to predict, within economic
and socially-acceptable error bounds, future states of the system. This viewpoint implies a compromise between complete understanding of natural phenomena
and the need to predict here and now. To the extent that efforts toward
"complete" understanding may lead to destructive testing or measurement or excessive interference with nature, one might argue that Heisenberg's uncertainty principle applies to the macroscopic world. Also complete understanding
may require never-ending study. These would be additional reasons for em-
bracing a pragmatic or operational viewpoint toward model validation. Even the
great potential of remote sensing for improved predictions should not deter
formal economic analyses of the tradeoff between basic understanding and current
needs for prediction.

A strong subjective consideration in accepting a mathematical model and
its predictions is the ranking of the relative importance of errors in the model
and its parameters. Decision theory gives a methodology for such ranking
(Deutsch, 1969, p. 269) when uncertainty exists in parameter estimates;
A decision-theoretic framework has basic merit because of its utilitarian
orientation and a potential for unifying the study of error analyses for
diverse subsystems. Actual and potential applications of this theory to
hydrologic problems will be discussed later in the section on parameter
estimation.

2.3 Relevance of notions of randomness and determinism to the validation problem

Recognition of the impossibility or cost of knowing all initial, boundary, and geometric conditions, either by destructive or non-destructive measurements as suggested by Heisenberg's uncertainty principle also propels some to a recognition of the statistical-dynamic dualism observable in nature. In this view, the causal and stochastic descriptions of nature are complementary. Basic causal principles of continuum mechanics, namely, conservation of mass, momentum, and energy are coupled to the constitutive equations for an "ideal" material in order to insure mathematical solution; the result is a set of dynamic equations, either in Newtonian or variational form (Hamilton-Lagrange), that describe the causal behavior of the system for point conditions. However, inherent in these dynamic equations is a limited capability for predicting or localizing events in space-time because of uncertainties in initial conditions, model, and parameters and because of stochastic character of forcing functions in space and time; the stochastic description is concerned with these "errors."

There is an apparent disagreement among hydrologists as to the origin of these "errors." Decomposition of these errors into their respective origins leads to a recognition of instrumental and sampling errors and prediction errors in space-time. The fluctuations observed in (x, y, z, t) space lead the analyst to an awareness of two forces operating simultaneously in nature: a decay toward equilibrium or maximum entropy as a result of earlier inputs and new disturbances. It is also noted that the new disturbances occur at random times {t} and at random points {x, y, z}. Any hydrograph may be observed to be the result of a random number of events in space and time. At issue is whether the entire domain of events in space-time is completely predictable in space-time. Dalinsky (1970) states that "...the stochastic process begins where understanding of the physical phenomenon ends." Penman, in a quote seconded by Budyko, states that all processes in the natural environment have a physical basis, and if a stochastic hydrologist cannot find a physical basis, it is his fault, not nature's (Simpson, 1970). There viewpoints reflect ignorance of the of the historical motivation for stochastic models whose physical bases are nicely presented by Blanc-Lapierre and Fortet (1965) and Jenkins and Watts (1968). There is substantial evidence on nature's behavior as a Bernoulli, Poisson, Gaussian or non-Gaussian process. Furthermore, randomness does not have to be given a physical basis in all instances except to specify a tendency for maximum disorder in nature.

There is no doubt that some errors may be reduced by improved models, more data, and better estimates of parameters as suggested by some; others argue that the "residual error" is not an "apparent" randomness but is due to inherent randomness in nature (Mann, 1970; Simpson and Smalley, 1970). The notion of apparent randomness, according to Mann, is interpreted as "...merely an accumulation of numerous deterministic events into a complex and undecipherable tangle...." However, arguing in behalf of inherent randomness as a concept, he points out that determinism and causality rest on the postulates of complete description within the spatial domain and period of time over which the process is observed, of complete isolation of the system from outside influences, and of a complete set of dynamic equations for all points and particles. Arguments against the first postulate were put forth in a previous paragraph. The second postulate is a major assumption of existing watershed, aquifer and hydrometeorological models based on causal descriptions. In the third assumption a large number, if not infinite, of equations would be required to obtain some kind of a solution; yet even in this case, required is a large number of guesses and experiments to get the constitutive equations (such as Darcy's law, Fick's law, and so on) according to Eringen (1967, p. 143). And when such constitutive equations are not available, the number of un- specified variables would be greater than the number of equations, thus leading to an infinity of solutions (and an infinite number of combinations of parameters that might reconstruct historical sequences). If hydrologists accept the above arguments, they are forced to agree with Bridgman (1959, p. 172) that "determinism and causality have only a generalized, nonspecific, and fuzzy meaning." Unique solutions are a figment of one's imagination. What is apparently needed is an evaluation of the classes of hydrologic problems for which each modeling approach (or combination) is "best."

2.4   On choosing lumped and distributed models

An important consideration in choosing models is the space-time scale of the phenomenon. These scales are at the heart of the problem of choosing a lumped or distributed model. Relevant here is the fact that most hydrologic stochastic process models proposed thus far are lumped except for multivariate streamflow synthesis models. Himmelblau and Bischoff (1968, p.43) suggest a rule of thumb for such a choice, namely, if the response of a subsystem is more or less instantaneous, then the subsystem parameters may be lumped. Such parameters become pseudo in character and represent a kind of spatial average if the instantaneous response property does not hold. The distributed-parameter model is justified if the response shows instantaneous differences along the element.

Efforts to get at the propriety of lumped or distributed-parameter models resort to frequency-domain methods (Roots, 1969, p. 64; Eagleson, 1969). Consider the relationship for wave length, $\lambda = c/f$, in which c is the velocity of propagation, f the circular frequency of the phenomenon under considera- tion. If the vector x defines the dimensions of the process, two diametrical- ly opposed interpretations are possible for a system with fixed c and time constant T. First, if $x \gg \lambda$, then free-field propagation is approximated. Second, if $x \ll \lambda$ and frequency of input disturbances is small, then the lumped- parameter model is invoked. More generally, the distributed-parameter model complies with the case when neither $x \gg \lambda$ nor $x \ll \lambda$, that is, $x \approx \lambda$. In this general and, strictly speaking, universal situation, the response of the process does not necessarily appear simultaneously in all parts of the process configuration. The finite-propagation velocity of these processes is deter- mined by their inertial or time constants. If these time constants T are large, then input disturbances are rapidly dampened. The above rationale is crude and needs strengthening by considering a form of the sampling theorem for both space and time simultaneously.

Terrestrial heat inputs into land masses are rapidly dampened by the soil mass such that at greater depths into the aquifer temperatures are virtually constant. In fact, this occurs a few centimeters below the soil surface (Lettau, 1967, p. 32). Effectively, the layer behaves as a cascade of expo- nential lag elements (same as the Nash model) and may be modeled by the classi- cal heat equation (Roots, p. 68). The resultant frequency response function has virtually the same frequency response function H(f) as the combination of pure delay and exponential decay, namely

$$H(f) = \frac{\exp(-j2\pi f\tau)}{(1+j2\pi fT)} \qquad (10)$$

in which τ is the extent of the pure delay. Of prime interest is exponential decay whose H(f) has the inverse transform

$$h(t) = \frac{1}{T} \exp\left(-\frac{t}{T}\right) \tag{11}$$

which is the kernel function for a first-order system. If a white noise sequence with Var Z(t) is used to force such a system, the response is a first-order Markov process whose autocorrelation function

$$\rho_{XX}(u) = \exp\left(-\frac{|u|}{T}\right) \tag{12}$$

is readily derived from the E[X(t) X(t+u)] upon substitution of the appropriate convolution relations. The spectrum of the linear process X(t) is

$$\Gamma_{XX}(f) = \text{Var } X(t) \, |H(f)|^2, \quad -\infty \le f \le \infty \tag{13}$$

which upon substitution of (10) becomes

$$\Gamma_{XX}(f) = \frac{\text{Var } X(t)}{1+(2\pi fT)^2} \tag{14}$$

Equations (12) and (14) may now be used to interpret the heat flow example. As T increases, the correlogram defined by (12) gets flatter and rapidly approaches unity typical of a correlation for a d-c current or mean value function. The spectrum rapidly approaches a spike at zero frequency. Hence, the observed time series at sufficient distances below the land surface are virtually a constant. Similarly, air temperatures in caves equilibrate at the value of the mean annual air temperature. Other segments of the hydrologic system may be evaluated in a similar vein by considering the scale of the phenomenon in relation to the dimensions of the lumped approximation.

The above result was based on a white noise input but which for the given system is not generally known except at a few locations. For many hydrologic systems the input is not known; only a univariate time series is at hand. By a systematic use of correlograms on the original time series and, first, second and higher-order differences until the residual is white noise, one is led to a stochastic non-causal model that embodies virtually all of the memory structure of the original time series. The residual white noise may be interpreted as a real but unknown input.

3.0 A suggested strategy for model validation

What strategy does one assume in the face of the above situation? An operational strategy for explicitly considering both inherent and apparent randomness in hydrologic processes must recognize that:

(a) Pursuit of absolute accuracy (zero bias) and zero imprecision in field measurements of the state vector and in estimation of model parameters is inconsistent with reality.
(b) "Errors" have meaning in an inferential, decision, and social framework. The consequences of errors in each context require clarification.
(c) Input-output relations and multivariate regression models that do not explicitly include prior knowledge of process dynamics may have operational advantages for solution of many hydrologic problems even in circumstances dominated at present by causal models.

Limited data on many distributed systems leads to errors of interpolation and errors in estimates of source functions and initial
state vector. For example, experience with a digital computer model
of the Tucson aquifer points up important difficulties such as error
growth in the use of numerical forecasts of future aquifer response
to controlled and natural disturbances (Gates and Kisiel, 1970;
Lovell, 1971). This state of affairs points up questions of
statistical inferences on partial differential equations when used
to model large scale systems because of errors in initial conditions,
model parameters, interpolation, and estimates of source functions
(recharge, pumpage, etc.); one may read this into a recent case
study by Paulson (1970) to verify distributed models of longitudinal
dispersion in the Delaware River Estuary.

Explicit and formal approaches to error analysis of hydrologic predictions has
been deterred by an educational tradition that is biased to a deterministic
view of nature, by an absence of computational speed, and by the late emergence
of a theory of model building, parameter estimation, and error analysis. A
strategy for systematic studies of the above issues might include:

(a) Computer simulation experiments and theoretical analyses to evaluate the relative importance of model assumptions, errors and inherent randomness (Eagleson, 1967; Grayman and Eagleson, 1969; Maddaus
and Eagleson, 1969). Still in this case the analyst is still away
from reality because his simulations revolve around assumed true
parameter values; to assume the role of hydrologic deity can be dangerou

(b) Determination of criteria for transfer of computer results to actual
hydrologic systems (Maddaus and Eagleson, 1969, p. 94, 105).
(c) Use of Turing tests for judging reasonableness of simulated sequences, that is, presenting such sequences to experienced hydrologists not familiar with their origin. Use of statistical tests
because two sequences may look alike to naked eye analysis but one
may reject the null hypothesis that their standard deviations are
identical.
(d) Use of decision theory (to be explored later in this paper). Included here is the cost of errors.
(e) More ex post facto studies of the goodness of hydrologic predictions.
Perhaps this should be made a matter of public record because of
the historical character of hydrology.
(f) More checks of hydrologic predictions by independent sets of data.[2]
(g) Degree of model validation that would be satisfactory for each
managerial use of the model.
(h) Study of optimal data collection schemes for more than one use or
model based on the data.
(i) Transfer of data and models from one site to ungaged sites by means
of regional models.

The reader is invited to suggest additions or deletions.

---

[2]A check of the hydrologic literature reveals that the word prediction
is too often misused. Strictly speaking, prediction signifies an estimate of
a future state $z(t)$ given an estimate of the present state $z(t_o)$ and a forecast
equation, $z(t) = f[z(t_o)]$, either deterministic or stochastic. More loosely,
prediction is frequently taken to mean the estimation of evolution of a single
event described by a flood or well hydrograph or of a sequence of these events.
See the next page.

3.1 Philosophical positions on the problem

Wold (1968) reminds us that the scientific method is at the heart of model building. Hammer (1968) emphasizes that "the process of making a model is a filtering process" and that these patterns or models arise because one's training has conditioned us to look at a set of data in a certain way and not in other ways. Hence, model validation is partly conditional on the various philosophical positions taken on the scientific method. Naylor and Finger (1967) review the three traditional positions on model verification: rationalism, empiricism, and positivism. In rationalism the problem of validation is "reduced to the problem of searching for a set of basic assumptions underlying the behavior of the system of interest." At the other end of the methodological spectrum is empiricism which relies on sense experiences for verification. It may be argued that science occupies more or less a middle ground between a priorism and empiricism. Positivism is not preoccupied with the validity of model assumptions but takes the operational view that empirical testing of predictions should be the sole criterion of validity. To many, the positivist approach is not attractive because it seemingly imparts no understanding. The statistician, M. G. Kendall (1968), espouses Bridgman's operational philosophy and, in a sense, a combination of the three positions. Naylor and Finger (1967) suggest that multi-stage verification, the fourth position on verification and a combination of the three philosophies, is increasingly feasible through computer simulation. They state that "multi-stage verification implies that each of the aforementioned methodological positions is a necessary procedure for solving the problem of verification." To support this viewpoint they argue that "the researcher cannot subject all possible postulates to formal empirical testing and must therefore select, on essentially a priori grounds, a limited number of postulates for further detailed study." The three-stage verification process is given as follows:

(a) Formulation of a set of postulates or hypotheses describing the behavior of the system of interest.
(b) An attempt on the part of the analyst to "verify" the postulates on which the model is based subject to the limitations of existing statistical tests, and
(c) Testing the model's ability to predict the behavior of the system under study.

---

[2] Often, however, the analyst fails to distinguish between reconstruction of the observed event and actual prediction of another independent event. The former is model calibration. When reconstructing an event, one intends to compare it with the event actually observed primarily as an internal check on the model or parameter optimization procedure. An independent set of input-output data is necessary to obtain a predictive check on the response given the new forcing function and the previously derived model and parameters. At issue here is not the adequacy of the sample size of the independent set of data used as a predictive check but the need for a routine clarification of what has been actually done. The matter is important to progress toward a solution of the model validation problem. Some of the traditional statistical literature does not help to resolve the matter, because quite often the commonly identified standard error of "prediction" really means standard error of estimate (a statement of the accuracy of the model whose parameters have been optimally estimated on the basis of certain assumptions). Both kinds of standard errors have distinct merit when using regression models.

Schrank and Holt (1968) emphasize that "the problems of building complex simulation models and getting them to operate on computers has consumed so much time and energy that the validation problem has been neglected." Verification or validation of a model requires specification of a set of criteria for discriminating between those models which are "true" and those which are "not true." But because definition of a set of criteria for testing models in itself requires choice of a criterion, Popper (1959) suggests that our focus should be on the degree of confirmation of a model instead of its absolute verifiability. He states that "so long as a theory withstands detailed and severe tests and is not superseded by another theory ..., we may say that it has 'proved its mettle' or that it is corroborated" (p. 33). On the other hand, Schrank and Holt argue that in applying Popper's criterion to simulation models "it is necessary to find a method to arrange the tests in order of importance, since innumerable tests could be devised for the complicated hypotheses represented by these models. By adopting the criterion of usefulness of the model as the key to its validation we shift the emphasis from a conception of its abstract truth or falsity to the question whether the errors in the model render it too weak to serve the intended purposes.... the validation problem in prediction and policy application concerns whether we can rely on the results generated by the model, and whether any particular model is the best available." Models are like statistical hypotheses; strictly speaking we do not accept them. We state that there is no basis to reject one.

3.2 Recent literature on model validation

In addition to the philosophical aspects of model validation, Naylor and Finger review specific measures and techniques for testing the "goodness of fit" between a simulated time series and observed data. After questioning the graphical techniques for validation of simulation models, they enumerate the following statistical techniques, by no means exhaustive, for testing goodness of fit: analysis of variance, chi - square test, factor analysis, Kolmogorov-Smirnov test, non-parametric tests, regression analysis, spectral analysis, and Theil's inequality coefficient. Schrank and Holt attach special importance to Theil's coefficient as a basis of comparison between several forecast models and suggest "that this type of analysis could provide a framework for a validation theory." Leuthold, MacCormick, Schmitz and Watts (1970) apply this criterion to the problem of choosing between two forecast models: an econometric model or a stochastic noncausal model. The former model is based on causal demand and supply equations and the latter is based on a study of correlograms of the raw data and higher-order differences. Theil's inequality coefficient, based on a quadratic loss function, is defined as:

$$U = (\frac{\Sigma (x_i - \hat{x}_i)^2}{\Sigma (x_i - x_{i-1})^2})^{1/2} \tag{15}$$

in which x_i denotes an observation made at time i and $\hat{x}_i$ denotes a predicted observation. Equation (15) is a comparison of the sum of squares of the one-step-ahead forecast errors of a model with those of a random walk model. $U = 1$ in the case of a random walk model because the best estimate of the one-step-ahead forecast is $\hat{x}_i = x_{i-1}$; hence, the numerator reflects redundancy or structure in the observed time series. The smaller U, the greater the structure. The stochastic noncausal models include nonstationary, moving average and autoregressive components that are one-one in correspondence to lumped conceptual models in hydrology (Jenkins and Watts, 1968; Box and Jenkins, 1970). For the problem of forecasting daily hog prices and quantities, the econometric model yields slightly superior results than the time series model. However, they suggest that the cost of making a slightly greater error using the stochastic noncausal model could be much less than the additional cost involved in setting up an econometric model and collection of the data; unfortunately, no cost figures were available to evaluate this hunch. Even so, these results raise a question about the actual worth of causal structure in terms of equivalent sample size assignable to human judgment. To implement the causal model required more data than for construction of the time series model. Could it be that these results suggest more parsimonious models for aquifers and watersheds?

Box and Henson (1969), in an effort to distinguish between empirical and mechanistic (causal) models, develop equations from the Bayesian point of view for the assignment of probabilities to theoretical models which have been fitted to data. In view of the smorgasbord of statistical tests available for analysis of simulated time series, criteria must be developed for choosing an appropriate set of tests for a given hydrologic model. Both Schrank and Holt (1968) and Arrison (1969) emphasize this point. Hydrologists have hardly scratched the surface of this subject.

3.3 System indeterminacy: degrees of freedom in modeling and parameter estimation

Frequently implied or seemingly taken for granted is the notion of degrees of freedom in modeling and parameter estimation. Because parameter estimation follows development of the hydrologic model, there is merit in reviewing the relationship of model building to optimization theory and system determinacy (Wilde and Beightler, 1967, p. 32). Generally speaking hydrologic problems are not well posed and hence have non-unique solutions. Basically hydrologic systems are physically underdetermined.

Optimization theory has applicability in at least three contexts: (a) design and planning, (b) system identification, and (c) process parameter estimation. Let M = number of variables and N = number of sources of information about the system. Three cases are of interest: $N > M$, $N = M$, $N < M$, or respectively, the overdetermined, completely determined, and underdetermined cases.

If $N > M$, a contradiction exists in the design problem because the greater number of independent design equations N generally makes it impossible to find consistent values of the M variables. However, in the case of the parameter estimation problem, N ordered pairs (x_i, y_i) of data are available to estimate the parameters β_j in an overdetermined system of equations of the form (Linnik, 1961, p. 135)

$$y_i = \sum_{j=1}^{M} \beta_j x_{ij} \text{ --------- } (j = 1, 2, \ldots, M) \tag{16}$$

The problem is of considerable concern to meteorologists and geophysicists in the estimation of space fields. A unique solution of Equation (16) is relative to the least square or quadratic error criterion and the assumed linear model of the system.

If $N = M$, the number of degrees of freedom $F = M-N = 0$. The system is determinate and the solution unique in the sense that the problem is well posed. Errors in the model and measurements must still condition one's acceptance of the results. Consider the pair of equations representing the kinematic wave model of overland flow:

$$\frac{y_{i-1}^{j+1} - y_{i-1}^{j} + y_i^{j+1} - y_i^j}{2\Delta t} = r - f - \frac{q_i^{j+1} - q_{i-1}^{j+1}}{\Delta x} \tag{17}$$

$$q_i = \frac{1.49}{n} (y_i^{j+1})^{5/3} S_o^{1/2} \tag{18}$$

in which y = water surface elevation
      q = volume rate of flow/unit width
      x = distance in direction of flow
      t = time
      n = Manning's roughness coefficient
     S_o = bed slope
      r = volume rate of lateral inflow as rainfall/unit channel length/ unit channel width
      f = volume rate of lateral outflow as infiltration/unit channel length/unit channel width
      i = spatial index in x - direction
      j = time step index

To obtain a unique solution, the analyst must prespecify the parameters, S_o and n. Usually S_o is known in the laboratory and an average value can be obtained in the field, but more judgment is necessary to specify n on an a priori basis. r and f are controllable in the laboratory (but generally not in the field); values of y and q are known for all points i along the x-axis at time j (this may not be true in the field). Hence, given all parameters and system states (y,q) at (i,j), solve for (y,q) at (i,j+1) with Equations (17) and (18) because N=M=2. This example of a determinate system is, however, for a highly idealized subsystem.

If N < M, the system is indeterminate; F = M-N degrees of freedom exist in specifying the F free or independent variables (or parameters), and hence an infinity of solutions exist. A ranking of these solutions according to a criterion of merit is bought at a price; the resulting solution is unique only with respect to this criterion. Unless the criterion is supreme in its capability to rank, any optimal answer must still be evaluated in terms of other subjective considerations not quantifiable for the moment. As a consequence, in system identification and parameter estimation the managerial use of models and parameters may dictate a utility or economic loss function as the basis of estimation instead of least squares or maximum likelihood estimators (Eykhoff, 1968; Folayan, Hoeg and Benjamin, 1970). This does not imply that estimation is totally a subjective activity but is a marriage of the subjective and objective dimensions of the problem.

If the parameter n in Equation (18) were not specified, then M-N = 1 degree of freedom exists; specification of an objective function is indicated. Schreiber (1970) chooses to minimize the quadratic error criterion:

$$V = \sum_{k=0}^{K} (Q_o (k) - Q_e(k))^2 \tag{19}$$

subject to the equality constraints specified by Equations (17) and (18). No inequality constraints are imposed so as to reduce the range of variation allowed in n. Q_o and Q_e are, respectively, the observed and estimated total discharge hydrographs for the experiment. The V-statistic is computed for deviations over the entire time domain K of the hydrograph. Note that Equation (19) assigns equal weight to positive and negative errors. Even in this simple problem, arguments against visual comparison as a basis for judging goodness of fit include the need to reduce human bias and to use the computer more efficiently. A stronger argument for parameter optimization arises if model parameters are to be related to watershed properties.

Dawdy and O'Donnell (1965) set up a watershed model with nine parameters to be manipulated. Although their model is not formally stated in terms of optimization or systems theory, one may presume that M-N = 9 degrees of freedom. Leeds (1967) suggests that the heuristic method of adjusting parameters to obtain convergence to the observed sequence tends to break down after about five parameters. He argues for use of both deterministic and stochastic identification methods. There is a strong hydrologic tradition that favors heuristic methods of parameter estimation. Perhaps a combination of the objective and subjective estimation methods becomes more practical as the interactive mode with the computer becomes more widely available. Experience with a large-scale computer model of the Tucson aquifer suggests the danger of discarding important hydrogeologic knowledge if brute force automatic optimization were employed (Gates and Kisiel, 1970; Lovell, 1971).

4.0 Bayes decision theory

It has been observed (Davis and Dvoranchik, 1970) that "investment requires justification, justification is prediction, prediction embodies uncertainty, uncertainty is reduced by information, getting information requires an investment, investment requires justification, etc. ad circulum." Decision theory is proposed as a means for cutting this cycle. It consists of the following steps (by no means exhaustive):

(a) Define the decision to be made and the possible alternatives: d
(b) Select goal or utility function: $V(d, b, y)$.
  (1) Define goal(s)
    i) Select state variables (arguments of goal function): y, b. The true parameters b are known from y or obtained a priori.
    ii) Develop stochastic properties of state variables: $p(y/b)$, $q(b)$, that is, respectively the probability density function (pdf) of the data y given the true parameter set b (constant) and the probability density function of b if b is uncertain.
  (2) Establish time preference and include risk aversion
(c) Making the decision
  (1) Evaluate present knowledge y by calculating the outcomes of the various alternatives and the stochastic properties of these outcomes.
  (2) Calculate the expected value of the goal function for each alternative. This is the Bayes risk for one value of d:

$$R(d, b) = E_b V(d, b, y) = \iint_{by} V(d, b, y)p(y/b)q(b)dydb \qquad (20)$$

in which $p(y/b)$ weights the goal function over all values of observed y for fixed b.
  (3) Choose alternative d* to maximize expected value of goal function

$$R(d^*, \beta) = \max_d E_b V(d, b, y) \qquad (21)$$

in which d* minimizes the Bayes risk R(d, ß) and represents the Bayes decision rule with respect to the distribution q(b) describing the uncertainty (ß - b) in the supposedly true parameter set b. ß can now be inserted into the Bayes risk as shown. q(b) weights the uncertainty in b as encoded in the Bayes risk.

(4) Analyzing uncertainties
    (a) Compute the expected opportunity loss XOL (due to uncertainty).
    (b) Evaluate information gathering programs
       i) Determine the expected reduction in XOL
      ii) Find full cost of getting more data.

The value of additional data is defined as the expected reduction of expected opportunity loss less the full cost of obtaining the data including lost benefits. Data is of value only if it leads to a change of decision or action.

To illustrate the above formalism, consider the annual extreme flows sampled from the stochastic process as observed over a recent 10-year period on Rillito Creek in Tucson, Arizona. Because worth of data is judged in the final analysis in relation to its managerial utility, consider the decision problem of designing the depth of piles h for the construction of bridge piers. The objective is to find the value of next year's observation of extreme flow $y(K + 1)$.

The 500-foot bridge is to rest on four piers with each containing 25 piles and with sinking cost of $4 per foot of pile. Cost of part of bridge that may be lost because of pier scour due to flood is $150,000. Employed is an empirical relation between scour depth h and streamflow $y(k)$. It is desired to minimize cost of sinking of the piles plus expected cost of bridge replacement, that is, minimize $V(h, b, y)$.

The parameter $b = \{\mu, \sigma^2\}$ in which μ and σ^2 are, respectively, the true mean and variance of the log-normal distribution of annual extreme flows. The Kolmogorov-Smirnov test did not challenge this frequency hypothesis. To choose another frequency hypothesis leads into the problem of choosing among models. In the context of Type I and II errors, Duckstein and Kisiel (1970) suggest an economic basis for making such choices. In this paper uncertainty arises only in the exactness of our knowledge of $\{\mu, \sigma^2\}$ and in the bridge scour relation. Assume that the latter relation is perfectly known. If knowledge of $\{\mu, \sigma^2\}$ were exact, choosing that depth h* that minimizes Equation (20) would solve the design problem provided the expected value criterion defined by (20) is subjectively acceptable as a basis for decision-making; it is an optimistic view and not as risk-averse as the minimax criterion which is the minimization of the maximum loss (see Equation (9)) and which guards against the situation that is unlikely to occur.

The parameters $\{\mu, \sigma^2\}$ would naturally arise from an analysis of a stochastic forcing of the kinematic wave model or the more complete equations for wave motion in river channels. Uncertainty in the stochastic properties of the response function would be the result of a compounding of uncertainties in the input forcing function, model, length of lumped reach of stream and channel properties over a long period of years.

Because $b = \{\mu, \sigma^2\}$ are not exactly known, they cannot be considered to be constant. Our actual knowledge of b is encoded in $\beta = \{m, s^2\}$ in which the mean m and sample variance s^2 are based on sample size K. The probability density function q(b) used to calculate the joint confidence limits of $b = \{\mu, \sigma^2\}$ is the one assigned to encode uncertainty in b. Here, it is the normal chi-square pdf with parameters $(m, s^2, K-1)$.

Following Davis and Dvoranchik, the worth of one more sample is obtained
as follows. The expected variable cost of the bridge or Bayes risk

$$R(h, m, s^2, K-1) = E_{\mu, \sigma^2} V(h, \mu, \sigma^2) \qquad (22)$$

is obtained by integrating numerically over the normal-chi square distribution because $\{\mu, \sigma^2\}$ sufficiently embodies the information in the data y.
Sought is the Bayes decision rule h* that minimizes (22) with respect to
$q(b) = q(\mu, \sigma^2)$, that is,

$$R(h^*, m, s^2, K-1) = \underset{h}{Min} \ E_{\mu, \sigma^2} \ V(h, \mu, \sigma^2) \qquad (23)$$

$$V(h_T, \mu_T, \sigma_T^2) = Min \ V(h, \mu_T, \sigma_T^2) \qquad (24)$$

gives the true decision rule h_T. The difference $|h_T - h^*|$ results in
an opportunity loss OL

$$OL(h^*, \mu_T, \sigma_T^2) = V(h^*, \mu_T, \sigma_T^2) - V(h_T, \mu_T, \sigma_T^2) \qquad (25)$$

that is a measure of the value of perfect information. To account for the
fact that $\{\mu_T, \sigma_T^2\}$ is not known, one must obtain the OL for each value of
$\{\mu, \sigma^2\}$, weight each OL by the appropriate ordinate of the normal chi-square
pdf, $q(m, s^2, K-1)$, and integrate. The resulting weighted average is the
expected opportunity loss

$$XOL(h^*, m, s^2, K-1) = E_{\mu, \sigma^2} [V(h^*, \mu, \sigma^2) - V(h_T, \mu, \sigma^2)] \qquad (26)$$

which is also interpreted as the expected value of the worth of perfect knowledge. Note that the design piling depth h* has been chosen on the basis of
present data. To augment present data with one more sample requires waiting
one full year to get one more extreme flow. The value of sample information
VSI is simply

$$VSI = XOL[h_y^*, m_y, s_y^2, K] - XOL[h^*, m, s^2, K-1] \qquad (27)$$

in which the subscript $y = y(K+1)$ indicates that m_y, s_y^2 is based on (K+1)
values. In interpreting VSI one must recognize that foreknowledge of y(K+1)
would be necessary because the decision, to build or not to build, must be
made before the additional sample is taken. Under such clairvoyance, the
decision would be to wait untill one more sample is taken if VSI < c[y(K+1)],
that is, the reduction in XOL is less than the cost of one more sample. In
the absence of clairvoyance, however, only an expected VSI is obtainable.
To do this requires weighting each possible value of y(k+1) by the log-normal
pdf p[y(K+1)] or, in other words, taking the average of next year's expected
opportunity loss, one has the expected expected opportunity loss:

$$XXOL(m, s^2, K) = E_{y(K+1)} [XOL(h^*_{y(K+1)}, m_{y(K+1)}, s^2_{y(K+1)}, K+1)] \qquad (28)$$

in which h^*_y, m_y and s^2_y are computed with the new observation $y(K+1)$ being included with the original set of K values. In (28) the expectation over y requires knowledge of $p[y(K+1)]$ whose parameters $\{\mu, \sigma^2\}$ are random; this problem is circumvented by taking expectations in (28) with respect to the normal chi-square pdf. A measure of the worth of one more sample is given by the expected value of sample information

$$EVSI = XOL - XXOL \qquad (29)$$

If the value of having perfect information about $\{\mu, \sigma^2\}$ as defined by XOL is greater than the costs (including loss of benefits in use of facility) of obtaining one more sample over the next year, then the decision might be to take that sample.

In the case of Rillito Creek data for a sample of 10 years, the Bayes decision rule $h^* = 16.1$ feet and corresponds to designing for a million year flood. The Bayes risk was $7479, XOL = $2930, and XXOL = $2756. Hence EVSI = $174. Comparing this figure with the loss of one year's benefits from use of the bridge, the decision is to build the bridge now on the basis of present data. The low value of EVSI may be explained by the relatively flat minimum found for the Bayes risk; a two-foot range between 15 and 17 feet in pier depth results in only a $90 range in Bayes risk. The computer program took only about 4 minutes to give the EVSI.

The approach applies to a single use of the data but there is reason to believe that the EVSI for each use is additive. The EVSI may be expected to change with changes in design parameters, model, loss function, and subjective criteria. The Bayes decision framework not only gives a mechanism for judging worth of hydrologic data but also seems to have the potential of serving as a unifying vehicle for communications among hydrologists with different economic and scientific persuasions.

The above formalism can be extended to include process parameter estimation and not just parameter estimates for input and output stochastic processes. In many hydrologic problems large sample sizes are not available to get unbiased, efficient and consistent estimates of parameters. Maximum likelihood, Gauss-Markov and least squares estimators have greatest meaning in the large-sample context. Generally, rates of convergence to limiting parameter values are not known for skewed populations. In this sense, decision theory gives a basis for parameter estimation and sampling in non-asymptotic situations. Extensions to nonstationary environments seem possible. The Bayesian methods, however, require considerable prior knowledge or the willingness to make guesses based on the present body of professional experience, when the luxury of waiting for larger samples and more definitive scientific hypotheses is not possible. Subjective prior probabilities q(b) may be elicited from the modeler or the practicing hydrologist in the manner employed by Folayan, et al (1970).

5.0 Closure

There is reason to believe that decision and systems theory provide a constructive framework for progress in unifying the diverse approaches in

hydrology. Presentation of philosophical issues reflects a conviction that
interaction at this level is necessary if there is to be progress toward the
next plateau of synthesis. These are the issues that in many ways determine
professional behavior in a given problem context. Of concern has been the
fact that "...the ability to accurately predict behavior is a severe test of
the adequacy of knowledge in any subject." (Crawford and Linsley, 1966). At
issue are the extent of accuracy required in a given prediction situation,
the best pathways for reaching a prediction, the criteria for judging goodness
of prediction and for choosing among models, and the cost of uncertainties
that exist in a data-constrained world.

6.0 Acknowledgments

     Some of the reported results have been supported by a matching grant (B-007-
ARIZ) on "Efficiency of data collection systems in hydrology and water resources
for prediction and control," from the Office of Water Resources Research, U. S.
Department of the Interior. Discussions with D. R. Davis and L. Duckstein have
been most helpful.

7.0 References

1. Amorocho, J. and W.E. Hart. 1964. A critique of current methods in hydrolo-
    logic systems investigation. Trans. Amer. Geophysical Union. 45(2): 307-321.
2. Arrison, James M, III. 1969. Procedures and Statistical Methodology of
    Model Validation. M.S. Thesis in Operations Research, U.S.Naval Post graduate
    Monterey, California.
3. Astrom, K.J. and P. Eykhoff. 1970. Identification and process parameter
    estimation, Proceedings, Second Prague Symposium (June 15-20, 1970)
4. Barrera, A. and F.E. Perkins. 1967. An extension of the role of linear
    systems analysis in hydrograph theory. MIT Hydrodynamics Lab., Cambridge,
    Mass. Report No. 106.
5. Bellman, R.E., H.H. Kagiwada and R.E. Kalaba. 1965. On the identification
    of systems and the unscrambling of data, I. Hidden periodicities. Proc.
    National Academy of Sciences. 53(5):907-910.
6. Blanc-Lapierre, A. and R.Fortet. 1965 and 1968. Theory of Random Functions.
    Vol. 1 & 2. New York: Gordon and Breach Science Publishers.
7. Box, G.E.P. and G.M. Jenkins. 1970. Statistical Models for Forecasting
    and Control, San Francisco: Holden-Day, Inc.
8. Box, G.E.P. and T.L. Henson. 1969. Model fitting and discrimination. Tech-
    nical Report No. 211, Department of Statistics, University of Wisconsin,
    Madison, Wisconsin.
9. Bridgman, P.W. 1959. The Way Things Are. Cambridge, Mass. Harvard Univ.
    Press. 329 pp.
10. Carlson, R.F., A.J.A. MacCormick, and D.G. Watts. 1970. Application of lin-
    ear random models to four annual streamflow series. Water Resources Re-
    search. 6(4): 1070-1078.
11. Chow, V.T. (Editor). 1969. The Progress of Hydrology. Proc. of the First
    International Seminar for Hydrology Professors. Vol. 1. Univ. of Illinois,
    Urbana.
12. Chow, V.T. (Editor). 1964. Handbook of Applied Hydrology. New York:
    McGraw-Hill Book Co.
13. Crawford, N.H. and R.K. Linsley. 1966. Digital simulation in hydrology:
    Stanford Watershed Model IV. Stanford Univ. Dept. of Civil Engineering.
    Tech. Rept. 39. 210 pp.

14. Dalinsky, J.S. 1970. An unconventional approach to flood frequency analysi
    Bull. International Assoc. Scientific Hydrology. XV(3):55-59.
15. Davis, D. R. 1971. Use of Bayesian decision theory in evaluating the worth
    of additional hydrologic data. Ph.D. dissertation (in process). Dept.
    of Systems Engineering, Univ. of Arizona, Tucson.
16. Davis, D.R. and W. Dvoranchik. 1970. Evaluation of the worth of additional
    data. Paper presented before Sixth American Water Resources Conference.
    Las Vegas, Nevada (October). To appear in Water Resources Bulletin (1971).
17. Dawdy, D.R. 1969. Considerations involved in evaluating mathematical
    modeling of urban hydrologic systems. Chapters 6 and 7, Appendix A of
    "Urban Water Resources Research," ASCE Report to Office of Water Resources
    Research, U.S. Department of the Interior, Washington, D.C.
18. Dawdy, D.R. and T. O'Donnell. 1965. Mathematical Models of catchment
    behavior. Proc. ASCE Journal of Hydraulics Div. 91 (HY 4): 123-137.
19. Deutsch, R. 1969. System Analysis Techniques. Englewood Cliffs, N.J.
    Prentice-Hall, Inc. 472 pp.
20. Dooge, J.C.I. 1967. The hydrologic system as a closed system. Proce.
    International Hydrology Symposium. Fort Collins, Colo. Vol. 2, 98-113.
21. Duckstein, L. and C. Kisiel. 1970. Efficiency of hydrologic data col-
    lection systems: Role of Type and Type II errors. Paper presented be-
    fore Sixth American Water Resources Conference, Las Vegas, Nevada (Octo-
    ber). To appear in Water Resources Bulletin (1971).
22. Dunsmore, I.R. 1968. A Bayesian approach to calibration. Journal Royal
    Statistical Society (Series B). 30(2): 39-405.
23. Eagleson, P.S. 1969. Modeling surface runoff in urban hydrology. Chapter
    4, Appendix A of "Urban Water Resources Research," ASCE Report to Office
    of Water Resources Research, U.S. Department of the Interior, Washington,
    D.C.
24. Eagleson, P.S. 1967. Optimum density of rainfall networks. Water
    Resources Research. 3(4):1021-1034.
25. Eringen, A.C. 1967. Mechanics of Continua. New York. John Wiley &
    Sons, Inc. 502 pp.
26. Eykhoff, P., 1968. Process parameter and state estimation, Automatica,
    4, pp. 205-233.
27. Folayan, J.I., K. Hoeg and J. R. Benjamin. 1970. Decision theory
    applied to settlement predictions. Proc. ASCE, Journal of Soil Mech.
    and Foundations Div. 96(SM4):1127-1141.
28. Freeze, R.A. and R.L. Harlan. 1969. Blueprint for a physically-based,
    digitally-simulated hydrologic response model. Journal of Hydrology.
    9:237-258.
29. Fritts, H.C. 1966. Growth-rings of trees: their correlation with
    climate. Science. 154:973-979.
30. Gandin, L.S. and R.L. Kagan. 1967. The economic approach to the plan-
    ning of a network of meteorological stations. Soviet Hydrology. Issue
    No. 6, 597.
31. Gates, J. and C. C. Kisiel. 1970. Efficiency of data collection systems
    in hydrology and water resources for prediction and control: Progress
    report. Water Resources Research Center. University of Arizona. Tucson.
32. Gleeson, T.A. 1970. Statistical-dynamical predictions. Journal of
    Applied Meteorology. 9(3):333-344.
33. Gould, L. 1969. Chemical Process Control. Reading, Mass.: Addison-
    Wesley Publishing Co.
34. Grayman, W.M. and P.S. Eagleson. 1969. Streamflow record length for
    modeling catchment dynamics. Report No. 114. Hydrodynamics Laboratory,
    Mass. Institute of Technology, Cambridge, Mass.
35. Hammer, Preston C. 1968. Patterns and information. Proc. Computer
    Applications in the Earth Sciences: Colloquium on Simulation, Computer
    Contribution No. 22, State Geological Survey, the University of Kansas,
    Lawrence.

12 .23

36. Himmelblau, D. M. 1970. Process Analysis by Statistical Methods. New York: John Wiley & Sons, Inc., 463 pp.

37. Himmelblau, D.M. and K.B. Bischoff. 1968. Process Analysis and Simulation: Deterministic Systems. New York: John Wiley & Sons, Inc. 348 pp.

38. James, I.C., II, B.T. Bower, and N.C. Matalas. 1979. Relative importance of variables in water resources planning. Water Resources Research. 5(6): 1165-1173.

39. Jenkins, G.M. and D.G. Watts, Jr. 1968. Spectral Analysis and Its Applications. San Francisco, California: Holden-Day, Inc. 525 pp.

40. Kendall, Maurice G. 1968. Model building and its problems, in Model Building in Economics and Industry, by CEIR, Inc. and CEIR, Ltd.

41. Kraijenhoff van de Leur and T. O'Donnell. 1966. Recent Trends in Hydrograph Synthesis. Chapters 2 and 3 of Proceedings of Technical Meeting 21, Netherlands Committee for Hydrological Research T.N.O. (#13): 31-103.

42. Leeds, J.V., Jr. 1967. Dynamic curve fitting: identification problem of system theory as applied to pollution dynamics. Paper. Joint Meeting of Instituto Mexicano de Ingenieros Quimicos and American Institute of Chemical Engineers. Mexico City.

43. Lettau, H. 1967. Problems of micrometeorological measurements. in The Collection and Processing of Field Data. Ed. by E.F. Bradley and O.T. Denmead. New York: John Wiley and Sons.

44. Leuthold, R.M., A.J.A. MacCormick, A. Schmitz and D. G. Watts. 1970. Forecasting daily hog prices and quantities: A study of alternative forecasting techniques, Journal of the American Statistical Association, 65, March, pp. 90-107.

45. Lindahl, L.E. and R.L. Hamrick. 1970. The potential and practicality of watershed models in operational water management. Proc. AM, ASCE National Water Res. Engineering Meeting, Memphis, Tenn., January 26-30, 1970.

46. Linnik, Yu. V. 1961. Method of Least Squares and Principles of the Theory of Observations. New York: Pergamon Press. 360 pp.

47. Lovell, R. 1971. Adjustment of parameters of an aquifer model. M.S. Thesis. Department of Systems Engineering, University of Arizona, Tucson.

48. Maddaus, W.O. and P.S. Eagleson. 1969. A distributed linear representation of surface runoff. Report No. 115. Hydrodynamics Laboratory. Massachusetts Institute of Technology, Cambridge, Mass.

49. Mandelbrot, B. and J. R. Wallis. 1969. Computer experiments with fractional Gaussian noises, Part 1, Averages and variances, Water Resources Res., 5(1), 228-241.

50. Mann, C. John. 1970. Randomness in nature. Geological Society of America Bulletin. 81:95-104.

51. Matalas, N.C. and B. Jacobs. 1964. A correlation procedure for augmenting hydrologic data. Geological Survey Professional Paper 434-E. U.S. GovernmentPrinting Office, Washington, D.C.

52. Morgenstern, Oskar. 1964. On some criticisms of game theory. Princeton, New Jersey. Princeton University. Econometric Research Program. Research Paper No. 8.

53. Naylor, T.H. and J.M. Finger. 1967. Verification of computer simulation models. Management Science. 14(2), B-92.

54. Papoulis, A. 1965. Probability, Random Variables, and Stochastic Processes. New York: McGraw-Hill Book Co. 583 pp.

55. Paulson, R.W. 1970. Variation of the longitudinal dispersion coefficient in the Delaware River Estuary as a function of freshwater inflow. Water Resources Research. 6(2):516-526.

56. Popper, Karl. 1959. The Logic of Scientific Discovery, New York: Basic Books, Inc.

57. Roots, W. K. 1969. Fundamentals of Temperature Control. New York: Academic Press.

58. Schrank, W.E. and C. C. Holt. 1968. Critique of "Verification of computer simulation models," Management Science, 15.

59. Schreiber, D.L. 1970. Overland flow simulation by a nonlinear distributed parameter model. Ph.D. dissertation. Washington State University, Pullman, Washington.

60. Simpson, G. G. and I.J. Smalley. 1970. On randomness and determinism: Discussion. Geological Society of America Bulletin. 81:3185-3186.

61. Simpson, E.S. 1970. Report on World Water Balance Symposium. Trans. Amer. Geophysical Union. 51(10):692-693.

62. Smallwood, R. D. 1968. A decision analysis of model selection. Institute of Electrical and Electronic Engineers. Transactions on Systems Science and Cybernetics, Vol. SSC-4, No. 3, pp. 333-341.

63. Tschannerl, G. 1970. Designing reservoirs with short streamflow records. Ph.D. Dissertation. Harvard University, Cambridge, Mass.

64. Vemuri, V. and N. Vemuri. 1970. On the systems approach in hydrology. Bulletin of the International Association for Scientific Hydrology. SV(2):17-38.

65. Wilde, D.J. and C. Beightler. 1967. Foundations of Optimization. Englewood Cliffs, N.J.: Prentice-Hall, Inc.

66. Wold, Herman. 1968. Model building and scientific method: a graphic introduction, in Model Building in Economics and Industry. by CEIR, Inc. and CEIR, Ltd.

67. Wold, Herman. 1967. Time as the realm of forecasting, in Interdisciplinary Perspectives of Time, Edited by E.M. Weyer and R. Fisher, New York: The New York Academy of Science, p. 525-560.

List of Symbols

b	true parameter vector
c	velocity of propagation of disturbances through system
d	decision vector or set of possible alternatives
d*	optimal alternative or decision
e	error of estimation
f	circular frequency of the phenomenon
f	volume rate of lateral outflow per unit channel length per unit channel width
h	scour depth for bridge pier
iae	integral absolute error
ise	integral square error
k	integer value of $t = k_\Delta t$
ℓ	integer index for number of L input-output pairs
m	sample mean
mse	mean square error
n	Manning roughness coefficient
n(k)	additive measurement noise

12 .25

p	real world
p(y/b)	probability density function of the data y given the true parameter set b
q	volume rate of flow per unit width
q	model (appears only on one page)
q(b)	probability density function of b
r	volume rate of lateral inflow per unit channel length per unit channel width
s	system
s^2	sample variance
t	continuous time
u	lag in continuous time
x	measured input signal
$\underline{x}$	dimensions of the process
y	measured output signal
y_M	model output signal
z(k)	state vector
E [ ]	expectation operator
EVSI	expected value of sample information
F	degrees of freedom
H(f)	frequence response function
K	number of values in discrete time series
L	number of input-output pairs used in estimation
M	number of variables
N	number of sources of information (equations and data on parameters)
$P\{(\beta(k)-b)=o)\}$	probability of parameter error
Q_e	ordinate of estimated hydrograph
Q_o	ordinate of observed hydrograph
R(d,b)	Bayes risk
S	set of systems
S_o	bed slope
T	time constant of system
U	Theil's inequality coefficient
V	loss function
VSI	value of sample information
XOL	expected opportunity loss
XXOL	expected expected opportunity loss
Z(t)	white noise input

12.26

β	estimate of b
$\Gamma_{XX}(f)$	spectrum of X(t) process
λ	wave length of phenomenon
μ_T	true mean value function
$\rho_{XX}(u)$	autocorrelation function of X(t) process
σ_T^2	true variance

DISCUSSION

M. HINO

As Prof. Kisiel said, the identification is a problem of fundamental importance in water resources systems. I would like to introduce my idea to the solution of identification problem together with an example.*) After some discussions with Prof. Kisiel yesterday, it is concluded that my idea may be entirely a new one although the technique is very popular.

This brief note is to describe an attempt to "Dynamic Programming Approach to the Identification Problems of Nonlinear System".

(1) A hydrologic system is described by a second order nonlinear ordinary differential equation, (Prasad (1967) model)

$$K_2 \frac{d^2Q}{dt^2} + K_1 m Q^m \frac{dQ}{dt} + Q = I \tag{1}$$

in which Q is the runoff rate, I is the rainfall, t is the time, and K_1, K_2, and m are constants or control variables. Equation (1) may be rewritten as

$$\frac{dQ}{dt} = P$$
$$\frac{dP}{dt} = -\frac{K_1 m}{K_2} Q^{m-1} \cdot P - \frac{1}{K_2} Q + \frac{1}{K_2} I \tag{2}$$

(2) The difference form of the above system equation yields equations (3) and (4)

$$Y_{N-1} = Y_N - Z_N(\Delta t/2) - Z_{N-1}(\Delta t/2) + (O_N - O_{N-1}) - \dot{O}_N \Delta t$$
$$= h_1(Y_N, Z_N; X_N, W_N) \tag{3}$$

---

*) Abstract from "On the problem of identification and adaptive control of hydrologic system" to be published in the Proceedings of Conference on Hydraulics, Feb. 12-13 (1971); Also Tech. Rep. No. 9, Dep. Civil Eng., Tokyo Inst. Tech.

$$Z_{N-1} = Z_N + \{X_N(Y_N + O_N)^{m-1} \cdot (Z_N + \dot{O}_N) + W_N(Y_N + O_N - I_N)\}\Delta t + (\dot{O}_N - \dot{O}_{N-1})$$

$$\cdot = h_2(Y_N, Z_N; X_N, W_N)$$

(4)

where $Y_N = Q_N - O_N$ and $Z_N = P_N - \dot{O}_N$ represent errors of system output from observed values at $t = N\Delta t$, and

$$X = K_1 m/K_2$$

$$W = 1/K_1$$

(5)

(m may be chosen as a control variable, however, for the reason of simplicity, it is considered a constant)

(3) The essential point of the discusser's idea of dynamic programming formulation is to consider the values of K_1 and K_2 to be time variant and control variables. As iteration proceeds, the range of variation is limited within a narrower range converging to constant values. Then the problem is reduced to a variational one.

$$J = \int_0^T Y^2(t)\ dt \rightarrow Min.$$

As result of the optimal principle, a recurrence formula is obtained,

$$f_N(Y, Z) = \underset{\substack{X \\ W}}{Min} [G(Y, Z; X, W) + f_{N-1} (h_1(Y, Z, X, W), h_2(Y, Z; X, W)]$$

(6)

in which $f_M(Y, Z)$; minimum of J at N step attained starting from initial states (Y, Z)--result of optimal decision for multiple decision process of N-order.

G(Y, Z; X, W) : evaluation function; in this case ($= Y_{N-1}^2$),

$h_i(Y, Z; X, W)$: resulting state after initial decision (eqs. (3) & (4)).

(4) Figure A shows an example of calculation of nonlinear system parameter identification where only the second iteration is sufficient for convergence of control variables, K_1 and K_2.

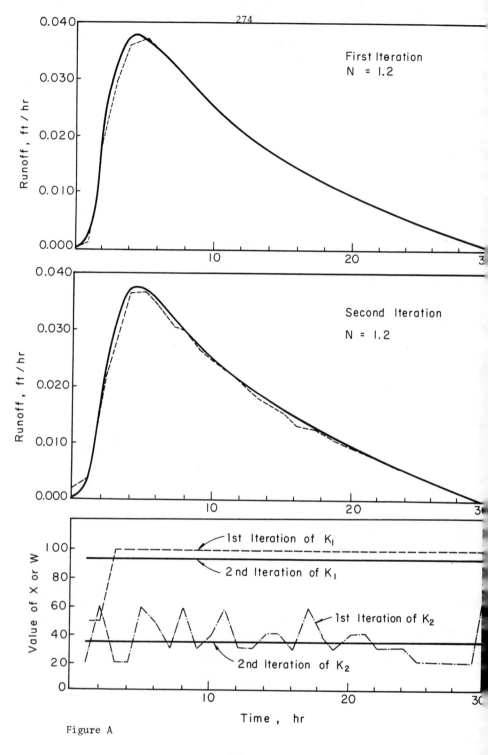

Figure A

12.29

J. PAUL RILEY

1. A very interesting review (survey) paper.

2. There are two basic "filtering stages between models and the real world.
    (a) our interpretation of the real world which frequently is based on our data collection or monitoring systems.
    (b) our ability to represent our interpretation in model form.

Your paper deals with the second stage, but we should never lose sight of the first stage in model development.

Y. TAKAHASI

What is the criterion to assume the hydrological model, as lumped or distributed, linear or non-linear, etc? Does it depend on the nature, the accuracy of the aim of the study in practice?

How to think the applicability and the limitation of decision and systems theory to hydrology? In what kind of hydrological problem Bayesian decision theory could apply, except the case of the cost of uncertainty of the bridge piers? In determining soci-economical factors, is it likely to judge subjectively?

V. YEVJEVICH

The central uncertainity involving mathematical modeling and the estimation of parameters in hydrology comes from sampling errors because of limited sample sizes, though random and systematic errors in data, as well as other sources of uncertainties, are usually also present in modeling and estimation.

When considering the use of the Bayesian approach in hydrology through the use of the Bayesian theorem or the formula of hypotheses, the crucial test is how the a priori probabilities, which serve for the computation of the a posteriori probabilities, are obtained. If the a priori probabilities are estimated from past observations, with a known degree of accuracy, the Bayesian approach may be considered objective. However, if the a priori probabilities are hypothesized, by intuition or assumption, this approach may become completely subjective, with extensive gray area between these two extremes.

The use of the split-sample approach in hydrology merits a much larger application than is given by the profession at present. The model selection, parameter estimation, and tests of hypotheses are carried out on one part of the split sample, then again tested on the remaining part, and if the model is accepted, the parameters are reestimated for the total sample size. Usually, the unanswered question is where to split the sample.

RESPONSE BY C. C. KISIEL

The response to discussion by M. Hino is as follows.

The author is to be commended for his efforts to apply optimal control theory to an identification problem in hydrology.

To relate back to my paper, the J-function that is minimized is in reality the quadratic loss function in continuous time given in my paper in discrete form as Equation (3).

It would be of interest to determine if the optimally estimated parameters K_1 and K_2 vary from each input-output data pair applied to the model. The stability of K_1 and K_2 from each data pair will determine the model's utility for similar watershed conditions.

The response to discussion by J. Paul Riley is as follows.

In my judgment my paper is a mixture of new results and a survey of previous work both in hydrology and elsewhere. The new results include: (a) a theoretical approach to judging when lumped models are adequate approximations to distributed systems, (b) clarification of the issues involved in the calibration and validation of hydrologic models, and (c) presentation of the role of decision theory in modeling and parameter estimation. Imbedded in the second point of the discussion is the distinction between model calibration and validation. I believe that too often model calibration (curve-fitting or model matching) has been wrongly equated to model validation. Theory established or "validated" under laboratory conditions is not necessarily transferrable in a direct manner to field conditions. Furthermore, because predictions by deterministic watershed models are for _future_ operating conditions, some measure of predictive reliability of such models should be defined and computed. In general, this is not being done at present. One of the conclusions of my paper is that, in the discharging of this responsibility, hydrologists should carefully evaluate the social or economic losses associated with model predictions. This goes beyond classical sensitivity analysis. Obviously, model predictions for periods of 15 minutes to 50 years are put forward to help in the solution of human problems and not to satisfy the hydrologist's ego. In the face of many uncertainties confronting the hydrologist, validation of models is a continuous iterative but never-ending process of intellectual activity.

I disagree that my paper focuses solely on "our ability to represent our interpretation in model form." As discussed above, the paper devoted considerable space to the problem of model validation. At the heart of validation is "our interpretation of the real world which frequently is based on our data collection or monitoring systems." My review of the philosophical positions on model building is expressly pursued to demonstrate the non-uniqueness and subjective nature of one's interpretation. If Professor Riley suggests that there are alternates to the use of models as the end products of the interpretive stage, I cannot agree because the alternates would be intuitive word models that are not necessarily communicated to others in an unambiguous and unbiased fashion. There is more than one way to interpret the same set of data and evidence of this diversity of interpretation is the current proliferation of hydrologic models -- even for the same managerial goal. Universities and government agencies develop their respective but different models; the outsider or young student or hydrologist comes along and may wonder what difference does it make! In my paper I conclude that decision analysis, as have other recent authors, is one way to ascertain if a chosen model does in fact make a difference in a given managerial context.

Some of the psychophysical aspects of our interpretation of the real world have been reviewed in an earlier paper[1] by this author. I believe that these issues are at the heart of the problem of diversity in hydrologic modeling. Reduction of biases in hydrologic models requires an honest interaction and a focus on the management aspects of the modeling problem.

12.31

The response on the first question by Y. Takahasi is as follows.

The basic message conveyed in my paper is that accuracy is not to be pursued as an end in itself. What is more important is the social and/or economic importance of that accuracy. This is incorporated into the loss function discussed in the paper. I believe that many of us have been doing this subjectively. But there is a need to formalize the process.

The paper also presents some criteria for choosing lumped as against distributed models. But each hydrologic situation must be evaluated on its own merits both from a scientific and economic standpoint. The paper only discusses the choice in scientific terms. Even here much research remains to be done. However, note that level pool routing is based on lumped models and that distributed models of flood routing in river channels allow greater generality than heretofore possible with lumped models. Distributed models of aquifers are necessary for local planning of water supply facilities whereas lumped models of aquifers allow for only mean-value or regional planning of water allocation to multiple users.

The criterion for using a linear or a nonlinear system model would once again depend on the sensitivity of the final answer to the chosen model. Preferably, the choice should be made on economic grounds and not just on the basis of "goodness of scientific fit."

In all of the above one should recognize that we need much more research to discern the relative importance of model choice (or error), lumping, linearity, time-invariance of system behavior, input functions and sampling errors on the overall prediction.

The response on the second question by Y. Takahasi is as follows.

As with all theory, the above theories are efforts to rationalize the thought processes in hydrology. The presumption is that thereby our intuition and subsequent acquisition of new experience is strengthened. Systems theory is increasingly put forward as an efficient way for organizing and transmitting human knowledge about systems between disciplines. Among other things, it also focuses on evolving complex systems and on inverse problems and their approximate solution. As with all theory, it cannot quantify that which is not quantifiable.

As indicated in the paper, decision theory promotes dialogue between diverse interests, provides an estimate of the cost of uncertainty (Bayes risk), and helps us to judge how much information to get on the hydrologic system. Much research remains in its development as a routine tool in hydrology and water resources. Its use, however, is not to be limited to bridge piers. Our research has also focused on its use in the design of flood levees and in aquifer modeling. It could be used to evaluate uncertainties in spillway design, study of nonstationary processes, design of hydrologic data networks, foundation design, water supply estimates, natural recharge estimates, business, marketing, medical diagnosis, population growth, etc. - in short, wherever uncertainty in model parameters arises, whether the model is of the input function, system, or output function. Limitations on its use arise from the need for numerical integration of the Bayes risk because conjugate distributions do not exist for virtually all two or three parameter probability distributions of interest to hydrologists. Also, only univariate objective or loss functions are at present considered; multiple uses for the same hydrologic data have not as yet been formally analyzed. Good physical models and loss functions are necessary to get "accurate" estimates of the Bayes risk. In short, much more research is necessary before the tool can be applied on a routine basis.

1. Kisiel, C. C., Mathematical methodology in hydrology, Volume 1 of Proceedings (World of Hydrology), Edited by Ven Te Chow, International Seminar of Hydrology Professors, Urbana, Illinois, 1969.

The response to discussion by V. Yevjevich is as follows.

1. It is <u>not</u> entirely clear that the central uncertainty in mathematical modeling and estimation of parameters comes from sampling errors. This implies that perfect sampling would be the solution to all of our hydrologic problems. As pointed out in my paper, Heisenberg's uncertainty principle has relevance in macroscopic measurements: the act of measuring modifies the system being observed -- the denser the sampling network, the greater the disturbance to the system. Obviously for economic, logical and logistical reasons we cannot ever achieve perfect sampling except under very special conditions.

There is an implied suggestion that large samples will resolve our modeling and estimation problems. But in the present and projected social contexts in which hydrologists must function will large samples be available at every future design or decision point in space? I believe not. The hydrologist, engineer or planner must decide with what information he has on hand at the time the decision is to be made, and <u>not with what he ought to have.</u> After some decision analysis, he may conclude to wait and get more data before making the final decision.

My paper suggests that decision analysis offers the best formalism of handling uncertainty engendered by "inadequate" information.

2. My response to the second paragraph naturally follows from the above. Because complete information is utopian, then hydrologists must rely on subjective knowledge or past experience. In the Bayesian viewpoint, prior probabilities must in part arise from such subjectivity. If prior probabilities are to be estimated solely from the data and to be estimated with a known degree of accuracy then by implication the hydrologist chooses (a) to discard his subjective knowledge about parameter and model uncertainty, (b) to rely on large samples to generate certainty or confidence in his parameters, and (c) to divorce himself from the decision context in which the data has meaning. In my view, it is doubtful that we can achieve complete objectivity in both deterministic and probabilistic models of environmental or hydrologic systems. Certainly, subjectively "estimated" prior probabilities are subject to error but one can perform a study on the sensitivity of the final answer to choice of prior knowledge. But the Bayesian approach gives a consistent approach to combining data and subjective knowledge. Its use in a decision framework has the potential for giving us a consistent basis for action (both scientific and managerial) in the face of uncertainty. However, there is no guarantee that computation of Bayes risk will lead to errorless or correct recommendations. I believe that the Bayesian approach is very consistent with the practice of zero-base hydrology in regions where virtually no measurement of the hydrologic system exists.

3. I agree that the split-sample approach is very basic. I would add that it should be mandatory in hydrologic practice. It is part of the model validation problem. I see no satisfactory answer, except in a decision-theoretic framework, to the unanswered question as to where to split the sample. In other words, what difference does it make in a social context?

Some hydrologists argue that the split-sample approach is not possible because the sample size is so small to begin with. Irrespective, the responsibility of validation still remains and decision analysis may be the only recourse in evaluating the model predictions -- that is, an economic analysis of the consequences of overestimation and underestimation with respect to unknown true parameters.

United States-Japan Bi-Lateral Seminar in Hydrology

Honolulu, January 1971

EFFECTS OF MOVEMENT OF PRECIPITATATION AREA

UPON RUNOFF PHENOMENA

by Yutaka TAKAHASI
Professor, Dept. of Civil Engineering, University of Tokyo, Tokyo, JAPAN

Katsumi MUSHIAKE
Assistant, Dept. of Civil Engineering, University of Tokyo, Tokyo, JAPAN

Takeshi HASHIMOTO
Engineer, La. of Hydrology, Public Works Research Institute, Ministry of Construction, Tokyo, JAPAN

Synopsis

Model simulation of streamflow hydrographs usually assumes that rainfall is distributed uniformly over the watershed. But, in reality, rainfall may vary considerably in time and in space. For floods in small river basins (less than several hundred square kilometers) which have been noted in recent years in Japan, effects of the spatial distribution and movement of precipitation storm cells especially cannot be ignored.
This paper reports on research studying the effects of the distribution of precipitation and its movement upon storm hydrographs. The use of a hydraulic runoff model is applied as the method of runoff analysis. The model is solved numerically through the use of the digital computer. Studies about effects of the various characteristics of storm area upon flood hydrographs are carried out by means of numerical experiments on two kinds of simplified catchment model. At the same time, several properties of the model catchment are studied. Characteristics of rain storms, such as scale, distribution, direction, and velocity, are investigated through analyses of hydrological data in the Kanna River Basin. Finally, comparisons are made between the computed and the observed hydrographs caused by a storm passing over the Kanna River Basin.

13.1

1. Introduction

In most linear models for runoff analysis that use the unit hydrograph method, the following basic assumptions are made[1] : (a) the input and output parameters are considered as "lumped", (b) the relations between input and output are time invariant, and (c) watersheds act as linear systems.

Such simplification for runoff phenomena has been widely adopted in the United States and in Europe. But it is dependent upon characteristics of watersheds and of the rainfall as to whether the above assumptions hold or not. In Japan many studies have been devoted to examine their applicabilities to a variety of watersheds. Gradually, it became evident that such treatment was hardly applicable in our country, where geomorphological and hydrometeorological conditions are extremely different from those in the United States.

Several methods of runoff analysis, based on the specific conditions in Japan, have been developed. For example, Iwagaki's method of characteristics[2], Sugawara's storage type model[3] and Kimura's method of storage function[4] have been published. In those studies, a major attempt was made to construct models of the runoff process by modifying assumptions (b) and (c) above. Concerning the first assumption (a), average depth of rainfall over the watershed is normally accepted as lumped input in any method.

Rainfall intensity actually varies considerably from place to place in the watershed. Although it may be adequate to use a lumped model if rainfall is distributed uniformly and covers the entire watershed, the same treatment cannot be adopted for runoff due to local intensive storms which have caused disastrous floods in small watersheds in recent years. It is intuitively known that characteristics of floods caused by local intensive storms in Japan differ considerably, due, in part, to the distribution of precipitation. Therefore, studies concerning the relative importance of assumption (a) and its modification should also be conducted.

This paper investigates the effects of the distribution and movement of precipitation upon flood hydrographs. A hydraulic runoff model is used as the method of runoff analysis and numerical solutions are made using a digital computer.

In the next chapter, the effects of various characteristics of precipitation patterns upon storm hydrographs are studied by means of numerical experiments utilizing two kinds of simplified catchment models. At the same time, analysis is made on the effects of some of the properties of the models. In chapter 3, characteristics of precipitation storms, such as scale, distribution, direction and velocity are studied using available hydrological data for the Kanna River Basin. Comparisons are then made between the computed and the observed hydrographs, caused by a storm moving over the Kanna River Basin.

1) Amorocho, J: Measures of the linearity of hydrologic systems, Jour. of Geo. Res. Vol. 68, No.8, pp.2237-2249, April, 1963.
2) Iwagaki, Y. : Fundamental studies on the runoff analysis by characteristics, Kyoto Univ. Disaster Prevention Res. Inst. Bull.10, Kyoto, Japan, December,1955.
3) Sugawara, M. and F. Maruyama : A method of revision of the river discharge by means of a rainfall model, Symposia Darcy, Intern. Assoc. Sci. Hydrology, Pub.42, Vol.3, pp.71-76, 1956.
4) Kimura, T : Flood runoff analysis by storage function, August, 1961.

2. Effects of movement of precipitation area over catchment models

2-1. Method of analysis

Various runoff models may be used to study the effects of variation in spatial distribution of precipitation. For example, Sugawara's storage type model connected in parallel which receives different inputs at the top vessels, or the unit hydrograph method which is applied to divided watersheds, could be adopted. But, from a practical point of view, it is very difficult to decide on the coefficient of each capillary tube, in the case of the storage type model, or on the unit graphs of sub-watersheds, in the case of the unit hydrograph method, because the rates of precipitation and discharge are rarely observed for each sub-watershed.

In the present study, the hydraulic runoff model is used, in which runoff phenomena are approximated as "unsteady flow in open channels with lateral inflow". This model has the following advantages: (1) the spatial distribution of precipitation can be reasonably estimated in comparison with the other models, (2) non-linearity of the catchment and stream flow is accounted for and, moreover, (3) the propagation of flood waves is easily followed along the stream. On the other hand, it has some of the following difficulties: (1) how to make the model of the actual watershed, (2) how to estimate the equivalent-roughness coefficient, and (3) how to separate losses from the precipitation.

Here, in order to investigate general effects of movement of storm area, numerical experiments are carried out for two catchment models as shown in figure 1; (1) a single slope model and (II) a combined V-shaped model. The single slope model is composed of a rectangular plane representing the catchment and a channel representing the main river. The combined V-shaped model is made up of a main channel (river) and ten tributary catchments which have a small channel (tributary) between two planes forming a V-shape. The overall length and width of the model catchments are 40 km and 5 km, respectively. The width of each sub-catchment in Model (II) is 4 km.

It is assumed that Manning's law can be applied to the catchment flow, and that the equation of steady flow can be used as the equation of motion. Strictly speaking, however, the equation of motion should also involve unsteady or non-uniform terms. The validity of such modeling assumptions for simulations of runoff phenomena was verified for actual river basins by Ueda[5].

The equations of continuity and motion for the catchment flow can be written as follows:

$$\partial h / \partial t + \partial q / \partial x = r \tag{1}$$

and

$$q = \frac{1}{n_c} \cdot h^{5/3} s_c^{1/2} \tag{2}$$

where h is the water depth in the channel, q is the discharge rate per unit width, r is the rate of the distributed inflow per unit area due to effective precipitation, n_c is Manning's roughness coefficient of the catchment, s_c is the slope of the catchment, x is the distance measured downstream from the top of the catchment, and t is the time.

Assuming the channel cross-section to be a parabola expressed as $ph=b^2$ (where b is the top width of flow and p is the coefficient), the equations may be rewritten as follows:

5) Ueda, T : Fundamental Study on the relation between precipitation and runoff, August, 1961.

For the flow of the tributary stream,

$$\partial A_B / \partial t + \partial Q_B / \partial x = q_I \qquad (3)$$

and

$$Q_B = A_B / n_B \cdot R^{2/3} S_B^{1/2} \qquad (4)$$

for the flow of the main river,

$$\partial A_R / \partial t + \partial Q_R / \partial x = q_{II} \qquad (5)$$

and

$$Q_R = A_R / n_R \cdot R^{2/3} s_R^{1/2} \qquad (6)$$

Where A is the flow cross-sectional area, Q is the discharge rate, q_I is the rate of the distributed inflow from the catchment, q_{II} is the rate of the distributed inflow from the catchment in Model (I), or the inflow rate from a tributary in Model (II), n is Manning's roughness coefficient, R is the hydraulic radius, s is the slope, and x is the distance measured downstream along the tributary or the river. The sub-scripts B and R denote the tributary and the river, respectively.

The relation between the hydraulic radius R and the flow cross-sectional area A is

$$R = \frac{2}{3} \left(\frac{3}{4} \cdot \frac{A_B}{\sqrt{P_B}} \right)^{2/3} \Big/ \left\{ 1 + \frac{2}{3 P_B} \left(\frac{3}{4} \cdot \frac{A_B}{\sqrt{P_B}} \right)^{2/3} \right\} \qquad (7)$$

for a tributary

and

$$R = \frac{2}{3} \left(\frac{3}{4} \cdot \frac{A_R}{\sqrt{P_R}} \right)^{2/3} \qquad (8)$$

for a river.

In order to solve the above differential equations numerically by a digital computer, the above equations are rewritten in the form of finite difference equations as follows:

$$h(i,\tau) = h(i,\tau-1) - \{ q(i,\tau-1) - q(i-1,\tau-1) - r(i,\tau)\Delta x \} \Delta t / \Delta x \qquad (1')$$

$$q(i,\tau) = 1/n_c \cdot h^{5/3}(i,\tau) \, s_c^{1/2} \qquad (2')$$

Where i is the index along the x-dimension and τ is the index in time.

Given the boundary and initial conditions, the water depth $h(i,\tau)$ is calculated by Eq. (1') and the discharge rate q (i,τ) by Eq. (2').

Similarly, Eqs. (3),(4) and Eqs. (5), (6) may be rewritten and solved for the appropriate variables.

2-2. Properties of catchment models used in the study

In order to assess the influences of variability of each model parameter, hydrographs using various values of parameters were calculated and compared with each other in both catchment models, using a uniform rainfall intensity of 20 mm/hr and duration of one hour.

13.4

The following parameters are involved in Model (I):

s_c : slope of catchment
n_c : equivalent-roughness coefficient of catchment
s_R : slope of river-bed
n_R : roughness coefficient of river-bed
p_R : coefficient determining river channel section

and in Model (II):

s_B : slope of tributary stream channel
n_B : roughness coefficient of tributary stream channel
p_B : coefficient determining tributary channel section

Models (I) and (II) have five and eight parameters, respectively. However, the number of factors affecting the hydrographs is reduced to three in Model (I) ($\sqrt{s_c}/n_c$, $\sqrt{s_R}/n_R$ and p_R) and five in Model (II) ($\sqrt{s_c}/n_c$, $\sqrt{s_B}/n_B$, $\sqrt{s_R}/n_R$, p_B and p_R) because slope s and roughness coefficient n tend to interact.

Figure 2 shows computed hydrographs at the outlet of model catchment (I). In figure 2 (a), the ratio $\sqrt{s_c}/n_c$ is varied while the other parameters are fixed as follows:
$\sqrt{s_R}/n_R$ = 2.86 (s_R =1/100, n_R =0.035) and p_R =50. In Figure 2 (b), the ratio $\sqrt{s_R}/n_R$ is varied and the others are fixed; $\sqrt{s_c}/n_c$ =2.24 (s_c =1/5, n_c =0.2) and p_R =50. Figure 3 presents the relations of peak-discharge rate and peak-arrival time to the ratio $\sqrt{s}/n$. It is found from these results that the variation of the ratio $\sqrt{s_c}/n_c$ has the more dominant influence upon the peak-discharge rate. Three hydrographs with the variation of p_R are given in figure 2 (c). The small variation of p_R does not significantly affect runoff hydrographs.

For Model (II), hydrographs at the outlet of each tributary catchment are considered in the same way as the entire catchment in Model (I). Figure 4 indicates the hydrographs for different values of ratio $\sqrt{s_c}/n_c$ and the following fixed parameters; $\sqrt{s_B}/n_B$ =5.59 (s_B =1/20, n_B =0.04) and p_B =10. The numerical experiments in which the ratio $\sqrt{s_B}/n_B$ is varied and the others are fixed ($\sqrt{s_c}/n_c$ =2.24, p_B =10) were also carried out. Figure 5 indicates the relation of peak-discharge rate and peak-arrival time at the outlet of a tributary catchment to ratio $\sqrt{s}/n$. The results show that the variation of the ratio $\sqrt{s_c}/n_c$ has much greater influence on runoff than that of the ratio $\sqrt{s_B}/n_B$.

Finally, for the fixed values of ratio $\sqrt{s}/n$ ($\sqrt{s_c}/n_c$ =2.24, $\sqrt{s_B}/n_B$ =5.59), hydrographs for three values of p_B (p_B =10,20,30) were computed and compared with each other. In each case of p_B =10,20 and 30, the peak-discharge rate is 33.0,32.9 and 32.9 m^3/sec respectively and the peak-arrival time is 75, 75 and 80 minutes, respectively. Thus the effect of variation in p_B is minimal.

2-3. Results of numerical experiments

Numerical experiments using a digital computer were performed to investigate general effects of the movement of precipitation area on runoff, using a precipitation area which has the triangular distribution and moves in direction parallel to the river. The precipitation intensity at a given storm center is assumed to be 50 mm/hr. The storm duration of one hour serves as an index to represent the scale of the storm area. The following four alternate precipitation storm velocities were used: 20 m/s (72 km/hr), 10 m/s (36 km/hr), 5 m/s (18 km/hr) and 2.5 m/s (9 km/hr). Each precipitation area is assumed to move either from upstream to downstream direction or from downstream to upstream.

In order to take into account the movement of precipitation area in Model (I), it is necessary to divide the model catchment in the direction

perpendicular to the river and give the appropriate inputs to each
segment of the larger catchment. The number of divisions has a considerable effect on the shape of the computed hydrographs. In general,
the lower the storm velocity is, the greater effect it causes. The
result of comparison of the computed hydrographs for various numbers of
divisions shows that almost identical hydrographs are derived when the
number of segments is more than ten. Therefore, the number of divisions
of the model catchment (I) was chosen as ten.

Figure 6 (a)-(d) indicates the results of numerical experiments for
Model (I). In each figure, two hydrographs are compared: the first is
due to precipitation area moving downstream and the other is due to a
storm pattern moving upstream. In general, the peak-discharge rate is
higher when the precipitation area moves downstream. The peak-arrival
time occurs later when the precipitation area is moving upstream.
However, when the storm velocity is high, the two hydrographs do not show
much difference. As the speed becomes lower, the difference between two
hydrographs becomes more apparent. It depends to some extent upon the
relation between the storm velocity of precipitation area and the speed of
runoff from upstream to downstream

In figure 7 (a)-(d), the results for Model (II) are shown. The
description of results concerning Model (I) is equally applicable to
Model (II).

From the view-point of modeling of the actual watershed, it is
necessary to notice that hydrographs for Model (I) are remarkably different from those for Model (II). A flat peak is more apt to occur in the
case of Model (I) because the catchment flow, which defines the flow to
the stream on a plane, is considerably slow compared to the streamflow.
It is possible to obtain hydrographs similar to those for Model (II) using
Model (I) by adjusting the equivalent-roughness coefficient. However,
in doing this, the physical interpretations of equivalent roughness become
ambiguous.

3. Characteristics of storm movement for an actual river basin and its
effects upon flood hydrographs.

3-1. Characteristics of precipitation area in the Kanna River Basin

To investigate the characteristics of movement of precipitation
area, the authors have taken precipitation data of the Kanna River Basin
as an example. The Kanna River, which is one tributary of the Tone River
passing through the Kanto Plain, has a drainage area of 374 km^2 and is
70 km in length.

The major reason for choosing this basin for study is the high
quality of hydrological data with self-recording precipitation and
discharge data for the years from 1948 to 1960.

The analysis of precipitation data proceeded as follows:
(a) record 10 min, 20 min, and 1 hour precipitation values from the
self-recording precipitation gage.
(b) develop isohyetal maps.
(c) define the movement of precipitation area,
1) from the isohyetal maps. (Fig. 8)
2) from precipitation data of each station (Fig. 9)
(d) determine the scale of precipitation area.
From the above analytical results of precipitation data, the rainfall
pattern is divided into three groups from a viewpoint of the movement
of precipitation storm area:
(I) an area consisting of a convective precipitation.
(II) rainfall which has the same effect as the movement of

13.6

precipitation, macroscopically, because of temporal
variation in area distribution of precipitation.

(III) rainfall which cannot discriminate the precipitation area, because of big scale of precipitation area relative to a given
basin.

Figure 8 shows the example of rainfall pattern (I) in the Kanna
River Basin. This pattern of rainfall has about 10 km in diameter and
the velocity of precipitation area varies from 5 to 10 km/hr. The
precipitation of pattern (I) can be approximated by triangular
distribution.

In the Kanna River Basin, the stream discharge caused by rainfall
pattern (I) is generally rather small under 100 m^3/sec. The rainfall
record at each station is shown in figure 9 from which the movement of
a storm-rainfall center could be seen. In this case, a storm center
moved apparently from downstream to upstream in the catchment within
5 and a half hours.

To determine the areal distribution of precipitation for this storm,
the ratios of the hourly precipitation at each station to the precipitation at a station where the maximum value is recorded are plotted as a
function of the distance from the maximum-value recorded station
(Fig. 10). These values are found from the isohyetal maps for every hour
increment.

The average curve for eleven curves in figure 10 is shown by curve
(a) in figure 11. Noticing that curve (a) shows about half the value of
the maximum rainfall intensity in 10 km, the distribution form is
represented by exponential function or normal distribution in curve (b)
and curve (c), respectively. The exponential function for curve (b) is
expressed as follows,

$$R\ (X) = R_o\ e^{-kx} \tag{9}$$

Where R_o is the maximum rainfall intensity in mm/hr in the precipitation
area, x is distance from the storm center, and k is a constant value
0.03.

3-2. Comparison of computed with the observed hydrograph

The catchment model of the Kanna River Basin is constructed, and the
hydrograph is computed for the rainfall caused by moving precipitation
area and compared with the observed one. Some consideration is given
to the applicability of this runoff model to the actual conditions in the
river basin.

First, a basin model was constructed. The natural river basin has
many tributary streams. To what extent the complicated basin could be
simplified, is dependent on the scale of precipitation area. By studying the topographical maps of scale 1:50,000, seventeen tributary
catchments and main catchments excluding them were taken as components
of the Kanna River Basin Model. A tributary catchment was represented
by a simple V-shaped model, and a main catchment was substituted for a
rectangular plane connecting directly with the main stream.

The slopes of catchment models and channels are estimated from the
topographical maps. Manning's roughness coefficients for the main river
and the tributaries are determined from prior knowledge and are estimated
as n_R =0.03 and n_B =0.05, respectively. The coefficients p_R and p_B
are 100 and 10, respectively. As for the equivalent-roughness
coefficient of the catchment, there is no sufficient information to
determine it. For this reason, it is assigned a value of 0.9 by the
method of trial and error.

The rainfall on 4th August in 1958 (see Fig. 8) and the corresponding runoff are used for the present analysis. This rainfall was caused by a frontal thunderstorm..The time distribution of the precipitation is represented approximately by a triangle.

The separation of effective precipitation is of particular importance in the hydraulic runoff model. Because properties of infiltration and the other losses do not become so apparent to date in the Kanna River Basin, the effective precipitation is determined in the simplest manner by multiplying the runoff coefficient by a constant value which is determined by the method of trial and error.

Figure 12 compares the computed and observed hydrographs for this storm. It is found that the peak and the rising part of the curve are nearly identical. The agreement between computed and observed hydrographs was not so good on the recession limb of the hydrograph.

There is no obvious explanation for this one example of model application. It may be possible to reduce this disagreement, if the infiltration of surface water after the rain ceases was taken into account. Such infiltration is not estimated in this study, and the losses are estimated in determining effective precipitation. In any case, the infiltration undoubtedly plays a significant role in the hydraulic runoff model.

4. Conclusions

From the result of the numerical experiments over two kinds of simplified catchment models, it was found that the movement of precipitation area had a significant effect upon the resultant storm hydrograph. When storm velocity is low and the precipitation area moves downstream, the peak-discharge rate is higher and the peak-arrival time is earlier than when it moves upstream.

In cases where the storm velocity is high, the two hydrographs resulting from the precipitation area moving upstream and from its moving downstream do not show much difference. As the storm velocity declines, the difference between two hydrographs becomes more distinguishable in this case study. Concerning the latter condition, it depends upon the relation between the storm velocity of precipitation area and the speed of runoff from upstream to downstream.

Through analyses of hydrological data in the Kanna River Basin, for the rainfall of pattern (I), the distribution form is represented by a triangle for which the base length is approximately 10 km. For the rainfall of pattern (II), it is represented by an exponential function or normal distribution function.

The catchment model of the Kanna River Basin was constructed and the flood hydrograph was computed using rainfall from a moving storm area. The agreement between the computed and observed hydrographs is fairly good for the rising hydrograph limb and peak flow.

Acknowledgment

The authors are much indebted to Dr. T. Takenouchi, Professor of Tokyo Institute of Technology, and Dr. M. Okuta, Chief of Typhoon Research Laboratory, Meteorological Research Institute, for valuable suggestions for the study. This study was initiated and greatly assisted by Mr. M. Furuki, civil engineer with the Kinki Regional Bureau of Construction, Ministry of Construction. Dr. T. Kinoshita, Chief of Laboratory of Hydrology, Public Works Research Institute, contributed much valuable discussion and helped with the numerical experiments.

13.8

LIST OF SYMBOLS

A_B	flow cross-sectional area of tributary stream channel
A_R	flow cross-sectional area of main river channel
h	water depth in catchment
k	exponential constant
n_c	equivalent roughness coefficient of catchment
n_B	roughness coefficient of tributary stream channel
n_R	roughness coefficient of river-bed
P_B	coefficient determining tributary channel section
P_R	coefficient determining river channel section
q	discharge rate per unit width of catchment
q_I	rate of distributed inflow from catchment to tributary channel
q_{II}	rate of distributed inflow from catchment to main channel in Model (I), or inflow rate from a tributary to main channel in Model (II)
Q_B	discharge rate of tributary stream channel
Q_R	discharge rate of main river channel
r	rate of distributed inflow per unit area due to effective precipitation
R	hydraulic radius
$R(X)$	rainfall intensity at distance X from storm center
R_0	maximum rainfall intensity in precipitation area
s_c	slope of catchment
s_B	slope of tributary stream channel
s_R	slope of river-bed
x	distance measured downstream from top of catchment
t	time
i	index along x-dimension
τ	index in time

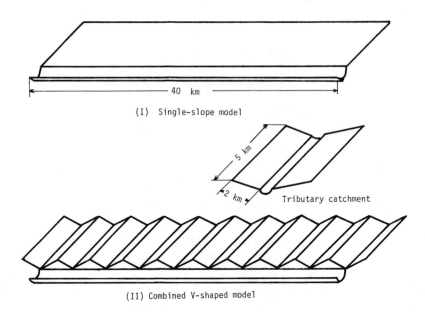

(I) Single-slope model

2 km →   Tributary catchment

(II) Combined V-shaped model

Fig. 1 Catchment model

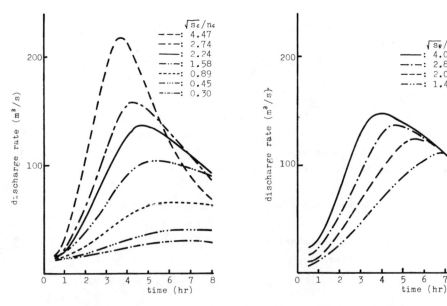

Fig. 2 (a) Comparison of computed
hydrographs in Model (I) for
variation of ratio $\sqrt{s_c}/n_c$

Fig. 2 (b) Comparison of computed
hydrographs in Model (I) for
variation of ratio $\sqrt{s_r}/n_r$

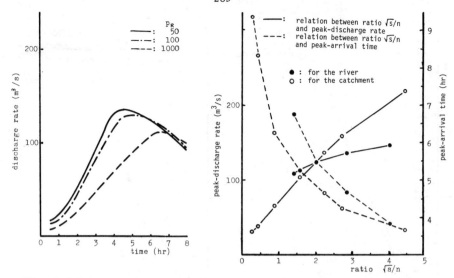

Fig. 2 (c) Comparison of computed
hydrographs in Model (I) for three
values of p_r

Fig. 3 Relations of peak-discharge
rate and peak-arrival time to ratio
$\sqrt{s}/n$

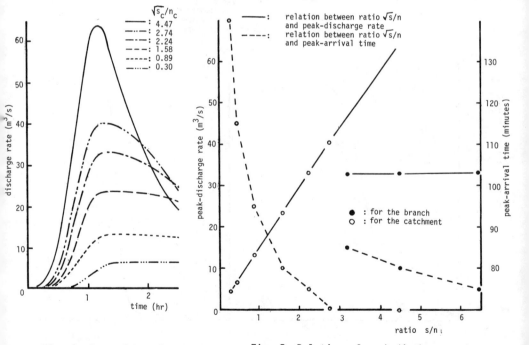

Fig. 4 Comparison of
computed hydrographs
at the outlet of tributary
catchment for variation
of ratio $\sqrt{s_c}/n_c$

Fig. 5 Relation of peak-discharge rate
and peak-arrival time at the outlet of
tributary catchment to ratio $\sqrt{s}/n$

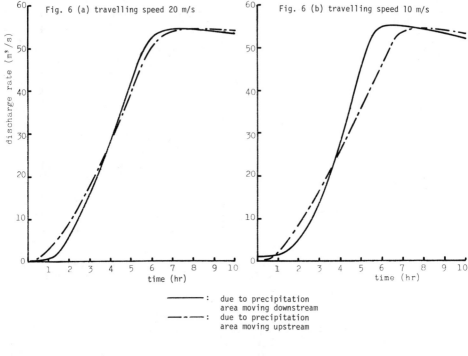

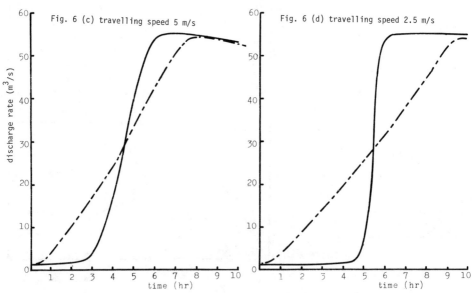

Fig. 6 Comparison between computed hydrograph due to precipitation area moving downstream and that due to the area moving upstream in Model (I)

13.12

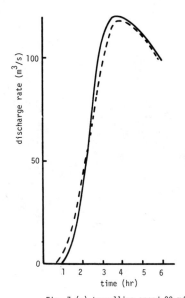

Fig. 7 (a) travelling speed 20 m/s

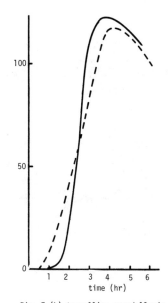

Fig. 7 (b) travelling speed 10 m/s

————: due to precipitation
      area moving downstream
— — —: due to precipitation
      area moving upstream

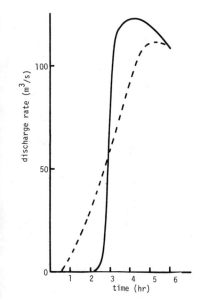

Fig. 7 (c) travelling speed 5 m/s

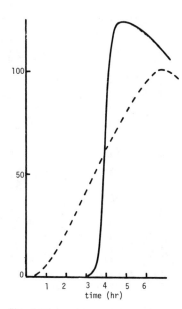

Fig. 7 (d) travelling speed 2.5 m/s

Fig. 7 Comparison between computed hydrograph due to precipitation area
moving downstream and that due to the area moving upstream
in Model (II)

13.13

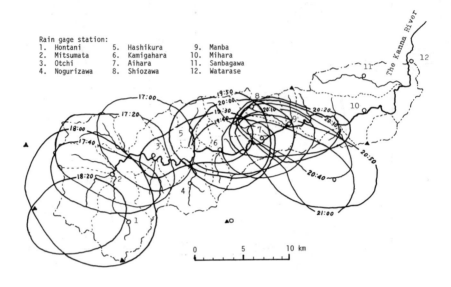

Rain gage station:
1. Hontani
2. Mitsumata
3. Otchi
4. Nogurizawa
5. Hashikura
6. Kamigahara
7. Aihara
8. Shiozawa
9. Manba
10. Mihara
11. Sanbagawa
12. Watarase

Fig. 8   An example of movement of precipitation area:
thunderstorm owing to a front on 4th August 1958

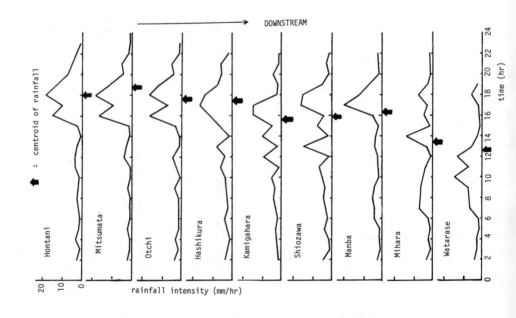

Fig. 9   Movement of time centroid of precipitation: rainfall on 25th
Sept. 1950

13.14

293

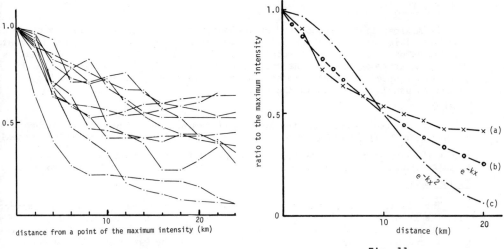

Fig. 10   Areal distribution of
          precipitation

Fig. 11

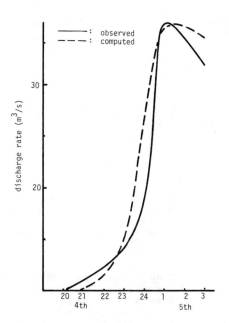

Fig. 12   Comparison of computed hydrograph
          with the observed one, for rain-
          fall due to moving storm on 4th
          August 1958

13.15

DISCUSSION

J. W. DELLEUR

The maximum travel speed used in the numerical experiment was of the order of 75 Km/hr. This speed is of the order of 10 to 20 times the travel speed of front movement as usually observed in continental USA. It is, therefore, asked what is the type of storm mechanism contemplated by the author? The example of Fig. 8 also shows a speed of about 5 Km/hour which seems to be more similar to the situations usually observed in the USA.

M. HINO

I would like to know how the authors determined the value of the catchment roughness, n_c? It is effected by several factors. Even the intensity of rainfall causes the change of it. However, the value of n = 0.9 seems to be too large. I would like to ask about the reasons of such large value of catchment roughness.

W. L. MOORE

The conclusion that the direction of storm movement had a significant effect upon the resultant flood hydrograph for low velocities of storm movement, but that the effect was reduced and became almost negligible for high rates of storm movement is reasonable and in agreement with what would be expected. The author rightly points out that more important than the absolute speed of the storm movement, is its speed in relation to "the speed of runoff from the catchment." The writer would like to suggest further development of this concept of relative speed as the important parameter. For example, a parameter giving the ratio of the travel time of the storm for the length of the drainage basin to the travel time of a particle of water moving through the drainage system to the outlet might be explored. Alternatively the base time might be that of the travel time of a flood wave through the drainage system rather than the travel time of a fluid particle. It would be interesting if some estimates of these parameters could be included in the paper.

M. OKUTA

Question:
For calculating the example of Kanna River Basin, which time unit of input data did you use, 1 hr, 10min. or 20 min.? For the input data, it may be better for your purpose that the time unit of rainfall is given shorter than one hour, because of same reason of my comment for Professor Ven Te Chow.

Comment:
I hope you and your colleague may treat the case when the storm rainfalls appear one after another from upstream or downstream to Kanna River Basin. It is the reason why that these cases appear very often in the time of heavy rainfall caused by typhoon and frontal system of Bai-U.

RESPONSE BY Y. TAKAHASI

A preliminary attempt was made to incorporate the concept of relative speed in another paper (M. Furuki: effects of travelling of precipitation area upon runoff phenomena - a study by a simplified watershed model (in Japanese), collected paper of Dep. of Civil Eng., Univ. of Tokyo, Vol. 6, 1969). The ratio of the speed of the storm movement to the stream velocity at the outlet of the catchment model was used as a parameter. In this case, the peak discharge rate indicated the maximum value when the ratio was about unity.

The authors intend to make further study about which parameter should be adopted.

United States - Japan Bi-Lateral Seminar in Hydrology
Honolulu, January 1971

NUMERICAL SIMULATION OF WATERSHED HYDROLOGY

Dr. Walter L. Moore, Professor of Civil Engineering
The University of Texas at Austin, Austin, Texas

Prof. B. J. Claborn, Assoc. Professor of Civil Engineering
Texas Tech University, Lubbock, Texas

SYNOPSIS

The possibility of simulating at a complex level most of the physical processes that are involved in the storage and movement of water in a watershed has become a reality on the current generation of high speed digital computers. This type of watershed simulation is potentially useful both for predicting hydrologic events of importance to the planning of water resources developments and as a tool for obtaining an improved understanding of the hydrological processes. Experience has shown that even very complex simulation programs can be operated at costs which are reasonable for application to problems of water resource evaluation.

In the process of translating the Stanford Watershed Model IV into Fortran IV computer language an understanding of the detailed working of that model was developed which led to the belief that important improvements could be made in the manner of treating concepts of depression storage, infiltration, soil moisture storage, and soil moisture movement. The result was a program for simulating at a fairly complex level most of the physical processes that occur in a watershed. The rainfall input is stored and transferred to various elements using mathematical relations that are based on realistic physical processes. Most of the parameters have a physical interpretation and it is hoped that with experience numerical values of most of them can be estimated using physical data. The simulation emphasizes surface storage, infiltration, and soil moisture phases as singificant in the determining the amount of stream flow. The time distribution of runoff is treated very simply by means of a distribution graph. Limited results are included for the application of the simulation program to two watersheds.

14.1

United States-Japan Bi-Lateral Seminar in Hydrology
Honolulu, January 1971

NUMERICAL SIMULATION OF WATERSHED HYDROLOGY

Dr. Walter L. Moore, Professor of Civil Engineering
The University of Texas at Austin, Austin, Texas

Prof. B. J. Claborn, Assoc. Professor of Civil Engineering
Texas Tech University, Lubbock, Texas

INTRODUCTION

Numerical simulation of the hydrological processes occurring in a watershed
has emerged as a potentially useful method both for predicting hydrologic events
and as a tool for obtaining an improved understanding of the hydrological processes.
From the standpoint of engineering application hydrology is usually called on to
supply information on the magnitude and frequency of flood events and on the severity and frequency of droughts. From the standpoint of scientific hydrology man is
interested in learning more about the internal working of the various physical
processes that occur as parts of the hydrologic cycle.

Conventional approaches to hydrologic analysis have usually been fragmentary
with different methods developed for each different problem. Methods of dealing
with problems of floods have included the analysis of historical stream flow
records, variations of the "rational" formula, variations of the unit hydrograph
method, multiple correlation analysis and various emperical formulas. In those
methods where the flood characteristics are estimated from a rainfall event, one
of the major uncertainties is the determination of rainfall excess as it is affected by antecedent conditions of the watershed. Evaluation of drought conditions has
been based almost entirely on analysis of historical stream flow records. An important constraint in the development and use of these conventional methods has been
the limited computational capacity of the pre-computer period.

The amazing capacity of modern high speed digital computers to perform massive
computation in a short time and at a low cost has opened up the possibility for new
approaches to the solution of problems in watershed hydrology. The possibility of
simulating at a fairly complex level most of the physical processes that occur in
the water cycle of a watershed has become a reality. For example, the Stanford
Watershed Model IV has demonstrated the ability to simulate a year's record of
stream flow on a one hour time interval in about ten seconds of central processer
time on the computer which at commercial rates would cost less than four dollars.

Simulation has been defined as, "The development and application of mathematical models to represent the time-variant interaction of physical processes."[1]
Numerical simulation appears to offer an important advance in the solution of
hydrologic problems because of the following propositions:

1. In many locations better information is available on historic rainfall or
    on probable rainfall sequences than is available on stream flow.

2. In many locations, rural as well as urban, changes occur in the watershed
    with the passage of time. Numerical simulation based on realistic physi-
    cal processes seems to offer the best possibility for evaluating the char-
    acteristics of stream flow as effected by known or anticipated changes.

---

[1]Hydrocomp International Simulation Newsletter, August 1, 1970.

14.2

While considering the promise and potential of numerical simulation, attention should also be given to some of its limitations. Concern is often expressed about the availability of adequate input data. In performing a numerical simulation, input data is needed on the evapotranspiration as a function of time and the rainfall as a function of time and position. In many locations, available rainfall data is inadequate either as to the number of locations or the frequency of measurement or both. The simulation process itself depends on the functional relationships chosen to represent various physical processes occurring in the watershed and on the parameters used to describe the various characteristics of the watershed. The art in developing a satisfactory simulation program is in achieving the proper degree of fidelity in simulating the various individual processes, and in omitting unnecessary and insignificant details which add unnecessarily to the complication of the program. In order to evaluate the validity of the program, it would be desirable to measure the time variation of many of the variables in the program as well as the stream flow which is the final output. Generally, only measurements of stream flow are available as a test of the output and no check can be made on the time variation of other variables such as soil moisture, overland flow, etc. This leaves the simulation process vulnerable to the charge that even though the stream flow is correctly simulated, one cannot be sure that each of the various physical processes is correctly simulated. However, the broader the range of conditions for which the stream flow output can be simulated by a particular program, the greater the confidence that the parameters and processes utilized have realistic physical meaning.

Historical Review of Numerical Simulation of Watersheds

One of the first and most successful efforts at simulation of the entire runoff process for watersheds was the "Stanford Watershed Model". It was conceived by Prof. Ray K. Linsley[2] at Stanford University in 1957 and evolved over the next few years with the aid of many people, especially Dr. Norman H. Crawford. It has been developed continuously passing through several identifiable models, the last one being Model IV. This model has been further developed and added to and is now being used commercially by Dr. Norman Crawford of Hydrocomp International.

A review of other models is included in the report by Claborn and Moore (1970)[3].

The Stanford Watershed Model IV

Watershed simulation at The University of Texas at Austin began with a study of the Stanford Watershed Model IV, Crawford and Linsley (1966)[2]. During the translation of this program from SUBALGOL to Fortran IV compiler language by B. J. Claborn for use on The University of Texas CDC-6600 computer, the detailed working of the model came to be understood. An overall picture of Model IV as interpreted at The University of Texas is presented in Figure 1. The Stanford Watershed Model operates by receiving precipitation, transferring moisture between various storage elements as shown in the Figure and discharging moisture through evapotranspiration, deep percolation and stream flow. It operates on basic accounting periods of fifteen minutes and one hour. Most of the moisture transfer within the storage

[2]Crawford, N. H., Linsley, Ray K., Digital Simulation in Hydrology: Stanford Watershed Model IV, Tech. Rep. 39, Dept. of Civil Engr. Stanford Univ., July 1966.

[3]Claborn, B. J., Moore, W. L., "Numerical Simulation of Watershed Hydrology," Technical Report to the Center for Research in Water Resources CRWR-54, Hydraulic Engineering Dept., HYD 14-7002, The University of Texas at Austin, Austin, Texas, August 1970.

14.3

elements operates on a fifteen minutes cycle while the removal of water from interception storage and the routing of stream flow takes place once each hour. It produces hourly stream flow data and if desired will produce peak flows or mean daily
or monthly flows. The total watershed area is divided into segments with the point
where the discharge from the segment is to be computed designated as a flow point.
The flow at several flow points may be routed and combined to give the flow at the
outlet of the watershed. For each watershed segment, the area is divided into pervious and impervious areas. For each fifteen minute interval, the rainfall volumes
falling on the impervious area move directly to the stream. The remaining volume
of water goes to interception storages whose maximum value is specified as an input
parameter. Since all model parameters are read into the computer at the beginning
of each year, it is possible to reflect yearly changes in the interception storage.
However, seasonal changes, which may be important in agricultural watershed, are
not provided for.

A rather complete description of the operation of the Stanford Watershed
Model is included in the report by Claborn and Moore (1970)[3].

The Stanford Watershed Model IV was applied to a 137 square mile watershed in
central Texas which is part of Mukewater Creek above the stream gauging station at
Trickham, Texas as a means to evaluate the effect of changes in this watershed,
Coskun, Claborn, and Moore (1969)[4]. By trial and error adjustment of parameters,
the model was able to simulate very satisfactorily both individual storm hydrographs and monthly and annual stream flow events for the period before any changes
occurred in the watershed. In this instance the entire watershed was treated as
one segment. Satisfactory results were obtained under quite extreme conditions of
rainfall and flow variability on both an annual and individual storm basis.

Although the Stanford Watershed Model IV was able to reproduce the stream flow
adequately, it was the opinion at The University of Texas at Austin that some of
the processes needed improvement to make them more compatible with realistic physical processes and to utilize parameters with a physically definable meaning. In
the Stanford Watershed Model, the most difficult parameters, which the user must
assign, seem to be the "nominal" values of storage for the upper and lower zones
and the infiltration index. These three parameters are interrelated which add considerably to the difficulty of determining their values. No clear physical interpretation could be given to them. The "nominal" upper zone storage seemed to include a depression storage factor as well as a shallow depth of top soil. It
seemed to be intended to have a small storage volume and a fast reaction time.

THE UNIVERSITY OF TEXAS AT AUSTIN SIMULATION PROGRAM

In considering important improvements to the Stanford Model it was felt that
the depression storage, infiltration, soil moisture storage, and soil moisture
movement should be modified to conform more realistically to accepted processes of
soil physics. With this in mind, a rather intensive study of unsaturated flow was
undertaken as a basis for developing a modified simulation program.

The mechanics of unsaturated flow are discussed at length by Remson (1962)[5].
Forces acting to produce motion of the water within a soil may be considered as:

---

[4]Coskun, Erdal, Claborn, B. J., and Moore, W. L., "Application of Continuous
Accounting Techniques to Evaluate the Effects of Small Structures on Mukewater
Creek, Texas," Proc., Conf. on the Effects of Watershed Changes on Streamflow,
University of Texas Press, Austin, Texas, 1969.

[5]Remson, I., Randolph, J. R., Review of Some Elements of Soil-Moisture
Theory, Geological Survey Professional Paper 411-D, U. S. Geological Survey, 1962.

1. The gravitational force which always acts in vertical direction,
2. The capillarity forces,
3. The chemical and osmotic forces, and
4. Forces due to partial pressure gradients acting on the water vapor.

Chemical and osmotic forces usually cause relatively slow movement and were not included in the analysis. The volume of water moved in the vapor state is small in comparison to that moved in the liquid so long as the liquid state is continuous. The study was therefore limited to motion under the first two types of forces mentioned.

Considerable time was spent initially studying the behavior of a finite difference model of a vertical soil column. This model was based on the use of a form of Darcy's equation for unsaturated flow

$$V = - K \frac{\partial (\psi + y)}{\partial y}$$ (1)

and the continuity equation

$$- \frac{\partial V}{\partial y} = \frac{\partial s}{\partial t}$$ (2)

where

V is the bulk velocity in the y direction (i.e. the flow rate through a gross unit area,
K is the permeability of the soil in L/t units,
ψ is the soil moisture tension potential or capillary potential with units of length,
y is the vertical distance from an arbitrary reference plane positive upward.

The form of the resulting equation was applicable to the unsaturated zone, but not the saturated zone. This led to the necessity of obtaining the location of the interface between the two zones as part of the solution with the proper form of Darcy's Law applied to each zone. Satisfactory methods for handling this problem and evaluating the finite difference forms of the derivatives in the region of the interface were not found and this line of inquiry was abandoned.

Some method which does not require differing forms of Darcy's law for the saturated and unsaturated zones will avoid these difficulties. Rubin (1966)[6] asserts his combination of permeability, soil moisture, and capillary potential accomplishes this feat. Based on such a model it may be possible to develop an infiltration model somewhat better than the one adopted and described in the following pages. However, it was not possible to carry out this approach as part of the recent investigation.

A Modified Watershed Model

In developing a modified watershed model extensive use was made of the processes of the Stanford Watershed Model IV, particularly relating to overland flow and stream routing. The study of unsaturated flow described previously was used in a guide to the unsaturated flow process. A diagram of the watershed model is shown in Figure 2. Each phase of the simulation process will be discussed.

The computer program written to implement the modified watershed model is included in the report by Claborn and Moore (1970)[3]. It was written to accommodate

---

[6]Rubin, J., "Theory of Rainfall Uptake by Soils Initially Drier than their Field Capacity and Its Application," Water Resources Research, Vol. 2, No. 4, page 739-749, 1966.

rainfall measured at irregular intervals in either accumulated form as from a
weighing gauge or as a rate from a tipping bucket gauge. Either of these records
is converted to a record with the average rate for the specified time period whic
may be as short as one minute or as long as one day. A similar record is prepare
from the measured stream flow when this is available. The maximum length of the
basic accounting cycle is set at fifteen minutes.

Interception Storage

All precipitation falling on the pervious area is routed through interceptio
storage. The volume of water in interception storage in inches at any time is li
ited by an input parameter, VINSTM, which may vary monthly. This parameter may b
estimated as a function of the type and density of material above ground. In agr
cultural areas, the maximum interception storage may be very small early in the
year, increasing to a maximum as the crops mature in the fall, and then drop shar
ly as the fields are prepared for the winter. On the other hand, in forest or
urban areas, the maximum volume may be relatively constant over the annual cycle.

Surface Storage

Water exceeding the maximum interception storage passes through interception
storage and arrives at the ground surface. It may fall into one of two types of
storage: depression storage or overland flow storage. Depression storage, or dea
storage, is that volume of storage within depressions of all sizes in the watershed. A depression is defined as a hole or low area with no outlet.

Within the pervious area of the watershed, three types of areas are delinen-
ated as shown in Figure 3. These areas are characterized as (A) areas from which
overland flow proceeds directly to the stream; (B) areas from which overland flow
proceeds into a depression; and (C) areas of depression storage. The areas of
depression storage vary from the hole caused by a woman's shoe to farm ponds and
other flow retarding structures. The surface area of the water in depression sto
age at any time is assumed to vary linearly with the volume of depression storage
Figure 4. Rainfall reaching the land surface is divided between overland flow
storage (OLS) and depression storage (DS) on the basis of the surface area of eac
type of storage. Overland flow storage is further divided between that flow goin
directly to the stream and the flow going into depression storage. Infiltration
and evaporation, also surface phenomena, are based on the surface area of each
type of storage.

The overland flow model used is taken from the Stanford Model. It is a quas
turbulent form of Izzard's overland flow equations

$$OLF = \frac{64200 \ s^{0.5}}{nL} \ \left(\frac{D}{L}\right)^{5/3} \ \left(1 + 0.6 \ \left(\frac{D}{D_e}\right)^3\right)^{5/3} \tag{(}$$

where OLF is the rate of runoff in inches per hour per unit area,
      n is the Manning roughness factor for overland flow (ROUGH),
      L is the length of the overland flow reach in feet (VLENGH),
      S is the slope of the overland flow surface (SLOPE),
      D is the storage in ft.^{3}/ft. and is defined as the average of the storage
        at the beginning of the time period and the storage at the end of the
        time period (OFSAVG),
      D_e is the storage in ft.^{3}/ft. for an equilibrium condition (OFSEQU), and i
        defined by

$$OFSEQU = \frac{0.000818 \ i^{0.6} \ n^{0.6} \ L^{1.6}}{s^{0.3}} \tag{(}$$

14 .6

where i is the precipitation rate, in inches per hour (XI). This model is based on the following empirical relationship between outflow depth and storage

$$y = \frac{D}{L} \left[1 + 0.6 \ (\frac{D}{D_e})^3\right] \tag{5}$$

where y is the depth, in feet, at the lower edge of the flow plane.

These equations were developed by Linsley and Crawford (1966)[2], and plots showing quite good agreement with a finite difference solution of the partial differential equation of varied flow were presented.

Overland flow generated on that portion of the watershed classified as contributing directly to stream flow is added to the variable RO. That part of overland flow originating on the area contributing to depression storage is added to depression storage. Some of the smaller depression storage areas will fill rapidly and surface runoff from areas originally designated as depression areas will commence when these areas are filled. For small indentions of the soil this will occur early in the storm, while for larger storage areas the runoff will not occur until much later. A typical relationship between area producing runoff through depression storage and the volume in depression storage is shown in Figure 5. The curve is assumed to be a parabolic with vertex at the origin and may be written as

$$X_a = (\frac{1}{C} \ \frac{DS}{DSMAX})^{0.5} \tag{6}$$

where X_a is the fraction of the pervious area which originally was designated as depression storage, or an area contributing flow to depression storage, but is now producing runoff,
DS is the actual depression storage volume, in inches of depth,
DSMAX is the maximum depression storage volume in inches of depth, and
C is a constant, normally with a value of 1.

The actual shape of this relation will vary from one basin to the next. However, it is felt that the parabola is adequate for most basins, based on an investigation reported in Claborn and Moore (1970)[3].

Infiltration

The infiltration is dependent on (A) the available water, i.e., the rainfall rate; or (B) the ability of the soil to conduct the water through the soil in its unsaturated condition, i.e., Rubin's preponding condition, or (C) the ponded depth, the thickness of the saturated zone, and the saturated permeability. Ponding of water occurs only for the third condition. The first is characterized by a rainfall rate less than the saturated permeability of the soil, and the second by a rainfall rate greater than the saturated permeability. Equation (1) may be rewritten as

$$V_o = - \ (K)_{y=0} \left[(\frac{d\psi}{dS}) \ (\frac{\partial S}{\partial y})_{y=0} + 1\right] \tag{7}$$

where V_o is the infiltration rate. This equation is applicable to both conditions (A) and (B) and $\partial S/\partial y$ should be viewed as the dependent variable.

Referring to Figure 6, the infiltration rate of ponded rainfall is given by

$$V_o = - \ K_{sat} \left[\frac{POND - \psi_{ae}}{SATDPH} + 1\right]$$

where POND and SATDPH have the meanings shown in the figure, and ψ_{ae} is the value of soil tension at air entry.

302

Holtan (1961)[7] proposed an infiltration equation

$$f = a\, F_p^n + f_c \qquad ($$

where f is the infiltration rate when supply is not the limiting factor,
  f_c is the constant infiltration rate, the saturated permeability of the soil
  F_p is the total volume which can be infiltrated before a constant rate of
    infiltration is reached,
  a and n are constants.

Holtan recommends a be taken as 0.62 and n as 1.387. F_p is a measure of the void
remaining in the soil column at any time, and hence is also a measure of the water
in storage in the column. Since Holtan's equation is for the period when rainfall
excess exists, i.e., ponding

$$-\left[K\right]_{y=0} = -K_{sat} = -f_c \qquad (1$$

where the minus sign is a matter of convention. Then to the extent that

$$K_{sat}\left[\frac{POND - \mathscr{Y}_{ae}}{SATDPH}\right] = a\, F_p^n \qquad (1$$

Holtan's equation approximates equation (8). Holtan found from experimental data
that F_p could be expressed as

$$\left[F_p\right]_0 = K\, S_0 \qquad (1$$

where the zero subscript indicates evaluation at time zero,
  K is a vegetative factor given in Table 1, and
  S is the available pore space in the 0-21 inch depth,

TABLE 1   HOLTAN'S VEGETATIVE FACTOR

Cover	Value of Vegetative Factor K
Bluegrass	1.00
Crabgrass and Alfalfa	.70
Lespedeza and Timothy	.45
Alfalfa	.35
Weeds	.30

Holtan's equation is particularly suited to a continuous accounting type watershed
model, since the independent variable is the unsaturated pore space within the top
layer of soil. Defining this layer to be the Upper Zone, equation (9) may be
written

$$f = a\,(UZST - UZS)^n + SATPRM$$
$$= C1\,(UZST - UZS)^{C2} + SATPRM \qquad (1$$

where UZST is the total pore space in the Upper Zone, porosity times thickness in
    inches^3/inch^2,
  UZS is the current volume of water in the Upper Zone in inches^3/inch^2,
  SATPRM is the saturated permeability of the Upper Zone, in inches per hour.

[7]Holtan, H. N., A Concept for Infiltration Estimates in Watershed Engineering
ARS 41-51, U. S. Department of Agriculture, 1961.

14.8

C1 and C2 are input constants, corresponding to Holtan's a · K and n. No allowance was made by Holtan for water leaving the Upper Zone, i.e., the volume of the pore space remaining at any time t after the storm began was computed as the pore space available at t_o to time t. The watershed model will reflect more accurately the actual volume of water in storage within the Upper Zone. Consequently, the Upper Zone can be thinner than Holtan's twenty-one inches. In agricultural lands, the depth to which cultivation takes place seems a reasonable thickness, while in uncultivated areas, the thickness may vary from one-half inch for very tight soils to several inches for sandy soils. The presence of any less permeable zone should terminate the Upper Zone. Equation (13) gives the infiltration rate for the period when supply is not the limiting factor, i.e., the potential infiltration. When the rainfall rate is less than this potential infiltration, all of the rainfall is infiltrated. This decreases the pore space available, and consequently decreases the infiltration potential for the next time period. Rubin (1966)[8] pointed out that for a uniform supply less than the potential infiltration rate, the soil column eventually reaches an equilibrium state in its upper reaches where the gradient

$$\frac{\partial K\,(\Psi + y)}{\partial y}$$

is just adequate to transfer the supply. This may also occur in the model, as the flow into the Upper Zone may be exactly equal to the flow out of the Upper Zone. Holtan's equation, while not exact, does seem to offer a good approximation to the infiltration process, both in the situation of infiltration limited by supply, and infiltration limited by the soil condition.

Flow Though the Unsaturated Zone

Ideally, one would describe flow through the unsaturated zone using some form of equation (1). However, in a watershed model this will have to be approximated. In the continuous accounting model, the volume of water within each interval of depth can be obtained. However, as the number of these intervals increases, the time to perform the calculations also increases, and soon reaches an economic limit. The number of such zones must be limited. The independent variables in equation (1) may be written as functions of the soil moisture, S

$$\Psi = f\,(S) \tag{14}$$

$$K = g\,(S) \tag{15}$$

Solution of equation (1) must yield

$$V = h\,(S) \tag{16}$$

Several forms of the functions f(S) and g(S) have been proposed and are discussed by Claborn and Moore (1970)[3]. The set of functions chosen for use in the simulation program are

$$K = A_1\,(S + B_1)^{C_1} + D_1 \tag{17}$$

and

$$-\Psi = A_2\,(S + B_2)^{C_2} + D_2 \tag{18}$$

Values of the coefficients for the various soils tested are shown in Table 2, which may be used as a guide in assigning the coefficients.

The program moves moisture from one zone to another using equation (1) rewritten as

---

[8]Rubin, J., "Numerical Analysis of Ponded Rainfall Infiltration," Proceedings, Symposium on Water in Unsaturated Zone, Wageningen, 1966.

14.9

Description and Source	A	B	C	D	Max. R.E.	Avg. R.E.	R^2
Permeability							
Geary Silt Loam Hanks and Bowers (1962)	797.7	-0.114	7.75	$2.9 \cdot 10^{-9}$	0.400	0.139	0.949
Yolo Light Clay Phillip (1957), Gardner (1958)	3.37	-0.103	6.01	$-3.0 \cdot 10^{-7}$	0.372	0.147	0.936
Watson (1967)	206.8	0.002	4.06	$-6.9 \cdot 10^{-4}$	0.231	0.091	0.919
Sarpy Loam Hanks and Bowers (1962)	1677.2	0.044	8.70	$-1.6 \cdot 10^{-6}$	0.652	0.284	0.936
Del Monte Sand (drying) Liakopoulos (1966)	1.689	0.026	2.45	$2.4 \cdot 10^{-3}$	0.233	0.079	0.899
Del Monte Sand (wetting) Liakopoulos (1966)	1.983	-0.00585	2.66	$2.2 \cdot 10^{-5}$	0.312	0.188	0.915
Vachaud (1966)	117.32	-0.1185	5.69	$7.1 \cdot 10^{-4}$	0.187	0.068	0.954
Remson (1965)	$1.6 \cdot 10^4$	0.087	25.16	$1.0 \cdot 10^{-9}$	1.790	1.179	0.883
Capillary Potential							
Geary Silt Loam	0.061	0.063	-7.67	-8.11	0.014	0.004	0.963
Yolo Light Clay	Data given in equation form:			= -7.87	$10^{-7}/12.2 \cdot K - 1$		0.5
Watson	-47.6	-0.047	-0.033	33.74	0.008	0.001	0.923
Sarpy Loam	26.20	.7745	-23.91	0.965	2.68	0.753	0.898
Del Monte Sand (drying)	225.3	1.0	-11.35	3.64	0.59	0.239	0.900
Vachaud	9.937	0.6555	-21.28	1.207	1.765	0.478	0.894
Remson	249.76	0.816	-30.89	-2.653	0.480	0.167	0.909

TABLE 2   COEFFICIENTS FOR PERMEABILITY AND CAPILLARY POTENTIAL APPROXIMATIONS

14.10

$$V = K \left(\frac{\partial \psi}{\partial y} + 1\right) \tag{19}$$

The value of permeability is the weighted average of the permeability in each zone as determined by equation (17). The value of $\partial \psi / \partial y$ is found from

$$\frac{\partial \psi}{\partial y} = \frac{\psi_1 - \psi_2}{y_1 - y_2} \tag{20}$$

where subscripts 1 and 2 refer to the two zones. The value of ψ is found using equation (18). The value of S for each zone is found by dividing the total moisture in the zone by the zone thickness.

Interflow

The phenomenon of interflow, while frequently observed in nature, has not been studied in detail. A simplified interflow model is shown in Figure 7. The occurrence of water at the seepage face is dependent on the slope of the less permeable zone, S, the permeability of this zone in relation to the permeability of the zone above it, the depth to the less permeable zone, and the area contributing water to the interflow process, i.e., the length L in Figure 7. These variables and perhaps others combine to change a portion of the infiltration hydrograph into the interflow hydrograph. The simplest mathematical formulation of the process would seem to be one which determines the volume of the interflow and produces the interflow hydrograph by lagging this volume. This method is used in the watershed model. The volume of interflow from the top level of the Intermediate Zone is determined by

$$\text{VINFLO} = C_{16} \, (\text{TIZS} - C_{10} \cdot \text{VINST}) \, \Delta t \tag{21}$$

where VINFLO is the volume of water added to the interflow process during the time period Δt,

TIZS   is the volume of water stored in the top half of the Intermediate Zone,

VINST   is the total volume of the Intermediate Zone, and

C_{10}, C_{16} are the input parameters which must reflect the difference in permeability between the two zones.

When the quantity $\text{TIZS} - C_{10} \cdot \text{VIST} \leq 0$, VINFLO is set to zero. C_{10} is seen to be a parameter which sets a lower limit on the volume of water which must be present before interflow can occur. The interflow hydrograph shape is determined by a lag function

$$X = (C_{14} \cdot \text{DELING} + C_{15}) \, \Delta t \tag{22}$$

where x is the volume of water discharged to the stream from interflow storage in time Δt,

DELING is the volume of water in interflow storage, and C_{14}, C_{15} are input parameters.

No rationale can be given for equation (22). Probably the parameter C_{15} can be taken as zero. By analogy to routing equations for stream, the outflow should be related to the volume in storage.

Groundwater Flow

Much of what was said about the difficulties of mathematically modeling the interflow process also applies to the flow of groundwater. The watershed model makes provision for groundwater flow to occur into the stream and also to flow out of the basin. The latter is termed "Underflow", and is determined as a function of the water stored in the saturated portion of the soil profile

$$Y = C_{13} \cdot \text{GWS} \cdot \Delta t \tag{23}$$

14.11

where Y is the volume of water leaving the basin as underflow in the period Δ
GWS is the volume of water in groundwater storage, and
C_{13} is an input parameter.

The flow into the stream is determined in a similar manner

$$S = (GWS - C_{11}) \cdot C_{12} \cdot \Delta t \qquad (2$$

where X is the volume of water flowing from the groundwater system into the
stream during time Δt,
C_{11} is the volume of water in groundwater storage below which no flow into
the stream occurs. (A slight modification here would allow influent
streams to be modeled).
C_{12} is an input parameter.

For the base flow period of the stream hydrograph, equation (24) is analogous to
the commonly used decay equation

$$q_i = k \cdot q_{i-1} = k^i \cdot q_0 \qquad (2$$

where q_i is the flow for the ith time period,
q_{i-1} is the flow for the $(i - 1)^{st}$ time period,
q_0 is the flow at the beginning of the first time period, and
k is the recession constant.

For equation (24),

$$K = \frac{1}{1 - C_{12} \, \Delta t \, \frac{GWS + C_{11}}{GWS - C_{11}}} \qquad (2$$

It is seen that k is not constant, but approaches zero as the groundwater storage
approaches the input parameter C_{11}. The result of the variable recession constant
is a steeper and shorter recession than given by equation (25). This is further
accentuated by the removal of a volume of water from groundwater storage for
underflow.

Evaporation and Evapotranspiration

The evaporation process is highly dependent on the energy received in the fo
of sunlight. The amount of energy received is reflected in both the total evapor
tion and in the time distribution of the evaporation. Other important climatic
factors in the evaporation process are wind and humidity. The average effect of
all three factors will be reflected in the amount of evaporation from an evaporation pan. Accordingly, the model makes use of monthly pan evaporation to establi
potential monthly evaporation for the basin. An average daily potential is deter
mined from the monthly potential, using a second order interpolating equation, an
finally an instantaneous potential evaporation rate is determined. Potential eva
poration is assumed to occur from thirty minutes past sunrise until one hour afte
sunset, and to reach a peak when three-fourths of this time has elapsed. A skewe
sine curve fitted to these three points is used for estimating the instantaneous
potential evaporation rate. The time distribution of the evaporation potential
agrees well with data reported by van Bavel (1966)[9] as shown in Figure 8.

Evaporation occurs first from Interception Storage. If there is insufficien
water stored in Interception Storage to satisfy the potential evaporation for thi
period, additional water is removed, in order, from Overland Flow Storage, Depres
ion Storage, and Upper Zone Storage. Evaporation is assumed to occur at the

[9] van Bavel, C. H. M., "Potential Evaporation: The Combination Concept and It
Experimental Verification," Water Reso. Res., Vol. 2, No. 3, pp 455-567, 1966.

---

potential rate from Overland Flow Storage and from Depression Storage. It will also occur at the potential rate from the Upper Zone Storage when the Upper Zone decreases, the evaporation also decreases because of the difficulty of the soil to deliver the necessary moisture to the surface. This is approximated in the model by using

$$E = EVAPOT \cdot \left(\frac{UZS - UZMIN}{UZST - UZMIN}\right)^{\alpha} \tag{27}$$

where E   is actual evaporation rate from the soil surface,
    EVAPOT is the potential evaporation,
    UZS   is the current volume of water stored in the Upper Zone,
    UZMIN is the minimum volume allowed in the Upper Zone (evaporation will not remove the chemically bonded water from the soil particles),
    UZST   is the total volume allowed in the Upper Zone, and
    α is a parameter describing the soil's ability to deliver water to the surface.

Transpiration of water from the soil by plant life seems to be independent of the soil moisture content when the content is above the wilting point. Consequently, during the months when transpiration is a factor, water is removed from the root zone (RTZONE) in addition to the evaporation. This removal is limited by the wilting point moisture content, assumed equal to the minimum volume for each zone. The root zone thickness does not necessarily coincide with the Upper Zone--for deep rooted trees and such crops as alfalfa it should be larger. The monthly evaporation as measured by the pan evaporation is augmented by the monthly consumptive use (TRANPO).

Stream Flow Routing

The runoff for any time period as calculated by the model thus far described must be routed through the basin in order to produce the hydrograph of stream flow. As in the Stanford Model IV, a distribution graph technique is used. The flow generated during this period is distributed according to input parameters into future runoff intervals, i.e., the flow reaching the stream during the present time interval will appear at the gauging point distributed in time.

Watersheds with Multiple Segments

The program will simulate a watershed composed of several subwatersheds or segments. The order in which the segments are simulated must be from upstream to downstream, and the precipitation tape must be prepared in this same sequence. This program processes the segments sequentially; segment numbering must conform to the above usage.

APPLICATION OF THE SIMULATION PROGRAM

Opportunities for application of the program have so far been very limited, but it has been applied to two watersheds with widely different characteristics and with different objectives.

The Edwardsville, Illinois Watershed

The first application was to a 27.22 acre watershed (WI) at the Soil Conservation Service experimental area near Edwardsville, Illinois. For this watershed quite complete information on the watershed was available to allow prior estimation of the parameters needed for application of the simulation program. In this application an ambitious objective was chosen, that is, to select the simulation

14.13

parameters in advance based on reported characteristics of the watershed. This is a rather severe test of the program and the ability to interpret the known physical characteristics of the watershed in relation to the physical processes being simulated. The test was also a severe one because of the small area. The watershed was agricultural with no impervious area.

Results of Computer Run

Before the computer runs were made, several hydrographs were chosen as typical of the various conditions encountered in the model. A comparison of some simulated and recorded flows are shown in Table 3 for monthly flows, Table 4 for individual storms, and in Figure 9 for individual storm hydrographs.

Although the results are not as good as might be desired, they are not disappointing considering the severity of the conditions where it was the first use of the model and all the parameters were chosen in advance of starting the computer run. A study of daily maximum and minimum temperatures during the winter months of the 1941-52 year showed that freezing conditions were affecting the runoff pattern for parts of January and probably extended well into March. The simulation program at present does not include any effects of snow melt or frozen soil condition

Applications to Mukewater Creek Watershed

The Mukewater Creek Watershed contained 70.4 square miles above the stream gauging station at Trickham in central Texas. About one-half of the watershed are is devoted to farming and the other half to ranching. Its stream flow runoff characteristics have been studied previously. Sauer (1965)[10] utilized a multicorrelation analysis and Coskun and Moore (1969)[11] utilized the Stanford Watershed Model IV. The new simulation program developed at The University of Texas at Austin was applied and the results compared both with recorded flows and with flow determined from the Stanford Watershed Model IV. Those parameters which are common to both the Stanford Watershed Model and the revised model were assigned the value that had been used by Coskun and Moore (1969)[11]. The other parameters were assigned values based on available information and then adjusted by trial to improve the agreement between the simulated and recorded flows. This was the same procedure that had been used in applying the Stanford Watershed Model IV.

The results of the simulation of individual storms are shown in Figure 10 and 11, of mean daily flows in Figure 12, and of monthly flows in Table 5.

It is quite likely that the correspondence between simulated and recorded flo would be improved by taking into account the areal distribution of rainfall. This was not done, however, either in the application of the Stanford Watershed Model I or in the revised University of Texas at Austin model.

Conclusions and Areas of Further Research

The validity of the various concepts incorporated into the model cannot be thoroughly tested by application to two watersheds. While the results of the appl cation to the Edwardsville Watershed were not as good as expected, those from the

---

[10]Sauer, S. P., "Hydrological Studies of Small Watersheds, Mukewater Creek, Colorado River Basin, Texas, 1952-60," Rep. 60, Texas Water Development Board, 196

[11]Coskun, Erdal, Moore, W. L., "Numerical Simulation of a Watershed as a Mean to Evaluate Some Effects of Floodwater - Retarding Structures on Runoff," Tech. Rep to CRWR-45, HYD 14-6901, The Univ. of Texas, Austin, Texas, December 1969.

TABLE 3   SUMMARY OF MONTHLY SIMULATED AND MEASURED VALUES

Month	Rainfall (inches)	Measured Runoff (inches)	Simulated Runoff (inches)	Simulated Evaporation (inches)
Oct	8.10	1.01	1.04	0.10
Nov	2.87	0.77	0.24	0
Dec	1.59	T	0	0
Jan	1.23	0.01	0	0
Feb	2.59	0.90	0.03	0
Mar	2.01	0.10	0.01	0.43
Apr	2.22	0.34	0.03	0.83
May	5.25	0.10	0.57	5.09
Jun	7.56	1.31	2.16	6.00
Jul	8.20	3.46	3.57	4.75
Aug	3.49	0.46	0.94	3.94
Sep	1.43	T	0.01	2.91
Annual	46.54	8.58	8.59	24.04

TABLE 4   COMPARISON OF SIMULATED AND MEASURED VALUES FOR EACH STORM

Date	Rainfall (inches)	Runoff (inches) Measured	Simulated	Correlation Coefficient
3- 4-42	0.03			
3- 5-42				
3- 7-42	0.71	0.1365		
3- 8-42				
3-12-42	0.65	0.0874	0.0073	0.4577
3-13-42				
3-20-42	0.07			
3-25-42	0.25			
3-26-42				
3-27-42	0.23			
3-30-42	0.07			
4- 6-42	1.16	0.0199	0.0215	0.9712
4- 7-42				
4- 8-42	1.17	0.3211	0.0019	0.5257
4-10-42				
4-24-42	0.02			
5- 2-42	0.17			
5- 3-42	1.05	0.0107	0.1629	0.3763
5- 5-42	1.11	0.0465	0.2928	0.8658
5- 6-42				
5-11-42	0.03			
5-13-42	0.60	0.0047	0.0792	0.6288
5-15-42	0.96	0.0288	0.1080	0.9270
5-17-42	0.10			
5-18-42	0.59	0.0098		
5-23-42	0.16			
5-26-42	0.07			
5-31-42	0.41		0.0002	0
6- 1-42	0.59	0.0058	0.1051	0.7161
6- 6-42	0.12			
6- 9-42	0.31			
6-10-42	0.07			
6-11-42	0.18			
6-13-42	1.35	0.1442	0.5503	0.9823
6-15-42	0.31			
6-18-42	0.52	0.0033	0.0322	0.0768
6-19-42	0.10			
6-20-42	0.03			
6-21-42	1.69	0.0275	0.6521	0.9685
6-25-42	0.50			
6-26-42	1.79	0.8281	0.8110	0.9064

14.15

Water Year	Source	Oct	Nov	Dec	Jan	Feb	Mar	Apr	May	June	July	Aug	Sep	Annual	Correlation Coefficient
1953 -1954	Recorded	0.50					0.17	0.25	0.18	0.02				1.10	
	Stanford	0.60					0.01	0.18	0.14					0.97	0.9500
	U. T.	0.77					0.03	0.49	0.17					1.46	0.9593
1954 -1955	Recorded		0.05			0.03	0.03		2.03	0.95	0.91	0.06	0.49	4.55	
	Stanford		0.02	0.01		0.01			1.80	0.42	1.27	0.01	0.53	4.10	0.9318
	U. T.								1.92	0.80	0.58	0.01	0.30	3.62	0.9434
1955 -1956	Recorded							0.10	2.15					2.25	
	Stanford		Data Not Available					0.25	2.31					2.57	0.9970
	U. T.														
1956 -1957	Recorded	0.07	0.05				0.08	2.03	2.75	0.20	0.01	0.01	0.01	5.19	
	Stanford	0.05	0.02	0.02		0.01	0.07	2.03	2.58	0.14			0.02	4.96	0.9550
	U. T.	0.06					0.16	2.10	2.03	0.30				4.65	0.9544
1957 -1958	Recorded	0.12	0.04		0.01	0.17	0.17	0.04	0.11	0.07		0.10		0.83	
	Stanford	0.18	0.07	0.03	0.04	0.13	0.14	0.09	0.08	0.11		0.16	0.03	1.06	0.9284
	U. T.	0.05	0.10			0.29	0.06	0.03	0.27	0.26		0.14		1.11	0.7402
1958 -1959	Recorded	0.01	0.01					0.01	0.01	2.24	2.00			4.25	
	Stanford								0.04	3.18	2.62	0.03	0.02	5.92	0.9766
	U. T.								0.11	2.50	1.67			4.31	0.9792

TABLE 5   COMPARISON OF RECORDED AND SIMULATED MONTHLY RUNOFF

VALUES IN INCHES

14.16

Mukewater Creek watershed are considerably more encouraging. Each of the 42 input parameters either has exact physical meaning or is an index of a physical quantity. The parameters in the latter category have been held to a minimum. There remain, however, many unsolved problems when modeling a watershed. Foremost of these problems is the spatial variation in most of the parameters. The Stanford Watershed Model attempted to solve this by assuming a linear distribution across the watershed. However, this is equivalent to assuming some average value of the parameter, such as has been done in the proposed model. The work reported by Holtan and Lopez (1969)[8] uses three zones of differing characteristics to account for the spatial variation. Quite possible, as digital computers become larger, the watershed can be modeled in smaller segments, thereby achieving a greater degree of homogeniety in each subarea.

The simulation of the infiltration process needs further improvement. While Holtan's approximation is more closely related to the physical phenomenon than other empirical equations, research using finite difference methods to model the flow in both the saturated and the unsaturated zones should yield even better approximations.

The Mukewater Creek application indicates a serious deficiency in the manner in which the interflow in handled. The classical, but empirical recession constant has not been utilized because it lacks physical significance. The Stanford Model does use this method, and the results are quite apparent in the correlation coefficients for 1957-1958 (Table 5). This water year contained twice as many (109) days of recession type flow as did any other year. Were these portions of the hydrograph closely modeled, the correlation coefficient would improve considerably. Future research needs to be directed toward defining a physically meaningful interflow model.

LIST OF SYMBOLS

a & n   constants.

C   constant, normally with a value of 1.

C_1, C_2 input constants.

C_{10}, C_{16} input parameters which must reflect the difference in permeability between the two zones.

C_{11} volume of water in groundwater storage below which no flow into the stream occurs.

C_{12}, C_{13} input parameters.

C_{14}, C_{15} input parameters.

D   storage in ft.^{3}/ft. and is defined as the average of the storage at the beginning of the time period and the storage at the end of the time period (OFSAVG).

D_e the storage in ft.^{3}/ft. for an equilibrium condition (OFSEQU), and is defined by
$$OFSEQU = \frac{0.000818 \ i^{0.6} \ n^{0.6} \ L^{1.6}}{s^{0.3}}$$

DELING   volume of water in interflow storage.

DS   actual depression storage volume, in inches of depth.

DSMAX   maximum depression storage, volume in inches of depth.

14.17

E	evaporation rate from the soil surface.
EVAPOT	potential evaporation.
f	infiltration rate when supply is not the limiting factor.
f_c	constant infiltration rate, the saturated permeability of the soil.
F_p	total volume which can be infiltrated before a constant rate of infiltration is reached.
GWS	volume of water in groundwater storage.
k	recession constant.
K	permeability of the soil in L/t units. (Equation 2)
K	vegetative factor given in Table 1. (Equation 12)
L	length of the overland flow reach in feet (VLENGH).
n	Manning roughness factor for overland (ROUGH).
OLF	rate of runoff in inches per hour per unit area.
q_i	flow for the ith time period.
q_0	flow at the beginning of the first time period.
s	volume of soil water per unit soil volume. (Equation 2)
S	slope of the overland flow surface (SLOPE). (Equation 3)
S	available pore space in the 0-21 inch depth. (Equation 12)
SATPRM	saturated permeability of the Upper Zone, in inches per hour.
t	time.
TIZS	volume of water stored in the top half of the Intermediate one.
UZMIN	minimum volume allowed in the Upper Zone.
UZS	corrent volume of water in the Upper Zone in $inches^3/inch^2$.
UZST	total pore space in the Upper Zone, porosity times thickness in inches $inch^2$.
V	bulk velocity in the y direction (i.e. the flow rate through a gross unit area).
V_o	infiltration rate.
VINFLO	volume of water added to the interflow process during the time period
VINST	total volume of the Intermediate Zone.
X	volume of water discharged to the stream from interflow storage in time Δt. (Equation 22).
X	volume of water flowing from the groundwater system into the stream during time Δt. (Equation 24).
X_a	fraction of the pervious area which originally was designated as depression storage, or an area contributing flow to depression storage, but is now producing runoff.
y	vertical distance from an arbitrary reference plane positive upward. (Equation 2).
y	depth, in feet, at the lower edge of the flow plane. (Equation 5).
Y	volume of water leaving the basin as underflow in the period Δt.
$\propto$	is a parameter describing the soil's ability to deliver water to the surface.
ψ	soil moisture tension potential or capillary potential with units of length.
ψae	value of soil tension at air entry.

14 .18

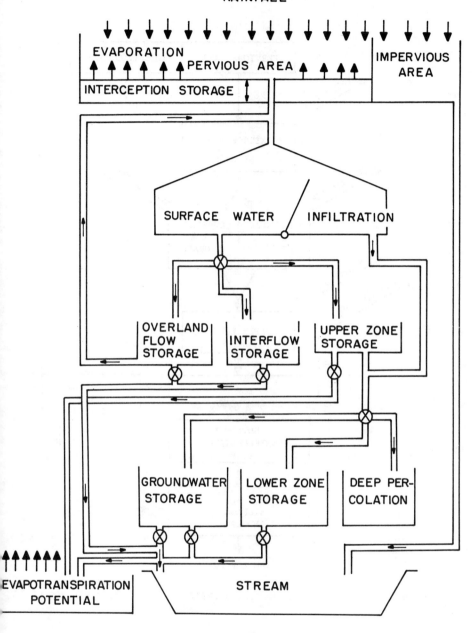

FIGURE 1   SCHEMATIC DIAGRAM OF STANFORD WATERSHED MODEL IV

14.19

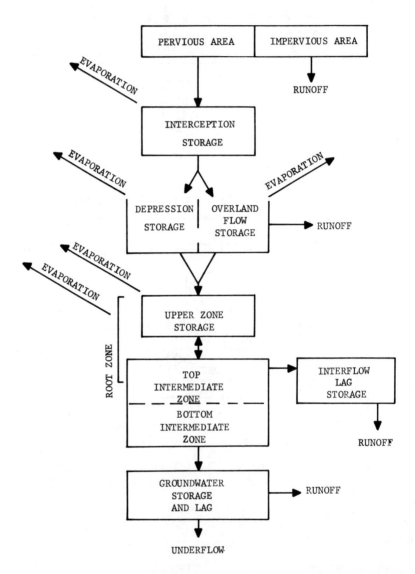

FIGURE 2   SCHEMATIC DIAGRAM OF UNIVERSITY OF TEXAS WATERSHED MODEL

14.20

315

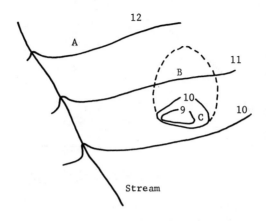

FIGURE 3   THREE TYPES OF AREAS WITHIN WATERSHED
            A) OVERLAND FLOW DIRECTLY TO STREAM
            B) OVERLAND FLOW TO DEPRESSION STORAGE
            C) DEPRESSION STORAGE

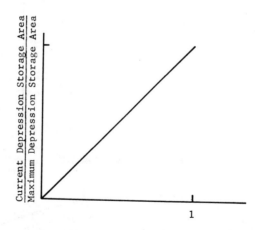

FIGURE 4   ASSUMED RELATION BETWEEN SURFACE AREA AND VOLUME OF
            DEPRESSION STORAGE

14.21

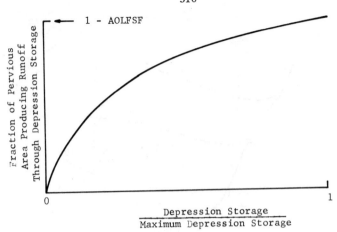

FIGURE 5   ASSUMED RELATION BETWEEN VOLUME OF DEPRESSION STORAGE,
             AND SURFACE RUNOFF FROM DEPRESSION STORAGE

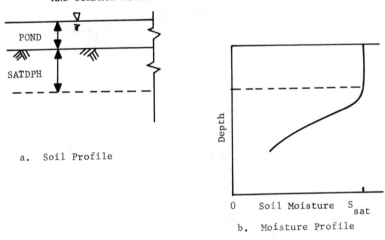

a. Soil Profile

b. Moisture Profile

FIGURE 6   INFILTRATION WITH PONDED RAINFALL

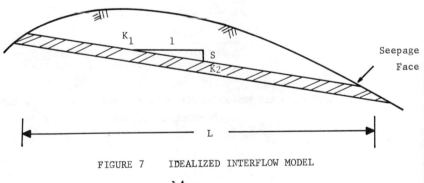

FIGURE 7   IDEALIZED INTERFLOW MODEL

14 .22

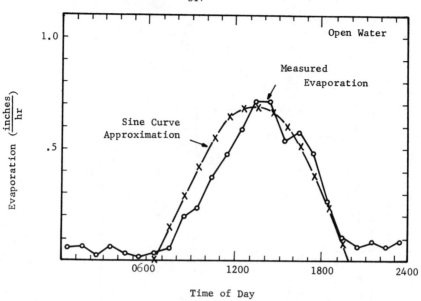

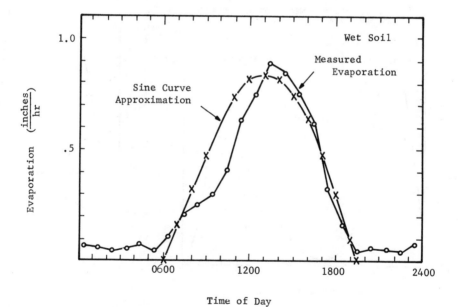

FIGURE 8   SINE CURVE APPROXIMATION OF van Bavel's (1966)
EVAPORATION MEASUREMENTS

14.23

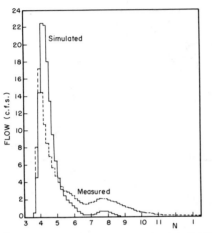

FIG. 9 COMPARISON OF MEASURED AND SIMULATED FLOW FOR STORM OF JUNE 26, 1942.

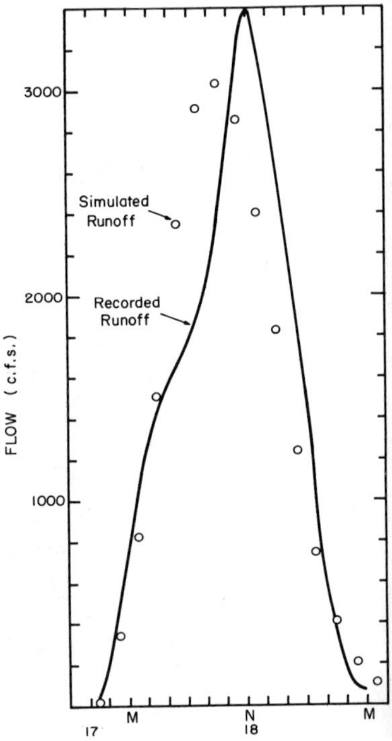

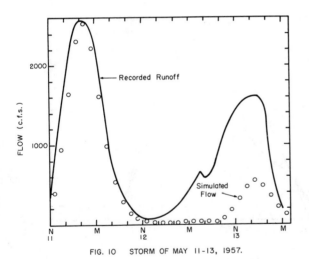

FIG. 10 STORM OF MAY 11-13, 1957.

FIG. 11 STORM OF MAY 17-18, 1957

14 .24

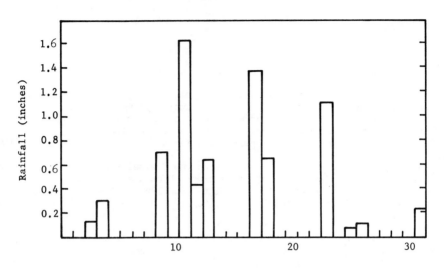

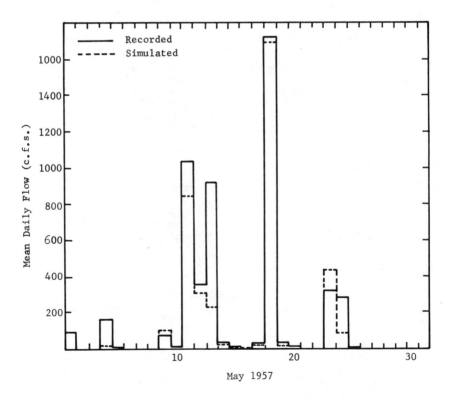

FIGURE 12   PRECIPATION AND RUNOFF FOR MAY 1957

14.25

DISCUSSION

C. KISIEL

1. How can we be sure that the most severe test has been applied to the mode

2. Of interest in future studies would be an explicit consideration of time-varying and nonlinear parameters. For example, permeability of unsaturated porous media varies in time and with depth or soil moisture states. The above augmentation does, however, require more data. But the problem with existing models is that they place all parameters for all events in the same population.

3. Modelers generally subscribe to the viewpoint of simplicity of the model and parsimony in the number of parameters. Unnecessary complexity is to be avoided. However, implied in some of the modeling philosophy is the notion that the sum of the parts is equal to the whole. What are the risks in this approach to watershed modeling?

4. More emphasis is being placed on the accuracy of prediction of important components of the simulated hydrograph -- for example, peaks, time to peak, total volume, low flows, runs (and other statistical properties). Based on your experience with the Texas model, how important are the observed discrepancies in relation to the potential uses of the model? What are appropriate criteria in judging the goodness of fit with respect to the earlier mentioned properties?

5. W. Snyder in his paper suggests "hopefully" that the model components are "extracted" or "processed" information. "They are a higher order of information." This seemingly is the presumption of watershed simulation models. I am troubled this view only with respect to the seeming neglect of questions of sample size, error criteria and uniqueness of solution. What sample size of data to be fitted would be adequate to obtain an adequate fit and subsequent confidence in use of model on "ungaged" watersheds? How important is the issue of nonuniqueness of solution? How good is the extracted information?

6. In Figure 12, the water balance does not seem to be preserved over the period of record. Should it not be?

7. How representative is the sine curve in Figure 8 for various other conditions on the watershed?

8. There is some evidence that the parameter C11 can be in serious error. Definition of groundwater reservoirs is not without its serious difficulties.

J. PAUL RILEY

1. You indicated that you had developed a complex model based upon small tir and space increments. Usually it is more fruitful to preceed from the simple to the complex.

2. With references to parameter evaluation, we have done this for a monthly simulation model over a period of 30 years, and from these results obtained a statistical distribution of the parameter values. Variations resulted from a number of sources, including periodicities, non-stationarity, sampling errors, fitting errors, and failure by the model to accurately represent the physical syst

3. As you know, much of our work has been based on the kind of conceptual model that you have discussed. There is a tendency to fragment this type of model beyond what is necessary and certainly often beyond what is justified from a verification standpoint. We need to find ways of reducing the number of "boxes" in the model. Perhaps the answer is less determinism and more stochasticity.

4. No analytical methods have been mentioned or cited from the literature. The distributed parameter system under consideration perhaps might be tackled with a little more success by analytical methods in which the various system parameters are identified.

T. D. STEELE

The Stanford Watershed Model and various modifications thereof may serve as an excellent educational tool and, given the appropriate circumstances, may be useful in water resources planning and design. In spite of your modifications in the Texas version of SWM IV, considerable "engineering" (subjective) judgement still must be exercised in estimating several of the model parameters, some of which are very critical in affecting model output, both in terms of hydrograph simulation and continuous moisture accounting over periods of several years.

In assessing the desireability of applying any form of the basic Stanford model to a particular basin, concern must be given to the availability of the appropriate input data and information on the drainage basin for model parameter estimation. Occasionally, the application of SWM has been proposed for hydrologic simulation without a sufficient and proper assessment of the program objectives and of the appropriate input information.

Y. TAKAHASI

(1) How to divide the pervious area and impervious area in practice? How about the accuracy of such a divide?

(2) Why the application to Mukewater Creek has a rather good result compared with Edwardsville case? What is the severity of the conditions to the latter?

(3) How to improve the simulation of interflow process?

(4) How to judge the validity to assume the hydrological model as linear, time-invariant, etc.?

V. YEVJEVICH

The method of rainfall-runoff simulation presented in this paper has an advantage when no runoff data is available and parameters of the model can be estimated from the river basin characteristics. When some runoff data are available, parallel to rainfall data, the estimates of the model parameters can be significantly improved. However, as soon as a sufficient amount of runoff data is available concurrently with the rainfall data, as well as known river basin characteristics, the multiple regression and correlation analysis may give such a relationship between runoff and all other variables that the transfer of other rainfall data into the runoff data shows a smaller standard error of estimate than the presented deterministic simulation model.

The main objection to the simulation method presented is its indeterminacy of parameter estimation, with more parameters needing to be estimated than the number of equations available.

RESPONSE BY W. L. MOORE

The response to discussion by C. Kisiel is as follows.

1. It may not be possible to be sure that the most severe test has been applied to the model. There is not a single most severe test. For adequate testing, the model must be applied over a wide range of hydrological conditions. Under some conditions, the infiltration and evaporation conditions may be extremely important, under other conditions overland flow and the evaluation of resistance may be very important, in another case the ground water storage and subsequent release may be dominant. The tests reported in the paper are only a start on evaluating the reliability of the proposed model. One condition that should normally be avoided in selecting a watershed for testing the model is regularity of rainfall and runoff patterns. In an area which has a regular and uniformly distributed rainfall with small variations in runoff, it should be relatively easy to simulate the runoff with a very simple model. One of the reasons for choosing the Mukewater Creek watershed was that it shows a great deal of variability in both rainfall and runoff patterns.

2. The authors agree that some parameters in the model should be time varying and non-linear; and, in fact, the model described provides for this. For example, the interception storage can be varied as a function of season to account for changes in vegetable cover, the value of the unsaturated permeability and the soil tension are expressed as function of the soil moisture (Equation 17 and 18) and thus do vary with time and with depth.

3. I am sure everyone agrees that unnecessary complexity is to be avoided. The problem is to determine what is necessary and what is unnecessary. If the notion referred to by Dr. Kisiel, that the sum of the parts is equal to the whole, is the one involved in breaking a linear phenomenon into pieces and adding the pieces together to get the results, I would agree whole heartedly that this is a dangerous notion when applied to non-linear systems. In fact, such a notion can lead not only to erroneous predictions, but to predictions that are opposite to the truth. The simulation procedure described in the paper is really a moisture accounting process in which the presence and transfer of water between various elements is monitored at frequent time intervals. Thus, it is not a question of adding the sum of parts to equal the whole but rather a continual application of the continuity principle.

4. The aim of watershed simulation is to simulate accurately the entire hydrograph in all of its aspects. Although this aim should be pursued, it will probably never be reached with complete accuracy. It seems probable to me that the model may be adjusted somewhat depending upon the potential use to which it is put. Thus, if one is interested in low flows, a relatively long time interval chould be used and more effort would be put on matching the flow volume than the instantaneous hydrograph peaks. On the other hand, if one is interested in levee height, it would be necessary to concentrate on magnitudes of peak flows. The question as to the appropriate criteria to use in judging the goodness of fit is an important one which deserves more careful study than it has received so far.

5. The questions raised as to sample size, error criteria, and uniqueness of solution are very important ones for which answers must be sought. These would seem to hinge on the previous question regarding the proper criteria for goodness of fit. Due to the complexity of the simulation process, it will probably be difficult to arrive at satisfying quantitative solutions to many of these problems.

6. The question is raised about preservation of the water balance over the period shown in Fig. 12. Of course, the water balance should be preserved for

14.28

each time period but at the present stage, at least, this is not exactly true. For the month of May 1957, the recorded runoff amounted to 2.75 inches and the simulated runoff 2.03 inches. More data on the comparison of recorded and simulated flows by the Stanford Watershed Model and the U. T. Watershed Model is shown in Fig. 6.5 of reference 3.

7. The data presented in Fig. 3 is from reference 9 which was taken to be representative and is not based on measurements on the Mukewater Watershed.

8. We would be interested in more information on the sources of error in the parameter C11, the volume of water in ground water storage below which no flow into the stream occurs.

The response to discussion by J. P. Riley is as follows.

1. I agree that it is usually more furitful to preceed from the simple to the complex when one is trying to understand or explain a physical process. In developing a watershed simulation scheme, one utilizes understanding and knowledge already available about the physical processes in a system to predict runoff, soil moisture, etc. In this process it may be beneficial to start using all the available knowledge and gradually cut out what proves to be unnecessary.

2. It is not surprising that a monthly simulation model would show a statistical distribution of the parameters over a period of thirty years resulting from the various sources mentioned. The aim in developing a model would be to accurately represent the physical system and have the parameters which were constant remain constant and those which represented periodic or non-stationary quantities vary in the ways they do in nature. This would imply that the various parameters must have a distinct physical interpretation that can be identified with some property of the physical system. This was the aim in our simulation model although it can surely be improved from its present form.

3. The statement is made that there is a tendency to fragment the model beyond "what is necessary" and ways need to be found to reduce the number of "boxes" in the model. The question as to what is necessary depends on how general the model is to be, that is, how widely will the conditions vary for which the model is to be used. If the same model is to be used under widely varying conditions, it will need to be fairly complex, but the relative importance of different "boxes" will change greatly depending on the particular conditions for which the model is being used. For example, under arid conditions, evaporation may be very important but ground water relatively unimportant, while in a more humid area evaporation is less significant and the contributions of ground water to base flow may be the dominant factor.

I find it difficult to subscribe to the idea that the answer is in less determinism and more stochasticity. Stochastic analysis is a procedure for making statements about the values of variables when the physical processes that control the variation are unknown or not fully understood. I favor utilizing to the full whatever understanding we have, recognizing it is incomplete, the models are approximate, and the data is insufficient. Thus there will probably always be stochastic variations present in the output of a model. The more we understand, however, and the more accurately the model represents the physical condition, the smaller will be the stochastic component. The pursuit of this goal of increased understanding is the basis for much of the productive work that has been done in science and engineering.

4. The suggestion should be explored.

The response to discussion by T. D. Steele is as follows.

These comments are all well stated, and I agree with them.

The response to discussion by Y. Takahasi is as follows.

(1) The pervious area may be determined from areal photographs where they are available or in some urban areas from records and plats kept by city offices. Where such detailed records are not available, the classification of areas may be made from data in similar regions, for example: downtown business, shopping centers, dense suburban (apartments), suburban, open suburban, and rural. Percent impervious cover for each type of area can be determined and used in those areas where such data is not available. Actually, a simpler classification with fewer classes would be accurate enough for many purposes.

(2) For the Edwardsville case all the parameters were estimated in advance from physical data available for the watershed. There was no trial and error adjustments of the parameters based on measured rainfall and runoff data. Also in the Edwardsville case, the results were distorted during the winter months by freezing of the ground. These conditions made a very severe test for the first application of the simulation procedure, and close agreement between measured and simulated runoff was not anticipated.

In the case of Mukewater Creek there was no freezing of the ground, and also the major simulation parameters were adjusted by trial and error based on a period of recorded rainfall and runoff data. This type of application is more typical of what has been done with other simulation models and the results are comporable to those obtained by the Stanford watershed model.

(3) This is a good question and the answer is not known. It seems that a better understanding of the physical processes of interflow is needed as a basis for an improved simulation method.

(4) The hydrological processes in nature are not linear and not time invariant and neither is the numerical simulation process described in the paper. The movement of water between the various storage elements is highly non-linear. The contribution of a given increment of rainfall to runoff depends in a complex non-linear manner on the condition of the watershed at any particular time. It is not intended that the parameters be time invariant; and in fact some, such as interception storage, change with season. Also, it might be anticipated that changes in the watershed on a long-term basis, such as changes in the impervious cover, changes in depression storage, or changes in ground cover, would be accounted for by corresponding lont-term changes in the related simulation parameters.

The response to discussion by V. Yevjevich is as follows.

I do not doubt that in particular instances a multiple regression and correlation analysis may give a relationship between a runoff and other variables that shows a smaller standard error of estimate than may occur with a deterministic simulation model. The main purpose of the simulation model approach is not to provide the relationship between existing data on runoff, rainfall, and other hydrologic parameters, but to deal with three types of predictions of runoff outsic the period of record.

14 .30

1.   Prediction of runoff from either recorded or generated rainfall in areas where there are no recorded runoff data. This will require estimation of parameters from physical characteristics of the watershed.

2.   Extension of runoff data for periods of measured or generated rainfall beyond that for which measurements are available.

3.   Making estimates of changes in runoff due to anticipated changes in watershed characteristics.

Where the multiple regression and correlation analysis can be used to provide acceptable estimates of runoff data for a particular purpose, it may be preferable to the simulation model approach.

The last comment about the indeterminacy of parameter estimation for the simulation model is related to the comments of Dr. Kisiel, and the reply to his comments is applicable here. With regard to the model requiring the estimation of more parameters than the number of equations available, I believe that depends on the length of record available. I do not know of any way to express the concept explicitly, but if a "fairly long period of record" is available involving a wide range of hydrological conditions in the watershed and many discrete hydrological events, the record contains a great deal of information as a basis for evaluating the parameters.

United States-Japan   Bi-lateral Seminar in Hydrology
Honolulu, January 1971

AN APPLICATION OF SIMULATED RAINFALL MODELS TO
FORECASTING OF THE LONG TERM VARIATION OF RIVER BED

by
Akira MUROTA
Professor of Civil Engineering,
Osaka University, Osaka, Japan.
Michio HASHINO
Lecturer of Construction Engineering,
Tokushima University, Tokushima, Japan.

Synopsis
        The long term variations of river bed being accompanied with the
transversal supply of sediment transported from the watershed to the river
channel, will be studied by numerical experiments.
        Enormous amount of debris production due to landslides in our moun-
tainous area has been caused by heavy rainfalls. A part of these debris
yields may tumble down directly into the river channel and humps of debris
in large scale on the river bed will be occasionally formed. These dunes
would move down slowly in the channel and our morphological question to be
answered is whether the long term variation of the bed profile will show
any trend of convergence to the stable bed under natural environments, or
not.
        For stochastical evaluations of debris yields, these authors dis-
covered the fact that the major factor affecting on landslide generation
and resulted debris yields is not directly the precipitation, but the
water storage in the drainage basin in the form of subsurface storage.
The functional relationship between the watershed storage and debris
yields was empirically established.
        If the rainfall sequence has been properly simulated and the water-
shed storage has been calculated by run-off analyses, the probable occur-
renences of landslide and resulted quantities of debris yields may be
forecasted by the watershed storge versus debris yields function.
Synthesis of rainfall simulations will be reported in this paper.
        After calculations of supplimental inflow of sediment from the water-
shed to channels and preparing simulated river flow, the river bed
variations at the 26km reach of our objective river are forecasted
extending over 10 years future and our analyses show some negative interpretations for possibility of stable bed profile under actual environments.

Introduction

        One of attractive themes in the recent river engineering is the
problem of possibility of stable river bed profile when some natural, or
man-made disturbunces are put in a river system. Due to the put-in of the
outer disturbance which may be either natural (for example, inflow of
massive amount of debris produced by landslides), or man-made (e.g.,
construction of dams), dynamic responce of river systems would be usually
very gradual relaxation process and the river bed variation should be
traced in sufficiently long period by field observations or simulation
analyses.
        Another difficulties for quantitative evaluation of river bed varia-
tion may be originated from our poor knowledge about sediment supply
transversally flowing into the channel from the watershed. To introduce
the effect of these sediment supply to our analyses, the mechanism of

production of transportable sediment and debris yields should be clarified.

Nearly all of debris production due to landslides in our country have been caused by heavy rainfall. Landslide phenomena, however, are of rare occurrence and in stochastic process. For making possible to treat the landslide phenomena as a stochastic analysis, we have to consider the problem in very long term because of rare frequency of the phenomena, not only by the reason of very gradual response of river bed variations.

To simulate the long term precipitation sequences which are the trigger of landslide outbreaks and the input for the output discharge, we will consider the daily rainfall for the landslide forecasting and the hourly rainfall for the simulation of discharge and we may reasonably assume that the precipitation sequences may be represented by their three components which are mutually independent, such as the intensity, frequency of occurrences and interval of adjacent daily rainfall. According to the statistical homogeneity of precipitation characteristics, one year will be divided into proper numbers of season. (In our simulation, the season having the statistical homogeneity is considered as a month.) By simulation techniques which are based on the convolution of probability evaluation for each component, simulated rainfalls have been generated extending over 700 years.

Based on the observation of our several times field-surveys at the target watershed (the Rv. Arita basin) as shown in Fig.1, these authors indicate the fact that the major factor affecting on the landslide generation and resulted debris yields is not directly the precipitation, but the water-mass-storage in the catchment, mainly in the form of subsurface storage. Surveying the bulk of produced debris by landslides and calculating the subsurface storage of precipitation by runoff analyses, we could establish empirically the functional relationship between the subsurface storage and debris yields. Moreover, it will be demonstrated that the critical watershed storage by which the landslide would set up to generate, is about 200mm. Using the fuction of watershed storage versus debris yield, we may be able to perform the simulation of landslide phenomena and to evaluate quantitatively debris yields.

Because we have prepared both probability distributions of the transportable sediment and the river discharge, forecasting of the river bed variation for our objective 26km reach are ready to perform. Simulations are extended over 10 years future starting from two initial bed profiles. One of the initial conditions corresponds to the profile after 1953 when the severe landslide damage was experienced along the Rv. Arita and tremendous bulk of debris collapsed into the channel forming the natural rockfill dam, and the other profile is the so-called dynamically stable bed slope.

Moreover, superposing two or three imaginary humps on the bed, we will trace the dynamic behavior of moving humps.

Among several results of our analyses, one of the interesting features is the tendency that we may expect some stable state of bed if the supplemental inflow of sediment from the whole watershed would be ignored, but if not so, any finally stable profiles should not be able to be expected.

I.   Modeling of Rainfall Sequences

Rainfall sequences will be represented stochastically by their three components, that is, the intensity $\{x\}$, frequency $\{r\}$ and interval $\{j\}$. We can reasonably assume that there will be no cross-correlations among these three components.

For modeling of daily rainfall sequences, we will calculate at first the joint probability of $\{r\}$ with $\{j\}$.

Probability G_r of r-days rainfall occurrences for n-days which

15.2

compose a season having a statistical homogeneity of hydrological characteristics, can be calculated by

$$G_r = M_r / \sum_{i=0}^{n} M_i \qquad (1.1)$$

, where M_r is the number of years in existing records having r -days
occurrences for n -days.

When $r = 1$ (that is, only one day rainfall in a season), probability
of a rainfall occurrence on the i_1 -day in a season, is $G_1 \times \frac{1}{n}$.

When $r = 2$, probability of the first rainfall occurrence on the i_1 -
day ($1 \leq i_1 \leq n-1$), is $G_2 \times \frac{1}{(n-1)}$, but the second one would be affected by the
first one because the nominal period of a season decreases from n to
($n - i_i$). Then, probability $K_{j_2 2}^{(i_1)}$ of serial occurrences being composed
of the first rainfall on the i_L -day and the second rainfall following after
the first with j_2 -days interval, is

$$K_{j_2 2}^{(i_1)} = H_{j_2 2} / \sum_{\ell=0}^{(n-i_i-1)} H_{\ell 2}, \qquad (1.2)$$

where $H_{j_2 2}$ is the empirical frequency of interval j_2 when $r = 2$.

Consequently, the joint probability of two rainfalls occurrences being
composed of the first on the i_1 -day and the second on the i_2 -day, is

$$G_2 \frac{1}{(n-1)} \cdot K_{j_2 2}^{(i_1)} \qquad (1.3)$$

Generally, probability of r -times occurrences of rainfalls on the
i_1 , i_2 , $\cdots$, i_r -day in a season, is

$$G_r \frac{1}{(n-r+1)} \prod_{k=2}^{r} K_{j_k r}^{(i_{k-1})}, \qquad (1.4)$$

provided that

$$K_{j_k r}^{(i_{k-1})} = H_{j_k r} / \sum_{\ell=0}^{n-i_{k-1}-(r+k+1)} H_{\ell r}, \qquad (1.5)$$

which show the probabability of occurrences of the k -th rainfall on the
i_k -day following the ($k-1$)-th rainfall on the i_{k-1} -day.

Moreover, we will convolute the probability of intensity to the joint
probability of rainfall occurrences and intervals given by Eq.(1.4).

Being $f(x)$ the probability density function of rainfall intensity,
probability corresponding to $x = x_1$, is

$$\Delta F(x_1) = \int_{x_1 - \Delta x/2}^{x_1 + \Delta x/2} f(x) \cdot dx. \qquad (1.6)$$

If there is no lag-correlation between x_1 and sequent x_2, probability of simultaneous occurrence of x_1 and x_2 is

$$P\{x_1, x_2\} = \Delta F(x_1) \Delta F(x_2). \qquad (1.7)$$

But, when sequent rainfalls have some correlation,

$$P\{x_1, x_2\} = P\{x_1\} \times P\{x_2 | x_1\}. \qquad (1.8)$$

If x_1 and x_2 are connected by the equation

$$x_2 = \rho x_1 + (1 - \rho) \bar{x} + \sigma_x (1 - \rho^2)^{\frac{1}{2}} \cdot \varepsilon_2 , \qquad (1.9)$$

where ρ : correlation coefficient,
$\bar{x}$: expected value,
σ_x : standard deviation,
ε_2 : noise.
From Eq.(1.9),

$$\varepsilon_2 = \frac{x_2 - \xi x_1 - (1-\xi)\bar{x}}{\sigma_x (1-\xi^2)^{1/2}} \qquad (1.10)$$

then,

$$\Delta\varepsilon_2 = \frac{\Delta x_2}{\sigma_x} (1-\xi^2)^{-\frac{1}{2}} \qquad (1.11)$$

At Eq.(1.8),

$$P\{x_2|x_1\} = \frac{1}{\sqrt{2\pi}} \int_{\varepsilon_2 - \Delta\varepsilon/2}^{\varepsilon_2 + \Delta\varepsilon/2} e^{-t^2/2} dt \equiv \Delta E(\varepsilon_2) \qquad (1.12)$$

Representing the rainfall on the i_a -day having intensity x_a by the symbol x_{i_a} , we get

$$P\{x_1, x_2\} \equiv P\{x_{i_1}, x_{i_2}\} = \Delta F(x_{i_1}) \times \Delta D(x_{i_2}|x_{i_1}), \qquad (1.13)$$

with

$$\Delta D(x_{i_2}|x_{i_1}) = \begin{bmatrix} \Delta E(\varepsilon_{i_2}) & \text{when } i_2 = i_1 + 1, \\ \Delta F(x_{i_2}) & \text{when } i_2 > i_1 + 1. \end{bmatrix} \qquad (1.14)$$

Generally,

$$P\{x_{i_1}, x_{i_2}, \cdots, x_{i_r}\} = \Delta F(x_{i_1}) \times \prod_{k=2}^{r} \Delta D(x_{i_k}|x_{i_{k-1}}), \qquad (1.15)$$

with

$$\Delta D(x_{i_k}|x_{i_{k-1}}) = \begin{bmatrix} \Delta E(\varepsilon_{i_k}) & \text{when } i_k = i_{k-1} + 1, \\ \Delta F(x_{i_k}) & \text{when } i_k > i_{k-1} + 1. \end{bmatrix} \qquad (1.16)$$

Finally, convoluting probabilities of rainfall occurrences, intervals and intensities, we can represent the rainfall model in stochastic process as follows.

(1) The probability of no rainfall in a season: $P(0)$ is

$$P(0) = G_0 \qquad (1.17)$$

(2) The probability of only one-time rainfall on the i_1 -day in a season having the intensity $x_1 \equiv x_{i_1}$: $P[x_{i_1}]$ is

$$P[x_{i_1}] = \frac{1}{n} G_1 \cdot \Delta F(x_{i_1}) \qquad (1.18)$$

(3) The probability of r -times occurrences of rainfalls which are a series of the first on i_1 -day with the intensity x_1 , the second on the i_2 -day with the intensity x_2 and so on, is

$$P[x_{i_1}, x_{i_2}, \cdots, x_{i_r}] =$$

$$\frac{1}{n-r+1} G_r \left[\prod_{k=2}^{r} K_{J_k r}^{(i_{k-1})} \right] \times \left[\Delta F(x_{i_1}) \prod_{\ell=2}^{r} \Delta D(x_{i_\ell}|x_{i_{\ell-1}}) \right]. \qquad (1.19)$$

As the first step of practical procedures of the simulation, we have to prepare the probability distributions of frequency G_r , interval $H_{j \cdot r}$ and intensity $F(x)$ of daily rainfall sequences from existing records by statistical calculations. These characteristics of rainfall sequences are set in memory of the electric digital computer.

We can get specialized random components of rainfall being conformed to the indicated probability distribution by generating normalized random numbers as shown schematically in Fig.2.

To examine an adequency of our simulation technique, comparisons of existing data of maximum daily rainfall intensity in a month with simulated ones are illustrated in Fig.3 and Fig.4. Both of existing and simulated extreme values were collected from data for 78 years at the Yawata gaging station in our target watershed and from simulated rainfall sequences generated for 700 years, respectively. Simulated extreme values were picked up from the arbitrarily abstracted sequence for same years to those of gaging performance, that is, 78 years for our case. Distributions of simulated values are sufficiently adequate on May, August and November, but not so on June, July and September, though coincidences are satisfactory in general.

We may reasonably guess that there will be little discrepancies between existing and simulated values both of frequency and interval of rainfall sequences, respectively.

II.   Simulation of Landslide Occurrences and
Forecasting of Debris Yields Produced by
Landslides

According to many researches on geomorphlogical surveys of landslide phenomena, we have some useful outlooks for the objective. The drainage density originally proposed by Horton (1945), or the ruggedness number and hypsometric integral which were offered by Strahler's analyses (1958), may be morphologically important indexes of landslide generation.

These conventional approaches to the problem, however, essentially base on multiple regression analyses, mainly using geomorphological factors as the inducements. Without insights for heavy rainfall or earthquake shock as the predominant causes for landslide generation, we can not depart from the descriptive stage of studies on landslide phenomena.

In our case, though the predominant cause of landslide occurrences is heavy rainfall, any distinct relationship between rainfall and landslide generation has not been discovered. The question that should be pursued is which component of rainfall is most directly correlated to incidental occurrences of landslides, concentrated intensity, long duration-time or large amount of totals?

Because total amount of rainfall or maximum intensity of rainfall has been usually taken as indexes of analyses for convenience sake, we primely investigated correlations between total or intensity of rainfalls and landslide occurrences at the Arita basin, but any significant correlation could not be recognized.

When we reflect upon the physical mechanism of landslide generation, it may be a common understanding that the infiltration part of precipitation or subsurface flow should act a leading role of landslide outbreak. In the case of well-weathered stratum loading on the inpermeable base-rock, landslides will generate because the infiltration makes the weathered stratum weight due to saturated water and makes the interface friction decrease due to labrication effect. Even in the case of poor permeable stratum, subsurface flow will concentratedly penetrate into faults or cracks and due to the pipping effect, local failure of mountainside stability being a trigger of massive movement of slope will occure.

Amount of infiltration or subsurface discharge may be summarized as a regime of short-term storage of water-mass in the watershed. Due to these physical interpretation, these authors would like to say that the leading role of landslide generation is not directly rainfall, but the water-mass storage in the watershed.

15.5

The water storage in a basin will be evaluated by the following relation.

$$\frac{dS(t)}{dt} = r - (q + e + q_L),$$ (2. 1)

where r : rainfall intensity,
  q : river discharge,
  e : loss due to evapotranspiration,
  q_L : perpetual storage as deep ground water.
For simplicity, neglecting e and q_L , we have

$$\frac{dS(t)}{dt} = r(t) - q(t).$$ (2. 2)

The intial value of storage: S_* may be calculated by the following empirical relation between the storage and river discharge for no-rainfall days.

$$S_*(t) = K_0\, q(t)^{P_0}.$$ (2. 3)

For no-rainfall days, Eq.(2.2) is

$$\frac{dS(t)}{dt} = -q(t).$$ (2. 4)

The solution of this equation is

$$S(t) = -\int_{t_*}^{t} q(t)\, dt + S_*$$

$$= \int_{t_*}^{t} \left\{ \frac{P_0 - 1}{K\,P_0} \cdot t - q(t_*)^{P_0-1} \right\}^{\frac{1}{P_0-1}} dt + S_*$$

$$= K_0\left[\left\{ \frac{P_0-1}{K_0 P_0} t - q(t_*)^{P_0-1} \right\}^{\frac{P_0}{P_0-1}} - \left\{ \frac{P_0-1}{K_0 P_0} t_* - q(t_*)^{P_0-1} \right\}^{\frac{P_0}{P_0-1}} \right] + K_0\, q(t_*)^{P_0}$$ (2 · 5)

For calculation by the digital computor, difference expressions of the solution of Eq.(2.4) are

$$S(t_* + \Delta t) = S(t_*) - \{ S(t_*)/K_0 \}^{1/P_0} \cdot \Delta t$$

$$S(t_* + 2\Delta t) = S(t_* + \Delta t) - \{ S(t_* + \Delta t)/K_0 \}^{1/P_0} \Delta t$$ (2. 6)

and so on.
If the rainfall starts at time t_0 and ends at time t_1 ,

$$S(t_c + \Delta t) = S(t_0) + \{ r(t_0) - q(t_0) \} \cdot \Delta t.$$ (2. 7)

Discharge $q(t)$ may be calculated by the storage function analysis as follows.

$$S = K_0'\, q(t_0 + \tau)^{P_0'}$$ (2. 8)

$$\frac{dS(t)}{dt} = r(t_0) - q(t_0 + \tau),$$ (2. 9)

or

$$\frac{dq}{dt} = \frac{r(t_0) - q(t_0 + \tau)}{K_0'\, P_0'\, q(t + \tau)^{P_0' - 1}}$$ (2. 10)

Putting $t_0 + \tau \equiv t$, the solution of Eq.(2.10) in difference expression, is

15.6

$$g(t+\Delta t)=\frac{r(t-\tau)-g(t)}{K_o' P_o' g(t)^{P_o'-1}}\Delta t + g(t).\qquad(2.11)$$

By using reciprocally Eq.(2.7) and (2.11), we can calculate $S(t)$ as follows.

Starting from intial values $S(t_o)=K_o\,g(t_o)^{P_o}$, $r(t_o)$ and $g(t_o)$ at $t=t_o$, the discharge at $t=t_o+\Delta t$ is

$$g(t_o+\Delta t)=\frac{r(t_o-\tau)+g(t_o)}{K_o' P_o' g(t_o)^{P_o'-1}}\Delta t + g(t_o),\qquad(2.12)$$

and the storage at $t=t_o+\Delta t$, is

$$S(t_o+\Delta t)=S(t_o)+\{r(t_o)-g(t_o)\}\Delta t.\qquad(2.13)$$

Sequently, at $t=t_o+2\Delta t$,

$$g(t_o+2\Delta t)=\frac{r(t_o+\Delta t-\tau)+g(t_o+\Delta t)}{K_o' P_o' g(t_o+\Delta t)^{P_o'-1}}\Delta t + g(t_o+\Delta t),$$

$$S(t_o+2\Delta t)=S(t_o+\Delta t)+\{r(t_o+\Delta t)-g(t_o+\Delta t)\}\Delta t$$

and so on.

At the Arita basin, we have 15 data of heavy rainfall groups since 1953 when the heaviest rainfall on record were experienced. (See Table 2.) By the 1953 disaster, the total rainfall was 583mm and the maximum storage of this rainfall group calculated by Eq.(2.13) is 494mm in depth, by which total debris production over the watershed was $2.1\times10^7 m^3$ and landslide scars were observed as about 2,300.

Among 15 records since 1953, detailed surveys were performed for 4 rainfall groups including the 1953 disaster and landslide occurrences were surely confirmed and not so surely for 5 groups and scarcely for 6 groups in spite of considerably heavy rainfalls.

By these field surveys and calculations of the maximum storage for each rainfall group, we can conclude that the criterion of landslide outbreak is about 200mm of storage in the watershed. This criterion has been verified to be appropriate for another watershed (the Ibi basin in middle Japan) by these authors.

The functional relationship between the maximum water storage S_{max} and total debris yields by landslides over the watershed is shown in Fig.5.

On the other hand, using records of the 1953 disaster, we have empirically the frequency distribution of debris yields per a landslide scar as shown in Fig.6. By this figure, we can see the fact that landslide may be scarcely affected by geological conditions and the watershed may be regarded as to be homogeneous so far as landslide occurrences are concerned.

These ensemble treatments of landslide-scars distribution for the particular disaster will not be stationary for every landslide occurrence. But, except for the 1953 disaster, we had not so many samples of landslide scars due to each heavy rainfall as we can evaluate the distribution, and this ensemble distribution profile would be assumed to be applicable to any generations of landslides.

Consequently, probability of occurrences of landslides can be expressed by Fig.5 and Fig.6. Distribution of landslide magnitude is prescribed by Fig.6 and integral amounts of debris yields are given by the relation o Fig.5 and these two constraints should not be mutually inconsistent.

The largest scar of landslides will be usually surveyed in high accuracy, but landslides in small scale may be missed in the field survey. Accordingly, in the frequency distribution of Fig.6, the largest magnitude would be fixed and integral amounts of debris yields which are produced by smaller landslides, will not invariably be equal to the volume observed by field surveys shown in Fig.5.

15.7

For consistency, the original curve has to be modified as shown in Fig.5. and the modified curve may be more reasonable than the original, because the former includes integral amounts of debris yields by smaller landslides which may be missed in the field survey.

Before advancing to the practice of landslide simulation, we have to mention about simulation techniques of hourly rainfalls and serial occurrences of landslides.

Rainfall sequences in hour unit generally have some lag-time correlations in their time-series. For our records of the Yawata gaging station, the hourly rainfall sequences have an autocorrelation coefficient $\rho = 0.345$ on an average. If it would be necessary to consider the autocorrelation, particular relations such as Eq.(1.9) will be applicable.

For simplicity, neglecting any autocorrelation in hourly rainfall sequences, we generate specialized random numbers being conformed to the empirically indicated probability distribution of hourly rainfalls and when sum of these random numbers is equal to the daily rainfall being generated in advance by the simulation already mentioned in the previous chapter, generations of the random numbers will stop.

Assumptions for serial occurrences of landslides are as follows. Considering the storage sequences as shown in Fig.7, we may expect that when $S > S_c$, the first outbreak of landslide will generate and as the storage increases, production of debris increases following to the functional relation of storage versus debris yields which was given by Fig.5. When S reaches the maximum S_2 , occurrences of landslides will stop. Over $S = S_2$, the storage is going to recess and rise again toward a next peak $S_4 (> S_2)$. Notwithstanding $S > S_c$ at the interval $t_2 < t < t_3$, any landslide would not occurre because landslides have previously occurred under the equivalent circumstance at $t_1 < t < t_2$. When S increases over S_2, landslides will be generated again. After decreasing under S_c at $t_5 < t < t_6$, the storage rises again over S_c and landslides will occurre at the interval $t_6 < t < t_7$.

But, the geological question arises on the reoccurrences at $t = t_6$, that is, the possibility of interference on the reoccurrence of forerunning stage of landslides. There is an opinion that the landslide phenomena will become immune from their reoccurrence because following landslides after overall occurrences of them at a watershed would be scarcely expected for very long periods. These interference effect of the phenomenon has to be geologically studied in future, but we will not consider the non-linear effect due to having no knowledge about them.

Procedures of the simulation are as follows.
1. Generate the simulated daily rainfall sequences.
2. Generate the simulated hourly rainfall sequences in the limit of the daily rainfall and make the hyetograph.
3. Calculate the discharge corresponding to the hyetograph by run-off analyses and make the hydrograph.
4. Calculate the initial storage S_* by Eq.(2.3).
5. Evaluate the storage $S(t)$ by Eq.(2.6).
6. When $S > S_c$, putting $S_1 = S_c + \Delta S$ after Δt from the instant of exceed over S_c , generate specialized random numbers being conformed to the frequency curve shown in Fig.6.
7. Stop the generation of random numbers when integral of debris yields is equal to V_1 which is given by the curve in Fig.5. corresponding to S_1 .
8. Advance to the next step: $S_2 = S_1 + \Delta S$
   Generate again specialized random numbers following to the curve of Fig.6.
   Stop the generation of random numbers when integral of debris yields is equal to $(V_2 - V_1)$.

15 .8

9. Repeat same processes till the time when $S = S_{max}$.

We adopt an annual period from May to November as the rainy season. Generating simulated daily rainfall sequences for 705 years, and picking up samples of the storage being over S_c , we immediately have the probability distribution of storage. Using both of the storage-debris yields curve and the probability distribution of storage, we may evaluate the probability distribution of debris yields produced by landslides for every month. Results of the evaluation are shown in Fig.8.

According to such probability estimation, we may conclude that (1) probabilities of debris production are very small on May and June, (2) most of debris production concentrate in months from July to September, (3) landslides in relatively small scale by which debris yields are less than 30×10^4 m^3/ 194km^2/month $\fallingdotseq$ 150m^3/km^2/month, occure on September and (4) landslides in comparatively large scale occure on July and August.

Convoluting probabilities of annual debris yields, we can show the probability distribution of debris yields in long term for 38 years and 128 years in Fig.9.

III.   Simulation of River Bed Variation

3.1   Fundamental equations

The equations of continuity and motion for open channel flow can be written in forms

$$\frac{\partial A}{\partial t} + \frac{\partial Q}{\partial x} = q .$$

(3. 1)

and

$$\frac{1}{gA}\left[\frac{\partial Q}{\partial t} - \frac{Q}{A}\frac{\partial A}{\partial t} + \frac{Q}{A}\frac{\partial Q}{\partial x} - \frac{Q^2}{A^2}\frac{\partial A}{\partial x}\right] + \frac{\partial H}{\partial x}$$

$$+ \frac{\partial z}{\partial x} + \frac{n^2 Q^2}{A^2 R^{4/3}} = \frac{1}{gA}\left[q U \cos\theta - \frac{Q}{A}q\right] ,$$

(3. 2)

where x being distance in the longitudinal direction along a channel bottom, t : elapsed time, z : bed elevation from the datum, A : cross-sectional area, Q : discharge, H : average depth of the cross section and R : hydraulic radius. q is transversal inflow per unit length, θ : angle between direction of q and x , and U : velocity.

In mountainous river basins with steep slopes ($> 1/500$), the bed slope $-\partial z/\partial x$ and the friction slope $n^2 Q^2/A^2 R^{4/3}$ may be assumed to be much more governing on the flow than other terms of Eq.(3.2). Accordingly, Eq.(3.2) can be written as

$$\frac{\partial z}{\partial x} + \frac{n^2 Q^2}{A^2 R^{4/3}} = 0 .$$

(3. 3)

On the other hand, the equation of continuity for sediment when the cross sectional profile is rectangular, can be expressed as follows.

$$\frac{\partial z}{\partial t} + \frac{1}{B(1-\lambda)}\frac{\partial(q_B B)}{\partial x} = \frac{q_{BL}}{B(1-\lambda)} ,$$

(3. 4)

where q_B is the longitudinal sediment discharge per unit width per unit time, q_{BL} : the lateral sediment inflow per unit length per unit time, B : the channel width, and λ : the void ratio.

With respect to the sediment discharge q_B , various formulas have been proposed. Since bed load has much more influence on the bed variation of the mountain river than suspended load or wash load, we may use

Sato-Kikkawa-Asida formula with regard to the bed load, namely,

$$q_B = \left(\frac{\tau_o}{\gamma}\right)^{3/2} \varphi \cdot F\left(\frac{\tau_o}{\tau_c}\right) / \left(\frac{\sigma}{\gamma} - 1\right) g, \qquad (3.5)$$

where τ_o is bed shear, τ_c : critical tractive shear, γ : density of water, σ : density of sediment, g : gravity acceleration, φ : the function of Manning's n , and F : the function of τ_o/τ_c .

Eq.(3.5) will be used in a sufficiently small time interval for unsteady flow being assumed to be steady flow.

Futhermore, according to Iwagaki' formula, the critical tractive shear τ_c can be expressed as follows.

$$
\begin{aligned}
\tau_c/\gamma &= 80.9\,d & (\quad d \geq 0.303^{cm}) \\
&= 134.6\,d^{31/22} & (\,0.118 \leq d \leq 0.303\,) \\
&= 55.0\,d & (0.0565 \leq d \leq 0.118\,) \\
&= 8.41\,d^{11/32} & (0.0065 \leq d \leq 0.0565) \\
&= 226\,d & (\quad 0 \leq d \leq 0.0065\,)
\end{aligned}
\qquad (3.6)
$$

In order to compute the river bed variation for unsteady flow, Eq. (3.1), (3.3) and (3.4) have to be transformed to corresponding finite difference equations, that is,

$$A(x, t+\Delta t) = A(x, t) + \left\{ q(x, t) + \frac{Q(x-\Delta x, t) - Q(x, t)}{\Delta x} \right\} \Delta t, \qquad (3.7)$$

$$Q(x, t+\Delta t) = \frac{A(x, t+\Delta t)}{n(x)} R(x, t+\Delta t)^{2/3} \times \left| \frac{z(x, t+\Delta t) - z(x+\Delta x, t+\Delta t)}{\Delta x} \right|^{1/2} \qquad (3.8)$$

$$z(x, t+\Delta t) = z(x, t) + \frac{1}{B(x)(1-\lambda)} \left\{ \frac{q_B(x-\Delta x, t)\,B(x-\Delta x) - q_B(x, t)\cdot B(x)}{\Delta x} + q_{Bi}(x, t) \right\} \Delta t \qquad (3.9)$$

Herein, the channel width B and Manning's n are assumed to be functions of x .

The intervals of space and time: Δx and Δt should be selected in such a way that

$$\frac{\Delta x}{\Delta t} > \frac{Q}{A} . \qquad (3.10)$$

3.2 Consideration on initial and boundary conditions

By using Eqs.(3.7) through (3.9), the river bed variation can be simulated under given initial and boundary conditions, namely, the discharge $Q(x, 0)$, $q(x, 0)$ and the bed elevation $z(x, 0)$ as initial conditions, and $Q(0, t)$, $q(x, t)$, $z(0\ t)$, $z(N\Delta x, t)$ and $q_{Bi}(x, t)$ as boundary conditions, in which 0 and N stand for upstream and downstream ends, respectively.

The boundary discharges $Q(0, t)$, $q(x, t)$ are determined by rainfall-runoff analyses at the upstream end and the junctions of the tributaries with the main channel and consequently, $q_{Bi}(x, t)$ can be determined through the sediment discharge formula.

The boundary values of the bed elevation, $z(0, t)$ and $z(N\Delta x, t)$ may be determined as follows. A fix end ($z =$ const.) should be adopted at such an end where z did not and will not vary. For example, a debris dam in full stage should be chosen as the downstream end. On the other hand, a free end ($z \neq$ const.) will be suitable for such an end as the downstream side of a dam. At a free end, the bed variation Δz during the interval Δt can be calculated on the assumption that Δz at the end might be equal to that at the adjacent section of it.

3.3   Simulation and performance cases for the Rv. Arita
The channel network of the upper basin of the Rv. Arita is shown in
Fig.1. Our objective reach for river bed variation covers 26km length
from Kitadera (a free end) to Yawata (a fixed end), and is divided into
twelve portions. Then, the interval Δx is 2,167m long. Each portion
has, or has not tributaries at both sides of the main channel. The bed
slopes of the main channel and the tributaries are in order from 1/100 to
1/200 and from 1/10 to 1/70, respectively. The average grain size is
about from 3 to 10cm.
According to the flow chart shown in Fig.10, procedures of simulation
are as follows.
Firstly, all invariable numerals are set up. They are three components of the rainfall model, some constants of the storage function used
in runoff analyses, the number of the cross section, the interval Δx ,
and Manning's n , the average grain size, the bed width of each cross
section, and the average bed slope of each tributary, etc.
Secondly, an objective month which the simulation will be performed is
set up and the discharge of each cross section and amount of sediment retained in each tributary are also set up.
Hourly rainfalls in a certain month are generated by simulations
mentioned in previous chapters. The resulting runoff in hours is estimated
by the method of storage function, and the estimation of boundary values
which are necessary for the calculation of river bed variation is carried
out. The boundary values are $Q(o,t)$, $q(x,t)$, $q_B(o,t)$, $q_{Bi}(x,t)$
and amounts of sediment retained in each tributary and upstream region of
the upstream end, etc.
The computation of river bed variation by means of Eq.(3.7) through
(3.9) is carried out, and after the performance, same procedure is repeated
exchanging the initial values in the next month.
In addition, if the unit times of the rainfall model and runoff analysis be four hours and one hour, respectively, the unit time interval
of river bed variation becomes from 3 to 6 minutes by Eq.(3.10).
Cases of our simulation performances of the river bed variation are
shown in Table 3. As the parameters of simulation, we will adopt the width
$B(x)$ of the main channel, the initial bed profile $Z(x)$, the sediment inflow G_u from the upstream end, and the lateral inflow of sediment G_s
from tributaries.
Two cases of $B(x)$ are given to examine the effect of the channel
width to the river bed variation. One is the width $B_L(x)$ which is one of
immediately after the 1953 disaster, and the other is the narrow width
$B_S(x)$ reduced by river improvements after the disaster.
With respect to the initial bed profile $Z(x)$, five cases are considered. The first is the profile $Z_A(x)$ in 1961 when last survey of leveling
has been performed, and the second is the so-called dynamically stable bed
slope calculated by the Aki's theory. The others are profiles with imaginary superposed humps $Z_{a1}(x)$, $Z_{a2}(x)$, and $Z_{a3}(x)$, each of which is
assumed to have one, two, and three humps on the bed, respectively.
By suitable combinations of the above parameters for simulation, seven
simulation cases are chosen, and the computations of them are carried out.

3.4   Results
Since the period in dominate variation of river bed is May through
October having intenser rainfalls than those in the other months, the
simulation was performed during this season.
To illustrate the degree with which simulated flows compare with
observed flows, both annual maximum values of river discharge are plotted
in Fig.11. Simulated and estimated discharges would be recognized to be

almost in the same order, although there are no observed data at Kitadera (the upstream end) and Yawata (the downstream end), therefore both of discharge are estimated by proportional allotments of basin area from existing records of discharge at the A-o gaging station.

Table 4 shows simulated and measured bed variations of the river. Measured bed variations were obtained from the survey of leveling performed in upstream reach from the cross section No.4, from August of 1957 to August of 1961. On the other hand, the comparative simulated variations are results of the performance case: No.1 which may be noticed to give an similar condition to the actual river regime during the period of the surveying. According to Table 4, simulated and measured bed variations would be recongnized to be in the same order on an average. But, in detail, the measured bed level varies complicatedly at each cross section, and on the contrary the simulated bed level of each section is ascendent or desendent monotonously. These discrepancies would be caused by the fact that sediments retained in tributaries will be transported into the main channel by several floods during that period, nevertheless, the lateral sediment inflow G_S was neglected in our computation.

After all, the simulated bed variations may be regarded as being reasonable considering the secondary discrepancies between the simulation condition and the actual river regime.

Although the so-called dynamically, or statically stable theory is based on possibility of a finally stable profile, the morphological questions to be answered are what condition of the river regime make the mentioned assumption reasonable, and how long it takes to attain some stable profile. These questions are very important for river engineers. For these reasons, in order to describe the degree of longitudinal bed unevenness, we define the bed deviation ΔZ_{dev} expressed as

$$\Delta Z_{dev} = Z_J - (Z_{J-1} + Z_{J+1})/2 , \qquad (3. 11)$$

in which Z_J is the bed elevation at J-th cross section.

If any finally stable profile is expected, the longitudinal bed unevenness will be smoothed, and therefore ΔZ_{dev} of each cross section will converge to a certain value with time. Figs.12.(a) through (d) shows the variations of ΔZ_{dev} with time, although the results of the simulation cases Nos.3 through 5 are not illustrated because of similarity to those of the simulation case No.1, 2 and 6 except No.7. It will be evident from these figures that if the lateral inflow G_S of sediment from the whole watershed is negligible, some stable state of bed will be expected, but if not so, any finally stable profiles will not be expected.

When the lateral inflow G_S is neglected, the velocities of convergence to stable state become high with the increasing values of $|\Delta Z_{dev}|$. From this $\Delta Z_{dev} \sim T$ curve the finally stable state and the required time to attain it will be able to be estimated.

As far as the Rv. Arita is concerned, the reason why any finally stable profiles could not be expected when $G_S \neq 0$, seems to be as follows.

As described in 3.3, in the upper region of the Rv. Arita, the average slopes of the tributaries are much more steep than that of the main channel, and consequently, transported sediments from the tributaries into the main channel are almost retained in it.

PARTIAL LIST OF SYMBOLS

Symbol	Definition
A	Sectional area of the channel
B	Top width of the channel
d	Diameter of sediment particles
Gs	Totals of lateral inflow of transported sediment
g	Gravitational acceleration
j	Interval of sequential rainfall groups
n	Manning's roughness coefficient
Q or q	River discharge
q_B	Transported sediment discharge per unit width of the channel
q_{Bi}	Lateral inflow discharge of transported sediment per unit length of the channel
r	Frequency of rainfall occurrences
S	Subsurface water storage in the watershed
V	Volume of debris yields by landslides
Z	Bed elevation from the datum
ε	Random noise
λ	Porosity of bed material
ρ	Auto-correlation coefficient
σ	Standard deviation
τ	Bed shear

Table 1. Characteristics of maximum daily rainfall in every month (calculated by Kadoya' theory)

	Mean (mm/day)	Stand. dev. (mm/day)	Skew. coef.	Daily rainfall for each return period		
				500 yrs.	50 yrs.	10 yrs.
Jan.	26.46	18.70	1.12	114.7	77.2	51.5
Feb.	29.79	25.11	1.52	127.9	82.1	53.9
Mar.	29.66	19.40	1.42	174.3	111.0	73.6
Apr.	55.43	25.65	0.72	171.7	124.0	90.0
May	54.15	24.20	0.52	163.9	118.9	86.8
June	78.81	45.42	0.98	284.7	200.3	140.0
July	87.05	73.74	2.92	616.8	283.2	154.5
Aug.	86.00	69.93	1.39	437.3	274.9	174.0
Sep.	94.54	56.86	1.01	352.2	246.6	171.2
Oct.	56.63	34.86	1.41	233.8	151.1	100.4
Nov.	40.68	27.36	1.55	188.0	116.3	74.6
Dec.	28.46	13.75	0.81	90.8	65.3	47.0

15.13

Table 2. Records of hydrological data and landslides at the Rv. Arita basin (since the 1953 disaster)

year	month	date	Total rain(mm)	Max. daily rain(mm/day)	Max.hourly rain(mm/hr)	Max. Storage Smax(mm)	Numbers of Landslides	Total volume of Debris yields Vd (m³)
1953	July	17~21	593	450?	93?	494	2272	2.1×10^7
1959	Aug.	11~13	259	194	44	237	1	4.0×10^4
1960	Aug.	28~30	375	346	49	309	4	1.1×10^5
1961	Sep.	12~16	330	230	60	287	2	6.2×10^4
1956	Sep.	25~28	353	266	26	286	more than 1	?
1965	Sep.	13~17	400	195	43	266	more than 2	?
1968	Aug.	24~29	343	136	26	232	more than 1	?
1954	June	25~30	398	136	26	269	?	?
1959	Sep.	23~26	232	149	23	207	?	?
1957	June	26~27	165	125	21	160	none	
1957	Sep.	5~11	332	112	30	142	none	
1958	Aug.	23~26	172	129	28	199	none	
1960	June	21~22	238	170	16	193	none	
1961	Nov.	27~28	235	190	18	160	none	
1962	July	1~3	312	109	36	162	none	

Table 3. Performance Cases of Simulation

Case No.	G_u	G_s	$B(x)$	$Z(x)$	Simulated period (year)
1	$\neq 0$	$= 0$	$B_S(x)$	$Z_\alpha(x)$	7
2	$\neq 0$	$= 0$	$B_S(x)$	$Z_b(x)$	11
3	$\neq 0$	$= 0$	$B_S(x)$	$Z_{\alpha 5}(x)$	6
4	$\neq 0$	$= 0$	$B_L(x)$	$Z_{\alpha 3}(x)$	6
5	$\neq 0$	$= 0$	$B_L(x)$	$Z_{\alpha 1}(x)$	11
6	$\neq 0$	$= 0$	$B_{\ddot u}(x)$	$Z_{\alpha 2}(x)$	10
7	$\neq 0$	$\neq 0$	$B_L(x)$	$Z_{\alpha 2}(x)$	6

Section No. $B(x)(m)$	1	2	3	4	5	6	7	8	9	10	11	12	13
$B_S(x)$	30	30	30	35	40	45	50	50	50	50	50	40	40
$B_L(x)$	40	40	40	45	50	65	80	80	80	80	80	60	40

Section No. $z(x)(m)$	1	2	3	4	5	6	7	8	9	10	11	12	13
$Z_\alpha(x)$	177	158	136	122	106	91	76	62	48	35	23	12	13
$Z_b(x)$	177	156	133	117	100	85	71	57	46	35	23	12	3
$Z_{\alpha 1}(x)$	177	160	142	125	108	91	79	62	48	35	23	12	3
$Z_{\alpha 2}(x)$	177	160	144	126	109	92	77	62	49	36	27	12	3
$Z_{\alpha 3}(x)$	177	160	148	126	109	92	79	63	51	36	28	13	3

Notes: the under line shows the top of a hump.

15.15

Table 4. Simulated and measured variations
of the river bed

(a) Measured variation $\Delta \bar{Z}$ in meters

Period	Cross section No.			Annual Rainfall (mm)	Rainfall during May~ Oct.(mm)
	1-2	2-3	3-4		
Aug.,1957 - Aug.,1958	-0.21	-0.01	-0.64	2274	1281
Aug.,1958 - Aug.,1959	-0.06	-0.05	-0.21	2680	1646
Aug.,1959 - Aug.,1960	0.29	0.28	0.73	2012	1385
Aug.,1960 - Aug.,1961	-0.10	0.29	-0.01	2241	1482
Annual average	-0.02	0.13	-0.03	2302	1449

(b) Simulated variation $\Delta \bar{Z}$ in meters
(The results of the simulation case No.1)

Period (year)	Cross section No.				Rainfall during May~ Oct.(mm)
	1	2	3	4	
0 - 1	-0.068	-0.068	0.082	-0.026	1499
1 - 2	-0.038	-0.038	0.046	-0.008	1382
2 - 3	-0.012	-0.012	0.014	-0.003	885
3 - 4	-0.049	-0.049	0.059	-0.012	1089
4 - 5	-0.067	-0.067	0.079	-0.022	1621
5 - 6	-0.049	-0.049	0.056	-0.008	1473
6 - 7	-0.033	-0.033	0.040	-0.006	1369
Annual average	-0.045	-0.045	0.054	-0.012	1331

Notes: the variation $\Delta \bar{Z}$ is herein defined as the difference
between the bed elevation in a year and that in the
preceding year, and positive and negative stand for
ascension and descent, respectively.

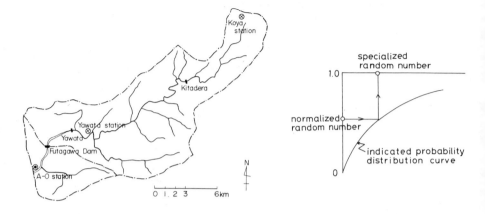

Fig. 1 Sketch of the upper region of
the Rv. Arita.

Fig. 2 Procedure of generation
of specialized random
numbers.

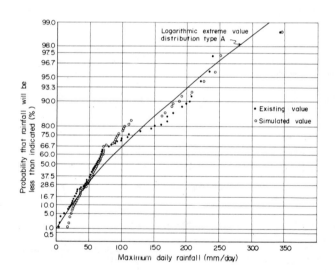

Fig. 3 Probability distribution of maximum
daily rainfalls on August (logarithmic
plotting).

15.17

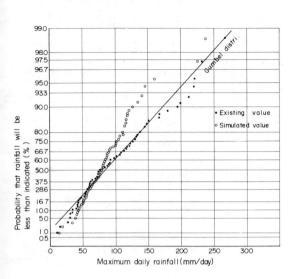

Fig. 4 Probability distribution of
maximum daily rainfalls on September
(Gumbel plotting).

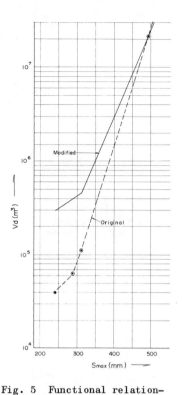

Fig. 5 Functional relationship between the maximum
water mass storage: S_{max}.
and bulk of debris
yields: V_d.

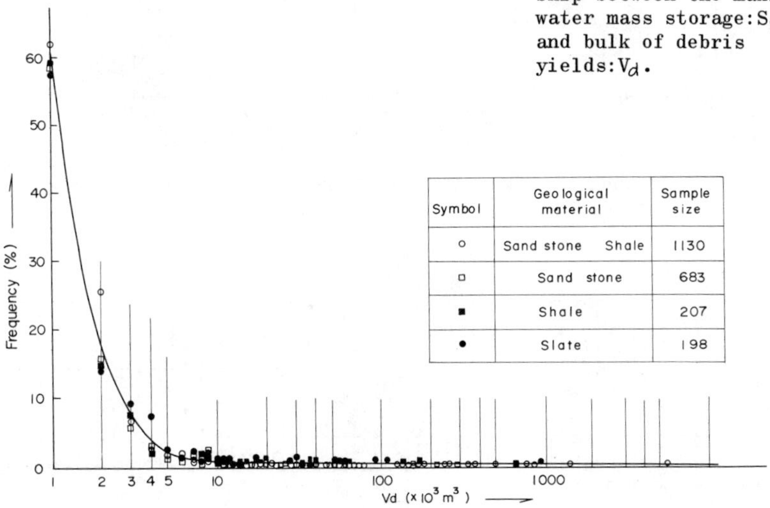

Symbol	Geological material	Sample size
○	Sand stone Shale	1130
□	Sand stone	683
■	Shale	207
●	Slate	198

Fig. 6 Frequency distribution of landslide scars being
represented by bulk of produced debris per a scar.

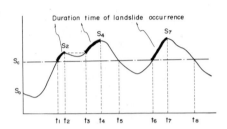

Fig. 7 Schematic feature of
storage sequence and
landslide occurrences.

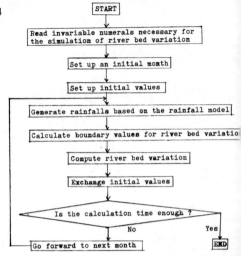

Fig.10 Flow chart for simulation
of river bed variation.

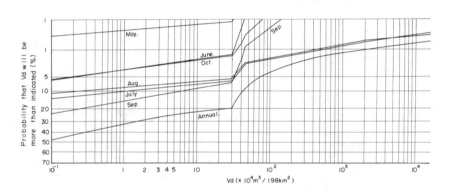

Fig. 8 Probability distribution of debris yields on each month
by landslides.

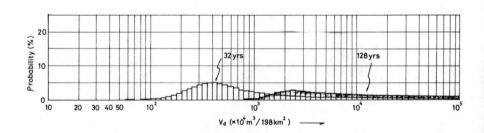

Fig. 9 Probability distribution of debris yields in long periods.

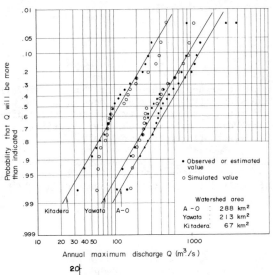

Fig.11
Comparisons of the
simulated with the
observed river
discharge.

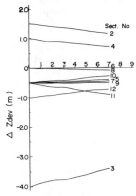

(a) For case No.1
($G_S = 0$).

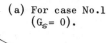

(b) For case No.2 ($G_S = 0$).

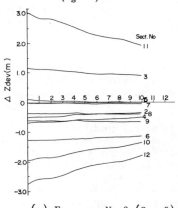

(c) For case No.6 ($G_S = 0$).

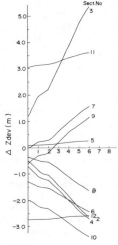

(d) For case No.7
($G_S \neq 0$).

Fig.12 $\triangle Z_{dev.}$ —— T curves.

15.20

DISCUSSION

J. W. DELLEUR

The dependence of landslide on watershed storage rather than on rainfall intensity is not fortuitous as the stability of landslopes depends on the position of the phreatic line. As a result the slope instability does not depend directly on the rainfall intensity. Similar results have been obtained regarding the stability of earth dams subject to fluctuating reservoir levels.

The speaker would like to know a) The reason for the discontinuities in debris probability curves (Fig. 8) for $Vd(x\ 10^4 m^3/198\ Km^2) \approx 30$; b) the definition of the symbol ϕ in equation 3.5, called the function of Mannings n. Is this a Strickler type relation?

J. PAUL RILEY and K. SAKHAN

The method is appropriate for the long-term prediction of river bed variation To clarify our understanding of the model, we view the concept in the following four steps:

1. River bed variation is function of landslide or debris yield.
2. Landslide or debris yield is function of subsurface storage.
3. Subsurface storage is function of rainfall and river discharge.
4. Stochastic rainfall with no cross-correlation between three components: frequency, interval, and intensity.

Our first general comment is that landslides are of rare occurrence as also stated by the authors. These landslides provide debris to the river channels. To assume that landslides alone are debris suppliers for the stream channel over the long run seems somewhat disputable. However, if this assumption is made, initial values for the stream bed elevation, stage, and discharge for the river must be known at the time when landslide debris reaches the stream channel. Between landslides, large amounts of debris could come from erosion due to sheet flow and rainfall splash, thus requiring new initial conditions each time Equations (3. (3.2), and (3.4) are applied. In this respect, the question is raised as to how initial values are determined at any time in the future when computations begin with new landslide debris reaching the stream. If debris provided by causes other than landslide are also included, initial values need be given only once at the very beginning of the computation.

We also wonder about the authors' assumption that in mountainous river basins only bed slope and friction slope are governing factors of stream discharge. This assumption means that the flow is nearly uniform, whereas, mountainous streams are generally formed of a series of pools and riffles. Therefore, although the equati of continuity of the bed material (Equation 3.4) is applicable, Equation (3.3) doe not necessarily give a good approximation of actual conditions.

To summarize, we suggest that consideration be given to refining the model of the river bed variation (part III of the paper). Also, it is considered that the applicability of the model would be increased by including (through a multi-channe time series approach) sediment input to the stream channel of debris from both landslides and erosion due to sheet flow and rainfall splash.

347

V. YEVJEVICH

This paper successfully attacts two problems that have not been analyzed until now by the advanced methods of probability theory and stochastic processes. The quantitative analysis presented in the paper shows that even the most difficult hydrologic problems do not need to be studied by only a quantitative discriptive method.

The question may be raised, however, whether the hypothesis of independence of rainfall intensity, the number of rainy days, and the time interval used to describe rainfall processes is a realistic assumption. Usually all discriptors of rainfall storms are mutually dependent parameters. In using the simulation approach for rainfall data only the probability distribution of variables, and not the time dependence, are taken into account. The first autocorrelation coefficient for rainfall intensities may be on the order of 0.15 - 0.40.

Similarly, because an area has a limited amount of material to supply in landslides, the volume of the sediment supplied to rivers by landslides must also be a time-dependent process. Besides, one should expect the landslide variables to be dependent on geological conditions, though some evidence in the paper implies that they are not.

Figure 9 poses the question of how a multi-peak distribution of landslide volumes is affected by the sample size. In other words, the sampling variation must be so large that the sample size significantly affects the estimation of probability distributions.

RESPONSE BY A. MUROTA

The response to the first question by J. W. Delleur is as follows. As you can see in Fig. 5, there is a bent on the modified curve for $V_d=4.5x10^5m^3$. This singular point just corresponds to the first discontinuity for $V_d=4.5x10^5m^3$ in Fig. 8.

In Fig. 5, the modified curve should be extended so as to connect the point for $V_d=3x10^5m^3$ with the point for $V_d\equiv0$ when Smax=200mm which is the critical storage for landslide outbreaks, and the point for $V_d=3.5x10^5m^3$ discontinuity for $V_d=3.5x10^5m^3$ in Fig. 8.

When more field data will be so sufficiently collected in the future to make it possible to draw the smooth modified curve in Fig. 5, these discontinuity should disappear.

The response to the second question by J. W. Delleur is as follows. Eq. (3.5) is one of the most commonly-used formulas for the discharge of tractional load in Japan. This formula was deduced from the idea that the momentum being given to the sediment particles by turbulent up-lift was equal to the momentum being given to the particles in the tractionally moving layer by the gravitational force.

In the figure included in this response, F is the function of τ_o/τ_c as shown in the right figure. α was decided by the experiment having performed at the Public Works Research Institute of Ministry of Construction in Japan and the experimental data by Gilbert as follows.

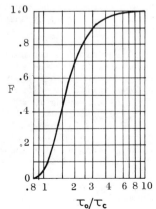

15.22

When $n > 0.025$, $\alpha = 0.62$.
When $n < 0.025$, $\alpha = 0.62(40n)^{-3.5}$,

where n is Manning's roughness coefficient in
meter-second system.

The response to questions and comments posed by J. P. Riley are as follows.

Due to saving our description about the stochastic evaluation for
transportation of sediments produced by landslides, a little lack of explanation might be inevitable.

Almost of comments by Dr. Riley seems to be summarized on the evaluation of sediments provided by causes other than landslides, that is, sheet
erosion.

By the quantitative observation of sheet erosion at the watershed of
well-weathered granite in Japan, we have some reasonable orders of produced
sediments by sheet erosion as follows.

$$20 \ m^3/km^2/year \qquad \text{from the planation area,}$$
$$3,900 \ m^3/km^2/year \qquad \text{from the bared area.}$$

These values were observed at the watershed with the mean annual
precipitation: 1,550 mm. For our target watershed which has similar geological conditions and the mean annual precipitation of 2,ooo mm, the
production of sediments by sheet erosion may be roughly estimated as follows
assuming the yields by sheet erosion should be proportional to the annual
rainfall.

$$26 \ m^3/km^2/year \ x \ 195km^2 \quad \text{for the plantation area,}$$
$$5,032 \ m^3/km^2/year \ x \ 3km^2 \quad \text{for the bared area.}$$

Totals of sediment yields by sheet erosion were estimated as $2.0x10^4$
$m^3/198km^2/year$ $(10^2 m^3/km^2/year)$. On the other hand, the mode and probable lower
limit of debris yields by landslides in return periods of 32 years, is
calculated to be about $4x10^6 m^3/198km^2$ and $8x10^5 m^3/198km^2$, respectively by our
stochastic analyses.

When we want to forecast the river-bed variation in longer term than
32 years, the ratio of the sediment production by sheet erosion to the
debris yields by landslides will go down smaller value than 1/200.

So far as forecasting of the long term variation of river-bed are
concerned, we may neglect the contribution of sheet erosion compared with
the debris yields by landslides. Our calculation, however, is limited for
11 years future at most and the relative importance of contribution of
sheet erosion must be considered as Dr. Riley emphasized and we will
evaluate the supply by sheet erosion and rainfall splash in our prospective
studies.

Proceeding to the next question, we have not experienced any landslide
occurrences before the 1953 disaster and the origin of sediment supply are
almost debris storage produced on the 1953 landslide disaster.

The initial condition is given as the bed profile $z_a(x)$ which is the
result of surveying in 1961 and possible sediment supply. Starting from
the $z_a(x)$ profile, we carry out the computation of river bed variation
using Eqs. (3.7) through (3.9). In this process, we have simulated data
of river discharge and subsurface storage in the basin which are deduced
by the generation of rainfall sequences and runoff analyses. Accordingly,
debris yields and the sediment supply reaching the stream are quantitatively provided and included in our computation process for each month.

After completing the computation in a month, same procedure will be
proceeded for next month using the new initial condition which has already

been set as the bed profile and possible sediment supply calculated in the preceding month.

Concerning the last question of Dr. Riley, it is theoretically deservedly that Eq.(3.3) does not necessarily give a good approximation of actual flood, because Eq.(3.3) represents the steady and uniform flow approximation.

Our time step of computation Δt, however, is taken the small value between 3 minutes and 6 minutes due to the restriction $\Delta x/\Delta t > Q/A$, where $\Delta x = 200m$. On the other hand, the duration time of the unit hydrograph being used in our run-off analyses is in order of 120 hours and time steps Δt would be negligibly small compared with the duration of flood.

Accordingly, we may assume for the sake of simplification of computation that the flood is represented by the quasi-steady and quasi-uniform in the small value of Δt and Δx. In another sequent step, the river discharge, of course, must be changed by the result of run-off analysis.

The response to questions and comments posed by V. Yevjevich are as follows.

We have formerly calculated cross-correlations among three components of rainfall for the generation of simulated rainfall sequences and some results are illustrated in Table-A, where $\sum R$ and T are totals and duration time of one-group of rainfall and Rp being the peak intensity.

Table-A: Cross-correlations between components of heavy rainfalls

Month	$\sum R \sim Rp$	$\sum R \sim T$	$Rp \sim T$	Samples
June	0.789	0.581	0.273	121
July	0.660	0.660	0.437	163
August	0.742	0.829	0.506	35
Sept.	0.509	0.630	0.061	91
Oct.	0.814	0.237	0.125	111

One group of rainfall is defined as a hyetograph which is separated from the preceding or sequent group of rainfalls with time interval more than four hours.

So far as the correlation among rainfall components of one group in hour unit are concerned, we may recognize some significant values of cross-correlation as shown in Table-A because the precipitations are governed by same meteorological cause. Moreover, we observed the significant auto-correlation coefficient in one group rainfall, which distributes in range between 0.238 and 0.440 when $\tau = 1.0$ hour. These estimations may be same order to the value proposed by Prof. Yevjevich.

We discuss in our paper, however, correlations among components of daily and heavy rainfall. Heavy rainfalls are usually caused by the meteorological disturbance in micro or mezzo scale, for example, moving front which results rainfall in only one or two days at most and we may reasonably assume that there are little correlations between totals of rainfall (rainfall intensity) and sequent rainy days.

We agree with Prof. Yevjevich's opinion that the supply of the sediment to river channel by landslides must be a time-dependent process.

On the viewpoint in very long term, this kind of discussions should be based on the knowledge of immunity of landslide phenomena, that is, after once occurrence of many number of landslides over the watershed, we may not experience so large number of landslides in the same basin for

many years. On this meaning, the landslide phenomena must be a Markoffian
process.

Discussing the problem in shorter term, we treated the supply process
of sediment after once occurrence of landslide as the stochastic and time-
dependent process. Debris being storaged in valleys or mountainsides will
be transported through each valley by river flows which are generated by
using the simulated precipitation and run-off analysis.

It is deservedly that the landslide phenomena depend on geological
conditions. In the case of complex geological status over the watershed,
we must survey the relation between the geological condition and landslide
occurrences. Of course, the functional relationship between debris yields
by landslides and maximum storage in the basin as shown in Fig.5 of our
paper should be changed for another geological condition.

By your kindly pointed-out for multi-peaks distribution in Fig.9, we
can have the chance of checking our calculations after the Seminar. Because
we found our unreasonable assumption which was setting the largest landslide
in unexpected scale, we calculated over again about Fig.9 and the revised
figure are to be presented.

United States-Japan Bi-Lateral Seminar on Hydrology
Honolulu, January 1971

SIMULATION OF THE SHORT-TIME SCOUR-FILL
PROCESS IN ERODIBLE STREAMS WITH STOCHASTIC
SEDIMENT TRANSFER AT THE STREAM BED

by

J. Paul Riley[1], Kousoum Sakhan[2], and Kenneth G. Renard[3]

SYNOPSIS:

In ephemeral streams, the occurrence of translatory waves causes the
shortening of the time of rise of the hydrograph which in turn results in channel instability. A simulation model is developed to describe the dynamics
of the channel in terms of: (1) two one-dimensional stream flow equations,
(2) a one-dimensional sediment transport equation, an equation for the
stream bed, and (3) a stochastic sediment transfer at the stream bed which
also includes the bed load.

The model as a whole is simulated on a hybrid computer. To demonstrate the operation of the model, real-time simulation is done using hypothetical data for a stream reach 24,000 feet in length. The results of this
study are presented in graphical form.

1. INTRODUCTION

Existing information is inadequate on channel stability influences in the
Southwest part of the United States. Under present conditions, many stream
channels are unstable. The major cause is believed to be the high-intensity,
short-duration convective thunderstorms, particularly during the summer
season, which result in flash floods moving over coarse-textured alluvial
stream beds with very high-intake rates. It has been observed by Renard and

---

[1] Associate Professor, Civil Engineering, Utah Water Research Laboratory, Utah State University, Logan, Utah.

[2] Graduate Research Assistant, Civil Engineering, Utah Water Research
Laboratory, Utah State University, Logan, Utah.

[3] Director, Southwest Watershed Research Center, Agricultural Research
Service, United States Department of Agriculture, Tucson, Arizona.

Hickok[4] that the occurrence of translatory waves is frequent. This phenomenon has a critical influence on the time of rise of the hydrograph, which in turn, affects the stability of the stream channel. The conventional theory of flood routing has been found to be inapplicable to these ephemeral streams. Therefore, it is necessary to account for the movement of these waves in order for the model to be descriptive of ephemeral streams. Besides these translatory waves, sedimemtns carried by the flow both as bed load and suspended load make the situation even more complicated.

It is the purpose of this investigation to develop a simulation model which accounts for the translatory waves, and sediments entrained by the flow both as bed load and suspended load, and yet is simple enough for practical uses. The system reported herein consists of two one-dimensional stream flow equations, a solid mass transport equation, and stochastic solid mass transfer at the stream bed.

2. CHANNEL DYNAMICS MODEL

Fluid Mass and Solid Mass Transport Equations

The three dimensional equations of conservation of fluid mass, flow momentum, and solid mass in the turbulent flow are

$$\nabla \cdot \vec{V} = 0 \tag{1}$$

$$\rho \frac{dV}{dt} = \rho \vec{g} - \nabla p + \mu \nabla^2 \vec{V} + [\nabla \cdot T^{(e)}] \tag{2}$$

$$\frac{\partial c}{\partial t} + \nabla \cdot (c\vec{V}) = \nabla \cdot (e\nabla c) \tag{3}$$

subject to the following boundary conditions (Figure 1)

$$\frac{\partial F}{\partial t} + \vec{V} \cdot \nabla F = \vec{R} \cdot \nabla F \tag{4}$$

$$c \frac{\partial F}{\partial t} - e \nabla c \cdot \nabla F = \vec{N} \cdot \nabla F + c \vec{R} \cdot \nabla F \tag{5}$$

where $T^{(e)}$ is the Reynolds stress tensor and $F(x, y, z, t) = 0$ is the equation of the moving boundary surface. After space averaging, Equations (1), (2) and (3) reduce to the following one-dimensional equations which describe the conservation of fluid mass, flow momentum, and solid mass in the flow of natural streams with movable boundaries,

$$\frac{\partial A}{\partial t} + \frac{\partial Q}{\partial x} - L - S = 0 \tag{6}$$

---

[4] Renard, Kenneth G., and Hickok, R. B., "Sedimentation Research Needs in Semi-Arid Regions," Proc. of the ASCE, Vol. 93, No. HY1, pp. 45-60, January, 1967.

$$\frac{\partial Q}{\partial t} + \frac{\partial}{\partial x}\left(\beta \frac{Q^2}{A}\right) + g\frac{\partial}{\partial x}\left(h_c A\right) + gA\frac{\partial \eta}{\partial x} + \frac{Q^2 F}{8R_h A} - \frac{Q}{A}\left(L+S\right) = 0 \tag{7}$$

$$\frac{\partial}{\partial t}\left(CA\right) + \frac{\partial}{\partial x}\left(CQ\right) - \frac{\partial}{\partial x}\left(G_{cx}A\frac{\partial C}{\partial x}\right) - C/_{y=\eta}\left[S + T\frac{\partial \eta}{\partial t}\right] - N = 0 \tag{8}$$

where the terms L, S, and N, as described in the terminology, have negative values if processes they represnet are influent, and positive values if processes are effluent. The scour-fill equation for the stream bed is

$$C/_{y=\eta} \; T\frac{\partial \eta}{\partial t} + \frac{\partial Q_B \, vol}{\partial x} + N = 0 \tag{9}$$

In natural streams, different bed configuration occurs depending upon the flow characteristics. Therefore, the friction factor, f, which appears in Equation (7) is by no means invariant. This friction factor can be decomposed into f' which represents the sand grain roughness and f" which represents the bed form roughness. These two friction factors are represented by the following equations

$$f' = 1/\left[2\log_{10}\left(2\,R_h/D_{50}\right) + 1.74\right]^2 \tag{10}$$

$$\log_{10} f" = -.45 - .04\frac{U}{\sqrt{gD_{50}}} + \left(.04\frac{U}{\sqrt{gD_{50}}} - 3.05\right)$$

$$\exp - 8\left[\log_{10}\frac{R_b}{D_{50}} - \left(1.9 + .04\frac{U}{\sqrt{gD_{50}}}\right)\right] \tag{11}$$

In the equation for the suspended sediment (Equation (8)), two variables must be determined: (1) the longitudinal sediment dispersivity G_{cx}, and (2) the sediment transfer rate N at the stream bed.

Following Chen[5] and assuming logarithmic velocity distribution in both vertical and lateral directions, the longitudinal sediment dispersivity can be derived and expressed as:

$$G_{cx} = \frac{\lambda k^2}{24}\frac{\sqrt{h}}{R_h}\frac{\left[\log_e \frac{h}{(\eta_0 - \eta_1)} - 1\right]}{\log_e\left(\frac{T/2}{\xi_0\,\xi_1}\right)}\,T^2 \tag{12}$$

in which λ is the ratio of the eddy mass diffusivity to the eddy kinematic viscosity of water, k is the von Karman universal constant, h is the depth of flow, T is

[5] Chen, C. L., "Dispersion of Sediment in Flow with Moving Boundaries," accepted for publication in the Proc. of the ASCE, Hydraulics Division, 1971.

the top width of flow, and η_o and ξ_o are the distances from the stream bed and the side walls, respectively, where the velocity is zero.

The rate of transfer of sediment N should be described by a stochastic process as a result of the random nature of the driving mechanism which is the flow turbulence. This process is treated in the following section.

Stochastic Sediment Transfer at the Stream Bed

It is proposed that at the interface between the flow region and the stream bed, there are three distinct states and at time, t, a solid particle may be in any one of these three states. The three states are: (A) the suspended load state, (B) the bed load state, and (C) the immobile bed state (Figure 2). The probability that a particle will move from one state to another or remain in a particular state is termed its transition probability. The future transition probabilities of a solid particle are independent of its transition probabilities in the past (a property of the Markov processes). For example, if a particle is in state (A) at time θ and in state (B) at time ξ the probability that is in state (C) at time t is given by the appropriate transition probabilities as follows:

$$P_{AC} (\theta,t) = P_{AB} (\theta,\xi) P_{BC} (\xi,t) \tag{13}$$

Generally, since the events corresponding to Equation (13) for different middle states are mutually exclusive, then the probability of going from state (A) at time θ to state (C) at time t is

$$P_{AC} (\theta,t) = \sum_{i=A}^{C} P_{Ai} (\theta,\xi) P_{iC} (\xi, t) \tag{14}$$

Equation (14) is the Chapman-Kolmogorov equation for a non-homogeneous Markovian process. If it is defined that

$$\psi_{AB} \Delta t + 0 (\Delta t) = P_r \{\text{a particle in state (A) at time } \xi \text{ will be in state (B)} \\ \text{at time } \xi + \Delta t\} \tag{15}$$

$$\psi_{AC} \Delta t + 0 (\Delta t) = P_r \{\text{a particle in state (A) at time } \xi \text{ will be in state (C)} \\ \text{at time } \xi + \Delta t\} \tag{16}$$

and

$$1 + \psi_{AA} \Delta t + 0 (\Delta t) = P_r \{\text{a particle in state (A) at time } \xi \text{ will remain} \\ \text{in state A during the interval } (\xi, \xi + \Delta t)\} \tag{17}$$

16.4

then it is clear that

$$\psi_{AA} = - \sum_{i=B}^{C} \psi_{Ai} \leq 0 \tag{18}$$

If ψ_{AA} is zero, then state Ⓐ is absorbing, that is, the particle is always in suspension. This case is not expected to happen for dense solid particles wandering in a natural stream.

Now consider two contiguous time intervals, (θ, t) and $(t, t + \Delta t)$. Using the definitions in Equations (15) through (17) with Equation (14) yields

$$P_{AA}(\theta, t + \Delta t) = P_{AA}(\theta,t)(1 + \psi_{AA}\Delta t) + P_{AB}(\theta,t)\psi_{BA}\Delta t$$

$$+ P_{AC}(\theta,t)\psi_{CA}\Delta t + 0(\Delta t) \tag{19}$$

$$P_{AB}(\theta, t + \Delta t) = P_{AA}(\theta,t)\psi_{AB}\Delta t + P_{AB}(\theta,t)(1 + \psi_{BB}\Delta t)$$

$$+ P_{AC}(\theta,t)\psi_{CA}\Delta t + 0(\Delta t) \tag{20}$$

and

$$P_{AC}(\theta, t + \Delta t) = P_{AA}(\theta,t)\psi_{AC}\Delta t + P_{AB}(\theta,t)\psi_{BC}\Delta t$$

$$+ P_{AC}(\theta,t)(1 + \psi_{CC}\Delta t) + 0(\Delta t) \tag{21}$$

Dividing Equation (19) through (21) by Δt and taking the limit as Δt approaches zero results in the following relationships:

$$\frac{\partial}{\partial t}P_{AA}(\theta,t) = P_{AA}(\theta,t)\psi_{AA}(t) + P_{AB}(\theta,t)\psi_{BA}(t) + P_{AC}(\theta,t)\psi_{CA}(t) \tag{22}$$

$$\frac{\partial}{\partial t}P_{AB}(\theta,t) = P_{AA}(\theta,t)\psi_{AB}(t) + P_{AB}(\theta,t)\psi_{BB}(t) + P_{AC}(\theta,t)\psi_{CB}(t) \tag{23}$$

$$\frac{\partial}{\partial t}P_{AC}(\theta,t) = P_{AA}(\theta,t)\psi_{AC}(t) + P_{AB}(\theta,t)\psi_{BC}(t) + P_{AC}(\theta,t)\psi_{CC}(t) \tag{24}$$

Equations (22) through (24) are known as the forward Kolmogorov differential equations. They are subject to the following initial conditions

$$P_{Ai}(\theta,\theta) = \delta_{Ai}, \quad i = A, B, C \tag{25}$$

where δ_{Ai} is the Kronecker delta symbol.

16.5

The ψ's are the intensities of solid mass transfer which are the main keys to the concept of stochastic solid mass transfer at the interface. They are functions of the instantaneous local hydrodynamic properties. Considering that the time interval (θ, t) is very short, then it can be assumed that the ψ's are constant over this interval. However, in general the ψ's are time-dependent.

The Kolmogorov differential equations for P_{BA}, P_{BB}, P_{BC}, P_{CA}, P_{CB}, and P_{CC} may be derived in a similar manner and presented in matrix format. Let the transition probability matrix be

$$\vec{P}(\theta,t) = \begin{array}{c} A \\ B \\ C \end{array} \begin{pmatrix} \overset{A}{P_{AA}}(\theta,t) & \overset{B}{P_{AB}}(\theta,t) & \overset{C}{P_{AC}}(\theta,t) \\ P_{BA}(\theta,t) & P_{BB}(\theta,t) & P_{BC}(\theta,t) \\ P_{CA}(\theta,t) & P_{CB}(\theta,t) & P_{CC}(\theta,t) \end{pmatrix} \tag{26}$$

and let the solid mass transfer intensity matrix be

$$\vec{\psi}(t) = \begin{array}{c} A \\ B \\ C \end{array} \begin{pmatrix} \overset{A}{\psi_{AA}}(t) & \overset{B}{\psi_{AB}}(t) & \overset{C}{\psi_{AC}}(t) \\ \psi_{BA}(t) & \psi_{BB}(t) & \psi_{BC}(t) \\ \psi_{CA}(t) & \psi_{CB}(t) & \psi_{CC}(t) \end{pmatrix} \tag{27}$$

Then the Chapman-Kolmogorov equation becomes

$$\vec{P}(\theta,t) = \vec{P}(\theta,\xi) \, \vec{P}(\xi,t) \tag{28}$$

In a similar manner the forward Kolmogorov differential equations become

$$\frac{\partial}{\partial t} \vec{P}(\theta,t) = \vec{P}(\theta,t) \, \vec{\psi}(t) \tag{29}$$

subject to the initial conditions

$$\vec{P}(\theta,t) = \vec{I} \tag{30}$$

where $\vec{I}$ is the identity matrix.

The task, now, is to determine the intensity matrix $\vec{\psi}(t)$. Referring to Figure 2, there are six from-state-to-state transfers and three within-state transfers. The terms state and zone should not be confused. With the complexity regarding the arrangement of solid particles at the interface and the instantaneous local hydrodynamic forces, it is impossible to draw a physical boundary between the bed load zone and the suspended load zone. However, it is possible to avoid this problem by considering states of a solid particle which do not have physical boundaries, but rather "process boundaries". The process boundaries are defined by the following relations (31) through (36) which define the process conditions for transfers between states. For example, relations (31) and (36) define the process boundaries for state Ⓑ.

Ⓐ Ⓑ - Transfer from suspended load state to bed load state occurs when the local upward hydrodynamic force $F_y\ (v'_{up})$ is less than the vertical resisting force $F_y\ (m)$ due to solid mass.

$$F_y\ (v'_{up}) \le F_y\ (m) \tag{31}$$

Ⓐ Ⓒ - Transfer from suspended load state directly to immobile bed state occurs when

$$F_y\ (v'_{up}) \le F_y\ (m) \tag{32}$$

Ⓑ Ⓐ - Transfer from bed load state to suspended load state takes place when

$$F_y\ (v'_{up}) > F_y\ (m) \tag{33}$$

Ⓑ Ⓒ - Transfer from bed load state to immobile bed state occurs when

$$F_x\ (\tau_0,\ u') \le F_x\ (m,\ \tau_0) \tag{34}$$

Ⓒ Ⓐ - Transfer from immobile bed state directly to suspended load takes place when

$$F_y\ (v'_{up}) > F_y\ (m) \tag{35}$$

Ⓒ Ⓑ - Transfer from immobile bed state to bed load state occurs when

$$F_x\ (\tau_0,\ u') > F_x\ (m,\ \tau_0) \tag{36}$$

As can be seen from Equation (18), within-state transfer are functions of transfers between states.

Let $u_{forward}$ be the forward velocity of the particle at the interface regions, and v_{rise} and v_{fall}, the rise and fall velocities of the particle, respectively. If a sediment particle moved with one of these three velocities, how many fictitious sediment particles similar to that real particle would move at maximum intensity, past a single "serving counter" per unit time? Let D be the diameter of the particle. Then there should be, for example, $u_{forward}/D$ particles per unit time which move in the forward horizontal direction. Under this concept, the intensity function matrix (27) becomes

$$
\vec{\psi}\,(t) = \begin{array}{c} A \\ B \\ C \end{array} \begin{array}{ccc} A & B & C \end{array}
\begin{bmatrix}
-\left(\dfrac{v_{fall}}{D} + \dfrac{v_{fall}}{D}\right) & \dfrac{v_{fall}}{D} & \dfrac{v_{fall}}{D} \\[12pt]
\dfrac{v_{rise}}{D} & -\left(\dfrac{v_{rise}}{D} + \dfrac{v_{fall}}{D}\right) & \dfrac{v_{fall}}{D} \\[12pt]
\dfrac{v_{rise}}{D} & \dfrac{u_{forward}}{D} & -\left(\dfrac{v_{rise}}{D} + \dfrac{u_{forward}}{D}\right)
\end{bmatrix}
\tag{37}
$$

subject to the process conditions (31) through (36). The entry which does not satisfy its respective process condition vanishes.

In order to evaluate the above matrix the three solid particle velocities, $u_{forward}$, v_{rise}, and v_{fall}, must be determined. In natural streams, various bed configurations are formed, depending upon the flow conditions, the characteristics of the bed material, and the stream geometry. In turn, bed features affect "wall" turbulence near the bed, which is a primary entrainment mechanism for solid particles. Another important entrainment mechanism is the mean bed shear stress. In the interface region of natural streams, the Newtonian law of motion is valid. Thus

$$
\vec{F} = \frac{d}{dt}\,(m\,\vec{V}_p) \tag{38}
$$

in which $\vec{F}$ is the total force vector on the particle; m is the mass of the particle, which is constant; and $\vec{V}_p$ is the velocity vector of the particle. Integrating Equation (38) from time t_1 to time t_2 yields

$$
\int_{t_1}^{t_2} \vec{F}\, dt = m\,\vec{V}_{p_2} - M\,\vec{V}_{p_1} \tag{39}
$$

where $\int_{t1}^{t2} \vec{F}\, dt$ is known as the impluse of the force $\vec{F}$ on the particle. Decomposing the force $\vec{F}$ into two parts, the hydrodynamic force, $\vec{F}_{hydro}$, and the resisting force, $\vec{F}_{resist}$, and integrating Equation (39) over the entire surface, Λ, of the bed feature yields

$$\int_\Lambda \int_{t_1}^{t_2} \vec{F}_{hydro} \, dt \, d\Lambda + \int_\Lambda \int_{t_1}^{t_2} \vec{F}_{resist} \, dt \, d\Lambda = m \int_\Lambda (\vec{V}_{p_2} - \vec{V}_{p_1}) \, d\Lambda \qquad (40)$$

Let $\vec{F}_{hydro}$, $\vec{F}_{resist}$, $\overline{(\vec{V}_{p2} - \vec{V}_{p1})}$ and $\bar{\Lambda}$ be the averages of $\vec{F}_{hydro}$, $\vec{F}_{resist}$, $(\vec{V}_{p2} - \vec{V}_{p1})$, and Λ and t in the domain, respectively. Then Equation (40) becomes

$$\bar{\Lambda} (t_2 - t_1) (\vec{F}_{hydro} + \vec{F}_{resist}) = \bar{\Lambda} m \overline{(\vec{V}_{p_2} - \vec{V}_{p_1})} \qquad (41)$$

In natural streams, the longitudinal and vertical motions of bed particles are usually the predominant processes. Hence, from Equation (41),

$$u_p = (u_{p_2} - u_{p_1}) = \frac{t_2 - t_1}{m} (\bar{F}_{hydro\ x} + \bar{F}_{resist\ x}) \qquad (42)$$

and

$$v_p = \overline{(v_{p_2} - v_{p_1})} = \frac{t_2 - t_1}{m} (\bar{F}_{hydro\ y} + \bar{F}_{resist\ y}) \qquad (43)$$

where u_p and v_p are the relative longitudinal and vertical particle velocities. The time of action (t_2-t_1) of the summation of forces $(\bar{F}_{hydro} + \bar{F}_{resist})$ is assumed, as can be deduced from the reasoning to obtain the intensity function matrix (37), to be:

$$t_2 - t_1 = \frac{D}{\pm (\vec{V}_{p_2} - \vec{V}_{p_1})} \qquad (44)$$

Because the time of action (t_2-t_1) should always be positive, the plus and minus signs in front of the expression $(\vec{V}_{p_2} - \vec{V}_{p_1})$ in Equation (44) are necessary.

Substituting Equation (44) into Equations (42) and (43) yields

$$\pm u_p^2 = \frac{D}{m} (\bar{F}_{hydro\ x} + \bar{F}_{resist\ x}) \qquad (45)$$

and

$$\pm v_p^2 = \frac{D}{m} (\bar{F}_{hydro\ y} + \bar{F}_{resist\ y}) \qquad (46)$$

16.9

Considering the fact that solid particles are sheared over a gravity bed in order to move in the longitudinal direction, one would expect that the particle to particle interaction is far greater in the longitudinal direction than in the vertical direction. Then the longitudinal resisting force for a spherical particle can be expressed as

$$\overline{F}_{resist\ x} = - (\gamma_s - \gamma) \frac{\pi}{6} D^3 \tan \alpha \tag{47}$$

in which $\tan \alpha$ is the dynamic friction factor, which as a result of Bagnold's[6] experiments can be expressed as

$$\tan \alpha = .375 + .375 \exp \left[- .00084 \left(\frac{\gamma_s\ D^2\ \tau_0}{14\ g\mu^2} - 100 \right) \right] \tag{48}$$

Since the particle to paricle interaction is negligible in the vertical direction, the vertical resisting force is due only to the submerged weight of the particle, or

$$\overline{F}_{resist\ y} = - (\gamma_s - \gamma) \frac{\pi}{6} D^3 \tag{49}$$

The total hydrodynamic force is the mean bed shear stress, $- \overline{\rho u'v'}$, superimposed by forces resulting from turbulent fluctuations u' and v'. Thus,

$$\overline{F}_{hydro\ x} = \frac{\pi}{4} D^2\ 1/2\ C_{Dx} \frac{\gamma}{g} (\overline{u'^2} - \overline{u'v'}) \tag{50}$$

and

$$\overline{F}_{hydro\ y} = \frac{\pi}{4} D^2 (1/2\ C_{Dy} \frac{\gamma}{g} \overline{v'^2_{up}}) \tag{51}$$

in which C_{Dx} and C_{Dy} are the drag coefficients in the longitudinal and vertical directions, respectively, and $\overline{v'^2_{up}}$ is the mean-square of the upward velocity fluctuation. If asymmetry of turbulent fluctuations is assumed to exist at the stream bed, then, for a maximum local momentum flux, the upward fluctuation can be derived and expressed as:

$$\overline{v'^2_{up}} = 2.415\ \overline{v'^2} \tag{52}$$

---

[6] Bagnold, R. A., "Flow of Cohesionless Grains in Fluid", Royal Society [London] Philos. Trans., Vol. 249, pp. 235-297, 1956.

Now let ϕ_x and ϕ_y be the correlation functions between the root-mean-square velocity fluctuations $\sqrt{\overline{u'^2}}$ and $\sqrt{\overline{v'^2}}$ and the root-mean-square shear velocity $\sqrt{-\overline{u'v'}}$, or

$$\phi_x = \sqrt{-\frac{\overline{u'^2}}{\overline{u'v'}}} \tag{53.a}$$

and

$$\phi_y = \sqrt{-\frac{\overline{v'^2}}{\overline{u'v'}}} \tag{53.b}$$

Substituting Equations (47) through (53) into Equations (45) and (46) yields

$$\pm u_p^2 = 3/4\ g\ \frac{C_{Dx}}{\gamma_s}\ (\phi_x^2 + 1)\ \tau_0 - g\ D\ (\frac{\gamma_s - \gamma}{\gamma_s})\ \tan \alpha \tag{54}$$

and

$$\pm v_p^2 = 1.81\ g\ \frac{C_{Dy}}{\gamma_s}\ \phi_y^2\ \tau_0 - g\ D\ (\frac{\gamma_s - \gamma}{\gamma}) \tag{55}$$

in which τ_0 is the mean bed shear stress $(-\overline{pu'v'})$.

The correlation functions ϕ_x and ϕ_y are functions of the friction Reynolds number (Laufer[7]) or

$$\phi_x = 2.5 - 2.5\ \exp\ (-.322\sqrt{\tau_0/\rho}\ D/\nu) \tag{56.a}$$

and

$$\phi_y = 1.0 - \exp\ (-.0525\sqrt{\tau_0/\rho}\ D/\nu) \tag{56.b}$$

Equations (54) and (55) provide estimates of the three particle velocities required for the intensity function matrix (37). The Kolmogorov differential equation (29) then can be integrated to obtain the probability for each process.

Once the probability for each process is obtained, the concentration, the rate of transfer, and the volume rate of flow of the sediment at the stream bed

---

[7]Laufer, J., "The Structure of Turbulence in Fully Developed Pipe Flow," National Advisory Committee for Aeronautics, Technical Report 1174, p. 17, 1954.

are given, respectively, by:

$$C_B(t) = C_A(t-\delta t) P_{AB}(t-1/2\delta t) + C_C(t-\delta t) P_{CB}(t-1/2\delta t)$$
$$- C_B(t-\delta t) [P_{BA}(t-1/2\delta t) + P_{BC}(t-1/2\delta t)] \tag{57}$$

$$N(t) = \frac{\partial}{\partial x}\left\{ BD_{50} C_C(t-\delta t) [\psi_{CB}(t-1/2\delta t) P_{CB}(t-1/2\delta t) \right.$$
$$+ \psi_{CA}(t-1/2\delta t) P_{CA}(t-1/2\delta t)] - C_A(t-\delta t) \psi_{AC}(t-1/2\delta t)$$
$$\left. P_{AC}(t-1/2\delta t) - C_B(t-\delta t) \psi_{BC}(t-1/2\delta t) P_{BC}(t-1/2\delta t)\right\} \tag{58}$$

and

$$Q_{B\ vol}(t) = \left\{ BD_{50} C_C(t-\delta t) \psi_{CB}(t-1/2\delta t) P_{CB}(t-1/2\delta t) \right.$$
$$+ C_A(t-\delta t) \psi_{AB}(t-1/2\delta t) P_{AB}(t-1/2\delta t) - \psi_{CB}(t-\delta t)$$
$$\left. [\psi_{BA}(t-1/2\delta t) P_{BA}(t-1/2\delta t) + \psi_{BC}(t-1/2\delta t) P_{BC}(t-1/2\delta t)]\right\} \tag{59}$$

Since the elevation of the stream bed is a function of both the rate of transfer of sediment between the stream bed and the bed load state and the stream bed and the suspended load state, Equation (9) can also be written

$$C/_{y=\eta} T \frac{\partial \eta}{\partial t} + \frac{\partial}{\partial x}(Q_{B\ vol} + Q_{B\ exc}) = 0 \tag{60}$$

where

$$Q_{B\ exc}(t) = \frac{\partial}{\partial x}\left\{ BD_{50} C_C(t-\delta t) [\psi_{CB}(t-1/2\delta t) P_{CB}(t-1/2\delta t) \right.$$
$$+ \psi_{CA}(t-1/2\delta t) P_{CA}(t-1/2\delta t)] - C_A(t-\delta t) \psi_{AC}(t-1/2\delta t)$$
$$\left. P_{AC}(t-1/2\delta t) - C_B(t-\delta t) \psi_{BC}(t-1/2\delta t) P_{BC}(t-1/2\delta t)\right\} \tag{61}$$

Completing the formulation, the mathematical model of the scour-fill process in erodible streams can be visualized by the illustration in Figure 3.

The particle diameter, D, used in the development of the stochastic model is for homogeneous bed material. For heterogeneous bed material, the mean particle diameter should be used.

Having arrived at this point, a question still remains. Is the Kolmogorov system (29), which described Markovian processes with time-dependent transition probabilities, a valid system to describe the stochastic sediment transfer at the interface; in other words, is the time spent within each state and from state-to-state exponentially distributed? Exponential distribution is a necessary, though no sufficient, condition of a Markov process, and since the time of particle stay or transfer is a function of the instantaneous particle velocity, this velocity has to possess a distribution which belongs to the exponential family.

To see that the instantaneous particle velocity, $\vec{V}_p$, has an exponential distribution, let $F(\vec{V}_p)$ be its distribution function with a range, Γ, or

$$F\,(\vec{V}_p) = \int_\Gamma f\,(\vec{V}_p)\, d\,\vec{V}_p \tag{62}$$

Going back to Equations (55) and (56) it can be seen that, at the interface,

$$\vec{V}_1' = +\sqrt{a\ \vec{V}_p^2 + b},\ \ \vec{V}_2' = -\sqrt{a\ \vec{V}_p^2 + b} \tag{63}$$

in which a and b are coefficient scalars. Equation (63) indicates that the density function of the random variable $\vec{V}_p$ is a double-valued function. Therefore, the density function $f(\vec{V}_p)$ can be obtained by partial differentiation of Equation (62) as

$$f(\vec{V}_p) = \frac{\partial\ F(\vec{V}_p)}{\partial\ \vec{V}'} \left| \frac{d\ \vec{V}_1'}{d\ \vec{V}_p} \right| + \frac{\partial\ F(\vec{V}_p)}{\partial\ \vec{V}_2'} \left| \frac{d\ \vec{V}_2'}{d\ \vec{V}_p} \right| \tag{64}$$

At the stream bed, the fluctuating velocity $\vec{V}'$ has a nearly Gaussian distribution. Hence,

$$\frac{\partial\ F(\vec{V}_p)}{\partial\ \vec{V}_1'} = \frac{1}{\sqrt{2\pi}\ \sigma_{\vec{V}'}}\ \exp\left[-\frac{(\vec{V}' - \vec{V}')^2}{2\ \sigma_{\vec{V}'}} \right] \tag{65}$$

and

$$\frac{\partial\ F(\vec{V}_p)}{\partial\ \vec{V}_2'} = \frac{1}{\sqrt{2\pi}\ \sigma_{\vec{V}'}}\ \exp\left[-\frac{(\vec{V}' + \vec{V}')^2}{2\ \sigma^2_{\vec{V}'}} \right] \tag{66}$$

where $\sigma_{\vec{V}'}$ is the standard deviation of $\vec{V}'$ about its mean $\overline{\vec{V}'}$.

Differentiating Equation (63) with respect to $\vec{V}_p$ yields

$$\left| \frac{d\ \vec{V}_1'}{d\ \vec{V}_p} \right| = \left| \frac{d\ \vec{V}_2'}{d\ \vec{V}_p} \right| = \frac{a\sqrt{c\ \vec{V}'^2 + d}}{\vec{V}'} \tag{67}$$

in which c and d are coefficient scalars. (See Equations (55) and (56)).

Then substituting Equations (65), (66), and (67) into Equation (64) yields

$$f(\vec{V}_p) = \frac{a\sqrt{c\ \vec{V}'^2 + d}}{\vec{V}'\ \sqrt{2\pi}\ \sigma_{\vec{V}'}} \left\{ \exp\left[-\frac{(\vec{V}' - \vec{V}')^2}{2\ \sigma^2_{\vec{V}'}} \right] + \exp\left[-\frac{(\vec{V}' + \vec{V}')^2}{2\ \sigma^2_{\vec{V}'}} \right] \right\} \tag{68}$$

16.13

Equation (68) indicates that $f(\vec{V}_p)$ has a Gamma distribution which belongs to the exponential family, and therefore suggests that it might be described by a Markovian process with discrete states in continuous time. If this is the case, the Kolmogorov system (29) is a valid description of stochastic sediment transfer at the interface as was assumed in the development presented herein.

3. METHODS OF SOLUTION

The essence of the model developed in this paper is to obtain the solution to systems of equations: (1) one-dimensional equations based on the conservation of fluid mass, flow momentum, and sediment mass in the flow, and (2) the Kolmogorov differential equations.

To obtain a high-accuracy approximation in the solution of Equations (6) and (7), the one-step Lax-Wendroff is adopted. Equations (6) and (7) are rewritten in the following form:

$$\frac{\partial \vec{W}}{\partial t} + \frac{\partial F(\vec{W})}{\partial x} + \vec{K} = 0 \tag{69}$$

where

$$\vec{W} = \begin{bmatrix} A \\ Q \end{bmatrix} , \quad F(\vec{W}) = \begin{bmatrix} Q \\ \frac{Q^2}{A} + gh_c A \end{bmatrix} , \quad \vec{K} = \begin{bmatrix} -L -S \\ gA \frac{\partial \eta}{\partial x} + \frac{Q^2}{8} \frac{f}{AR_h} \end{bmatrix} \tag{70}$$

The vector $\vec{W}$ can be expressed in Taylor series as follows:

$$\vec{W}_i^{j+1} = \vec{W}_i^{j} + \Delta t \left(\frac{\partial \vec{W}}{\partial t}\right)_i^{j} + \frac{\Delta t^2}{2} \left(\frac{\partial^2 \vec{W}}{\partial t^2}\right)_i^{j} + \dots . \tag{71}$$

Since this is an explicit scheme in time, t, the second order term is preserved in order to obtain high order accuracy. Equation (71) can also be written

$$\vec{W}_i^{j+1} = \vec{W}_i^{j} - \Delta t \left[\frac{\partial F(\vec{W})}{\partial x} + \vec{K}\right]_i^{j} + \frac{\Delta t^2}{2}\left[\frac{\partial}{\partial x}\left[\vec{J}_F\left[\frac{\partial F(\vec{W})}{\partial x} + \vec{K}\right]\right]\right]_i^{j}$$

$$+ \frac{\Delta t^2}{2}\left[\vec{J}_K\left[\frac{\partial F(\vec{W})}{\partial x} + \vec{K}\right]\right]_i^{j} \tag{72}$$

in which $\vec{J}_F$ and $\vec{J}_K$ are the Jacobians of $F(\vec{W})$ and $\vec{K}$ with respect to $\vec{W}$, respectively, or

$$\vec{J}_F = \begin{bmatrix} 0 & 1 \\ \frac{\partial}{\partial A}(gh_cA) - U^2 & 2U \end{bmatrix} \tag{73}$$

and

$$\vec{J}_K = \begin{bmatrix} -\frac{\partial S}{\partial A} & 0 \\ g\frac{\partial \eta}{\partial x} - \frac{U^2}{8}\frac{f}{R_h} - \frac{Q^2}{8}\frac{f}{AR_h^2}\frac{R_h}{A} + \frac{Q^2}{8AR_h}\frac{\partial f}{\partial A} & \frac{Uf}{4R_h} + \frac{Q^2}{8AR_h}\frac{\partial f}{\partial Q} \end{bmatrix} \tag{74}$$

All space derivatives are approximated by centered differences. Using the von Newmann stability criterion, it can be shown that the following condition must hold for stability in the solution

$$\left[U_{max} + \sqrt{\frac{\partial}{\partial A}(gh_cA)_{max}} \right] \frac{\Delta t}{\Delta x} < 1 \tag{75}$$

Characteristic of the Lax-Wendroff scheme is the presence of short-wave oscillations behind the shock front, particularly when the shock is strong. If these oscillations are allowed to be carried with the computation long enough, they might cause the solution to explode. Therefore, it might be necessary to add, in some cases, a filtering term or artificial viscosity to Equation (72) to minimize these oscillations.

The solution to the suspended sediment Equation (8) can be approximated by the following explicit difference scheme

$$c_i^{j+1} A_i^{j+1} = \frac{c_{i+1}^j A_{i+1}^j + c_{i-1}^j A_{i-1}^j}{2} - \frac{\Delta t}{\Delta x}(c_{i+1}^j Q_{i+1}^j - c_i^j Q_i^j)$$
$$+ \frac{\Delta t}{2(\Delta x)^2}\left((G_{cx_{i+1}}^j A_{i+1}^j + G_{cx_i}^j A_i^j)(c_{i+1}^j - c_i^j) - (G_{cx_i}^j A_i^j \right.$$
$$\left. + G_{cx_{i-1}}^j A_{i-1}^j)(c_i^j - c_{i-1}^j) \right) + \Delta t\, C_{B_i}^j S_i^j - \frac{\Delta t}{2\Delta x}(Q_B vol_{i+1}^{j+1} - Q_B vol_{i-1}^{j+1}) \tag{76}$$

In most practical cases, Equation (76) is of positive type; and, therefore, it is always stable.

The Kolmogorov system (29) which consists of nine ordinary differential equations, is solved directly on the analog computer. As far as stability in the solution is concerned, the analog technique is particularly suited for the Kolmogorov system because the intensities of sediment transfer within each state are negative. This causes the errors associated with the computation to decay exponentially with time. The analog diagram for this system is shown in Figure 4.

4. HYBRID COMPUTER EXPERIMENTS

The model as a whole is being synthesized on a hybrid computer available at the Utah Water Research Laboratory. The model will be tested by simulating conditions within an ephemeral reach of the Walnut Gulch Watershed in southern Arizona. This is a highly instrumental watershed operated by the Southwest Watershed Research Center, Agricultural Research Service, Tucson, Arizona. Measured input and control data will be used for calibration and testing of the processes modeled, and the model subsequently will be used for preditive purposes on this watershed.

Since field data are not yet available hypothetical input data are used to demonstrate the operation of the model. The movement of flood wave and sediment is simulated in a reach which is 24,000 feet long. This reach is divided into 20 space intervals, each 1,200 feet long. To stay within the stability limits of the difference equations used, the time increment is taken as one minute. The average slope is about .005.

With the input hydrograph as shown in Figure 5, the wave reaches the downstream end after 35 minutes. It is attenuated to about half the size of the input. This is due mainly to the high intake rate of the stream bed. Figure 5 also show that the peak of the hydrograph occurs at about the same time as the peak of the suspended sediment graph, while, as expected, the peak of the bed load graph lags behind the hydrograph peak. These phenomena are illustrated by Figures 6, 7, and 8, which show the profiles of the water discharge, bed load discharge, and suspended load discharge, respectively.

A sample of the probability profiles is shown in Figure 9 for the transfer of sediment from immobile bed state to bed load state. The profiles tend to have relatively flat lee-side slopes which are similar to those of the velocity profiles.

5. SUMMARY

A mathematical model of the sediment transport process in ephemeral streams is presented. The main advantage of the approach adopted is that the problem of separating bed load from suspended load is avoided by dealing with states of occurrence rather than physical zones. Stochastic processes are used to describe sediment transfer between states.

The model is being synthesized on a hybrid computer. It was found that the computational schemes used are stable. The term associated with the friction factor in the equation of momentum controls the stability in the solution. The responses of sediment load to change in water discharge are as expected. The suspended load tends to change instantaneously with the water hydrograph, while there is some lag in the response function associated with the bed load.

PARTIAL LIST OF SYMBOLS

Symbol	Definition
A	Cross sectional area of flow
A_C	Cross sectional area of the stream bed
Ⓐ	Suspended load state at the interface
Ⓑ	Bed load state at the interface
Ⓒ	Immobile bed state at the interface
C	Overall average concentration of suspended sediment
C_C	Specific weight of the bed material
C_i	Concentration of sediment at state i at the interface
$C/_{y=\eta} = C_B$	Bed load concentration
c	Point sediment concentration in 3-dimensional field
C_D	Drag coefficient
D	Sediment diameter
D_{50}	Median sediment diameter
e	Mass diffusivity in the 3-dimensional field
$\vec{F}$	Vector force on the particle
$F(x, y, z, t) = 0$	Boundary surface in the 3-dimensional field
f	Friction factor
f'	Friction factor due to grain roughness
f''	Friction factor due to bed forms
G_{cx}	Longitudinal solid dispersivity
$\vec{g}$	Gravitational acceleration
h	Flow depth
h_c	Depth from free stream surface to centroid of flow cross sectional area
I	Intensity of turbulence
$\vec{I}$	Identity vector
L	Lateral flow into or from the channel per unit length

Partial List of Symbols (Continued)

Symbol	Definition
m	Mass of solid particle
N	Local total sediment transfer rate at the stream bed
P_{AB}	Probability that a particle moves from state Ⓐ to state Ⓑ
p	Porosity of the bed at static state
p	Point pressure
Q	Total fluid discharge
$\vec{R}$	Vector flow across stream boundary surface
R_h	Hydraulic radius
S	Total seepage into or from the channel bed per unit length
T	Top width of flow
$T^{(e)}$	Reynolds stress tensor
U	Mean stream velocity
U*	Friction velocity
$\vec{V}$	Temporal average fluid velocity vector
$\vec{V'}$	Temporal fluid velocity fluctuation vector
$\vec{V}_p$	Solid particle velocity vector at the interface
u', v'	Turbulent velocity fluctuations
α	Average angle of encounter between individual particles
β	Momentum correction factor
γ	Fluid specific weight
γ_s	Solid particle specific weight
δ_{ij}	Kronecker delta symbol
η	Stream bed elevation above some datum
μ	Fluid dynamic viscosity
υ	Fluid kinematic viscosity
ρ	Fluid density
ρ_s	Solid particle density
τ_o	Bed shear stress
$\vec{\psi}$	Vector intensity of sediment motion at the interface

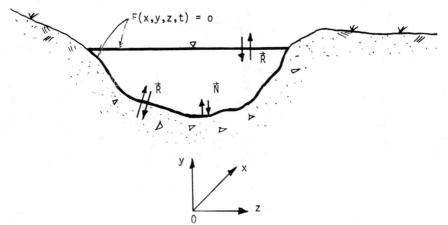

Figure 1. Illustration of a stream cross section.

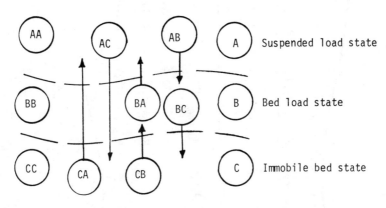

AA	AC	AB	A Suspended load state
BB	BA BC		B Bed load state
CC CA	CB		C Immobile bed state

Figure 2. Illustration of solid mass transfer at the interface

16.19

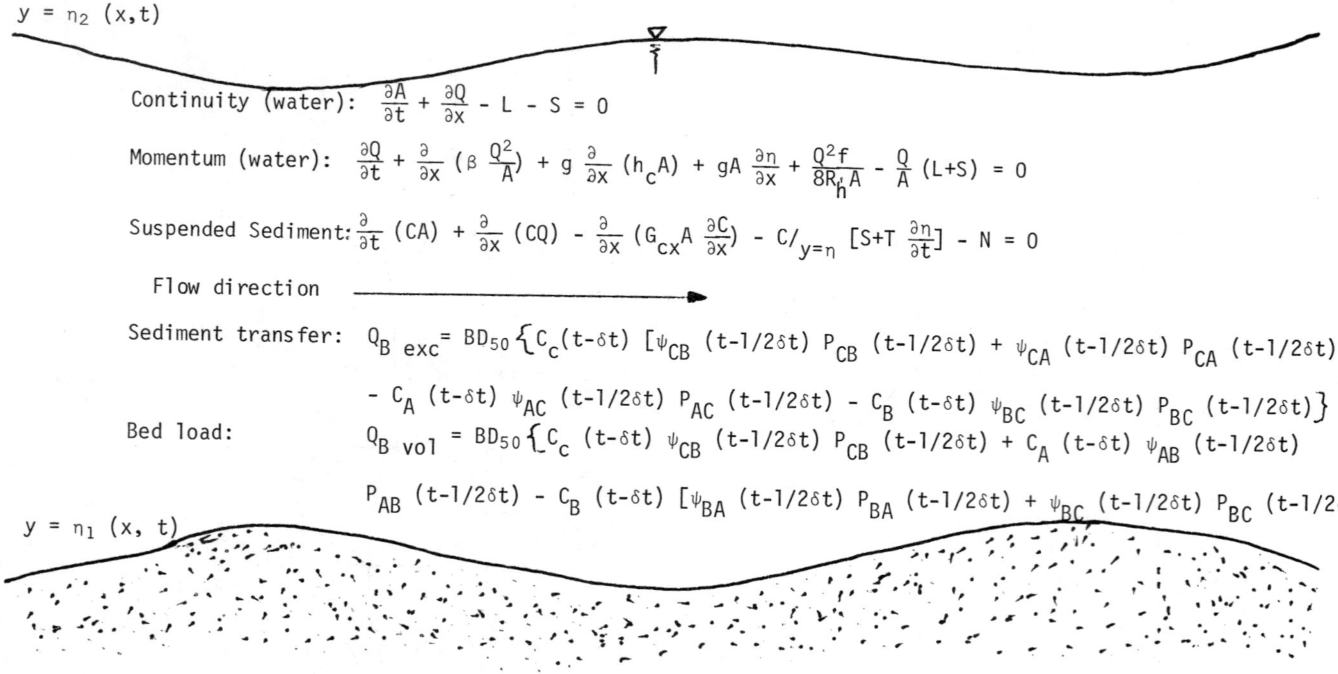

$y = \eta_2\,(x,t)$

Continuity (water): $\dfrac{\partial A}{\partial t} + \dfrac{\partial Q}{\partial x} - L - S = 0$

Momentum (water): $\dfrac{\partial Q}{\partial t} + \dfrac{\partial}{\partial x}\left(\beta\,\dfrac{Q^2}{A}\right) + g\,\dfrac{\partial}{\partial x}(h_c A) + gA\,\dfrac{\partial \eta}{\partial x} + \dfrac{Q^2 f}{8R_h A} - \dfrac{Q}{A}(L+S) = 0$

Suspended Sediment: $\dfrac{\partial}{\partial t}(CA) + \dfrac{\partial}{\partial x}(CQ) - \dfrac{\partial}{\partial x}\left(G_{cx} A\,\dfrac{\partial C}{\partial x}\right) - C/_{y=\eta}\left[S+T\,\dfrac{\partial \eta}{\partial t}\right] - N = 0$

Flow direction →

Sediment transfer: $Q_{B\,exc} = BD_{50}\big\{C_C(t-\delta t)\,[\psi_{CB}(t-1/2\delta t)\,P_{CB}(t-1/2\delta t) + \psi_{CA}(t-1/2\delta t)\,P_{CA}(t-1/2\delta t)]$

$-\,C_A(t-\delta t)\,\psi_{AC}(t-1/2\delta t)\,P_{AC}(t-1/2\delta t) - C_B(t-\delta t)\,\psi_{BC}(t-1/2\delta t)\,P_{BC}(t-1/2\delta t)\big\}$

Bed load: $Q_{B\,vol} = BD_{50}\big\{C_C(t-\delta t)\,\psi_{CB}(t-1/2\delta t)\,P_{CB}(t-1/2\delta t) + C_A(t-\delta t)\,\psi_{AB}(t-1/2\delta t)$

$P_{AB}(t-1/2\delta t) - C_B(t-\delta t)\,[\psi_{BA}(t-1/2\delta t)\,P_{BA}(t-1/2\delta t) + \psi_{BC}(t-1/2\delta t)\,P_{BC}(t-1/2\delta t)]\big\}$

Bed scour-fill: $C/_{y=\eta}\ T\,\dfrac{\partial \eta}{\partial t} + \dfrac{\partial Q_B}{\partial x} + N = 0$

$y = \eta_1\,(x,\,t)$

370

16.20

Figure 3.   Schematic diagram showing the various equations used in the sediment movement model.

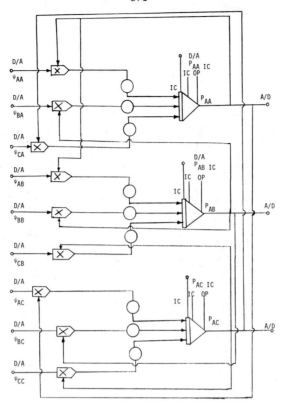

Figure 4. Sample analog diagram for the Kolmogorov System.

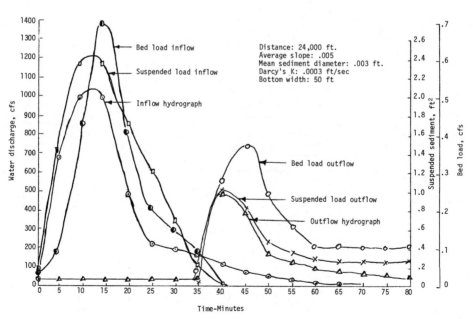

Figure 5. Inflows and simulated outflows

16.21

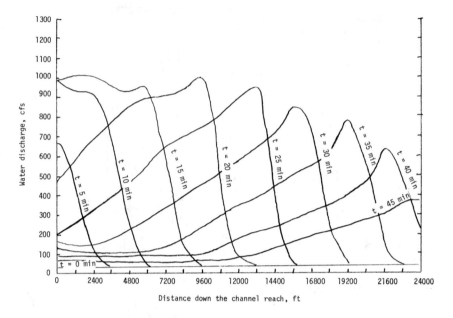

Figure 6. Water discharge profiles

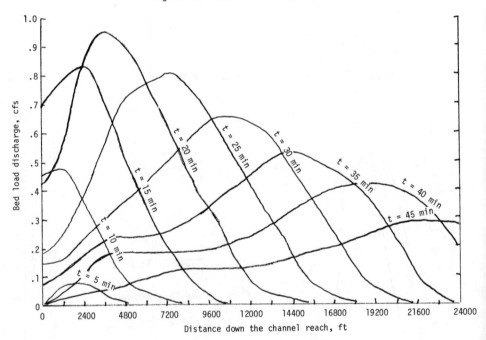

Figure 7. Bed load discharge profiles

16.22

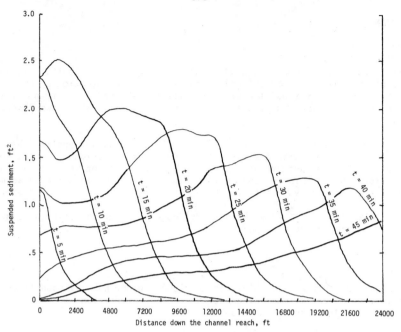

Figure 8. Suspended load profiles

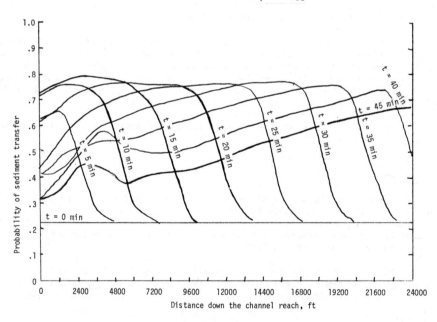

Figure 9. Profiles of the probability of the transfer of sediment from the immobile bed state to bed load state, P_{CB}.

16.23

DISCUSSION

M. HINO

(1) The authors' model is a one-dimensional one (Egs. (6)-(8)). I would like to ask whether the authors' model can simulate the formation of dunes, i.e. the instability of river bed (Kelvin-Helmholtz instability). Is it possible to simulate the dune formation process, if the model is extended to two-dimensional one?

(2) In the middle part of page 16, eq. (58), the author applies the Bagnolds concept on relatively large asymmetry of turbulent fluctuations. While, in page 1 eqs. (68) & (69), the authors ascert that the fluctuation of velocity has a nearly Gausian distribution. These discriptions are a contradiction, because asymmetry of fluctuations is equivalent to the non-Gaussianity of fluctuation probability.

(3) I would like to know the authors' opinion about the effects of sediment suspension on turbulence of flow?

C. KISIEL

1. How are initial probabilities obtained? Under natural conditions, the errors in initial conditions may cause the model's predictions to "blow up," for example, if meanders have been established in nature.

2. The focus is on a micro-stochastic model. Would not a macro-stochastic model be appropriate to the objective of building a sediment model to be used in connection with a watershed model? M. Negev constructed a sediment model for use in connection with the Stanford Watershed Model.

3. Computer time becomes a problem in stochastic modeling of micro processes Hence, the results to be realized by this approach are constrained by the availabl computer size (in addition to the basic assumptions on the physics of the process) Although it is premature at times to prejudge the future merits of a new approach, there are at present certain realities that can guide its pursuit: real time prediction versus simulation of equally likely sediment patterns.

4. In Equation (53), what is the nature of the averaging in $(\upsilon)^2$: temporal or spatial? Why the difference?

W. L. MOORE

Since the analysis of the stream flow is on a relatively large scale both in time and space, is it desirable to treat the sediment motion on such a fine scale and in such detail? It appears that the number of relations and the number of parameters used to describe the sediment motion might be reduced by using a simpler sediment transport function.

The simple assumptions about the turbulence characteristics (based on laboratory measurements) may actually eliminate much of the potential of the detailed sediment analysis.

A. MUROTA

I appreciate your paper in which the definition of "states" of transported sediment was originally proposed using the transition probability.

16.24

(1) Depending on the characteristics of progressive waves, mainly on the time of rise of the hydrograph, analytical treatments should be reasonably decided which approach is more preferable, by the dynamic wave analysis, or by the kinematic wave approximation.

Because the presentation of profiles of "translatory waves" observed in the southwest part of the United States are not given in the paper, it is difficult to decide whether your proposed Lax-Wendroff scheme is applicable.

(2) Analytical approach by the one-dimensional equation of flow momentum should not lead us to describe local variation of velocity near the bed, which is one of very important factors in your definition of states of flow-bed interface. I think that the problem in the short-time scour-fill process should be solved by introducing the internal mechanism of translatory waves from results of one-dimensional analyses.

How the local velocity variation of unsteady flows can be introduced from the solution of one-dimensional equations? Several researchers of our laboratory are studying at present the problems of river flow simulations, optimum operation of reservoirs, and spectra of sand waves in the alluvial channel, and similar.

T. D. STEELE

Continuing with C. Kisiel's comments, some concern might be given to the amounts of data required for sediment model testing and calibration. With the microscale and detailed refinement of your model, do you anticipate eventual operational application of the model on a large scale? If so, considerable costs in data-collection programs could be anticipated.

V. YEVJEVICH

In this paper the objective is to mathematically model to predict sediment yield from water discharge by using the basic laws of fluid mechanics. However, if the observed concurrent series of sediment transport and water discharge are studied, the relations between these two variables show that usually only up to about 25 percent of the variance of sediment discharge is explained by the water discharge variable. The relationship between the two variables can be accounted for through transition probabilities or through the proper regression equation. However, the number of states selected for these variables affect the results.

It is not clear why the model of runoff-rainfall should be tied to the model of sediment discharge--water discharge, because the information has twice the chance of being lost by the double transition from one variable to the other.

RESPONSE BY J. P. RILEY

The response to discussion by M. Hino is as follows.

1. This one-dimensional model does not simulate directly, but indirectly, the Kelvin-Helmholtz instability at the interface region. Since the pressure fluctuation varies inversely with the intensity of turbulence, any increase in velocity tends to reduce the pressure and, therefore, to induce the sediment particles to leave the bed, and vice-versa.

If the model were extended to include two-dimensions, an improved description of the sediment suspension would be accomplished. However, with a certain degree of approximation, the simulation of dune formation is possible even with a one-dimensional model. A process that should be taken into account is the separation behind the dune crest. This separation process is neglected in the present model which is still in the formative stages.

2. Dr. Hino poses a very critical question here. It is true that the asymmetry of velocity fluctuations is equivalent to the non-Gaussianity of fluctuation probability. The probability density curve for the vertical fluctuations is skewed to the left while the probability density for the horizontal fluctuations maintains the Gaussian distribution. The aim in this section of the paper is to show that the density distribution for the sediment particle velocity belongs to the exponential family. It is therefore assumed that the resultant of the vertical and horizontal velocity fluctuations have what is termed in the paper as being a "nearly Gaussian distribution". Admittedly, the term "nearly Gaussian" is not an accurate description of the process, but the intent is to imply the exponential pattern.

3. Because the sediment suspension has a damping effect on the intensity of turbulence, the turbulent eddy diffusivity for the mixture of water and sediment is less than that for water alone. This damping of turbulence means a reduction in the root-mean-square shear velocity. However, this reduction in shear velocity caused by sediment suspension is very small compared to the increase in resistance to flow brought about by stream bed irregularities.

The response to discussion by C. Kisiel is as follows.

Professor Kisiel has a good point in the fact that initial conditions may cause the model's predictions to "blow up". Initial probabilities are not critica but the initial amount of sediment in each of the three states control subsequent results. However, from model tests it was found that the initial conditions in the sediment portion affect the output only for a short period of time. Beyond that time the instantaneous bulk flow variables tend to represent the primary control. For ephemeral streams, it is easy to determine the initial conditions, and for perennial streams, an estimation based on some empirical relationship seems adequate.

As far as scale is concerned, it would be desirable to develop a macro-stochastic model, but in that case, the probabilities would need to be based on the intensity and frequency of rainfall input or stream inflow. Timer series analysis might be adopted for this purpose. In a sense, however, the model presented falls in the macro-stochastic model category because the relations and parameters on which the model is based are all reduced to functions of bulk flow parameters and other variables as mentioned in the reply to Professor Moore.

The computation time is not a problem. The sediment part of the model takes about the same time as the water part. Since a short-time prediction of the stream bed variation is the objective, a distributed model is necessary. In Equation (53), u^2 was originally used, but no way was found to predict this temporal and spatial mean velocity at the stream bed. The correlation functions between the mean square (spatial and temporal) velocity fluctuations $\overline{u'^2}$ and $\overline{v'^2}$ and the mean-square shear velocity $-\overline{u'v'}$ are introduced instead, or

$$\phi_x = - \frac{\overline{u'^2}}{\overline{u'v'}} = 2.5 - 2.5e^{-.322 \, \mathbb{R}_f}$$

and

$$\phi_y = - \frac{\overline{v'^2}}{\overline{u'v'}} = 1.0 - e^{-.0525 \, \mathbb{R}_f}$$

where $\mathbb{R}_f$ is the friction Reynolds number, or

$$\mathbb{R}_f = \frac{\sqrt{\tau_o/\rho} \; D_{50}}{\nu}$$

Equations (55) and (56) become

$$\pm u_p^2 = 3/4 \, g \, \frac{C_{Dx}}{\gamma_s} \, (\phi_x + 1) \, \tau_o - gD \, (\frac{\gamma_s - \gamma}{\gamma_s}) \tan \gamma$$

$$\pm v_p^2 = 1.81 \, g \, \frac{C_{Dy}}{\gamma_s} \, \phi_y \, \tau_o - gD \, (\frac{\gamma_s - \gamma}{\gamma_s})$$

The response to discussion by W. L. Moore is as follows.

The model is intended to be applied to a large system of rivers. Although several relationships and parameters are involved in the formulation of the model, these are all reduced to functions of the following: (1) shear velocity, which determines the friction slope, (2) bulk flow parameters, and (3) channel and sediment characteristics. Because the simulation of an integrated sediment movement as caused by floods is the objective of the model, the involvement of several equations which describe the unsteady nature of the processes is unavoidable.

The response to discussion by A. Murota is as follows.

In the southwest part of the United States convective thunderstorms occur during the summer season. These high-intensity, short-duration storms cause flood waves to move downstream, and these waves tend to override each other. The usually prevailing high-intake rates of the stream beds adds to the complexity of the situation. These phenomena tend to produce hydrograph rise times which decrease with increasing watershed area.

Most of the ephemeral stream in the Southwest are formed on steep slopes (about one percent slope on the average), and meandering is usually not extensive,

16.27

although a stream may change its course rapidly. Most stream are wide and shallow with uniform bed elevations over the top width of flow.

Since the purpose of the model is to be applicable to field conditions, all the parameters are expressed in terms of the bulk flow parameters. Local variations of velocity near the bed are approximated by the mean by shear stress.

The response to discussion by T.D. Steele is as follows.

The model is intended to predict sediment flow in a system of rivers on a short time basis. As far as data collection is concerned, only in flows to and outflows from the system and initial conditions are needed in addition to the mean channel geometry and sediment characteristics. These data requirements would not add considerably to costs involved in data collection for flood simulation in a system of rivers.

The response to discussion by V. Yevjevich is as follows.

It is true that, if a time series analysis involving only the water discharge and the sediment discharge is adopted, only a small percent of the variance of the sediment discharge is explained by the water discharge variable. However, this is more likely to be the case for a lumped parameter model. In the case of a distributed parameter model, not only is the water discharge considered, but also several other conditions such as local flow variables, channel geometry, and sediment characteristics. Also the suspended load, the bed load, and the immobile bed interact on each other. This could explain why there is a low cross-correlation between the concurrent sediment discharge and water discharge series.

In this model, only the sediment transfer at the stream bed is considered as a stochastic process. In this region, only three states may exist: (1) the suspended load state, (2) the bed load state, and (3) the immobile bed state. Transition probabilities describe the change of states in this region only, not in the main body of flow.

On the short-time basis, sediment contribution from the sloping lands to the stream channel is negligible. In the model of our study, only water runoff from these slopes is considered because these inflow partly affect the movement of sediments already in the stream channel. In a small watershed, particularly in the upper portion, lateral inflows into the channel are the main source of water supply.

United States-Japan Bi-Lateral Seminar in Hydrology

Honolulu, January 1971

METEORO-HYDROLOGICAL ASPECTS OF RAINFALL IN JAPAN

By Minoru Okuta

Chief of the 2nd Lab. of Typhoon Research Laboratory
Meteorological Research Institute
Japan Meteorological Agency
Tokyo Japan

Synopsis

The distribution of the regional division of heavy rainfalls in Japan and its meteorological causes are described in brief. Those distributions very well coincide with that of the climatic provinces.

Based on the results of climatological studies in Japan, the author suggests in this paper that the climatic province is available for estimation of the various hydrological values as follows:
The characteristics of depth-duration and intensity-duration curve,
Regional change of rainfall amount and its intensity,
Recurrence interval of rainfall amount, etc.

1. Introduction

The reason why we take up this subject is as follows:
The characteristically severe climate of Japan is due to the existence of the vast area of the Eurasian Continent on the West and the expanse of open sea of the Pacific Ocean on the east which give rise to a special circulation of the atmosphere. Thus, besides the summer and winter monsoon, the formation of the principal frontal zones creates the Baiu, typhoon, and frequent barometric depressions which bring forth floods and strorms; morever, details of the climate of Japan are affected by surrounding oceanic bodies and the complicated mountain topography, and there are significant regional differences in precipitation in Japan.

The climatic provinces which were introduced by many climatologists very well coincide with the regional disvision of heavy rainfalls that the author introduced by using the characteristics of frequencies of heavy rainfalls. His regional division of heavy rainfalls gives us many available informations related to hydrology. Now, we will describe them in the following sections.

17.1

2. Regional divisions of heavy rainfalls in Japan and their relation-
    ships with the climatic provinces

According to the seasonal variation of frequency and the total
number of heavy rainfalls of each station, we can classify the heavy
rainfalls in Japan into four main regional types and some transitional ones (Figs. 1 and 2).

Type I with low frequency throughout the year (the period of
1951-60); total sum of the frequency of heavy rainfalls more than 50
mm in daily precipitation amount is less than 30 days, heavy rainfalls
occuring only in the warm season.

Type II with high frequency throughout the year; the frequency is
more than 80 days, heavy rainfalls appearing throughout the year.

Type III with high frequency in winter; the maximum in the year
appears in the season of winter monsoon but heavy rainfalls more than
100 mm are rather frequent in the warm season.

Type IV with high frequency in the warm season; the frequency is
more than 80 days.

Transitional Types; Type I to Type II and Type I to Type III
appear in Fig. 1.

Then combining those types and comparing frequencies of heavy
rainfalls between the Baiu and the Typhoon Season or between June and
July by using the data of the entrusted rain-gauge stations in western
part of Japan, it is suggested that subdivision of the regional division of heavy rainfalls is possible. Fig. 2 indicates the synthetic
subclassification of regions in the Western Japan. In Fig. 2, Types
I, II, III and IV are same as Fig. 1, and I : frequencty of daily
precipitation amount $\geqq$ 50 mm is 31-39 days during the ten years,
I : same as I , but for 40-49 days, I : same as I , but for 50-79
days.

The regional divisions of heavy rainfalls that we suggested in
this paper very well coincide with the climatic provinces proposed by
Professor E. Fukui (1933) and other climatologists as shown in Figs.
3 and 4.

3. The primary conditions causing the areal characteristics of heavy
    rainfalls

The primary conditions causing the areal characteristics of heavy
rainfalls may be divided roughly into two as follows:

   (1) Whether or not large quantities of water vapour are suppli-
        ed continuously into a certain area.
   (2) Whether or not strong ascending currents occur continuously
        in a certain area.

   (1) The frequency of heavy rainfalls as controlled by water
        vapour contents:

The water vapour content in the atmosphere is controlled mainly by
temperature and also affected by the distributions of ocean currents.

The fact that the frequency of heavy rainfalls increases rapidly as one goes southward from the border line at about 36°-37° N in Japan is caused by the latitudinal distribution of the water vapour content as shown in Fig. 5. In the area with less than 13 mb of annual mean water vapour pressure, the variation of the frequency of heavy rainfalls with vapour pressure is small, and in the area with more than 13 mb it is large.

Supply of water vapour into the atmosphere is done mostly by the process of evaporation, and the higher the sea-surface-temperature rises above the atmospheric temperature, the more is the evaporation generated. So, water vapour is supplied into the atmosphere over Japan in the area of warm currents in the South and Japanese waters, and the areas of frequent heavy rainfalls are naturally found in the regions where the wet air current can easily flow in after having been modified during its passage over the warm ocean current for a long time and distance.

The areas of extremely low frequency belonging to the region of Type I are the under the influence of the screening effect of mountains upon the wet air current flowing in from the ocean.

We can easily understand the relationship above mentioned by combining Fig. 2 with Fig. 6. As a typical example of this, we show the relation between the wind direction and speed at 850 mb level and the difference of frequency of heavy rainfalls on the east and the west side of the Kii Peninsula as shown in Fig. 7.

(2) Primary conditions causing the ascending current:

The conditions causing the ascending current are considered under the following four heads:

   i) Meteorological disturbance on a synoptic scale is strong.
   ii) Stratification of the atmosphere is unstable.
 iii) Dissolution of convective instability concentrates locally.
  iv) Forced ascending current is produced by orographic effect and strong forced convergence occurs.

Those four conditions are examined closely in relation to the areal characteristics of heavy rainfalls. Meteorological disturbances on a synoptic scale are responsible for the areal characteristics and the seasonal variation of the frequency of heavy rainfalls. It is shown that the seasonal variation of heavy rainfalls can be explained by that of the circulation systems in East Asia.

Near cyclones and fronts, the stratification of the atmosphere is unstable, and the areal concentration of the dissolution of convective instability appears frequently in the Western Japan at the time when the wet air currents flows into that area in the shape of tongue at the edge of anti-cyclone of the North Pacific Ocean. And also, the heavy snow-falls on the coast of the Japan Sea in winter belonging to the region of Type III, are caused by the dissolution of convective instability accumulated gradually in the cold air mass as it crossed the Japan Sea.

In addition to the screening effect of mountains upon the transportation of the water vapour contents, there are the following effects of topography upon the areal characteristics of heavy rainfalls:

  1) Forced ascending current due to mountainous topography.
  2) Ascending by forced convergence due to topography.

3) Ascending by forced convergence by relief.
4) Rapid decay of meteorological disturbances by relief.

Among these effects, the third one has not yet been examined sufficiently.

Last year, the author explained the formation of the zone of frequent heavy rainfalls near the coastal region and at the edge of a mountainous region by forced convergence caused by the difference of roughness between land and sea or plain and mountain. A good example of the zone of frequent heavy rainfalls by this effect of roughness is found along the coast of the Kii Peninsula at a distance of 20-25 km from the seashore.

4. The characteristics of depth-duration and intensity-duration
   curve related to climatic provinces

By using the data of official observation, Dr. M. Yoshino calculated the constants, k and n, for an experimental equation of the depth-duration curve, $R = kt^n$, where t is time (in minutes) and R, rainfall amount (in mm), were then calculated. As for the rainfall amount, R, the mean values obtained from the 1st to 5th ranking in the official records of the Japan Meteorological Agency from 1941-50, as observed every 10, 20 and 30 minutes and 1,3. 6. 24 and 36 hours for each of the 109 stations in Japan, were used. Seperating the time periods into those between 10 minutes and 1 hour and those between 6 and 36 hours, it was shown that the k and n values exhibited a wide range according to geographical regions and the time periods mentioned above. These facts are shown in the accompanying Fig. 8.

Dr. M. Yoshino obtained also the constants, b, k and n, for an experimental equation for the intensity-duration curve $i = k/(t+ b)^n$, where t is time (in minutes) and i, the rainfall intensity (in mm per minutes) by calculating the intensity values by the same method as is described above for the mean rainfall values. The distribution b, k and n values revealed marked localization as is shown in Fig. 9.

Comparing those figures with the figures which indicate the areal distribution of the climatic provinves, we can see that the areal characteristics of rainfall intensity appear related to the climatic provinces.

5. Relation between the climatic provinces and the rainfall amount
   and its intensity

The regional division that we introduced by statistical method is also useful for estimation of the areal variation of the rainfall amount and its intensity by the passage of meteorological disturbances.

For example, on July 9, 1967 when a typhoon of small scale approaching from south-west was decaying rapidly, the precipitating area of extreme intensity moved eastward along the Japan Islands bringing severe damages from place to place. In this case, rainfall amount and its intensity changed regionally by the climatic provinces as is evident by comparing Fig. 10 with Fig. 2. In Fig. 10, small typhoon appeared lefthand side, where the total rainfall amount inicates 350 mm, and passed across the central part of this figure to the right hand side. And in Fig. 10, the bar graphs indicate the time sequences of hourly precipitation amount at the stations that locations are pointed by the arrow. There are more

17.4

precipitation amount and strong rainfall intensity in the area of Type II and Type IV, and few precipitation amount and weak rainfall intensity in area of Type I.

6. Relation between the climatic province and the recurrence interval

It is very important for the water-resources planning to decide the reasonable recurrence-interval of heavy rainfall.

The author already described in this paper that the regional division of heavy rainfalls indicates good agreement with the areal distribution of the climatic provinces.

The frequencies of daily precipitation amount at every station for each of the classes $\geq$ 0.1 mm, $\geq$ 1.0 mm, $\geq$ 5.0 mm $\geq$ 10 mm, $\geq$ 30 mm, $\geq$ 50 mm, $\geq$ 100 mm, $\geq$ 150 mm, $\geq$ 200 mm, $\geq$ 300 mm, ... are found to be expressed by some exponential function. But it is clear from Fig. 11 that the cumulative frequency distribution curves of those classes are differnt according to the climatic types. In Fig. 11, the location of Takada is in the climatic province of Japan Sea side and belong to the region of Type III, Nagano is in that of the basin in inland area and belong to the region of Type I, Shizuoka is in that of Pacific side and belong to the region of Type II, as shown in Fig. 1.

From this nature, we can easily suppose that the types of recurrence curve plotted on logarithmic graph paper will be different by climatic provinces. For example, in Fig. 12, the recurrence curves of rainfall amount of the same stations of Fig. 11 are shown. And then, from Fig. 13 to Fig. 18, the author indicates that we can easily get similar recurrence curves in each same climatic province and different curves by the different climatic provinces. The location of those stations in Fig. 13 to 18 are indicated in Fig. 6.

So, if we want to obtain a recurrence interval of rainfall amount, at first time, we must check up on the division of the region by climatic provinces.

At last, the author points out that the other areal characteristics of rainfall are also almost always brought to light by using the climatic provinces, for example, periods of rainfall interval, distribution of the power-spectra of rainfall intensity and diurnal variation of rainfall intensity in the time of heavy rainfalls, etc.

References

Fukui, E., 1933: Climatic provinces in Japan (II), Geographical Rev. of Japan, Vol. 9, 271-300, (in Japanese).
Okuta, M., 1968: Climatological characteristics of heavy rains in Japan (I), Pap. in Met. & Geophy., XIX, 277-308, (in Japanese).
Sekiguchi, T., 1959: Climatic provinces in Japan, Tokyo Geography Pap. of Tokyo Kyoiku Univ., III, 65-78, (in Japanese).
Yoshino, M., 1960: The distribution of maximum observed rainfall and the characteristics of depth-duration and intensity duration curves in Japan, Jour. of the Met. Soc. of Japan, Ser. II, Vol. 38, 27-46, (in Japanese).

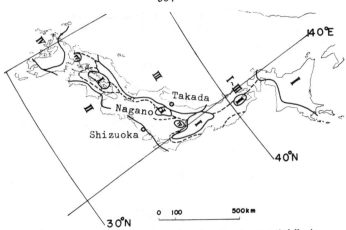

Fig. 1   Synthetic classification of regions for heavy rainfalls in Japan.
    I: low frequency through the whole year.
    II: high frequency through the whole year.
    III: high frequency in winter.
    IV: high frequency in the warm season.

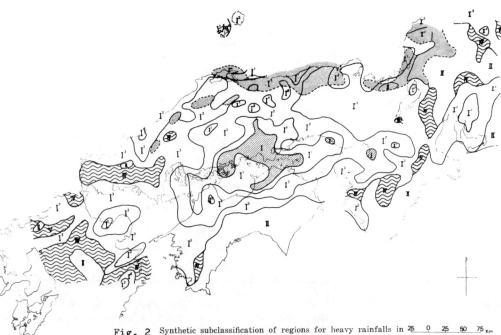

Fig. 2   Synthetic subclassification of regions for heavy rainfalls in Western Japan.
    I, II, III, IV are the same as Fig. 1
    I¹: frequency of daily precipitation amount $\geqq 50$ mm is 31–39 days during the ten years,
    I²: same as I¹, but for 40–49 days,
    I³: same as I¹, but for 50–79 days.

17.6

Fig. 3 Distribution of the climatic provinces in Japan, after E. Fukui.

Fig. 4 Same as Fig. 3, but after T. Sekiguchi.

17 .7

386

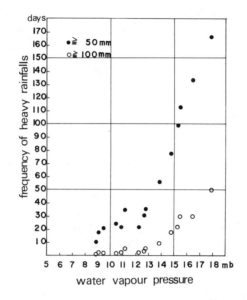

Fig. 5. Relation between the latitudinal mean frequency of heavy rainfalls and the latitudinal mean of the normal of water vapour
pressure in each degree of latitude in Japan (1951-60).

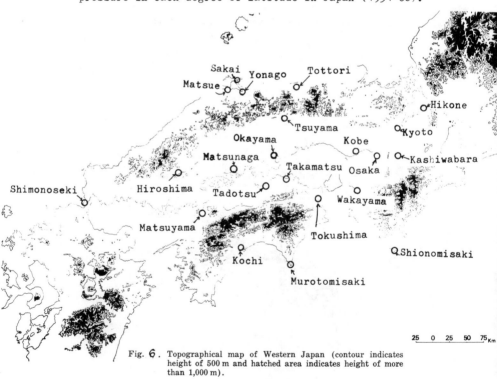

Fig. 6. Topographical map of Western Japan (contour indicates
height of 500 m and hatched area indicates height of more
than 1,000 m).

17.8

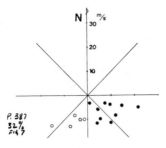

P. 387
32%
Fi. 7

Fig. 7. Relation between appearance of heavy rainfalls at Wakayama and
Owashi and upper wind of 850mb level observed at Shionomisaki.
The white circle indicates that the daily precipitation amount
at Wakayama is more than 50mm but that the amount at Owashi is
less than 50mm or that the amount at Wakayama exceeds that of
Owashi by more than 50mm; the black circle indicates an opposite
relationship. Location of Wakayama is on the west side of Kii-
Peninsula and that of Owashi is on the east side, and that of
Shionomisaki is southern point of the Kii-Peninsula.

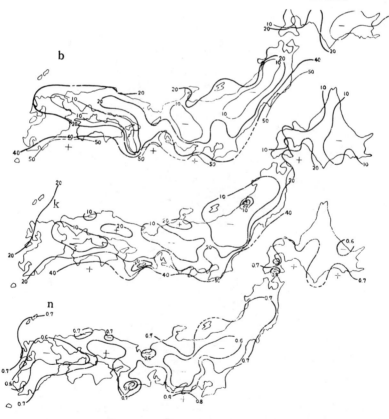

Fig. 9. Distributions of constants, b, k, and n, for equation $i = k/(b+t)^n$.

17.9

388

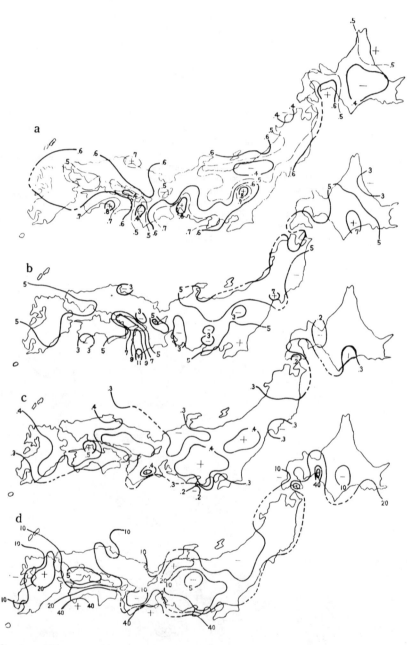

Fig. 8. Distribution of constants, k and n, for equation $R = kt^n$. (a) n and (b) k for short duration, 10-30 minutes. (c) n and (d) k for long duration, 6-36 hours.

17.10

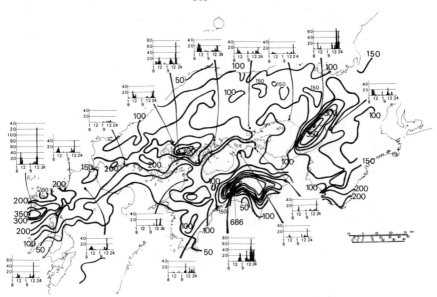

Fig.10. Areal distribution of the total precipitation amount and time
sequences of hourly precipitation amount in western Japan on
July 7-9th 1967.

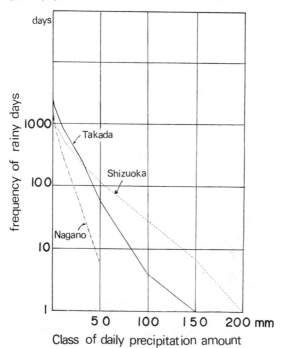

Fig.11. Examples of the frequency distribution of classified daily
precipitation amount.

17.11

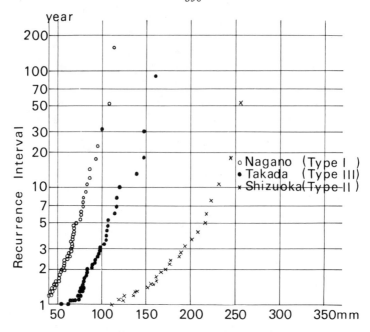

Fig. 12. Recurrence curves of daily precipitation amount in
same stations of Fig. 11.

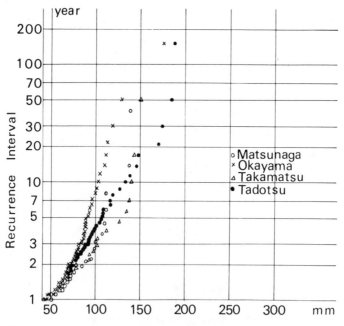

Fig. 13. Recurrence curves of daily precipitation amount in the climat
province of Type I.

17.12

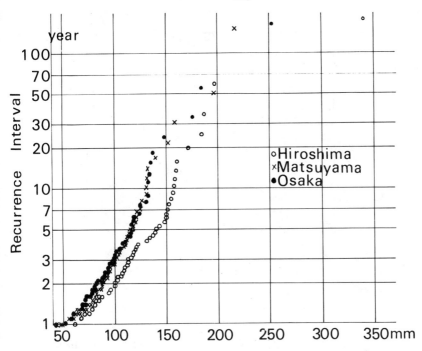

Fig. 14. Same as Fig. 13, but for Type I².

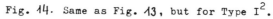

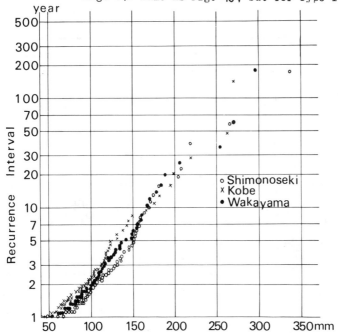

Fig. 15. Same as Fig. 13, but for Type I³.

17 .13

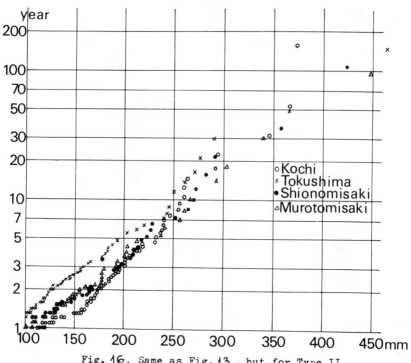

Fig. 16. Same as Fig. 13, but for Type II.

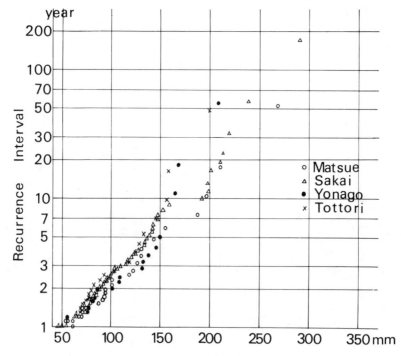

Fig. 17. Same as Fig. 13, but for Type III.

17.14

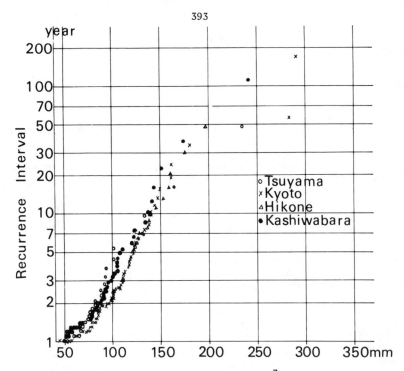

Fig. 18. Same as Fig. 13, but for Type I^3 (inland area).

DISCUSSION

C. KISIEL

1. How can the use of Hazen's method for obtaining plotting positions be justified? In particular, the approximate maximum value of the recurrence interval is set by Hazen's method to be twice the period of record. Does this really make sense?

2. Are PMP (probable maximum precipitation) estimates made in Japan? If so, how do these compare with the results of the probability analysis undertaken in this paper?

V. YEVJEVICH

Figures 12-18 give the points of a recurrence interval of more than 100 years for precipitation data while the length of time series used seem to be of a shorter period. How this recurrence interval, particularly of more than 100 years of length, has been obtained is unclear.

RESPONSE BY M. OKUTA

As a response to the question by V. Yevjevich, I obtained the points of a recurrence interval for precipitation amount by the Hazen's method: when $X_j (j=1,2,\ldots, N)$ is the annual maximum series of precipitation data in the order of their magnitude for N years, and T_j is an empirical recurrence interval corresponding to X_j, T_j is obtained by following equation

$$T_j = \frac{2N}{2j-1} \quad , \quad (j = 1, 2, \ldots, N) \quad .$$

I am aware of many criticisms of the Hazen's method. However, the purpose of my paper was not to estimate the probabilities of extreme values of precipitation amounts, but to clarify the relationships between the climatic province in Japan and the probability distribution curve. For the purpose the Hazen's method was used as easy to apply.

I have the same doubt as to C. Kisiel's question about the Hazen's method. The reason for which I used the Hazen's method is explained in answering the question by V. Yevjevich.

We tried to estimate the Probable Maximum Precipitation for an arbitrary region but to present have not succeeded in doing it for Japan or other parts of the world. Evaluation of topographic effects on rainfall is difficult. The presented paper is among the results obtained in our study for the evaluation of topographic effects on rainfall.

In comparing the observed rainfall (as independent data for the analysis) with the probability analysis of rainfall by various methods (Hazen's, Gumbel's, and others), these methods did not produce acceptable results.

United States - Japan Bi-Lateral Seminar in Hydrology
Honolulu, January 1971

THE ROLE OF NETWORK DESIGN IN THE MANAGEMENT AND CONTROL OF STREAMFLOW WATER QUALITY 1/

by Timothy Doak Steele 2/

SYNOPSIS

A generalized cost function for annual operation of sampling
sites of a streamflow water-quality network is proposed for use in
testing alternative designs in terms of frequency of sample collection, number of constituents determined directly by field or
laboratory analysis, and areal coverage. The objective function
may be stated in two ways: (1) given that the annual budgeted
costs for station operation is fixed, derive the most effective
design for station operation towards achieving the desired statistical measures for the various water-quality variables selected;
or (2) given that certain accuracy goals of certain measures of
water quality are to be achieved at a streamflow site, derive the
annual costs of station operation. The decision matrix of station-
operation strategies is dynamic in that each design should be
reviewed periodically to reflect the addition of new criteria and
the fulfillment of existing criteria. This paper discusses various
trade-offs between the cost function and the accuracy goals and
objectives (e.g., benefits) as applied to three major categories
of networks associated with management and control of streamflow
water quality: basin accounting, stream surveillance, and areal
synthesis.

INTRODUCTION

Streamflow water quality has come to the public limelight
as a more and more critical component of the problems in environmental quality facing planners and managers of our natural
resources. The adequacy of both historical data for detecting
changes in streamflow water quality and of data-collection programs
for assessing water-quality conditions is being seriously evaluated. Given constraints on money and manpower, the problem arises
as how to allocate these limited resources effectively for developing and maintaining a workable information system in order to
satisfy the various needs for managing and controlling streamflow
water quality. It is recognized, however, that management and
control of streamflow quality is not a closed system. Due consideration must be given to evaluating the impact of management policy
concerning streamflow quality on other sectors of the environment.
This paper describes several alternative schemes for deriving
water-quality information in terms of station schedules and data-
collection methodology. It should be kept in mind that an analysis
of water-quality networks involves a multivariate, multidimensional
process significantly more complex than analysis of surface-water
networks, where water quantity is the single variable involved.

1/ Publication authorized by the Director, U.S. Geological Survey.
2/ Research Hydrologist, U.S. Geological Survey,
          Washington, D.C., 20242, U.S.A.

The objectives and accuracy requirements of the various needs of water-quality data frequently are not specified. However, the water-quality standards established by individual states of the United States for interstate waters as authorized by the Water Quality Act of 1965 have begun to form a quantitative base upon which water-quality networks can be realigned. In many states' water-quality standards, consideration is given to different dominant uses of streamflow by development of classification schemes However, the initial class designation of a stream undoubtedly will be reviewed so that planning data networks to a large extent is or should be a dynamic process involving periodic modification.

Historical Data

Past records of streamflow water-quality data are important (1) for providing a historical information base on water-quality conditions, (2) for delineating existing problem areas with respect to certain water-quality variables, and (3) in testing for long-term trends in streamflow water quality resulting from economic development and population growth in the drainage basin. The information contained in basic water-quality data must frequentl be condensed into a manageable form amenable to data analysis and network evaluation. However, certain limitations in the methods of collection or in types of water-quality data should be kept in mind while carrying out statistical and analytical manipulation of historical records. Although many sampling sites are operated on a systematic frequency (e.g., daily, weekly, monthly, etc.), many data are collected at irregular time intervals and may be biased unintentionally by any seasonal hydrologic pattern. Data can represent grab samples or samples composited from several grab samples, and the time represented by the composite frequently is of a variable time interval. Determinations of certain constituents may be staggered throughout the schedule of samples. For example, although constituents A and B were determined for each of 12 monthly samples, constituent C may have been determined only for samples collected in February, May, and December, and constituent D for samples in April and November. Systematic sampling schedules may often be plagued with missing values or gaps in the record. Often, only a few years of record are available for making an assessment of trends in water-quality conditions. Presence of any or all of these factors may complicate rigorous statistical treatment of much of the available historical water-quality data.
A sampling program may advocate continuing coverage of several constituents measured over a historical period which provides additional information with few benefits. In extreme cases, perhaps the water-quality variables measured historically do not provide any information on current water-quality problems. For example, continued data-collection programs for major ionic constituents in surface waters of many areas of the United States may tie up funds that might more justifiably be used for measuring biologically-related variables, trace elements, and other important characteristics of water quality. Frequently, in verifying physical or management models of water quality or in testing compliance with water-quality standards, we may be plagued more with inappropriate data than with insufficient data.

18.2

Data Analysis

Data analysis should be complementary to data collection
and automatic data processing (ADP). The data analysis should
consider the water-quality program objectives and accuracy
requirements, either specified or assumed, of the particular
network associated with the data. As objectives are fulfilled
and as new objectives are added, areal configuration, suite of
constituents determined, and sampling frequency of the network
must be modified.

In this paper, concern is limited to data collected specifically for management and control of streamflow quality.
Included in these purposes are three general functions of networks applied to water quality: (1) regional basin accounting
(e.g., fulfilling National objectives for the major subregion
(Water Resources Council) or areal unit (Office of Water Data
Coordination)) divisions of the United States, (2) surveillance
(specifically, fulfillment of the various water-quality standards,
particularly, with respect to interstate streams), and (3) areal
synthesis of water-quality conditions. Relative emphasis in
spatial and temporal dimensions of the three networks may be
depicted as follows:

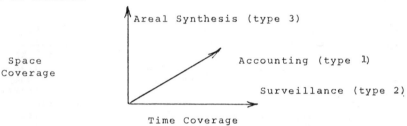

For areal synthesis, emphasis is placed on identifying areal variability of water-quality. Surveillance concerns itself with temporal
changes in quality, either on the long or short term, relative to
historical conditions or to set standards. Major basin accounting
combines aspects of both dimensions where areal variations on a
broad scale are accounted for over the long term. Data collected
for special research studies or for gaining scientific knowledge
in hydrologic, biological or hydrochemical processes are outside
of the scope of this paper.

APPROACH

Network Input Specifications

The Office of Water Data Coordination (OWDC, 1969) has
catagorized the national objectives of water-data needs into
the three major types of networks stated above. Although
products of all three networks may be interrelated, OWDC has
attempted to define each uniquely, and certain aspects of each
type must be considered in water-quality management and control.
Within the framework of each network, as applied to water quality,
the following basic questions must be considered in designing
the areal layout and annual operation of sampling stations or of
automatic monitoring equipment: (1) what water-quality constituents to analyze for, (2) where to sample, and (3) how often and

when to sample. Design criteria for all three networks must be described in terms of these three components, given due consideration to budgetary constraints and accuracy criteria for the appropriate statistical measures. This paper will deal more with selection of constituents to be considered and sampling strategies than with areal coverage. This latter aspect, although critical in areal synthesis, is more severely constrained in accounting and surveillance networks by regional basin subdivisions and major sources of pollution, respectively.

Figure 1 attempts to show how specifications for each type of network translate into the network design, which in turn determines to a major extent the workloads in data processing and data analysis. From a systems viewpoint, it should be stressed that the network--data--network cycle should be initiated by objectives specified from the planning level and not by the capacity of data loadings as viewed from the operational level (fig. 1). Traditionally, among massive data-collection programs, setting of objectives in sufficiently quantitative terms prior to implementation and subsequent expansion of data-collection programs has unfortunately been the exception rather than the rule.

A General Cost Function

In an attempt to derive a more quantitative assessment of design alternatives, a generalized cost function specifically for water-quality networks is developed below by which the economic impact of each of several alternatives can be weighed, based upon decisions regarding the basic design components of areal configuration, sampling frequency, and required constituent analyses. The cost function might be considered an economic model which includes as major components (1) costs of field visitations, (2) constituent analysis (including maintenance of water-quality automated stream monitors), and (3) data processing. Examples of the application of the cost function to evaluating alternative designs of each of the three types of networks will serve as a focal point for discussion on the role of such cost analysis in station design as well as management and control of stream quality.

Throughout the paper, discussion of accuracy levels will connote statistical errors in data analysis rather than errors in field sample-collection procedures or analytical errors in laboratory determinations. The magnitudes of these latter errors are fairly well known in the case of conservative water-quality variables. Accuracy ramifications of alternative network designs as discussed in this paper refer to those statistical errors over and above errors of the latter types. Less is known concerning the sampling and analytical errors inherent in determination of non-conservative pollutants, and only an intuitive statistical base can be built on top of this lack of knowledge.

The annual costs of operating a data-collection program at sampling site j in network type t, $Z_{T(j,t)}$ can be thought of as being comprised of three components:

$$Z_{T(j,t)} = Z_{V(j,t)} + Z_{M(j,t)} + Z_{P(j,t)} , \qquad (1)$$

where Z_V is that portion of operating costs associated with field site visitations, Z_M is the cost involving actual measurement of water-quality constituents specified for the station (laboratory analyses, field determinations of monitoring instrumentation), and Z_p covers data-processing costs. Each cost component, in turn, can normally be broken down into a product of frequency (or number of occurrences) and unit cost per number of occurrences. Thus,

$$Z_V = F_V \times C_V , \qquad (2)$$

where F_V is the frequency of field trips or observer visitations to a given site and C_V is the unit cost associated with each station visit. Next,

$$Z_M = F_M \times C_M , \qquad (3)$$

where F_M is the frequency of sample collection for constituent analyses and C_M is the aggregate cost associated with the total number of constituent determinations. Because the possible combinations of constituents and frequencies of determination are so widely variable, Z_M is more practically the sum over k of the products of the number of determinations made for constituent k (f_k) times its associated analytical charge (C_k):

$$Z_M = \sum_{k=1}^{N} (f_k \times C_k). \qquad (3a)$$

For a surveillance (type 2) station utilizing an automatic monitor, Z_M cannot be broken down readily by constituents, and operating charges for the various types of automatic monitoring equipment tend to be independent of the number of constituents measured and more dependent upon the type and electronic sophistication of the instrument. Also, the possible combinations of constituents monitored is not so widely variable. Finally,

$$Z_P = F_P \times C_P , \qquad (4)$$

where F_P is the number of data processing elements (in units of numbers of samples or constituent-years) and C_P reflects all the data processing costs (coding, punching, computer storage and data-file maintenance) associated with that element. Frequently, for basin accounting (type 1) or areal synthesis (type 3) stations, F_P will approximately equal the number of samples collected for analysis, which in turn equals the number of field visitations, so that

$$F_P = F_V \qquad (5)$$

in the overall cost function. Combining equations (2) through (5) back into the operating cost function (eqn. 1), we have the following:

$$Z_{T(j,t)} = F_V \times (C_V + C_P) + \sum_{k=1}^{N} (f_k \times C_k) , \qquad (6)$$

where t equals 1 or 3, and, in the special case for surveillance monitors (type 2):

$$Z_{T(j,2)} = F_V \times C_V + Z_M + F_P \times C_P . \qquad (7)$$

The operating cost function deals with the various charges associated with operating stations in a given type of network. Charges generally reflect certain overhead items (administrative, office supplies, etc.) and depreciation write-offs or capitalized items (equipment, laboratory supplies, instruments, analytical methods, etc.) as well as the direct cost items, such as field personnel, laboratory operating costs, and data processing.

Table 1 lists the various cost components and unit costs or charges associated with water-quality station operations. Because standard costs for the various components and elements of the cost function are, for the most part, lacking, these estimates, obtained from the available sources of information (e.g., professionals involved in network planning or monitoring instrumentation) are used only for purposes of demonstrating cost-analysis techniques in this paper and should not be accepted per se as guidelines for future planning. The laboratory cost factors for standard constituents were derived from laboratory charges of the U.S. Geological Survey and have become fairly stabilized. Laboratory charges for supplementary constituents listed in the appendix will vary by as much as 100 percent for individual laboratories within the Survey. This variation is dependent upon several factors, including economy of scale of sample loading, the analytical methods used, and geographical pertinence of measuring for the constituent. The cost components for the three types of monitors (table 1) are gross estimates from highly variable overall cost figures for operating monitors. Cost estimates for monitors have not been broken out into the three components, which were felt necessary for the analysis in this paper.

In evaluating the economics of water-quality network design, the annual operating cost function can be utilized in two directions. First, given a monetary constraint on operating a given water-quality station or network of stations, those funds allocated to station operation can be translated into the three cost components to arrive at effective operating rules or alternatives for assessing the degree that accuracy objectives or guidelines can be achieved. This option may not be too realistic in the case of surveillance stations using automated monitoring equipment. Here Z_M is quite high and fairly insensitive to the number of constituents monitored and frequency of constituent determination (eqn. 7). However, impacts of alternative schedules of operation on Z_V and Z_P may be studied in comparison to the high Z_M charge for monitoring equipment.

Alternatively, specified constituents, statistical measures of those constituents, and accuracy requirements of the statistical measures may be transformed into the estimated component charges Z_V, Z_M, and Z_P to compute Z_T for those specifications of a given type station. Interplay between these two options should hopefully provide the basis for arriving at design for station operation agreeable to both the water-resources manager who must use the resultant data and the network planner who must provide the data. The sensitivity and relative weighting of the three cost components in a cost analysis of any alternative mode of station operation

in a network must also be considered. A distinct advantage in attempting to develop a simplified cost function of several components and a series of standard costs is that the causes of variances from standard costs can be studied in a meaningful and quantitative manner.

In the application of the cost function, some bias may become apparent in handling conservative over non-conservative water-quality constituents. This bias stems from the fact that the behavior of non-conservative pollutants in the environment is often not too well understood, and that the statistical parameters used to assess these classes of water-quality variables may well differ from those generally accepted for conservative constituents.

With the advent of water-quality standards, more data, especially concerning biologically-related variables, will have to be collected. However, more data-collection programs must be set within the framework of statistical analysis.

Typical Cost Analyses

Designs of stations designated for a basin accounting network are particularly amenable to analysis using the proposed cost function. The number of designated accounting stations, located on major tributaries, main streams, and near terminal outflow points in major basins, might be expected to remain fairly stabilized in long-term operation. Hence, the major considerations are selection of constituents determined, frequency of sample collection and frequency of constituent determinations. In the United States, over 300 water-quality stations currently in operation have been designated as having an accounting function. The eventual number recommended approaches 400 stations for the 306 accounting units (OWDC, 1969). In evaluating the suggested procedures for basin accounting stations, it seems that, after a sufficient historical data base of certain inorganic constituents covering up to five years has been established, a station's design could be modified to provide some operating cost savings that could be applied to sampling sites of other networks or for other constituent determinations at existing accounting sites. For example, determinations for such variables as Ca, Mg, Na, K, HCO_3, SO_4, Cl, Fe, SiO_2, dissolved solids, and pH might readily be reduced from the suggested monthly sampling schedule for the duration of station operation to as little as a quarterly frequency and yet provide sufficient information on long-term trends for those variables. With such a reduction in those constituent determinations only (sample collection and other constituent determinations would remain at the suggested frequencies), an estimated annual cost savings of over $110,000* nationwide would be realized. One possible application of these funds could be for monthly determinations in the current accounting network for three or more trace elements (for example, Pb, Hg, and Zn could be analyzed monthly at over 300 accounting stations) which might possibly have more significance and about which very little is known on a regional basis. Technical justification for some of the above suggested reductions will be described in later case studies. The philosophy conveyed here in basin accounting is that the currently suggested procedures may be requiring too much detail and refinement on a limited number of water-quality variables at the expense of not doing justice to numerous other constituents which may become or have already become apparent as much more critical, for the purpose and time-frame in which accounting stations operate.

As another general example, an assumption that may be implicit in surveillance station design is that time coverage must be continuous or equal-spaced samples throughout the entire year and for year after year ad infinitum. Intuitively, we may realize that certain water-quality problems and existing or potential noncompliance of stream water-quality standards may take place with much higher probabilities at certain times of the year than at others (assuming a favorable spatial configuration). Seasonal variability in probabilities of water-

---

* ($44.00/sample x 8⁻ samples/station-year x 306 stations = $107,712).

quality problems, in turn, can be translated through the cost
function in terms of possible savings in stratifying sampling
procedures or in promoting intermittent continuous monitoring
for certain water-quality variables, given due consideration
for the risks involved in these schedules and for other difficulties with manpower allocation and equipment maintenance.

With respect to areal synthesis, the general tendency in
station design is to implement a definite pattern of areal
coverage but to not stipulate a desirable number of years for
station operation. The network planner may neglect to delin-
eate the functions of areal synthesis from those of basin
accounting or surveillance where prolonged longer-term coverage
is more critical in fulfilling the networks' functions. The
subject of areal synthesis of streamflow water-quality conditions is amenable to water-quality regionalizing statistical
analyses and models. Required levels of accuracy for the
statistical measures in areal synthesis are much less stringent
than for surveillance stations, another fact often disregarded
in designing station operation for areal synthesis. Extra-
polation in space of water-quality data at point sampling sites
is required in areal synthesis, delineation of problem areas
for specified water uses is of primary importance, and existing
or proposed sampling stations should not attempt to be operated
or even designed at every flowpoint where information on water-
quality conditions is desired.

RESULTS

Alternative Sampling Frequencies

A distinction is made between frequency of sample collection
and frequency of constituent determination. Sample collection
schedules should reflect the most refined time coverage required
for any one constituent to fulfill the desired accuracy objective.
However, no reluctance should be shown in station design for
reducing wherever possible the frequencies of constituent determination as much as possible to keep analytical (Z_M) and processing (Z_p) costs down.

Sample Collection

A principal function of the basin accounting network is to
measure the annual quantities of various water-quality variables
removed by streamflow from the designated accounting units. Stations operating for areal synthesis function primarily to record
general levels and variability of water-quality conditions for
the short term, so that these stations might be set up to operate
for between two and five years and thereafter reactivated on a
rotating schedule. Both types of networks are readily subject
to evaluation of alternative frequencies of sample collection.
Accuracy levels for the desired statistical measures of streamflow
water quality for these networks often have not been clearly
defined, although some accuracy guidelines can be inferred from
the suggested frequencies of sampling for the various specified
constituents. Assume that no conjunctive function of surveillance
is required by a station operated for basin accounting or areal
synthesis. The cost function can be applied to analyzing the
trade-off between operating costs and accuracy of sampling frequency

for the annual mean statistic, which is used to describe general
levels and long-term trends in streamflow water quality.

Figure 2 shows the estimated range of average relative error
in the annual mean statistic as a function of measurement frequency
to compute the annual mean statistic. The range of errors (y-axis,
fig. 2) are relative to an annual mean computed from a daily schedule of grab samples (Steele, 1970). The x-axis of the graph refers
to the number of measurements made systematically throughout the
year. The range of relative errors will approach zero as the
sample frequency approaches a schedule of daily measurements.
No attempt was made to adjust the frequency of measurement to an
effective sample size in order to compensate for the effects of
serial correlation of the records used in the analysis.

Although records of daily specific conductance, K_{sc}, were
used for seven long-term stations (9-24 years) exhibiting a wide
range of salinity conditions (mean annual K_{sc} ranging from 63 to
12,800 μmhos/cm) in constructing the graph, relative errors as a
function of sampling frequency would be comparable for most other
conservative water-quality constituents. The magnitude of relative error is quite dependent upon the levels of salinity for a
particular stream; relative errors of annual mean K_{sc} tend to
increase as overall levels of salinity increase for any fixed
schedule of measurements.

To test alternative operating rules for stations in the
accounting or areal synthesis networks, we see that sampling
frequency might be reduced from a daily frequency to a monthly
schedule with an average additional error of at most 13 percent
for very saline streams in the annual mean statistic. A simplified cost analysis of several reduced sampling frequencies
is given as follows:

Frequency	Maximum relative error (percent)	Z_T**	Percent of daily frequency cost
daily	0.0	$815	100.0
weekly	4.0	125	15.4
biweekly	9.0	65	8.0
monthly	13.0	36	4.5

In using a monthly schedule, an additional 13 percent maximum
error (on the average for highly saline streams) in annual mean
values has been added with a corresponding reduction of over 95
percent in operating costs. A better feel for the overall magnitude of potential cost savings would be to multiply the above
figures by the number of actual or proposed stations in the accounting or areal systhesis network for any one year. Even though other
constituents and statistical measures must also be taken into
consideration, the intangible benefit of such an analysis is the
exercise in deriving realistic design alternatives for more
effective utilization and reallocation of funds. In the above
example, realized cost savings could be passed on to better areal
coverage or to additional analyses for constituents ignored in
previous data-collection programs.

**Assume that a local observer is paid to sample for all frequencies.
Samples are then picked up monthly on routine field trips for laboratory determination of K_{sc}. Assume daily constituent option for
data is processing used. Component costs that make up Z_T have not
been shown.

Constituent Determination

Specific conductance (K_{sc}) is an index of overall salinity levels and can frequently be used to estimate concentrations of the major inorganic constituents of streamflow, assuming that sufficient information is available for the functional relationships between concentration of solute i, C_i, and K_{sc} (Steele, 1970). The premise of design flexibility in constituent determinations is based on a philosophy that, if water-quality variable A can be shown directly or by inference to be highly correlated with variable B at some flowpoint in a stream system, the additional information on one of the variables provided by continued concurrent measurements of A and B quickly becomes redundant.

In considering C_i-K_{sc} relationships, linear regression models of the form $C_i = a_i + b_i K_{sc}$, where a_i and b_i are regression parameters, have been derived from water-quality data at a site consisting of up to 1000 samples or more with correlation coefficients often exceeding 0.95 (Steele, 1969; Steele, in preparation). These C_i-K_{sc} relationships may be used in a predictive capacity both in time and in space. Using split-sample testing, data covering 22 years of record (1591 composited samples of chemical analyses) for a water-quality station in the lower Arkansas River was analyzed with regression analysis in the above form. No significant changes or trends in the C_i-K_{sc} regression parameters for selected constituents were detected for the period of record. Moreover, regression equations for the dominant ions in streamflow at two downstream sites with concurrent records were essentially identical, even though salinity levels were diluted by approximately 20 percent at the station furthest downstream.

Figure 3 shows C_i-K_{sc} graphs for chloride concentrations, C_{Cl}, measured on samples collected during the 1968 water year(WY) at four water-quality stations located on the Pecos River in New Mexico and Texas. Both chemical composition and K_{sc} have been measured concurrently at all four sites since July, 1937, and, if the results of the Arkansas River data analysis can be extended in this case, the relationships between C_{Cl} and K_{sc} at each flowpoint have remained unchanged over this time span. Techniques for transferring information on chemical composition from K_{sc} measurement using the C_{Cl}-K_{sc} regression relationships for Pecos River water-quality stations (fig. 3) will be discussed below.

Each instance that the chemical composition of a sample can be estimated using C_i-K_{sc} relationships, cost savings in reduced laboratory charges of up to \$30 can be made (of up to \$36 if dissolved-solids residue values are determined). Extrapolate this cost savings over the number of standard chemical analyses performed on samples collected at stations with five years of historical record or more, and the true impact on overall network operating costs becomes more apparent.

Compliance with Water-Quality Standards

Stream standards have been described for various classes of water-quality variables. In the following paragraphs, scheduling strategies in station operation are explored which would satisfy the surveillance needs for verifying compliance or violation of stream standards but yet represent a net reduction in operating costs.

Mineral Quality

Standards on mineral quality typically allow for no substantial rise above "existing" salinity levels. Occasionally,

specific indices of mineral quality are incorporated into standards,
such as concentrations of chloride, hardness, and dissolved solids.
Mineral quality of most major streams are no longer contributed
solely from natural geochemical processes, and rarely can the
portion of "natural" contributions of major inorganic solutes be
separated out from the total solute loads removed by streamflow
from a highly developed drainage basin. However, it may frequently
be the case, as was inferred above, that the proportions of the
major solutes at any given salinity level have not changed appreciably in the course of basin development. As a result, errors
in estimating C_i using appropriate C_i-K_{sc} regression relationships
may be so low that, for purposes of testing against standards for
stream mineral quality, C_i might be estimated from field measurements
of K_{sc} rather than measured directly. Such a practice might be
highly desirable in irrigation areas, where cationic ratios as well
as total salinity levels are critical. Possible legal ramifications
in testing compliance to states' water-quality standards cannot be
anticipated fully, but the potential cost savings in the operation
of surveillance stations can be substantial.

Dissolved Oxygen

With the advent of standards to implement the Water Quality
Act of 1965, much more emphasis has been given to streamflow quality characteristics and patterns other than mineral quality. In
many areas of the United States, existing or potential water-quality
problems do not involve levels of salinity but rather deal with trace
elements, pesticides, temperature, and many biologically-related
variables such as dissolved oxygen (DO) and biological oxygen demand
(BOD). Dissolved oxygen has generally been accepted as one indicator
of overall biological quality of a stream, and minimum DO standards
set by the states often reflect water use and anticipated DO needs
of certain forms of aquatic life in the stream.

Despite heavy loadings of organic wastes throughout the year, DO
levels of streams may still exhibit a strong seasonal cycle. During
the winter months, colder water temperatures increase the solubility
of oxygen in water while at the same time slowing down biological
activity and thus, oxygen consumption, in the stream. With warmer
temperatures, solubility of oxygen declines and biological activity
increases. Both effects combine to make the summer months the
critical season of the year in terms of DO.

A system of water-quality monitors operating along the Delaware River estuary provides an excellent case and point. Dissolved
oxygen has been monitored at five locations between Trenton, New
Jersey, and the Delaware Memorial Bridge downstream near Wilmington,
Delaware, beginning with the 1965 WY (Merk, 1970). A strong seasonal
cycle of DO prevails in the Delaware above Philadelphia and, with
heavy organic loadings from the Philadelphia metropolitan area, DO
levels are consistently lower than upstream. Average DO levels at
Delaware Memorial Bridge, over 30 miles below Philadelphia, ranged
from 5 to 10 mg/l between December 16 and March 31 during the
1965-69 WY period, well above the stream standard of 4.5 mg/l for
that period.

Figure 4 depicts the variability of DO levels as reported by
Merk (1970) measured by an automatic monitor located on the Delaware River upstream from Philadelphia at Trenton, N.J. The horizontal bars in the graph indicate the stream-quality (DO) objectives
for zone 2 of the river set by the Delaware River Basin Commission.

Suppose that it would be politically feasible to propose intermittent operation of selected monitors on the Delaware, based on
the historical pattern of DO variability in conjunction with
compliance or non-compliance with the stream-quality objectives.
Using the example of the automatic monitoring station operated at
Trenton (fig. 4), it appears that continuous surveillance throughout
the entire year would not be necessary. For example, continuous
monitoring might be maintained only between May 1 and October 30,
assuming that the other water-quality variables monitored concurrently are not critical at other times. Allowing for random
periodic grab samples to serve as checks during the proposed
period of shutdown, estimated cost savings could be computed as
follows (see assumed charges, table 1):

Option	Z_V	Z_M	Z_P	Z_T
all year operation	$1560	$2500	$68	$4128
1/2 year operation	1040	2000	40	3080
estimated savings	$ 520	$ 500	$28	$1048

Several factors have been considered in the above cost analysis
Life of monitoring equipment may or may not be extended by intermittent operation. Some component parts will deteriorate whether
in actual use or not. On the other hand, because the shut-down
period commonly would coincide with more severe climatic conditions,
certain critical electronic parts and sensors possibly could be
removed and stored when not in field operation. In this way, some
maintenance and calibration could be carried out in the laboratory
prior to each field season's installation, and field trips during
the winter would be limited to collecting samples periodically
as checks against the historical seasonal pattern. Summer field
assistants could be employed where possible and could be trained
to maintain the surveillance monitors. However, manpower scheduling
problems could be foreseen in starting up and checking field
operation of monitors each spring.

If anticipated overall savings were in the order of 25 percent,
as shown above, an additional automatic monitor could be operated
seasonally for every three monitors maintained only during critical
periods. Savings in data-processing costs, small relative to Z_V
and Z_M, become more significant when compared with Z_P for all-
year operation and taken in aggregate for considering the total
monitoring network.

pH

The pH value is another water-quality variable whose
permissible limits are frequently specified in water-quality
standards and which is included among those variables requiring
surveillance. Whether or not pH requires continuous monitoring throughout the entire year depends upon the standards
imposed, on possible seasonal patterns in pH variability, and upon
the terms for assessing compliance or non-compliance with the
standards. Several states' pH stream standards refer to "natural"
and "normal" pH variations which are not to be affected appreciably
by introduction of additional wastes. Inclusion of "normal" into
the standard is probably to cover the numerous streams where
"natural" pH levels will probably never be known.

Figure 5 summarizes daily pH records for two streams which
exhibit periods of possible non-compliance with the appropriate
state's standard. Arkansas' pH stream standard is summarized as

18.12

follows (Arkansas Pollution Control Commission, 1969):

"The pH of water in the stream must not fluctuate in excess of 1.0 pH unit, within the range of 6.0-9.0, over a period of 24 hours. The pH shall not be below 6.0 or above 9.0 due to wastes discharged to the receiving stream."

Three Creek near Three Creeks, Ark. (USGS station number 7-3659.00) during the 1960 WY had a total of 14 days out of 362 daily samples collected when the measured pH was below the lower limit of the standard of 6.0. On consecutive days, pH measurements changed by as much as 2.4 pH units. Stream quality of Three Creek is known to be affected by oil-brine wastes, certainly contributing a large portion of salinity loads of the stream, as shown by concurrent daily determinations of C_{Cl} and K_{sc} over the 1950-62 WY period. It remains to be shown what "normal" pH levels are in Three Creek and how pH varies over time without the influence of the brines. If a seasonal pattern of pH persists, as was shown for Three Creek (fig. 5), surveillance for compliance of stream standards might more economically be achieved by stratifying sampling in favor of the time period during which low pH values can be anticipated with a greater probability. Data analysis of the historical pH records covering more than nine years would confirm the possibility of consistent seasonal lows in stream pH and would test the impact of abatement of oil-brine pollution on salinity as well as on pH levels.

The Alafia River at Lithia, Fla. (USGS station number 2-3015.00), during the 1967 WY showed numerous daily pH measurements below 5.0 during the period from April through September (fig. 5). Streams in the southeastern United States are influenced, particularly during periods of storm runoff, by highly-organic suspended material picked up in swampy areas. Occasionally, a reciprocal relationship between pH and stream discharge is observed. The North Prong of the Alafia River is further influenced by the effects of phosphate mining, contributing a waste effluent to the stream that is low in pH and high in fluoride and phosphate concentrations (Kaufman, 1970). An assessment of the relative impact on pH levels in the Alafia River from natural swamp drainage and from mining wastes would be required in attempting to enforce compliance with Florida's stream pH standard. Moreover, from a design standpoint, the available data indicate that station operation for surveillance could be limited to time coverage during approximately six months of the year instead of the entire year.

Temperature

In absence of effects of excessive thermal pollution, stream temperatures exhibit a persistent annual seasonal cycle. Stream temperatures are strongly controlled by overlying air temperatures, and, because of the enormous heat absorption capacity of water, stream temperatures tend to dampen out the effects of more-widely varying air temperatures. Figure 6 depicts the typically strong seasonal character of stream temperature. Daily stream temperatures recorded at two water-quality stations on the Arkansas River (USGS station numbers 7-2505.00 and 7-2635.00) have more than fulfilled the needs of basin accounting. Annual mean temperatures at each site have varied less than 5 percent with no discernible trend in time. Annual mean temperatures determined for the Rappahannock River at Remington, Va. (USGS station number 1-6640.00), have gradually increased, but the unknown effects of changing sampling location are difficult to mask out. If the current function of these temperature stations is for surveillance, a sufficient historical base has been gathered on annual variability, and future testing for satisfying stream temperature standards might well be reduced to detailed coverage annually only during the three months of June, July, and August (fig. 6).

Of course, periodic random check measurements could be made during the remaining months of the year to check if stream temperatures for those periods differed consistently from the "norm" or base levels indicated by the historical record. Quality variables such as streamflow temperature commonly exhibit a diurnal fluctuation as well as a seasonal cycle. Comparison of measurements from grab samples must be adjusted for this short-term time-dependence when being checked against base levels for assessment of significant changes. T following cost analysis reflects estimated savings in station operat costs brought about by reducing daily or continuous coverage to a critical three-month period as suggested above (assume use of a servo-programmer (SP) or thermograph (TG) type of monitor):

Option - Type	Z_V	Z_M	Z_P	Z_T	Cost Savings
all year - SP	$300	$700	$ 17	$1017	
3 months - SP	100	300	10	410	$607
all year - TG	$250	$50	$200	$500	
3 months - TG	100	50	70	220	$280

In both cases, cost savings are estimated to be approximately 60 percent of the cost of continual operation throughout the entire year.

Regionalization

Regionalization techniques become extremely useful in generalizing water-quality conditions from a fixed configuration of stations functioning in an areal systhesis network. Emphasis would be placed upon the following:(1) transferring information to streamflow sites with little or no information at a flowpoint located between sampling stations or located in drainage basins with similar lithology and other environmental factors affecting water quality, and (2) extrapolating from short-term records gathered by the areal synthesis network to obtain water-quality average and extreme characteristics over a variety of flow conditions (Steele, 1969).

A regionalization technique for conservative water-quality constituents in streamflow has been documented, utilizing the a_i and b_i regression parameters from the appropriate C_i-K_{sc} relationships (Steele, 1970). For purposes of demonstration, consider the C_{Cl}-K_{sc} (fig. 3) and C_{DS}-K_{sc} relationships for the three upstream stations on the Pecos River in New Mexico. Table 2A summarizes the regression relationships fitting the plotted data, ignoring, for the moment, the slightly curvilinear effect for low K_{sc} values exhibited by many constituents. Assume that no chemical data had been collected during the 1968 WY for the middle station (08-3965.00 Table 2B lists the average and extreme C_{Cl} and C_{DS} values computed from regression relationships formed by simple averaging of the appropriate a_i and b_i regression parameters fitting data for the upstream and downstream stations. The computed maximum and annual mean C_{Cl} and C_{DS} values are within 5 percent of the values actually determined. Both minimum estimates were lower than actual measurements, primarily because both C_i-K_{sc} relationships had large negativ slopes due to slight curvilinearity at low K_{sc} (Steele, 1970;

18.14

Hem, 1959). Estimating C_{Cl} and C_{DS} in this manner, total laboratory charges of \$567 in analytical costs could have been saved in not performing the two chemical analyses on the 63 composited samples at station 8-3965.00 during the 1968 WY.

Possible regionalization of stream temperatures might follow similar lines. Ward (1963) demonstrated the use of harmonic analysis in fitting stream temperature data. Regional comparison of the resultant parameters of the sine function used by Ward to fit data for Arkansas streams showed promising results, in terms of forecasting and estimating stream temperatures, knowing the time of year. A major exception would be directly below impoundments, where the annual cycle of stream temperatures may become greatly distorted due to reservoir releases. However, even the highly re-gulated lower Arkansas River has shown little deviation from a simple harmonic coinciding with a seasonal cycle for the past 24 years. The persistence of a seasonal cycle at both sites (fig. 6) in conjunction with a highly correlated time series of stream temperatures would indicate that measurement frequency at one of the stations could be substantially reduced.

Regionalization techniques for biologically-related variables remain an area for further research. Very few detailed and compat-ible data are available for testing regional models for nutrients or indicators of organic stream quality. But, for most purposes of areal synthesis, quite crude estimates of these water-quality characteristics are tolerated, insofar as delineating existing or potential problem areas or critical times of the year. By evaluat-ing the sensitivity of errors in these estimates on design criteria of water and waste treatment facilities, water planners may justify allocating more funds for reducing the errors in those estimates rather than advocating higher 'safety' factors in designing for plant construction.

Long-Term Trends

'Long-term' trends in water quality may imply data analysis of a period of record usually much shorter than 'long-term' records of precipitation or streamflow. Environmental scientists analyzing streamflow water-quality data for trends frequently find themselves in a quandry due to insufficient or inappropriate data in trying to assess quality degradation or abatement or to forecast water-quality conditions. If a relationship is found in analyzing historical data between a water-quality variable and stream discharge, the statistical characteristics of that variable may often be improved using longer-term records of streamflow at the site (Steele, 1969).

However, quality-flow relationships may not always be static over time. Figure 7 gives an example of apparent salinity degrad-ation in the St. Johns River, Florida. The annual mean K_{sc} time series was separated into two periods: 1954-56 WY (period A) and 1957-69 WY (period B). This particular separation was based upon visual inspection of the salinity-flow relationship for the total period of record for the site (fig. 7). The statistical t test was used to test the hypothesis that $\overline{K}_{sc}$ for period A equals $\overline{K}_{sc}$ for period B. Based on the analysis, this hypothesis was rejected at the 95 percent confidence level. A corresponding test for no difference in $\overline{Q}$ for the two periods was accepted at the 95 percent confidence level.

In using the above analysis for certain types of water-quality variables whose levels are predominately flow-dependent, values for the two periods of record must be adjusted if average Q for the periods differs significantly. In the above example, mean annual streamflows for periods A and B were 1020 and 1052 cfs, respectively; whereas, average K_{sc} increased from 262 to 424 µmhos/cm. Had Q_A been significantly greater than Q_B, then the reduction in average Q would have had a positive but undetermined effect causing the observed increase in K_{sc} unless the effects of dilution by higher flows could be masked out. Water-quality variables as stream temperature and dissolved oxygen should not require this type of modification in analysis of annual time series.

Other statistical techniques for assessment of long-term trends in streamflow quality are currently being investigated. Long-term trends for numerous water-quality variables are difficult to assess, either due to sampling schedules imposed at irregular intervals or due to insufficient periods of record.

An assessment of long-term trends of streamflow water quality does not require continuous or daily sampling frequency. In the following example, using data for the San Lorenzo River in California, K_{sc} was determined for monthly samples during the 1952-67 WY period. Annual mean time-weighted K_{sc} values were computed from the number of samples collected during each year. Next, regression relationships of the form $K_{sc} = k_{sc} / Q^{n_{sc}}$, where k_{sc} and n_{sc} are regression parameters, were obtained from the historical data (Steele, 1969). Making the assumption that the K_{sc}-Q relationships were static over the 1952-67 WY period, annual mean time-weighted K_{sc} values were estimated by simulating K_{sc} from available streamflow records for the period. Comparison of simulated (S) and reported (A) annual mean K_{sc} values (table 3) indicates a sign shift in the residuals between the 1960 and 1961 WY values. The inherent statistical error in computing annual mean K_{sc} with monthly measurements should not produce that degree of trend in the residuals. The results of the analysis provide conclusive evidence that the assumed K_{sc}-Q relationships indeed have not been static over the 1952-67 WY period, and that the salinity of the San Lorenzo River had degraded by about 9 percent, on the average, during the 1961-67 WY relative to the 1952-60 WY period. Further analysis indicates that some of the increase in annual mean K_{sc} may have resulted from a reduction of Q between the two periods, caused, in part, by construction of one or more permanent reservoirs in the basin. However, the average increase in simulated annual mean time-weighted K_{sc} was about one percent relative to a decline of reduced flows on this measure of salinity has been minimal. The example indeed served its intended purpose in showing that monthly systematic sampling of a water-quality variable is just as satisfactory as a more frequent sample schedule for assessing long-term changes in streamflow quality.

SUMMARY

The objectives and accuracy requirements for designated water-quality variables for each of the national networks associated with management and control of streamflow water quality provide the opportunity for alternative designs in station operation. Each feasible alternative can be evaluated with the aid of a generalized operational cost function for an assessment of relative magnitudes of possible savings, impacts of budgeted standard costs, and anti-

cipated manpower requirements. An information base of historical
water-quality data is most useful in the scheduling of station
operations in terms of critical variables to measure, types of
sampling procedures for field collection and constituent determination, and techniques for indirectly transferring information in
time and in space as alternatives to direct measurement. Network
design should be as dynamically changing as is necessary to gain
maximum knowledge and problem-solving ability, given a budgetary
constraint. Network evaluation should incorporate new problem
areas as they are unveiled and reduce ongoing programs whose
objectives have been fulfilled. However, water-quality networks
must maintain sufficient continuity in several facets of data
collection for a systematic and objective reappraisal of the effects
of environmental changes on the nation's stream resources.

Selected Bibliography

Arkansas Pollution Control Commission, 1969, Water quality
    standards summary: U. S. Dept. of the Interior,
    FWPCA, 21 p.

Bramhall, D. F. and Mills, E. S., 1966, Alternative methods
    of improving stream quality: an economic and policy
    analysis: Water Resources Research, v. 2, no. 3,
    pp. 355-363.

Busch, A. W., 1968, A suggested approach to the problem of
    water quality standards: Proc. 23rd Industrial Waste
    Conf., Purdue Univ., pp. 458-461.

Cleary, E. J., 1967, the ORSANCO story -- water quality
    management in the Ohio Valley under an interstate compact:
    Resources for the Future, Inc., Johns Hopkins Press, 335 p.

Davis, R. K., 1968, The range of choice in water management:
    a study of dissolved oxygen in the Potomac estuary:
    Resources for the Future, Inc., Johns Hopkins Press, 196 p.

Dysart, B. C., III, and Hines, W. W., 1969, Development and
    application of a rational water quality planning model:
    Georgia Inst. of Tech., Water Resources Center, Atlanta,
    Ga. WRC-0668.

Gunnerson, C. G., 1967, Streamflow and quality in the Columbia
    River basin: Jour. Sanitary Engr. Div., ASCE, v. 93, no.
    SA6, p. 1-16.

Hem, J. D., 1959, Study and interpretation of the chemical
    characteristics of natural water: U. S. Geol. Survey
    Water-Supply Paper 1473, 269 p.

James, I. C., II, Bower, B. T., and Matalas, N. C., 1969,
    Relative importance of variables in water resources
    planning: Water Resources Research, v. 5, no. 6,
    pp. 1165-1173.

Kaufman, M. I., 1970, The pH of water in Florida streams and
    canals: Fla. Dept. of Natural Resources, map series no. 37

Kisiel, C. C., 1969, Time series analysis of hydrologic data:
    in Advances in Hydroscience, edited by V. T. Chow, Aca-
    demic Press, Inc., v. 5, pp. 1-119.

Kittrell, F. W., 1969, A practical guide to water quality
    studies of streams:. U. S. Dept. of the Interior,
    FWPCA, 135 p.

Kneese, A. V. and Bower, B. T., 1968, Managing water quality:
    economics, technology, institutions: Resources for the
    Future, Inc., Johns Hopkins Press, 328 p.

Langbein, W. B., 1965, National networks of hydrological
    data: WMO-IASH Symposium on Designing of meteorologi-
    cal networks, Quebec City, Canada, 21 p.

Merk, C. F., 1970, A graphical summary of dissolved-oxygen
    data for the Delaware River estuary for water years
    1965-69: U. S. Geol. Survey open-file report, 15 p.

National Technical Advisory Comm., 1968, Water quality
    criteria: U. S. Dept. of the Interior, FWPCA, 234 p.

NUS Corporation, Cyrum Wm. Rice Div., 1970, Designing of
    water quality surveillance systems; phase 1 - systems
    analysis framework: report for FWQA, program no.
    16090 DBJ, 303 p.

Office of Water Data Coordination, 1969, An approach to net-
    work design: (preliminary report); U. S. Geol. Survey.

Rainwater, F. H. and Avrett, J. R., 1962, Error inference in
    systematic-sample statistics in stream quality studies:
    Jour. AWWA, June, 1962, pp. 757-768.

Smith, E. T. and Morris, A. R., 1969, Systems analysis for
    optimal water quality management: Jour. WPCF, v. 41,
    no. 9, pp. 1636-1646.

Steele, T. D., 1969, A technique for improving estimates of
    long-term chemical-quality characteristics of streams:
    Am. Geophys. Union National Fall Meeting, San Francisco,
    Calif., December, 1969 (abstract + 60 p. handout).

_____, 1970, Beneficial uses and pitfalls of histori-
    cal water-quality data: National Symposium on Data and
    Instrumentation for Water Quality Management; Conference
    of State Sanitary Engineers, Madison, Wisc., July 1970,
    14 p.

_____, in preparation, A study of chemical quality of
    streamflow in Arkansas: U. S. Geol. Survey open-file
    report, 89 p.

Swenson, H. A., 1963, Purpose and operation of USGS water quality networks: Jour. AWWA, August, 1963, pp. 1010-1026.

Thomas, D. M. and Benson, M. A., 1970, Generalization of streamflow characteristics from drainage-basin characteristics: U. S. Geol. Survey Water-Supply Paper 1975, 55 p.

Vice, R. B. and Swenson, H. A., 1965, A network design for water quality: WMO-IASH Symposium on Design of Hydro-meteorological Networks, Quebec City, Canada, 19 p.

Ward, J. C., 1963, Annual variation of stream water temperature: Jour. Sanitary Engr. Div., ASCE, v. 89, no. SA 6, pp. 1-16.

Water Resources Engineers, Inc. 1966, An interagency system for water quality management: report prepared for Calif. State Legislature and Water Pollution Control Board, 186 p.

Woods, P. C., 1967, Management of hydrologic systems for water quality control: Univ. of Calif. Sanitary Engr. Research Laboratory, contribution no. 121, 121 p.

LIST OF SYMBOLS

$Z_T(j,t)$ = annaul operating costs of sampling station j of type t

$Z_V(j,t)$ = portion of operating costs associated with field visitations

$Z_M(j,t)$ = costs of chemical laboratory analyses or monitoring instrumentation

$Z_P(j,t)$ = costs of data processing

F_K = frequency or number of units annually of type K (K = V or P)

C_K = unit costs associated with K (K = V or P)

K_{sc} = specific conductance, in micromhos per centimeter at 25° Centigrade

C_i = concentration of solute i, in milligrams per liter

$\underline{a}_i, \underline{b}_i$ = regression parameters (C_i-K_{sc} relationships)

DO = dissolved-oxygen concentration, in milligrams per liter

Q = stream discharge, in cubic feet per second

Cl = chloride

DS = dissolved solids

$\underline{k}_{sc}, \underline{n}_{sc}$ = regression parameters (K_{sc}-Q relationships)

S = simulated

A = reported or published

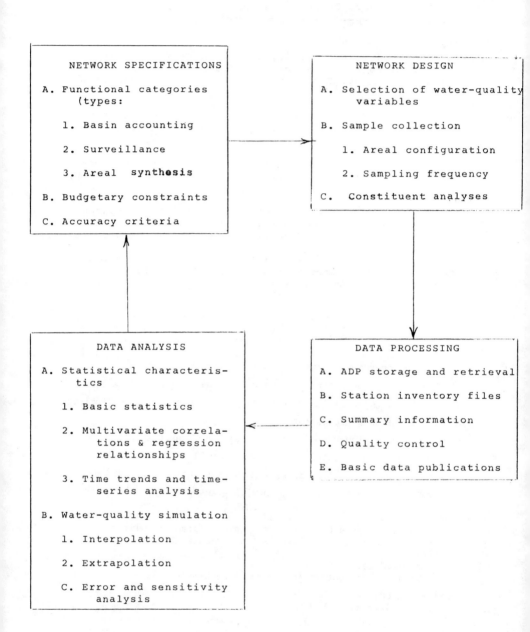

Figure 1.--The cycle of a water-quality
data-collection system

18.20

Table 1.--Schedule of approximate unit costs,
monitor charges, and other costs

A. Unit costs of laboratory analyses for selected constituents:

1. Standard constituents	C_k (per determination)	2. Supplementary constituents	C_k (per determination)
Q (field)	$20.00	Al	$ 5.40
T (field)	0.50	NH_3	9.00
SiO_2	3.60	As	9.00
Fe	3.60	Ba	9.00
Mn	4.80	B	11.00
@ Ca	4.20	Br	9.00
@ Mg	4.20	BOD_5	9.60
@ Na	4.80	Cr	4.80
@ K	4.80	coliform	12.00
@ HCO_3	3.00	color	1.20
@ SO_4	6.00	Cu	4.80
@ Cl	3.00	CN	9.00
F	3.60	detergents	12.00
NO_3	6.00	DO	6.00
@ DS residue	6.00	Pb	9.00
K_{sc}	1.20	Hg	11.00
pH	1.20	Ni	7.20
		NO_2	6.00
		N-total	9.00
		Sr	6.00
		Zn	7.20

@ These major inorganics frequently can
be determined indirectly using C_i-K_{sc}
regression equations within required
levels of accuracy for use of the data.

C_k unit costs are based on average prorated factors using $60 per
standard chemical analysis.

B. Annual cost components for automatic monitors (estimated):

1. Electrochemical sensors*
(generally four or five channels)

Z_V $1560
Z_M 2500
Z_P (see C)

*sensors available for DO, K_{sc}, pH,
temperature, turbidity, and Cl

2. Servo-programmer (T and K_{sc})

Z_V $300
Z_M T only   700
   T and K_{sc} 1200
Z_P (see C)

3. Thermograph or RQ recorder

Z_V $250
Z_M 50
Z_P 200

C. Other charges:

C_V field trip - $25/visit;
   observer - $1/sample

C_P lab sample - $1/sample;
   daily observer - $10/constituent;
   automatic monitor - $17 x S per
constituent, where S is the number of
values recorded per hour for each
constituent.

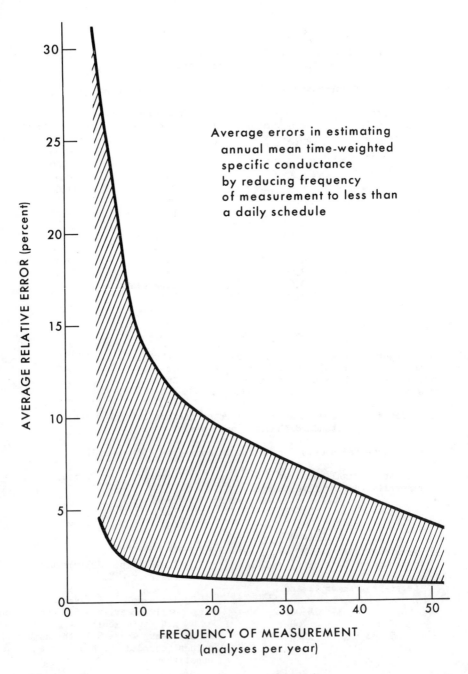

Figure 2.--Impact of reduced sampling frequencies on accuracy
of the annual mean (adapted from Steele, 1970).

18.22

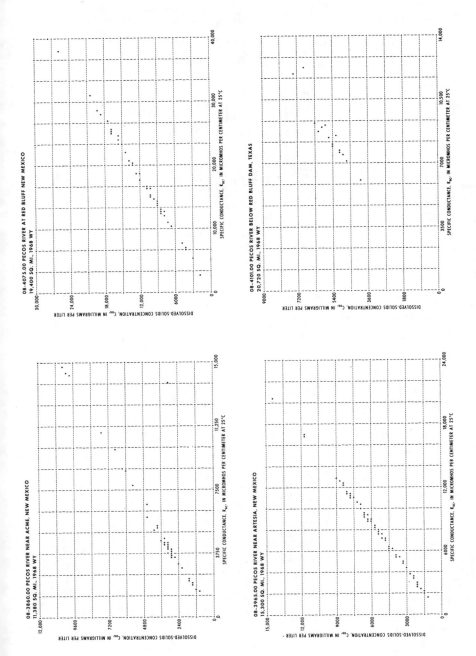

Figure 3.--Selected C_j-K_{sc} graphs for water-quality stations on the Pecos River, New Mexico and Texas (1968 WY).--cont.

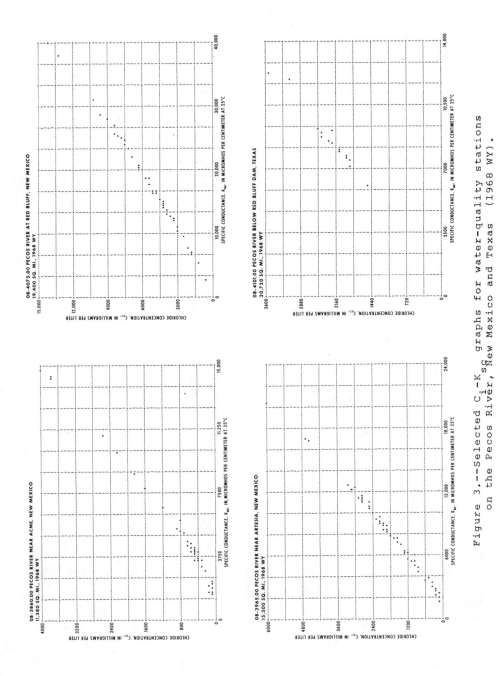

Figure 3.--Selected C_i-K graphs for water-quality stations on the Pecos River, New Mexico and Texas (1968 WY).

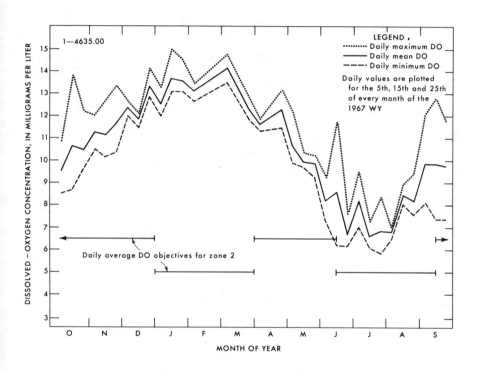

Figure 4.--Annual variability of dissolved oxygen in the Delaware River at Trenton, N. J., for 1967 water year (after Merk, 1970).

18.25

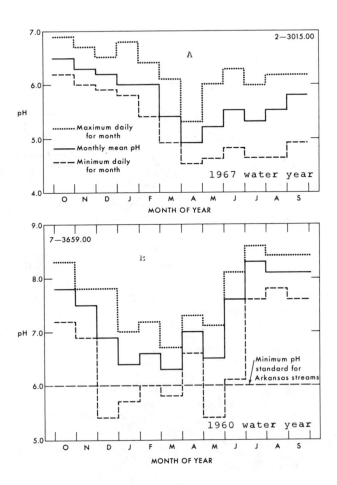

Figure 5.--Annual variability of pH of selected streams.
A.   Alphia River at Lithia, Florida;
B.   Three Creek near Three Creeks, Arkansas.

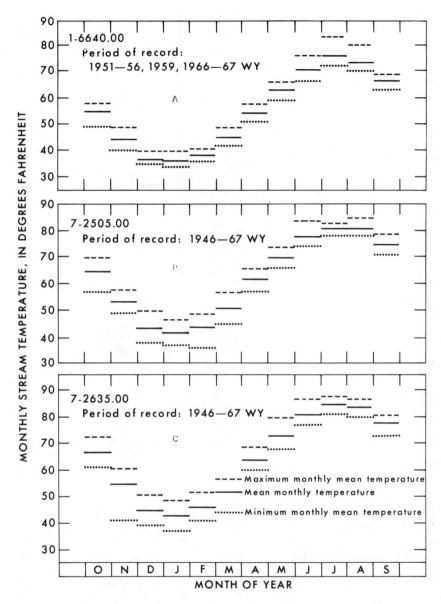

ure 6.--Annual variability of water temperatures for selected streams
A. Rappahannock River at Remington, Virginia;
B. Arkansas River at Van Buren, Arkansas;
C. Arkansas River at Little Rock, Arkansas.

18.27

Table 2.--Regionalization of streamflow chemical-quality information --
Pecos River, New Mexico

A. Results of regression analysis (1968 WY):

Station	DA (sq. mi.)	$\bar{K}_{sc}$ (range)	Simple regression equation	N	SE_e	r	$\bar{C}_i$
8-3860.00	11,380	4850	$C_{Cl} = -615 + 0.292\ K_{sc}$	49	125	0.99	800
		(1440-14800)	$C_{DS} = +268 + 0.684\ K_{sc}$	49	117	0.99	3590
8-3965.00	15,300	7810	$C_{Cl} = -591 + 0.302\ K_{sc}$	63	94	0.99	1780
		(1630-20400)	$C_{DS} = + 47 + 0.690\ K_{sc}$	63	99	0.99	5440
8-4075.00	19,540	17910	$C_{Cl} = -906 + 0.358\ K_{sc}$	47	224	0.99	5500
		(2720-40000)	$C_{DS} = -548 + 0.686\ K_{sc}$	47	260	0.99	11700

B. Estimating C_{Cl} and C_{DS} characteristics at station 8-3965.00 by interpolation of upstream-downstream regression parameters:

| | C_i Estimates (Actual values) | | |
Estimated regression equations:	Minimum	Mean	Maximum
$C'_{Cl} = -760 + 0.325\ K_{sc}$	0*(150)	1780(1780)	5870(5960)
$C'_{DS} = -140 + 0.685\ K_{sc}$	980(1100)	5210(5440)	13830(14300)

* negative value computed

Notation: N = number of paired analyses; SE_e = standard error of estimate, r = correlation coefficient, C_i = constituent mean, DA = drainage area.

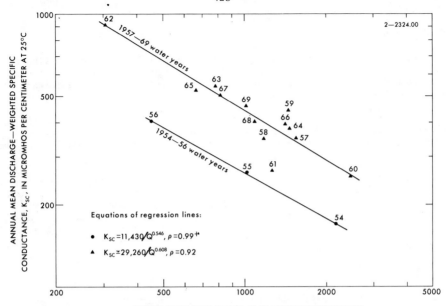

Figure 7.--Long-term changes in streamflow chemical quality --
St. Johns River near Cocoa, Fla. (USGS station number 2-2324.00)

Table 3.--Assessment of salinity degradation --
San Lorenzo River at Big Trees, Calif. (USGS
station number 11-1605.00)

| Water Year WY | Annual mean values | | | Difference A - S | Difference relative to A (percent) |
	Q (cfs)	K_{sc}(S)* (μmhos/cm)	K_{sc}(A)* (μmhos/cm)	(μmhos/cm)	
1952	285	320	291	-29	-9.06
1953	125	342	325	-17	-4.97
1954	76.1	349	335	-14	-4.01
1955	71.8	352	334	-18	-5.11
1956	258	330	329	-1	-0.30
1957	58.7	354	338	-16	-4.52
1958	284	322	315	-7	-2.17
1959	85.1	350	342	-8	-2.29
1960	48.1	357	348	-9	-2.52
1961	25.8	362	376	+14	3.87
1962	89.6	351	383	+32	9.12
1963	188	334	361	+27	8.08
1964	48.4	356	369	+13	3.65
1965	159	338	341	+3	0.89
1966	60.7	353	368	+15	4.25
1967	226	327	355	+28	8.56
avg.52-60	144	342	329	-13	-3.88
avg.61-67	114	346	365	+19	5.49

*S = simulated from K_{sc}-Q regression relationships
 A = computed from the published data

18.29

DISCUSSION

P. S. EAGLESON

First a comment: As a taxpayer as well as a hydrologist, I would like to compliment you on this refreshing approach to the problem of data collection. I have two questions related more to my own ignorance than to any deficiency in your presentation:

1. How are the samples taken so that the values are representative of cross-sectional averages? Certainly at many locations, variables such as salinity, temperature, dissolved oxygen etc. must have wide variation with depth at a given instant.

2. When designing a data gathering system for a single purpose we can estimate the value of information as well as its cost and hence can arrive at a system which is economically satisfactory to us. You have addressed the issue of costs but how does the Federal Agency, which must serve a spectrum of "customers" with varying needs, address the "benefit" side of the data gathering picture? Can we generalize on this issue or is this strictly a function of each particular data use?

C. KISIEL

1. How far can we extend the notion of proxy water quality variables as a substitute for other variables not so easily measured?

2. A "final" judgment on worth of water quality data requires concurrent consideration of multiple objectives or multiple use of the same data. But there is the problem of finding meaningful benefit and loss functions for each use. Even if we had these functions, would they be directly additive? In the face of the above situation, is there really a final answer to the problem?

3. To what extent must the hydrodynamic, chemical and biological "equations" for behavior of pollutants and natural species in streams be eventually included in worth of data studies? Admittedly, this leads to great complexities. Implied here are the limits on the use of correlation and other statistical methods for judging worth of water quality data.

4. Irregular spacing of samples can lead to important loss of information on severe events (producing important economic losses). A formal probability analysis of the risk of missing of such information is desirable for each potential use of the data.

M. OKUTA

Question:
About pH data, there is a large time lag in seasonal variation in two stations, and is large difference between max. and min. in Dec., May and June in bottom part of the Fig.. By what reason do they appear?

Comment:
Why don't you use the wind data for watching the water quality?
Many pollutants are transported by wind, and strong winds agitate the surface water and transport. So, I think it is better that you may introduce the wind observation system into your watching network of water quality.

R. G. QUIMPO

In trying to develop predictive models, one of the difficulties that I have with analyzing water quality data is that observations are taken at unequal time intervals, thus making standard time-series analysis techniques inapplicable. The problem may be resolved either by going into continuous monitoring or by developing techniques of analysis for time series sampled at unequal time intervals. I gather from the paper that the expense of continuous sampling makes the first alternative prohibitive. In this regard then, is the U.S.G.S. doing research on the other alternative, i.e., developing techniques for the analysis of "non-equi-spaced" time series?

A second question is with regards to regionalizing a water quality parameter. Since the causal factor affecting the variation of water quantity indicators acts over relatively large areas, regionalization has been quite successful. In many water quality problems however, the cause of variation is very often a point source (e.g., a single polluter) and so, point values are usually critical. Would you comment on the usefulness of regional values in specific problems?

J. PAUL RILEY

Accuracy goals and objectives in the establishment and operation of a data network require a knowledge of the needs of the data user. Are there any organized attempts now being made or planned by the U.S.G.S. to continuously appraise user needs in terms of the data collection activities of the agency?

V. YEVJEVICH

In transferring information on river flows into information on water quality variables, the question arises whether the interest should be in only the mean of these random variables or in all other parameters of major importance. Even if the mean is only of interest, the interest is in determining the standard error of estimate of the mean incurred by this transfer of information.

The river discharge variable explains only up to 25 percent of the variation of water quality variables in a large number of cases. If the water conductivity is assumed as measuring the water quality variables, in general and in lumped terms, because it has a large correlation with various chemical constituents dissolved in the water, it is legitimate to ask what is the real potential of transferring the information from water discharge variables to water quality variables.

Because the number of chemical constituents is very large in measuring water quality, the problem is in selecting the most important variables of water quality to monitor in such a way that they exhibit the largest correlative relation with all non-monitored variables of practical importance.

RESPONSE BY T. D. STEELE

The response to discussion by P. S. Eagleson is as follows.

1. Small streams are assumed to be uniformly-mixed over the cross-section for most purposes of basic data collection. For larger streams, initial and intermittent reconnaissance surveys are occasionally made (but unfortunately probably not frequently enough) to determine the variability over a channel cross-section and to locate one or more positions for determining average conditions in the stream (especially with regard to sediment stations). Where special

conditions warrant, water-quality data for a large or multi-channelled cross-sectio in a stream are collected and reported at several points in a cross section.

2. Benefits from the water-quality data-collection programs of the U. S. Geological Survey generally are difficult to compute until a specific study is made to assess the various uses of the data provided. I believe that, at the Federal level, some general benefits of data should and can be estimated to fulfill certain national objectives. Spin-off benefits at a regional or local level are significant in the case of our basic-data programs and must be included in any economic analysis, inasmuch as a large portion of our funding comes from state cooperators.

The response to discussion by C. Kisiel is as follows.

1. I have limited my discussion on use of an index variable to the inter-relationships between concentrations of the dominant ionic species and specific conductance. There is a theoretical base for relating the behavior of charged ionic species in aqueous solution (e.g., ionic activities) with the electrical conductivity of the solution as determined by measurements of specific conductance. Specific conductance as an index variable would only by accident show a significant correlation with such water-quality variables as stream temperature, concentra-tions of nutrient species, trace elements, or biologically-related constituents.

2. Benefit-loss functions for the multiple uses of water-quality information have not been clearly defined. Even if they were, I agree with you that they would not be additive. Nonetheless, I feel that we can intuitively develop some feel for the uses of water-quality data and, through an economic analysis, develop some priorities as to what facets of the myriad of water-quality problems facing us today justify a larger portion of the limited available manpower and monetary resources.

3. It would depend to a considerable degree on the magnitude of the particular water-quality problem and on the desired accuracy of the solution. For certain purposes of regional water-resources planning at the national level, for example, quite large errors of estimate can undoubtedly be tolerated, especi-ally considering the uncertainties of other aspects of the planning process. The proposed empirical methods of analysis certainly have limits of application, but the philosophy to be conveyed is that we should not use any more complex a methodology than we need.

4. I would only hope that such statements of acceptable risk could be made and followed for each data use. Unfortunately, to date, many uses of water-quality data have steered away from any stipulation of requirements on a probabilistic basis. A case and point would be a hard look at the wording of some of the states' water-quality standards.

The response to discussion by M. Okuta is as follows.

(1) As mentioned in the text of the paper (pages 13-14), the pH of both streams cited in fig. 5 are significantly affected by mining or drilling operations. The shift in seasonal variations of pH observed in the two streams reflects, in part, a difference in timing and effects of the rainy season. During the 1967 water year in the Alphia River at Liphia (fig. 3a), pH of the stream declined through April, and when the summer rains began in June, pH levels gradually increased again. During the driest period (April through May), average pH was at a minimum, reflecting the close association of H^+ levels with maximum concen-trations of phosphate and fluoride ions occurring simultaneously in the stream. In contrast, Three Creek near Three Creeks (fig. 3b) exhibited lower pH with higher stream discharges between December and June. During the winter months of the 1960 water year, rains apparently washed out significant portions of low-pH

18.32

brines into Three Creek. This might also explain the larger variations of pH exhibited during the relatively wet months of December, May, and June.

(2) Wind is one of several hydrologic variables that can play a role in geochemical processes. Wind can serve as a significant source of solutes, especially in near-coastal environments such as in Japan, where uptake of ions from the ocean takes place. In evaluating the effects of physical processes on streamflow water quality, the effects of such variables as wind, rainfall intensities and distribution, vegetative and soil patterns, and evapotranspiration losses should be considered.

The response to discussion by R. Quimpo is as follows.

1. For certain purposes, 'continuous' sampling at selected sites for analysis of several critical water-quality variables will be funded with no time limit. My implication in the paper was merely that we should review those sites where continuous sampling for data collection has taken place for many years without adequate review of the need for continuous data for the variables being measured. The U. S. Geological Survey as well as other agencies also collect data stratified in time, such as in low-flow areal surveys or studies of critical periods. Much research needs to be done in studying the statistical properties of water-quality data for different variables.

2. In regionalizing information on water-quality conditions in streams, we are working in a macro-scale and tend to smooth over any anomalous point-sources of pollution, natural or man-made. Regional values of water quality often may serve as a reference level from which changes in streamflow quality induced by man's activities can be estimated relative to regional or past conditions.

The response to discussion by J. P. Riley is as follows.

1. I understnad that a contract requesting an evaluation of user needs in water-quality data provided by Federal agencies has been announced for bidding.

The response to discussion by V. Yevjevich is as follows.

1. I did not intend to imply in the paper that the only important statistical measure in water-quality assessment is the mean. Unfortunately, data sets of specific water-quality variables are often highly skewed in either a positive or negative direction. This skew has occasionally been enhanced by irregular sampling in time. As a consequence, some type of transformation generally must be imposed on the data before the statistical by-products of normally-distributed data can be provided. Much has yet to be learned concerning the statistical properties of water-quality data.

2. In dealing with concentration-discharge relationships, we must restrict ourselves predominately to conservative water-quality variables. The potential of transferring information on water quality from stream discharge is quite real where the hydrologic regime is tied closely with the geochemical controls on streamflow chemical quality. Small drainage basins and basins of uniform lithology would be typical cases for application. In larger drainage basins where variable storm patterns pass over areas of different lithology, or where a pronounced wet-dry seasonal pattern takes place, quite varied conditions in streamflow chemical quality may result for an equivalent level of flow.

3. Inherent in your comment, however, is the need to stipulate what constitutes an acceptable level of correlation. Also, some surveillance of certain water-quality variables will be imposed by society regardless of any correlation (or lack of correlation) with other variables. Take the recent case of mercury in our hydrologic environment.

United States-Japan Bi-Lateral Seminar in Hydrology

Honolulu - January 1971

A THREE-COMPONENT, NONLINEAR WATER-YIELD MODEL

by

Willard M. Snyder[a], William C. Mills[b], and John C. Stephens[c]

a. Hydraulic Engineer; b. Res. Hydr. Engineer
Southeast Watershed Research Center
Soil and Water Conservation Research Division, ARS-USDA
Athens, Georgia

and

c. Chief, Northwest Branch
Soil and Water Conservation Research Division, ARS-USDA
Boise, Idaho

SYNOPSIS

A three-component, nonlinear model was developed and tested on three experimental watersheds. Input data are rainfall in 5-day periods. Output is volume of streamflow for synchronous 5-day periods.

The first component of the model is a characteristic function which is constant for all 5-day periods in the record analyzed. It is intended as a representation of the physical characteristics of the watershed expressed as a potential for water yield. The second component is a state function. It is intended as a representation of the transmission of the potential yield to the watershed outlet. It is variable with the wetness state of the watershed. Convolution of the characteristic function and the state function produces variable unit-yield functions, a different one for each 5-day period.

The third component of the model is a seasonal-loss function. Input rainfall is diminished by this function to produce 5-day amounts of rainfall, which are effective in production of streamflow. Convolution of the effective rainfall with the variable unit-yield function produces the 5-day volumes of runoff.

Parameters expressing the forms of the three components were given optimal numeric values by fitting to rainfall-runoff data from the three watersheds. The derived structures are hydrologically rational, and differ rationally for the three areas. This initial testing showed that the basic concepts are acceptable but minor modifications of the structures are required.

INTRODUCTION

The estimation of water yield by a linear convolution model has been presented previously (1). Other methods for prediction of water yield are generally based

---

(1) Snyder, W. M. A water yield model derived from monthly runoff data. Pub. No. 63, Symposium on Surface Water, IASH, Belgium. 1963.

on multiple regression (2) or auto- or cross-regression in time series analysis
(3). One feature of the convolution approach to yield analysis is the derivation of unit-yield functions operationally identical to unit-response functions
in storm analysis. Such unit-yield functions are, hopefully, expressible by
relationship to physical properties of the drainage area.

Recent work has shown that two-stage convolution in storm hydrograph analysis
appears to offer a means of exploring for relationships between hydrologic and
physical properties (4). The first stage of two-stage convolution produces a
variable unit-response function from a static characteristic function and a
variable state function. The second stage convolution is similar to conventional
procedure, producing a storm hydrograph from input effective rain and the variable unit-response function. The elemental characteristic and state functions
are considered to represent more fundamental watershed properties than usually
expressed in a unit-response function or unit hydrograph.

This paper explores two-stage convolution in a nonlinear water-yield model.
The study represents continued concern for the need to predict the availability
of a precious resource through natural delivery from the watershed.

For brevity in this discussion, it is presumed that the reader is familiar with
basic concepts of two-stage convolution given in reference (4).

THE MATHEMATICAL MODEL

The nonlinear model for water yield analysis cannot be presented simply as a
mathematical equation. The model is made up of three components representing
watershed physical processes. These components operate on each other numerically, again representing physical interaction of watershed processes. The
components and the linkages through the mathematical procedure of convolution
are presented below.

The model is designed to use input volumes of rain and output volumes of streamflow in 5-day units. There are thus 73 periods in a standard year, and period
74 corresponds exactly in season to period 1.

The Characteristic Function

The characteristic function expresses the ability of a drainage area to receive
input effective rainfall and store it for future delivery. This potential for
delivery is a function of time measured from time zero at the gaging point of
the stream. The actual time scale cannot be specified initially but results
from optimization of the model parameters using historical data.

The characteristic function is static, remaining unchanged for each 5-day period in the record. It would be a unit-yield function under the idealized situation of passage of a unit input of water out of the area with no attenuation.

(2) Sharp, A. L., A. E. Gibbs, W. J. Owen, and B. Harris. Application of multiple regression approach in evaluating parameters affecting water yields of river
basins. Jour. Geophys. Res., Vol. 65. 1960.

(3) Matalas, N. C. Time-series analysis. Water Resources Res., Vol. 3. 1967.

(4) Snyder, W. M., W. C. Mills, and J. C. Stephens. A method of derivation of
nonconstant watershed response functions. Water Resources Res., Vol. 6, No. 1.
1970.

Because the characteristic function must represent real-world watersheds, its form cannot be, at least initially, specified deterministically. The essentially form-free device of connected linear segments was therefore used. Hinge points of the segments were set at 1, 2, 3, 5, and 15 5-day periods. The function was required to be zero at the 30th period and beyond. All ordinates of the function between hinge points were expressed by linear interpolation expressions so that all ordinates entered into the numerical optimization.

Optimization will give numerical value of the ordinates of the characteristic functions at the hinge points. The function can shape itself in detail through the early close spacing of these points, but the averaging through linear interpolation will filter out oscillatory "noise" in the tail of the function.

The State Function

The state function is used to "route" the characteristic function. The result is a unit-yield function representing the actual passage of a unit yield of water through the watershed with storage attenuation. Such attenuation is not constant. When the watershed is "wet", additional input effective rain will pass rapidly to stream channels, and down channel to the gage. When the watershed is "dry", input effective rain will tend to penetrate more deeply into the soil profile and take longer to drain from the soil profile into the stream channels.

Variable attenuation can be accomplished by making the state function depend on the watershed "wetness". The functional form used in this study is given in equation 1:

$$S(t) = \frac{1/t_i^m}{\sum_i 1/t_i^m}$$ (1)

In this equation, t is time in 5-day periods, and $t_1 = 1$, $t_2 = 2$, and $t_3 = 3$. The parameter, "m", is computed from regression equation 2:

$$m = b_1 (5.0 - PPR) + b_2$$ (2)

where PPR is the runoff during the 5-day period previous to the current period, and b_1 and b_2 are regression coefficients.

Briefly, three ordinates of the state function are used to "route" the characteristic function. The relative values of the three ordinates depend on the "wetness" of the watershed as indicated by runoff in the previous 5-day period. Equation 1 shows that the ordinates are standardized so that their sum is unity. It was found by trial that the form (5.0 - PPR) in equation 2 had to be used to decrease the sensitivity of coefficient b_1 for values of PPR at or near zero.

If the attenuation is not variable, that is, if the watershed acts as a linear system in delivery of yield, b_1 will be small and m will be nearly invariant with state of the watershed.

The Seasonal-Loss Function

Some method is necessary to reduce rain falling on the drainage area to a volume equivalent to the volume of streamflow. Water not passing the gage must be lost from the soil and from the surface by evapotranspiration or lost by deep seepage. Evapotranspirative return of moisture to the atmosphere has a seasonal

431

cyclic pattern controlled by the seasonal march of incoming solar energy and the available water stored in the profile. Deep seepage, when it occurs, should have a maximum when soil moisture storage is maximum during the year.

Two general approaches to volumetric reduction of rain are possible: 1. Losses can be computed from physical principles and the effective rain computed by subtracting these losses prior to model optimization. 2. A functional loss can be formulated, incorporated in the model, and its parameters evaluated by the optimization. The second approach was used in this study, since little was known quantitatively about deep seepage, and because too many assumptions would have to be made to allow deterministic evaluation of evapotranspirative loss from an entire watershed.

When evaluated statistically through some optimization procedure, the loss function represents a seasonal pattern averaged across all years in the record analyzed. The function must be cyclic, but not necessarily mirror-symetric in its crests and troughs. In the earlier water-yield model (1) a rather cumbersome iterative procedure was used. In this present study the structure was made more computer efficient by using a form-free interpolation method (5) modified to a cyclic structure.

Ordinates for evaluation of the continuous parabolic interpolation function were specified at five points. The first point was at period 1 and the interval was 14.6 periods, thus providing a uniform spacing which repeats exactly each year. Seasonal loss for each 5-day period was calculated by interpolation between the five base points. Interpolation is always in the middle range of a four-point set. A cyclic function is generated by the annual cycling of the five base values.

The full seasonal-loss function is made up of the form-free, but continuous, cyclic curve passing through the five ordinate values, and a scaling term, (5.0 - PPR), previously defined with equation 2. This scaling term is a multiplier of the cyclic curve and allows loss to vary with wetness of the area.

Model Summarization

The water-yield model is made up of three components: a static characteristic function, a variable state function, and a seasonal-loss function. The state function operates on the characteristic function in first-stage convolution to produce variable unit-yield functions. Input rainfall is diminished by a seasonal-loss function to produce effective rain. In second-stage convolution the unit-yield function operates on effective rain to produce a 5-day volume of runoff.

The characteristic function is described by five ordinates in preset locations. The state function is described by a mathematical expression containing two regression coefficients. The seasonal-loss function is described by interpolation through five preset ordinates. The model thus contains a total of 12 "unknowns" which must be quantified by optimization against historical data. In practice, one of the five ordinates of the characteristic function was removed from direct solution by use of the principle of continuity, which requires the sum of 29 ordinates to be unity. Therefore, 11 values in the total model must be quantified by "fitting".

---

(5) Snyder, W. M. Continuous parabolic interpolation. Proc. ASCE, Vol. 87, No. HY4. 1961.

WATERSHEDS USED IN TESTING

Rainfall and runoff data from three experimental watersheds were used to test
the water-yield model. These watersheds are at widely separated locations in
the Southeastern United States. Taylor Creek (Fla. W-2) is in southern Florida
Pigeon Roost Creek (Miss. W-34) in northern Mississippi, and Ahoskie Creek (N.C
W-Al) in the northeastern section of North Carolina. They represent a variation in climate as well as physical characteristics and conditions.

Detailed physical characteristics and other basic data for Taylor Creek and
Pigeon Roost Creek watersheds have been presented in the Agricultural Research
Service's hydrologic data series (6). Similar information for Ahoskie Creek
will be published in the next edition of that series. Also, physical features
of Taylor Creek watershed are described in more detail in a progress report on
hydrologic investigations of the ARS, Florida experimental watersheds (7). Sum
maries of physical characteristics of the three areas are given in the followin
sections.

Taylor Creek

Taylor Creek watershed contains an area of 98.7 square miles. It is in the
Southern Florida flatwoods, where land slopes are very small. Soils in the
basin are highly permeable sands and a permanent water table exists within
5 ft. of the surface. For the period considered in the test, the stream channel system was very poorly defined and surface drainage was sluggish. Land
use in the watershed is predominately improved pasture and undeveloped range
and forest, both of which provide good hydrologic cover. Taylor Creek watershed is underlain by a thick bed of impermeable sediments. These sediments
form an aquiclude called the Hawthorn Formation that essentially seals off
water movement from the phreatic aquifer to the underlying Floridian aquifer.
Thus, very little surface water is lost to deep seepage.

Pigeon Roost Creek

Pigeon Roost Creek watershed is an area of 117.2 square miles in the transitional zone between the Southern Coastal Plains and the Southern Mississippi
Valley Silty Uplands. Soils in the basin are either loess or derived from
Coastal Plain material. Permeability of most basin soils is moderate to mod-
erately rapid. The entire watershed is underlain by the Meridian Formation,
which is an extensive water-saturated stratum. This Formation is the source
of a relatively constant base flow from seepage along the lower reaches of
the main channel. Pigeon Roost Creek has a well-defined channel system and
surface drainage is good. However, flow from about 15% of the watershed in
the upper reaches is controlled by retention dams.

Proportions of the Pigeon Roost Creek watershed in various land slopes are as
follows: 0.22 is in the 0-2% class; 0.24 is in the 2-5% range; 0.08 is 5-8%;
0.10 is 8-12%; 0.19 is 12-17%; and 0.17 is in the 17% and above range.

Land use in the watershed is mixed, with about 22% of the area in row crops,
55% in pasture and idle land, 21% in woods, and 2% in bare gullies.

(6) Hobbs, H. W., Editor. Hydrologic data for experimental watersheds in the
United States. USDA Misc. Pub. 1070, pp. 29 and 318. 1968.

(7) Speir, W. H., W. C. Mills, and J. C. Stephens. Hydrology of three experimental watersheds in southern Florida - A progress report. USDA-ARS 41-152,
50 pp. 1969.

Ahoskie Creek

Ahoskie Creek watershed is a 57-square-mile drainage basin in the Southern
Coastal Plain land resource area. Soils in the basin are largely fine sandy
loams and silt loams with moderate permeability. Land slopes are predominately
in the 0-2% range with less than 5% of the area steeper than this. The channel
drainage system is well defined, since all major channels were recently exca-
vated for drainage and flood prevention. Land use is largely woodland (65%)
and mixed row crops (30%), with the remainder in pasture, home sites, and mis-
cellaneous. Ahoskie Creek watershed is underlain by sedimentary formations
that vary in composition. Groundwater moves laterally in the surficial aquifer and discharges as effluent seepage into stream channels or moves out of
the basin as subsurface alluvial flow; only minor amounts seem to be lost to
the underlying artesian formations.

OPTIMIZATION

The 11 coefficients and parameters of the total water-yield model were quantified simultaneously using the principle of optimization presented by DeCoursey
and Snyder (8). This procedure is called by the various names of nonlinear
least squares, differential correction, or sensitivity analysis. Basically,
the method consists of setting initial trial values of all 11 coefficients,
computing runoff values, and using the resultant observed versus computed errors to achieve improved estimates of all 11 coefficients simultaneously. The
process continues until the sum of squares of residual errors stabilizes at
some minimum value.

A master computer program accomplishes all major steps listed above. The only
specific program for the yield model consisted of a subroutine to compute runoff values from rainfall and values of the coefficients.

One difference between convolution for storm analysis and convolution for
yield analyis is the normal length of the data set. Convolution for a storm
ends after a few hours or a few days. Convolution for yield is continuous
from beginning to end of the input record. Up to four years were used in
these analyses. The programming procedure used was to construct an operator
matrix of unit-yield function ordinates. As the computation of runoff proceeded through the record, a vector was "spilled off" one side of the operator matrix and a new vector was added on the other side.

Program Iteration

Figure 1 is an example of changing values of the coefficients during successive approximations of the optimizing procedure. All values of the coefficients become relatively stable after a few rounds. The right-hand set of
rounds shows the effect of having reset coefficients 3 and 6 to new initial
values. All coefficients are affected by such a reset but recover quickly
from the perturbation and stabilize near their original values.

Table 1 shows the basic statistical properties of the data and the fitting
for the three stations analyzed. Two runs are shown for Pigeon Roost Creek.
These correspond to the end values of the two series shown in Figure 1. The
two measures of fitting, reduction of standard deviations and the correlation
coefficients show reasonably good, but not excellent, correspondence between
model and data.

(8) DeCoursey, D. G. and W. M. Snyder. Computer-oriented method of optimizing model parameters. Jour. Hydr., Vol. 9, North-Holland Pub. Co., Amsterdam.
1969.

Table 2 shows the derived numerical values for the coefficients of the yield
model. Physical interpretation of these values will be attempted in the following section.

Analysis of Errors

Following quantification of the yield model, graphs were plotted showing the
observed 5-day runoff against the calculated runoff. In general, these graphs
showed acceptable error patterns for the levels of correlation shown in Table 1.

Approximately 50% reduction in standard deviation is not extremely good adjustment of data, and the graphs confirmed this in the wide scattering of the plotted
runoff values. However, the graphs showed a reasonable balance of positive and
negative errors for a wide range of runoff values, thus diminishing the chance
of bias in the resultant structure of the model.

A consistent bias in low values of runoff was noted. Observed low flows are
often higher than the flows calculated with the model. Calculated flows often
become zero, whereas the observed low flows rarely do. This low-flow bias in
the model casts some doubt on the structure of the recession portion of the
derived characteristic function. The low-flow bias was greatest for Pigeon
Roost Creek and least for Ahoskie Creek.

The low-flow bias may be due to the extremely large range of values of observed
runoff. The 5-day runoff for Taylor Creek, for example, ranged from zero to
4.83 inches. Period-to-period variation in the extremely large events is many
times the variation in the near-zero events. Since the optimization process
adjusts the "residual squared error", the few extremely large events tend to
control and the error pattern of small events is overshadowed.

It is doubtful if a model using input rainfall totalled over 5 days can serve
to predict any single event precisely. Rain can fall in a few minutes, or
extend over days. It can fall near the beginning, near the end, or in the
middle of a 5-day period. But such precise prediction is more appropriately
the function of a "storm" model. Yield models are intended for derivation of
average long-term response, and significant variation about the average response
must be expected.

MODEL COMPONENTS

Characteristic Functions

The characteristic functions derived for the three test streams are shown in
Figure 2. The three areas are similar to the extent that a large proportion
of water yield is characteristically delivered as streamflow in about 15 or
20 days. However, the areas differ greatly in the way in which this significant early portion of yield is delivered.

Pigeon Roost Creek delivers nearly 76% of its characteristic yield in the 5-day
period in which the effective rain occurs. An abrupt decrease to near zero at
period 2 is followed by a small secondary peak at period 5. The precision of
the characteristic function across the section from 2 to 15 periods cannot be
judged. This station has a typical streamflow pattern of abrupt recession
immediately following rainfall, and a very flat, sustained flow between rains.
The characteristic function for Pigeon Roost Creek is probably the best representation of this typical abrupt pattern that can be attained by the linear-
segmented form.

The characteristic function for Ahoskie Creek shows the lesser figure of about
50% of yield delivered in the period in which effective rain occurs. A smoother
transition to low flows is also evident

Taylor Creek has a characteristic function somewhat surprising on initial inspection, but probably rational for the area. Only about 40% of yield is delivered in the first 5-day period, and a high delivery of nearly 45% occurs in the second period. A likely explanation is that the sandy soils absorb a large portion of the effective rainfall. The high delivery in the second period is caused by rapid percolation through and from the soil profile.

The rapid initial delivery from Pigeon Roost Creek can be attributed to the steep slopes, significant proportion of agricultural land use, and soils of intermediate permeability. Ahoskie Creek is similar to Taylor Creek in having shallow slopes and is similar to Pigeon Roost Creek in having a significant proportion of agricultural land use. Ahoskie Creek does not have the high permeability associated with the sandy soils of Taylor Creek and, therefore, its characteristic function falls logically between those of Pigeon Roost and Taylor Creeks.

Pigeon Roost Creek and Ahoskie Creek are similar in that about 83% of characteristic yield is delivered in the first 25 days, leaving 17% for sustained streamflow. Taylor Creek, on the other hand, delivers about 97% in 25 days. These sandy soils can, therefore, hold only 3% of water for sustained streamflow.

Unit-Yield Functions

Unit-yield functions can be computed by convolving the characteristic and state functions. The coefficients b_1 and b_2, given in Table 2, can be used in equations 1 and 2 to produce the three ordinates of the state function. These in turn operate on the characteristic functions in the convolution.

The unit-yield functions are variable, since the state functions vary. Yield functions for three "wetness" states are shown for the three drainage areas in Figures 3, 4, and 5. A similar effect of wetness is noted in all three figures. When runoff in the previous period is high, the attenuation of the characteristic function is slight. But when runoff in the previous period is low, attenuation becomes greater. About 10% of yield can be withheld from the current period. A balancing increase in flow takes place around the third or fourth periods. Effect beyond about 30 days is too small to be shown graphically.

The greatest variability is exhibited by Taylor Creek. This variability is an indication of the nonlinear response between effective rainfall and rate of yield of water. It is probably most extreme in Taylor Creek because the sandy soils have rapid water intake when dry. However, as the limited capacity for soils storage is exhausted, further intake is prohibited and yield response becomes very rapid.

Seasonal-Loss Functions

The seasonal-loss functions for the three streams analyzed are shown in Figures 6, 7, and 8. The curves shown are for zero runoff in the previous period. The curves would be lowered if scaled by the term (5.0 - PPR). In the lower portion of each figure is a histogram of average rainfall for six consecutive 5-day periods, also averaged across corresponding periods in all years of the record analyzed.

The derived loss curves are variable from station to station, but this variability can be rationally explained. In Pigeon Roost Creek the highest rainfall occurs in the winter season. The soil profile becomes wet and only moderate loss occurs from rain falling on this soil. As rainfall amounts decrease and insolational energy increases to its June maximum, the soil dries out and losses from rainfall increase. With low rainfall and sustained evapotranspiration during the summer season, the losses reach their maximum in the autumn. However, a very rapid reduction in loss takes place in late autumn and early winter.

The seasonal-loss pattern for Ahoskie Creek is similar to that for Pigeon Roost Creek with two exceptions. The losses are appreciably smaller, and a pronounced secondary minimum of loss occurs in August. The losses are smaller in Ahoskie Creek, since appreciably smaller rainfall produces runoff nearly equal to that of Pigeon Roost Creek. This difference can be seen in the 5-day mean rainfall and runoff values in Table 1. The summer secondary minimum of loss is caused by the high summer rainfall in June, July, and August.

The seasonal-loss pattern for Taylor Creek is quite different from the pattern for Pigeon Roost Creek and Ahoskie Creek. Losses are fairly high during the entire year, but have a minimum in late summer about the time the other two stations have their maxima. This reversal of loss pattern is caused by the very high average rainfall from June through October.

CONCLUSIONS

The concept of a nonlinear water-yield model based on two-stage convolution was adequately verified in an initial analysis of three drainage areas. The yield model is constructed of three operational components. Two of the components, the characteristic function and the seasonal-loss function, varied significantly from area to area. These variations were, in all cases, in the directions expected by variations in physical characteristics of the areas.

The third component, the state function, which is variable from runoff period to runoff period, did not show as great a difference between areas. The difference that did appear was rational.

Of the three components, the seasonal-loss function is very likely the best defined. This function was quite stable in numerous trials with modified forms of the other components.

The calculation of low flows is biased. Two possible causes must be investigated. These causes may be separate, or may be interactive. The first possible cause of bias is the action of the optimization method. It may be necessary to weigh the runoff events to compensate for nonuniformity of variance. The second cause may be the form of the recession portion of the characteristic function.

Table 1. Statistical Properties

Watershed	No. of Rounds in Fitting	No. of Observations	Mean 5-Day Rainfall (inches)	Mean 5-Day Runoff (inches)	Std. Dev. of Runoff (inches)	Std. Dev. of Residuals (inches)	Cor. Coef.
Ahoskie Creek, N. C.	13	219 1/	0.51	0.17	0.30	0.16	0.85
Pigeon R. Creek, Miss. (run 1)	10	292 2/	0.64	0.18	0.37	0.14	0.93
Pigeon R. Creek, Miss. (run 2)	11	292 2/	0.64	0.18	0.37	0.14	0.93
Taylor Creek, Fla.	5	292 3/	0.76	0.29	0.53	0.20	0.93

Records used in analysis: 1/ 1965-67, 2/ 1962-65, 3/ 1956-59

Table 1a. Statistical Properties, Metric Units

Watershed	No. of Rounds in Fitting	No. of Observations	Mean 5-Day Rainfall (cm)	Mean 5-Day Runoff (cm)	Std. Dev. of Runoff (cm)	Std. Dev. of Residuals (cm)	Cor. Coef.
Ahoskie Creek, N. C.	13	219 1/	1.30	0.43	0.76	0.41	0.85
Pigeon R. Creek, Miss. (run 1)	10	292 2/	1.63	0.46	0.94	0.36	0.93
Pigeon R. Creek, Miss. (run 2)	11	292 2/	1.63	0.46	0.94	0.36	0.93
Taylor Creek, Fla.	5	292 3/	1.93	0.74	1.35	0.51	0.93

Records used in analysis: 1/ 1965-67, 2/ 1962-65, 3/ 1956-59.

Table 2. Derived Model Coefficients

Watershed	Characteristic Function					State Function		Loss Function				
	C1*	C2	C3	C5	C15	b_1	b_2	L_a	L_b	L_c	L_d	L_e
Ahoskie Creek, N. C.	0.505	0.290	0.022	0.000	0.013	-2.12	12.5	0.095	0.014	0.346	0.241	0.349
Pigeon R. Creek, Miss. (run 1)	0.757	0.000	0.007	0.039	0.000	-2.09	12.8	0.225	0.181	0.432	0.485	0.585
Pigeon R. Creek, Miss. (run 2)	0.757	0.000	0.009	0.038	0.000	-2.13	12.9	0.224	0.181	0.431	0.484	0.585
Taylor Creek, Fla.	0.403	0.485	0.046	0.007	0.000	-3.15	17.4	0.334	0.287	0.317	0.258	0.183

* From continuity.

SUPPLEMENTAL INFORMATION

Watershed Areas	sq. mi.	sq. km.
Ahoskie Creek	57.0	148
Pigeon Roost Creek	117.2	303
Taylor Creek	98.7	256

Conversion of Model Coefficients (Table 2)

	coef. b_1 for input in	
	in.	cm.
Ahoskie Creek	-2.12	-0.83
Pigeon Roost Creek (run 1)	-2.09	-0.82
Pigeon Roost Creek (run 2)	-2.13	-0.84
Taylor Creek	-3.15	-1.24

All other coefficients remain unchanged.

19.11

439

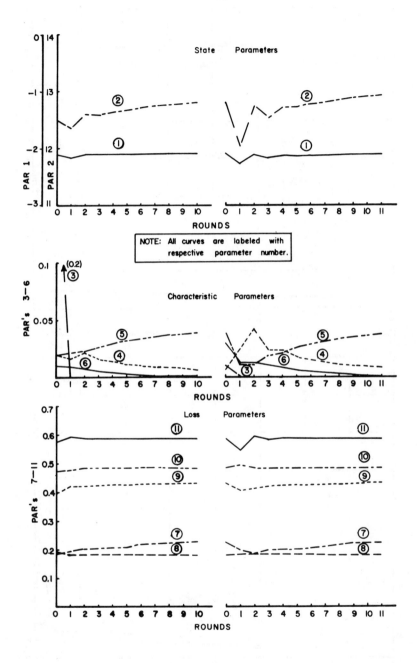

Figure 1.   Successive values of parameters for Pigeon Roost Creek.

19 .12

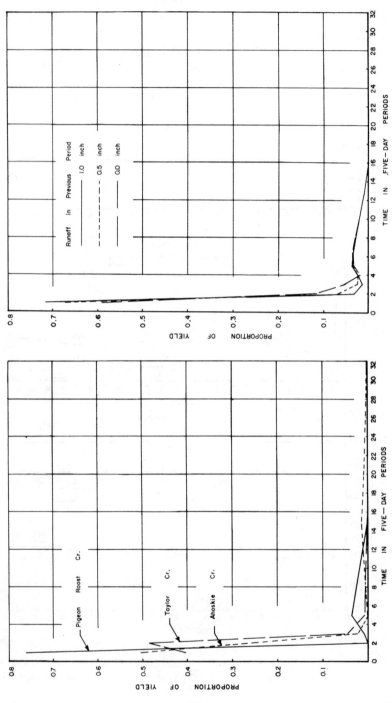

Figure 4. Unit-yield functions for Pigeon Roost Creek.

441

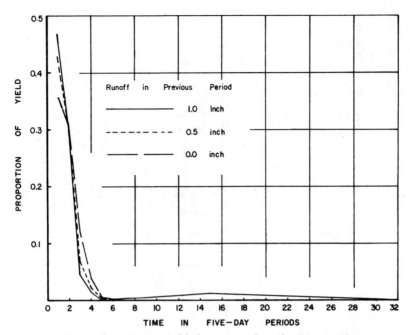

Figure 3.   Unit-yield functions for Ahoskie Creek.

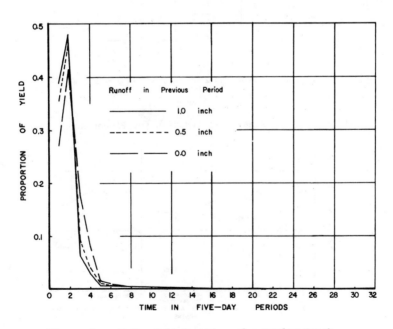

Figure 5.   Unit-yield functions for Taylor Creek.

19.14

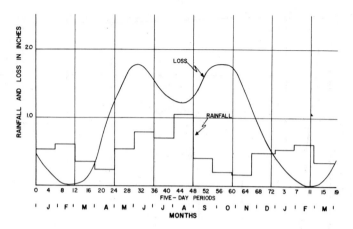

Figure 6.   Seasonal loss function for Ahoskie Creek.

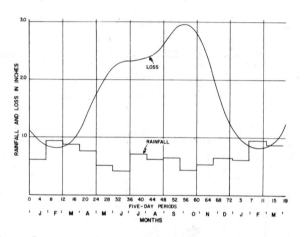

Figure 7.   Seasonal loss function for Pigeon Roost Creek.

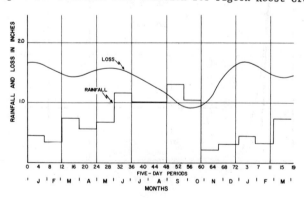

Figure 8.   Seasonal loss function for Taylor Creek.

19.15

DISCUSSION

M. HINO

(1) I would like to know about the existence of the conservation condition in the authors' model, i.e. the equality of total amounts of effective rainfall and runoff.

(2) In the authors' model, the following six parameters are involved; they are

$$b \quad : \quad eq. \ (4) \ or \ (7)$$
$$f, \ g \quad ; \quad eq. \ (5)$$
$$B_1, \ B_2, \ B_3, \quad : \quad eq. \ (8)$$

Is it possible to find any relationships between such parameters in order to reduce the degree of freedom? I believe that a simple model is preferable to a model which gives better predictions but contains more parameters.

RESPONSE BY W. M. SNYDER

The response to discussion by M. Hino is as follows.

Conservation of mass is accomplished in several ways. First, equation 1 defines the state function as three operating coefficients whose sum is unity. Second, Figure 2 shows that the characteristic functions, which are distributed proportions of yield, total approximately unity. The unit yield functions which are produced by convolution of these two functions must, therefore, also be approximately unity. Finally, the correlation coefficients are reasonably good. This must mean reasonable correspondence between values computed by the model and the observed streamflow values. This establishes continuity of mass insofar as the reduction of rainfall to effective rainfall is concerned.

It may be possible to find relationships among the parameters and thus reduce the total number of such parameters. While it is correct that, all things considered, simple models are preferred, the definition of what is simple is subjective. The authors feel that application of the model to data provides the best answer as to an adequate number of parameters. If the model is over-determined -- that is, has an excess number of parameters -- then optimization will cause some of these excess degrees of freedom to be used to absorb some of the random error always present in data. Numerical values of the parameters would tend to fluctuate randomly from data set to data set if they expressed such random components of data. Therefore, consistent results of optimization, with rational interpretation, would imply that the parameters express real, not random, information contained in the data.

United States-Japan Bi-Lateral Seminar in Hydrology

Honolulu, January 1971

HYDROLOGICAL STUDIES OF EVAPOTRANSPIRATION

AND GROUNDWATER FLOW IN SANDY LAND

by RYO KANEKO

DIRECTOR

NATIONAL RESEARCH INSTITUTE OF AGRICULTURAL ENGINEERING

MINISTRY OF AGRICULTURE AND FORESTRY

HIRATSUKA, KANAGAWA, 254 JAPAN

Synopsis

With the groundwater level record from 1953 through 1965 at the observation field in Hiratsuka located on a sand dune, a water balance calculation
around the field was performed to estimate groundwater flow and evapotranspiration. Since no surface flow takes place around the field, the water balance
equation is given as

$$P = E + M + G \qquad (1)$$
$$G = (G_2 - G_1) + H \cdot Pa \qquad (2)$$

and, each term being explained in the text.

If as many cases of $G \doteq 0$ are chosen as possible for obtaining the relationship between the groundwater level and $(G_2 - G_1)$, the value of the latter can
be obtained for each period throughout the year when the groundwater level is
known, since this relationship can also be applied to the case of $G \doteq 0$. $(G_2 - G_1)$
was calculated for each month continuously for 13 years, and G in Eq(2) was substituted to Eq(1) to find the monthly value of E.

Deep wells are gradually developing in Hiratsuka and the confined groundwater level lowers year by year, consequently, the unconfined groundwater level
falls and the relationship between the groundwater level and $(G_2 - G_1)$ changes
in a long term. Therefore, different relationships between the groundwater level
and $(G_2 - G_1)$ had to be used for different years (or sets of several years).

Chapter I
INTRODUCTION

The investigation site is in the National Research institute of Agricultural Engineering in Hiratsuka City, which is located about 60 km south-west of Tokyo. As shown in Fig. 1, the site is about 3.5 km far from the coast, and is on an almost flat coastal sand dune, the elevation of which is about eight meters above sea level.

Because of the sandy soil, all precipitation infiltrates into the ground and there is no surface runoff. Soil moisture, groundwater level and evapotranspiration from lysimeters were measured at the investigation site in addition to meteorological observation. The data have been recorded continuously from 1953 up to present. Here, water balance in the sandy land is discussed with the data recorded for 13 years, from 1953 through 1965. During the period, the increase of population and the development of industry in Hiratsuka caused a rapid increase of pumped discharge of groundwater. Accordingly, the groundwater level in deep wells gradually fell, and also unconfined groundwater table lowered owing to percolation into deeper strata. Consequently, these factors made the water balance system complicated.

In this study, transpiration from sandy land is estimated by providing precipitation, groundwater flow, groundwater stage, and the relationship between groundwater level and its drawdown corresponding to the change of environments.

The value of evapotranspiration indirectly obtained by water balance calculation on an area in question better represents the true evapotranspiration of the area than direct measurement in such a limited plot as lysimeters.

Chapter II
ANNUAL FLUCTUATION OF THE UNCONFINED GROUNDWATER LEVEL

Groundwater records from 1952 to 1953 at the meteorological observation field show that the annual mean was about two meters under the ground surface and that the level in the dry season was about two and a half meters: After 1960, the annual mean was about three meters, and the mean in dry season was four meters The falling rate of the groundwater level increases year after year. Since the unconfined groundwater in the city zone of Hiratsuka, which is to the south of the site in question, is percolating simultaneously into deeper strata, groundwater level lowered on the whole, and the gradient of groundwater table is about 1/500 downward to the south. Groundwater level rapidly rises after presipitation, and falls exponentially with the increase of groundwater flow. Annually it rises or falls with the range of more or less one meter. The peak appears in June through July and in September through October, and the valley formed by drought appears in March through April and in August, and the above tendency is common to every year. Fig. 2 is an example of the curves showing such changes of groundwater level.

Chapter III
THE RELATIONSHIP BETWEEN THE UNCONFINED
GROUNDWATER AND CONFINED GROUNDWATER

Though the unconfined groundwater in Hiratsuka is almost completely separated from the confined groundwater by an impermeable bed, some amount of unconfined groundwater percolates through the impermeable bed into the confined aquifer, and the groundwater in each aquifer is conected through the break at the terminal stretch of the impermeable formation.

The geological profile of the area compiled from deep well logs is as follows:

I A : Dune sand through about five meters below the ground surface.

I B : Coarse sand and small-grained gravel about five to ten or fifteen meters in thickness.

I C : Sand and fine sand, ten or fifteen through about thirty meters, in which lens-shaped silt and sandy clay are inter bedded.

I D : Impermeable bed consisting of sandy clay, about thirty to fifty or sixty meters.

II A : Sand and gravel bed of a great specific yield, fifty or sixty to eighty or ninety meters.

II B : Sandy silt stratum inter bedded in the sand and gravel bed II A.

III : Bedrock

The unconfined groundwater is held on the silt bed and sandy clay bed of IC in general. The groundwater in IC was once confined, but the water table has fallen below the sea level since. II A and II B are Diluvium. Bedrock of Tertiary in III forms a buried hill at the coast and serves as a tide embankment which prevents the sea water from intruding. Owing to the above geological structure, the deep wells near the seashore of Hiratsuka have no sea water even though groundwater table is staying forty meters below the sea level at present.

According to a record of 1922, artesian wells were seen about five through eight meters above sea level, but the groundwater level gradually fell and declined to the sea level in 1950, when the total pumped discharge was 10,000 m³/day. The total pumped discharge reached 18,000 m³/day in 1955; hence the groundwater table fell rapidly and declined to about thirty meters below sea level at the central part of the pumping area in 1965. The discharge increased to 22,000 m³/day around 1960, further 70,000 m³/day in 1965, and the lowering rate of the groundwater level reached two to three meters per year. In 1969, the discharge increased further to 90,000 m³/day by seventy-eight wells, the lowering rate reached three to four meters per year, and the groundwater level declined to forty meters below sea level.

As the result of the above, the sea water began to intrude over the depressed part of the buried hill at the mouth of Sagami River, and silt and sandy clay inter bedded in IC layer are facing to contraction.

With the increase of pumped discharge, the unconfined aquifer was separated from the confined aquifer and the unconfined groundwater began to percolate into the unsatulated part. Even though groundwater flow hardly occurs, the unconfined groundwater level goes down at the rate of 2 mm/day. This rate can be regarded as corresponding to the water depth of 0.7 mm/day, if the air capacity is supposed to be 0.35. The measurement of the density of natural tritium in the samples taken from deep wells in Hiratsuka showed that almost all the confined groundwater was mixed with the percolated unconfined groundwater. The fundamental equation of water balance in the confined aquifer at Hiratsuka area is given by

$$G_1 + L = G_2 + W + \triangle S \qquad (1)$$

where,

G_1 is groundwater inflow,

G_2, groundwater outflow,

L, percolation from the unconfined aquifer,

W, discharge pumped by deep wells, and

ΔS, change in water storage in the confined aquifer.

The object area is a part of the Hiratsuka groundwater basin of about 20 km^2 where the groundwater utilization is extensive. The Hiratsuka groundwater basin corresponds with the distribution of stratum IIIΛof a prominent specific yield which extends between the submerged hill at the coast and the inland hills, the area of which is about 68 km^2. In Eq (1), G_2 is supposed to be zero owing to the submerged hill at the coast and L is given by 14,000 m^3/day if the value of 0.7 mm/day measured at the National Research Institute of Agricultural Engineering is applied to the area in question. W is set equal to 70,000 m^3/day which is a discharge actually measured in 1965. ΔS is assumed to be 10,000 m^3/day or 0.5 mm/day, which is the mean of the groundwater drawdown in the groundwater basin 20 km^2 in area. The above value is derived by the assumption that the yearly drop of the groundwater level at the central part is 10 mm/day and the air capacity of the aquifer is 0.1. As a result, G_1 comes to be 46,000 m^3/day.

On the other hand, the value of G_1 is given by 40,000 m^3/day from Darcy's formula with 1/100 of the gradient of the confined groundwater in the environs, 16 km of the total length of the environs except the coastal part, and 250 m^2/day of the transmissibility measured by deep well pumping tests.

Since the both values derived in the different ways are quite close, the reliability that L is equal to 0.7 mm/day seems to be proper on the whole.

Within 20 km^2 of the investigation area, L cannot surpass a certain limit, even though the pumped discharge W increases. The increase in W mainly is accompanied by negative value of ΔS, and G_1 increases with some amount with the increase in the groundwater gradient.

Chapter IV

ESTIMATION OF GROUNDWATER FLOW AND EVAPOTRANSPIRATION

Since no surface runoff takes place, the water balance in the sandy land is given by the following equation:

$$P = E + M + G \qquad (2)$$
$$G = (G_2 - G_1) + HPa \qquad (3)$$

where,

P is precipitation,

E, evapotranspiration,

M, change of soil moisture retention,

G, groundwater supplied from ground surface,

G_1, groundwater inflow,

G_2, groundwater outflow,

H, variation of groundwater level, and

Pa, air capacity around groundwater level in question.

L in Eq(1) is included in G_2.

The investigation area to which Eq(2) and (3) are to be applied is supposed to be close to the mentioned meteorological observation field in Hiratsuka. The site is covered by lawn grasses on sandy soil, some of which is bare land or road, and at the border of which fruit trees are planted. Paticular case that G is equal to zero because of no or little precipitation, $(G_2 - G_1)$ is given by $(G_2 - G_1) = -HPa$. An approximation curve, which is almost a straight line, is obtained by selecting such a case that G is assumed to be zero from the yearly fluctuation curve of the groundwater level and plotting the relationship between the groundwater level and its fall. This relationship is also effective in the case of $G \doteq 0$. Therefore, when the groundwater level is measured, corresponding $(G_2 - G_1)$ is always obtained. Through the above process, G in Eq(2) comes to be known, and finally E in Eq(2) is calculated.

In the normal case, the fluctuation curve of the groundwater level and its fall is specific to site, and there should exist only one curve. However, in

this area, the curve varies year by year. For this reason, (G2 - G1) is calculated by using the different curves shown in Fig. 3.

The change of soil moisture M, consists of Md, the decreased soil moisture
below normal soil moisture (field capacity) by evapotranspiration, i.e., the lack
of soil moisture, and Me, the temporary retained soil moisture over normal moisture because of the infiltration of precipitation.

Md in sandy soil is up to about 40 mm at the maximum, and the maximum of Me
is inferred to be about 70 mm. Me is cannot be retained for a long time. M and
other data are compared and checked with the data measured at times, and the
cumulative M by the water balance calculation of a long time should correspond
to the soil property of the test field.

Chapter V
CONSIDERATION ON THE RESULTS OF THE
WATER BALANCE CALCULATION

The property of evapotranspiration and groundwater flow at the investigation
site are as follows: The monthly E and E/Ep of each year are shown in Figs. 4
and 5. (Ep: evaporation from pan 20 cm in diameter. This standard was formerly
used in Japan.)

1. Annual E is about 700 mm, 726 mm, in maximum, 633 mm in minimum and 683 mm in
average (the standard deviation being 29 mm), and the yearly variation is not so
large.

2. The ratio of yearly E to Ep (pan evaporation) is 0.75 in maximum, 0.61 in
minimum and 0.67 in average (standard deviation being 0.03), and the yearly variation is not so large. This value is slightly small as compared with the standard
value of wood land and upland measured by water balance calculation or lysimeter.
This is based on the fact that the upper layer of the sandy land is apt to dry,
and that evapotranspiration from the grassland is smaller than that from the ordinary upland cropping area.

3. E is not affected by the yearly fall of the groundwater level, since in the
sandy land of comparatively large amount of precipitation, the capillary rise of
the groundwater accompanied with evapotranspiration can be ignored, except the
case in which groundwater level is less than about 1.5 m below the ground surface. Though the trees on the investigation site grew during the observation
period, the increase in evapotranspiration was not clear.

4. The minimum of the monthly mean of E of 13 years is 30 mm in February, and
the maximum is 92 mm in August. The minimum monthly value is 21 mm in February,
and the maximum, 107 mm in August.

The standard deviation in each month is with about 5 to 10 mm through 13
years. The standard value of E is 1 mm/day in the dried period of low temperature, and in the humid period of high temperature it is 3 mm/day, which is small
as compared to the value approximately 7 mm/day in the paddy or irrigated field.
The above seems to show the characteristics of the sandy land.

The following is the general tendency of the monthly value arranged from
small to large values (February, January, December), (November, March), (April,
October), (May, June), September, July, August.

5. The maximum of the monthly E/Ep is 0.88 in October, the minimum is 0.44 in
February, 0.44 to 0.53 in January through April, 0.64 in May, 0.71 - 0.74 in June
through August, 0.87 - 0.88 in September through November, and 0.76 in December.
The reason for the small value of E/Ep in winter and spring is that Ep is relatively large because of low humidity and strong wind, but that E is small because
of the dried soil and little transpiration. The value of E/Ep is large in fall,
because Ep decreases with the fall of temperature, and E, on the other hand,
is still large because of the relatively humid soil and still unweakened transpiration. E/Ep is also large in December because of weak wind and small Ep.

This general tendency is almost common to each year. During the investigation period minimum value of E/Ep is 0.28 in February and the maximum is 1.19 in November. The variation of the monthly E/Ep is small with the standard deviation of 0.1 to 0.2.

On the Pacific side of Japan where yearly pan evaporation is about 1,000 mm, the ratio of evapotranspiration at the sandy land to pan evaporation can be estimated as follows, except the cropping land with very good vegetation: 0.4 - 0.5 in January through April, 0.6 in May, 0.7 in June through August, 0.8 - 0.9 in September through November, and 0.7 in December.

6. The fact that the monthly E/Ep is comparatively fixed without any considerable yearly variation, and that E corresponds to Ep indicates that transpiration, as a physiological phenomenon of plants, is strongly affected by meteorological conditions, i.e., moisture release from stomata is affected by humidity, temperature or wind velocity just like pan-evaporation is.

7. Evaporation from soil surface is influenced by soil moisture of the surface layer, and sometimes, even transpiration decreases when the surface layer drys intensively. For this season, E/Ep becomes small exceptionally in the dry month of high temperature. Some examples of the above are: (p=92 mm, E=92 mm, Ep=171 mm, E/Ep=0.54) in July, 1955, (P=41 mm, E=93 mm, Ep=177 mm, E/Ep=0.52) in August, 1962, (P=51 mm, E=63 mm, Ep=120 mm, E/Ep=0.52) in September, 1962.

In winter and spring, transpiration is small, and it mostly consists of evaporation from soil surface, which is intensively affected by soil moisture of the surface layer. In the month of scarce precipitation, E/Ep is especially small. Some examples are: (P=35 mm, E=21 mm, E/Ep=0.34) in January, 1960, (P=9 mm, E=24 mm, E/Ep=0.32) in February, 1960, (P=23 mm, E=24mm, E/Ep=0.31) in February, 1961, (P=15 mm, E=20 mm, E/Ep=0.28) in February, 1962.

8. E is especially large in the humid month of high temperature and large Ep. Some examples are: (E=107 mm, P=260 mm, Ep=142 mm) in August, 1960, (E=101 mm, P=281 mm, Ep=123 mm) in August, 1963, (E=97 mm, P=174 mm, Ep=152 mm) in August, 1964. However, when precipitation is excessively heavy, Ep, and E, in consequence, become small.

Chapter VI
COMPARISON WITH E MEASURED BY LYSIMETER

In the pot experiments in which water is supplied in accordance with evapotranspiration, E appears to be larger than that from natural soil. However, comparison here is concerned with E measured by lysimeter to which there is no water supply except natural precipitation.

The water balance equation for lysimeter is as follows: $P = E + F + \Delta S$ provided that no surface runoff takes place. Here P is precipitation, E is evapotranspiration, F is seepage, and S is the change of soil moisture in the lysimeter. The calculation is done serially in each month. The annual values of evapotranspiration measured by the lysimeter are about 550 mm and are smaller than the value at the investigation field obtained by water balance calculation. The reason for this is that the value is especially small from July through September, because of the bare land, intense dryness inside the lysimeter in summer, and the formation of a dry zone in the surface soil where capillaries are disconnected.

Except the special reason in summer, the general monthly tendency of the result of the water balance calculation seems to be proper as compared to that of the lysimeter measurements.

Fig.1. Location of Hiratsuka

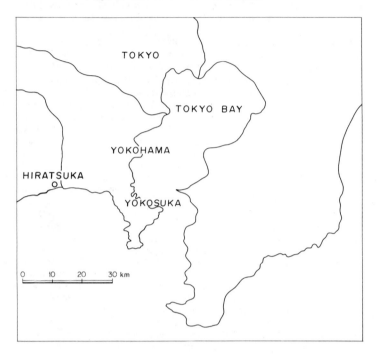

Fig.2. Fluctuation of groundwater level. (1969)

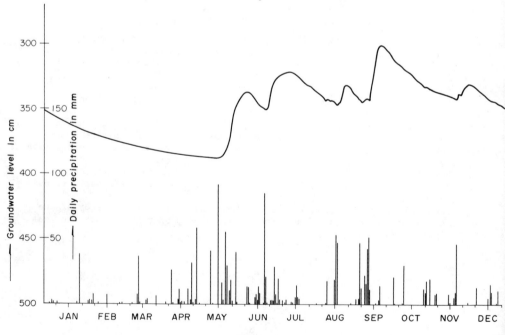

20.7

Fig. 3. Relation between groundwater level and lowering rate.

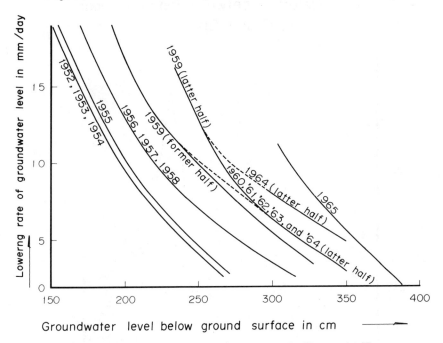

Groundwater level below ground surface in cm

Fig. 4. Relation between annual E and Ep.

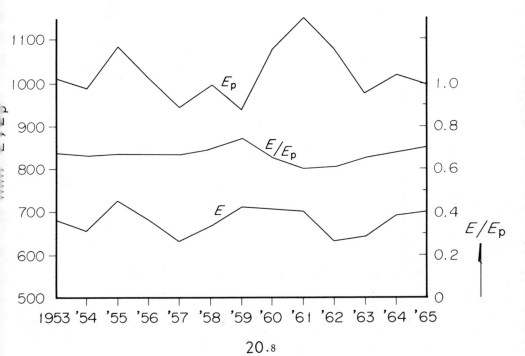

20.8

Fig. 5. Relation between monthly mean of P, E and Ep.

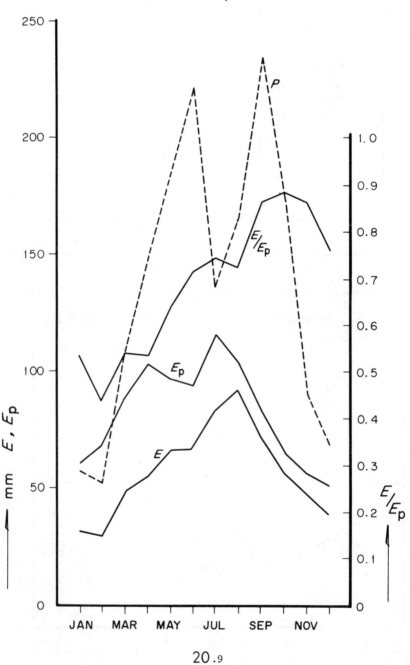

GENERAL DISCUSSION

on

A.   RESPONSE HYDROLOGY

B.   BRIDGE BETWEEN SCIENTIFIC AND APPLIED HYDROLOGY

C.   RELEVANT FUTURE HYDROLOGIC RESEARCH AREAS

Discussion is Presented in Alphabetical Order
of Discussers' Names for Each of the Three
Subjects, as Summaries Submitted by Discussers
After the Seminar.

454

A. RESPONSE HYDROLOGY

J. W. DELLEUR

In formulating a model of the response of a watershed we conceptualize the physical processes and express them in mathematical terms. These conceptualization may be deterministic or stochastic, linear or nonlinear, lumped or distributed, time independent or time varying, stationary or nonstationary or some combination of these. The choice of the model is determined by the type of problem to be solved. For example, stochastic models have been used successfully for the simulation of monthly flows. The St. Venant's equations provide a nonlinear deterministic model of the flood wave propagation which has been used successfully in modeling floods in large streams as the Ohio River, and its simplified version known as the kinematic wave theory has been successfully and particularly used in modeling the overland flow process. As may be seen from these examples, the time scale of the problem and the signal to noise ratio govern to a great extent the choice of the model.

In the paper presented at this symposium the authors addressed themselves to the modeling of transient phenomena due to a single storm on a relatively small rural watershed, smaller than 500 square miles, for example. This problem is effectively treated by a deterministic model as the storm and runoff signals are usually large compared to the noise or error that they may contain. Among the several deterministic models possible the lumped linear system is the simplest. It has the advantage of being a generalization of the unit hydrograph, a familiar tool to hydrologists. The lumping of the input may appear to be an oversimplification. However, the average number of raingages in Indiana, for example, is one per 250 square miles, and there is no simple alternative to that of lumping the rainfall excess input. The assumption of linearity may also appear as an oversimplification. However, the impulsive response calculated by the linear system theory is the leading term of a sequence of responses of pure first, second, third, etc. order systems. The sum of r of these responses is the output of a nonlinear polynomial system of order r. As a result, in the majority of the cases the linear system approach yields a method of estimation of runoff with a degree of accuracy that is sufficient for many engineering design purposes. The assumption of linearity may be limited to the storm under analysis by allowing the parameters of an otherwise linear model to vary from storm to storm as a function of the input. Sarma, et al. (1) have used this type of "Quasilinear" system to model the rainfall-runoff process in urbanized watersheds.

P. S. EAGLESON

I define the term "response hydrology" as the use of kernel functions to characterize the input-output behavior of hydrologic systems. When the system is (or is represented as being) linear, calculation of the response or output involves convolution of the input with the indicial response function or kernel. In these cases the kernel is usually called the unit impulse response or Green's function. When the system is represented as being non-linear, most response methods involve multiple kernels each representing a successively higher order

[1] Sarma, P. B. S., Delleur, J. W., and Rao, R. A., "A Program in Urban Hydrology. Part II "An Evolution of Rainfall-Runoff Models for Small Urbanized Watersheds and the Effect of Urbanization on Runoff" Purdue Water Resources Research Center, Techn. Rept. N-9, Oct. 1969 (Available from Clearinghouse for Federal Scientific and Technical Information, Springfield, Va. 22151, call number: PB 189043)

of non-linearity. Output calculation in such cases thus involves operating on the input with each of these kernels in turn (in a fashion dependent upon the particular non-linear scheme being followed) and then adding the results.

Response hydrology may be of three types:

1. Black Box - where no attempt is made to model the system behavior. The kernel is obtained by the "identification" process using pairs of observed input and output records. This method contributes little to an understanding of system behavior but is a valuable expedient for making predictions in the absence of a knowledge of system structure.

2. Gray Box - where the general nature of the system function is known (i.e. storage, delay, transduction) but the detailed structure is not. The system is represented conceptually by a kernel having the desired general behavior but with parameters which must be obtained from observations. Knowledge of the best conceptual structure and the appropriate parameter levels contributes to our physical understanding.

3. White Box - where the nature and properties of the physical system are both known (such as for flood routing in a river channel). Here the system is represented "exactly" by the appropriate differential equation. If the equation is linear or can be linearized without destroying its utility, the kernel may be derived therefrom. This method retains the knowledge of the system in the kernel parameters which are physically significant and hence provides a good basis for predicting the effect of system changes as well as for forecasting response.

T. ISHIHARA

The distributed models will become with time very important in the response hydrology in passing from rainfall to river discharge. These models will be essential for predicting the flood runoff, because the regional distribution of rainfall and the catchment topography have great effects on flood runoff. Moreover, the effects of urban development (urbanization) on flood discharges may be clarified only by using the distributed models. At present, we investigate the above effects by characteristic method after dividing the basin into subregions.

C. C. KISIEL

There seems to be a prevailing opinion that black-box analysis or input-output analysis requires very little hydrologic skill or that it does not concern itself with physical laws. This is far from true. It is a system identification problem and is partly discussed in my paper for this Seminar. Proper use of system identification procedures requires specification of initial conditions, boundary conditions, and an explicit mathematical relation that connects the input and output data. That mathematical relation may be for a linear or nonlinear system and for a time-invariant or time-variable system. The objective is to obtain best (in some sense) estimates of the parameters of the unit impulse response function. These estimates are obtained subject to mass balance, stability and physical realizability constraints. It should be clear that the whole procedure is concerned with physical laws but from a systems theory vantage point. The main difference between black-box analysis in the interest of tractability frequently leads to an imposition of the analyst's will onto nature -- a practice akin to assuming the role of a deity. As an example, consider that once the kinematic wave model is applied to larger and larger areas with more and more surface nonhomogeneities, it has less physical meaning and assumes some obscure grey character as a model. It is not so unique for subsequent predictive purposes. Can anyone claim otherwise!

456

At times, unit impulse response functions are taken to have meaning only in systems analysis. It actual fact, such functions constitute the kernel function in the integral equation representation of physical systems. They are synonymous with the well-known Green's functions that may be derived from the ordinary and partial differential equation models of hydrologic systems. Much more can be done with this approach in hydrology. Given the unit impulse response functions derived in this manner, the analyst now has some basis for evaluations of the kernels derived by "black-box" methods. Might I also suggest that black-box kernels may suggest the need to formulate more realistic "physically based" models.

There is a danger of over-selling the viewpoint that, to predict the behavior of changing hydrologic environments, we require bigger and better "white-box" model. But nothing is said about the price tag and the consequent uncertainty in goodness of prediction of more complex models. Simple correlation models or black-box models may be adequate to many tasks. Such models may be quite adequate for many controlled hydrologic systems. The choice of lumped as against a more involved distributed model may be justified in terms of the velocity of propagation of the system disturbance in relation to the dimensions of the system transmitting the disturbance (see my Seminar paper). All of this leads into the "proper" criteria for choosing among hydrologic models.

It should be noted that in all of the above I have not just had in mind rain-fall-runoff models. Included have been the full gamut of input-output conditions encountered in hydrology - including those arising from water quality and ecologic problems.

W. L. MOORE

In this seminar several different approaches were presented for determining the response of a watershed. There is often a desire to identify the "best" approach so it can be utilized and developed to the exclusion of other methods. The concept of a "best" approach fails to recognize the various purposes for which a response analysis may be made. Sometimes a very preliminary analysis for stationary conditions in the watershed is adequate. Other times a detailed analysis with maximum attainable precision may be required which will also account for changing conditions within the watershed. It seems clear that the best approach for a particular situation depends on the nature and purpose of the analysis to be made.

Water development schemes are usually planned for a long time horizon, and it is likely that physical changes will occur in the watershed during that time. The method of hydrologic analysis should then allow for incorporating these physical changes into the analysis. Under these conditions the parameters used in determining the response of the watershed should have physical meaning and be capable of being related to the physical changes that will occur. It may be possible to relate mathematically derived parameters of a response function analysis to physical parameters of the watershed and thus account for changing watershed conditions. This seems to be an avenue worthy of exploration. It seems more likely to the writer, however, that an analysis that starts with physical concepts and parameters with physical meaning will be more capable of adjustment to changing watershed conditions.

In attempting to determine fully the response of a watershed to rainfall input, it seems desirable to utilize in a deterministic fashion all the data and knowledge about physical processes that are available. In all cases both the data and the knowledge will be incomplete and simplifications must be made to obtain a workable simulation process. As a result of the simplifications and the inadequacy of the input data, the output of a "deterministic" simulation will differ from that of the real watershed. These differences represent the unexplained portion of the response and effort is needed to analyse these differences. Methods are needed to assess the degree of uncertainty in the simulation results, both for comparing the value of different simulation schemes and for evaluating the significance of the results for water resources planning activities.

A. MUROTA, M. HINO, AND T. TAKASAO

Several reports presented to this seminar showed that the methods of approaching the responses of hydrologic environments can be classified into the physical models and the mathematical models.

In the present stage of study it can be said that no priority should be given to either of the two methods. A significant progress is expected by their interconnection in the form of a hybrid of the two methods.

So far, many of the runoff theories have been constructed on the assumptions of stationarity and linearity of hydrologic phenomena. However, even for a linear system, the effects of noises should be studied in more detail, since inputs and outputs to the hydrologic systems are subjected to noises which come from the stochastic nature of hydrologic quantities. Furthermore, we often encounter the cases where the above assumptions do not necessarily hold. For instance, in the analysis of the long-term runoff which is required for the water resources development the non-stationarity and periodicity of hydrologic phenomena cannot be ignored. Some authors in this seminar shed some light on the treatment of the non-stationary and periodic processes.

The non-linearity of phenomena becomes evident especially for the short-term storm runoff. The introduction of stochastic inputs into the non-linear system which was made by some authors with different view points seemed to be a new development in the analysis of the non-linear runoff models.

T. D. STEELE

In selection of an approach for solving hydrologic problems, the ends (e.g., clear specification of the objectives to be achieved) will justify the means. It must be recognized that solutions to many problems involving hydrology in whole or in part require little knowledge or understanding of the physical processes taking place. Yet some empirical and very simple approaches may be used to transfer hydrologic information in time and in space and even to predict the effects of environmental changes on various hydrologic outputs. In any approach, as stated by Kisiel, the uncertainties associated with the results of an analysis should be clearly stated, and the costs associated with reducing those uncertainties must be weighed against anticipated benefits or objectives of the analysis.

V. YEVJEVICH

The problems associated with responses to their inputs of hydrologic environments conceived as systems are not as simply solved as may be implied by the present hydrologic practice. These system response functions are in reality very complex.

The response function of a hydrologic linear system is a function of frequency only when represented in the frequency domain (as spectral or variance densities). For a nonlinear system the weighting function $W(\tau)$, or the response function in the lag domain, is a function of the applied input, $x(t)$, with this function now designated by $W(\tau,x)$. The response function in the frequency domain $\eta(f)$, and consequently $R(f)$, as the attenuation or modification function, and $\theta(f)$, as the phase shift function, are also functions of input, $x(t)$, and frequency, f , and they may be designated by $\eta(f,x)$, $R(f,x)$, and $\theta(f,x)$. Furthermore, if the system is nonstationary, or its components vary with time, the weighting and response functions depend also on the absolute time t , so that they are $W(\tau,x,t)$, $\eta(f,x,t)$, $R(f,x,t)$, and $\theta(f,x,t)$. Changes of vegetation, soil permeability, evaporation and evapotranspiration, and other river basin factors, with seasonal changes, make the response functions of many hydrologic environments also nonstationary.

Strictly speaking, the seasonality measured by the nonstationarity in $W(\tau)$ and $\eta(f)$ must include the stochastic factors, ξ_t , of random changes in nature so that $W(\tau,x,t,\xi)$ and $\eta(f,x,t,\xi)$ are real weighting and response functions, and include frequency or lag, absolute values of input, time, and a stochastic factor of random changes in each hydrologic environment. Some investigators, in practice, simplify the analysis of response functions by neglecting the random factor and seasonality and by linearizing the systems (prevailing concepts of unit and instantaneous unit hydrographs, for example). In this manner, average annual responses are measured, and seasonality and randomness are passed on to as another problem, the problem of computing infiltration and evaporation for the effective surface runoff part of precipitation. This passing of one problem on to another should not be done. The development of response hydrology is at the stage where the linear and nonlinear response functions for many current hydrologic problems should be supplemented by both the seasonality and randomness of a realistic physical response of a natural environment.

B. BRIDGE BETWEEN SCIENTIFIC AND APPLIED HYDROLOGY

J. W. DELLEUR

The gap between the scientific levels of theory and practice seems to be greater in hydrology than in many other fields of knowledge. One example to illustrate this fact is the current practice in urban hydrology. Ardis et al.[1] have shown that the majority of municipalities in the United States are designing their drainage systems on the basis of the so-called "rational formula". This formula, according to Chow[2], was probably developed in Ireland by Mulvaney[3] in 1851. This 120 year old formula was introduced in this country by Kuichling[4] in 1889. The misnomer of "rational" has allowed this formula to persist. The word "rational" has even such an appeal in certain academic circles, that even today there are universities where this 19th century formula is the only approach to drainage estimation taught to undergraduate civil engineers. This situation, often due to curriculum inadequacies, perpetuates the gap instead of closing it.

Scientists working in the field of hydrology are in part to be blamed for this state of affairs. They have had the tendency of continually developing new models of the hydrologic cycle with a rapidly increasing degree of sophistication in the mathematical development rather than ascertaining the wide applicability of the models and developing the criteria for choices between them. In addition, there seems to be a gap between the level of sophistication in several areas of hydrology. For example, the models describing the dynamics of runoff are based on the laws of fluid mechanics whereas the estimation of the effective rainfall is still made in an entirely empirical and subjective way. Certain practitioners thus find it difficult to apply fairly sophisticated methods of analysis in part of their work when other parts, of necessity, remain empirical and subjective.

Three suggestions are offered to bridge the gap between applied and scientific hydrology. The first is addressed to the researchers in scientific hydrology. Additional research is needed in some areas of hydrology which are still in a fairly empirical and subjective stage, and an evaluation of the several models of the hydrologic cycle is as important as the development of new models. The second suggestion is addressed to the people responsible for engineering curricula. The inclusion of at least one course in hydrology is a necessity in all civil engineering curricula. Too often hydrology is not taught. An introduction to drainage calculations is sometimes offered in courses on highway design, for example, with the result that inaccurate and obsolete concepts are presented to the student giving them the false impression of knowledge. The third suggestion is addressed to sponsors of research in the academic establishment. Often this research results in pieces of scholarly work such as a doctoral thesis which fulfill the academic and scientific requirements but are essentially inaccessible to the practitioners. It is therefore, desirable to prepare summaries of the research

[1] Ardis, C.V., Dueker, K. J. and Lenz, A.T. "Storm Drainage Practice of Thirty-Two Cities", Journal of the Hydraulics Division ASCE. Vol. 95, N1 HY1, January 1969.

[2] Chow, Ven Te, "Runoff", sect. 14 in "Handbook of Applied Hydrology" V.T. Chow ed. McGraw-Hill 1964.

[3] Mulvaney, T.J. "On the Use of Self-Registering Rain and Flood Gauges in Making Observations of the Relations of Rainfall and Flood Discharges in a Given Catchment. Trans. Inst. Civil Engrs. Ireland (Dublin) Vol. 4, pt. 2, p. 18, 1851.

[4] Kuichling, E. "The Relation Between the Rainfall and the Discharge of Sewers in Populous Districts" Trans. ASCE, Vol. 20, pp. 1-56, 1889.

results in terms understandable to the practitioner. This, of course, requires
time and expenditure beyond those usually considered at the present. The preparation of result summaries would require the retention of doctoral students for
perhaps two semesters beyond the completion of their degrees. Time from universit
staff and from the staff of the agencies which are the ultimate users of the
research results should also be budgeted for the purpose of preparing these
summaries.

P. S. EAGLESON

We have two serious and urgent problems in this area. First - there is a
serious lack of public confidence in the ability of science and engineering to
contribute to the solution of the important problems of the day. In our own field
we must make a far greater effort to illustrate to the lay public how progress in
scientific hydrology will lead to improvements in the quality of life. Second -
because of the great demands upon limited research resources and the need for
rapid progress at the applications level, we should collectively focus our work
more on the problems which need to be solved.

T. ISHIHARA

From a combination of runoff response models and the simulation of rainfall
series, we may simulate the river discharge series as the input information into
the water resources development systems. On the other hand, the structure of the
water demands, as the output information, is very complex because of their correlations. Particularly in Japan, the irrigation demand is antagonistic to other
demands such as the industry and domestic water use. So, in order to design the
water resource systems, we must synthesize the input by using the methods of
scientific hydrology (runoff response models), the output from the water demand
structure and the control problems from input to output by using the research
results in the fields such as hydrology, economy, law, history and so on.

Y. IWASA AND M. OKUTA

Not only the science of hydrology but also all other scientific and technolog:
cal arts are reflections of man's activities to search sincerely for truth and
nature itself. The research activities are of multiple objectives, and the
simplest classification of all objectives will make them either basic or applied.

The scientific hydrology described in this discussion will be basic, in
view of the above mentioned concept, and the applied hydrology will be its counterpart. However, the Janus-faced activities are always fixed and as a system they
are mutually connected and connected with the environment. We may have a possible
distinction between scientific and applied, if we treat a particular problem from
a specified standpoint. A clear and fixed distinction between scientific and
applied is not recommended.

C. C. KISIEL

Too often research results are so involved that it increasingly seems desirable to communicate in some part of the report or paper, say in the conclusions,
the sum total of the assumptions and limitations of the effort. Not all readers

are going to dig this out of the paper as well as the authors of the paper might. Not all derivations are easily followed.

At times some models are put forward as the final answer (at least by implication) to the problem when in fact they are not. Is there such a thing as absolute certainty in modeling? No! Some scientific uncertainty surely lurks behind the scenes and should somehow be evaluated in relation to their social implications. I believe that scientific hydrologists must increasingly assume this reponsibility and carefully evaluate the social costs of Type II or beta errors (in the statistical sense).

We need more generalists in the overall subject of scientific hydrology. Even though development of such trained people is increasingly difficult, systems theory seems to offer an efficient pathway for achievement of that goal. Such people must increasingly be steeped in applications from the standpoint of operations research and economic analysis.

Team approaches increasingly seem to be the most efficient way to minimize individual biases in the solution of major hydrologic problems or the construction of major hydrologic or water resources models.

T. D. STEELE

Hydrologists must be more aware of social needs. The products of basic hydrologic research finds relevance only when it is translated and spelled out in laymen's terms. In communicating with the public at large, scientific hydrologists may attempt to translate by themselves the products of their efforts for application in the social world or they may rely on others to serve in this function. The choice of communicating as a scientist to the public should be a combined matter of desire and ability. Often we should depend upon other individuals or groups to serve as liaison between basic scientific research and application to general problems involving hydrology.

V. YEVJEVICH

It has been very beneficial in the past in having parallel development of both the scientific and the applied hydrology. The mathematical physics description of hydrologic physical processes and the mathematical statistical analysis of hydrologic stochastic processes, whether in basic or in applied research, are the best bridges between the scientific and the applied hydrology. Our society may be inclined to support only those basic scientific research programs that have the highest chances of stimulating the applied research and technological developments, and contributing direct and applicable results.

C. RELEVANT FUTURE HYDROLOGIC RESEARCH AREAS

J. W. DELLEUR

This symposium summarizes the state of the art in the mathematical modeling of hydrologic systems. The papers show that an interplay of mathematics, statistics, and physics is necessary for the description and analysis of the hydrologic cycle. Progress can thus be made by adopting and using more appropriate methods in each of these basic sciences to obtain better models of hydrologic phenomena.

The many natural phenomena that hydrologists attempt to model are more often nonlinear than linear, usually more unsteady than in equilibrium, probably more stochastic than deterministic, certainly more nonuniformly distributed in time and space than homogeneous. As a result, simplifications and assumptions are necessary to yield tractable mathematical solutions, and numerous mathematical models have been proposed. Many of these are valid under limited conditions. Further work would appear necessary to test and evaluate these models and to compare their relative merits.

Once reliable models of hydrologic phenomena are available, their use should be directed with some priority to the solution of socially relevant problems such as the effects of man-made changes on the hydrologic cycle. The effects of urbanization, the consequences of deforestation, and other impacts of changes in land use on the hydrologic response of watersheds; the effect of the discharge of vast amounts of particles and heat into the atmosphere, the effect of cloud seeding etc., on the temporal and spacial distribution of rainfall are some of the broad problems which are socially relevant.

Among more specific and immediate unsolved problems is the quantitative description of the infiltration process on a watershed scale. Considerable effort has been made towards the understanding of infiltration at a point, but the quantification of this process on a watershed scale has yet to be developed.

P. S. EAGLESON

I believe that the most important future research area is that concerning the prediction of the effect of man's activity upon weather and climate and upon the response of hydrologic systems.

T. ISHIHARA, T. KISHI, AND Y. TAKAHASI

The aim of the present seminar from the scientific viewpoint was the development of new scientific approaches in order to promote our understanding of hydrologic processes and environments.

It is very important in hydrology, as well as in other sciences, to make rearrangements of the huge amount of past knowledge and data by investigating and classifying the structure of hydrologic processes within the natural systems in which inputs are transformed into outputs.

From the above understanding we have selected the systems approach as one of the new ways of research in hydrology. The systems approach is a useful tool especially in the analysis of the processes such as hydrologic processes in which the stochastic nature of the phenomena is evident. It can be said, we believe, that the methods of describing the hydrologic processes have advanced in many respects during the present seminar.

In considering the future research areas of relevance to hydrology it is natural and reasonable to extend and refine the methods of analysis presented at this seminar. Studies on mathematical procedures for systems analysis and the physical and/or chemical mechanics of hydrologic processes are both undoubtedly important.

However, besides the above studies, the attempts to develop the new fields of application of the technology of systems analysis for the conservation, reclamation and control of hydrologic environments would also be important. In this meaning, "the optimization of the temporal and spacial distribution of water quantity and quality" would be suitable as the second target of systems analysis.

Along the above direction, the Japanese participants are proposing that the next U.S.-Japan bilateral seminar to be held in Japan.

Proposal for the Second U.S.-Japan Bilateral Seminar to be held in Japan in 1974 is as follows. The title of the Seminar will be: CONSERVATION, RECLAMATION AND CONTROL OF HYDROLOGIC ENVIRONMENTS. The two subjects of the Seminar will be:

(1) Advanced hydrologic methods in water resources planning and control.

(2) Physical approaches for conservation, reclamation and control of hydrologic environments, with case histories of successful water pollution control in over-populated areas.

T. ISHIHARA

The economical analysis should be introduced much more to analysis of hydrologic processes than at present. At the same time, the management of hydrologic information with computer systems and the water-quality hydrology will become important subjects of the future.

C.C. KISIEL

I would list the following:

(a) Careful evaluation of the social and economic importance of scientific uncertainties in hydrologic models or hypotheses. Implied here is the assessment of relative importance of Type I and II errors.
(b) Interfacing of hydrologic models with ecologic and water quality models.
(c) Space-time sampling of hydrologic processes in an economic decision framework. Implied here is the efficient design of hydrologic data network.
(d) Probabilistic reliability of hydrologic predictions into short-term, medium-range, and long-range future. Implied here is the problem of error growth in hydrologic models.
(e) Relative importance of hydrologic uncertainty in relation to physical (chemical and biological), economic and political uncertainty. Implied here is the fact that budgetary constraints will increasingly force an economic assessment of the proposed research. Admittedly, this is acquiescing to social relevance, but what other basis do we use to chart the course of hydrologic research?

T.D. STEELE

Hydrology must recognize its component role in the assessment and management of environmental quality. This recent emphasis is reflected in the proposed title for a second bi-lateral seminar in hydrology. Hydrology, itself an integrated science, drawing from such basic diciplines as engineering, mathematics, chemistry,

physics, biology, meteorology, oceanography, and economics must now recognize the
necessity to combine with other integrated fields, particularly in the social
sciences, concerned with the environment, in order to attack and to resolve some
real and pressing problems. Associated with this need are the tasks of (1) findi
current relevance for much of our past research efforts and (2) assigning priorities and allocating resources to new research programs that attempt to overcome
apparent deficiencies, either in knowledge of hydrologic phenomena or in analytica
tools for problem-solving.

V. YEVJEVICH

Response hydrology, based on finding relationships of hydrologic variables fo
given unit time inputs and unit lengths, unit areas or unit spaces of hydrologic
environments, has for a long time dominated research in hydrology. This response
hydrology, however, is quite likely out of proportion to its importance for applie
hydrology. For the complex social, economic, and environmental conditions of
hydrologic processes, with increasing human influences on both the environments an
the hydrologic processes, the study of nonhomogeneity of hydrologic processes and
changes in the environment represent a set of research topics of paramount importance. This includes the problems in reducing historical data to homogeneous
samples, and attempting to extrapolate future properties of hydrologic processes
for decision making.

The techniques for extracting hydrologic information from individual historic
time series were well developed before the advent of computers; these techniques
were tailored to the available computational devices. Now the problems of
transferring information from all points of observations into points of interest,
knowing when the maximum information has been transferred, and measuring how much
information has been concentrated at the points of interest are becoming central
problems in using the hydrologic information for planning water resources development, conservation, and control. The previous concepts of homogeneous hydrologic
regions, based on vague criteria of climatic homogeneity, need new approaches in
separating those parameters by proper techniques that are nonhomogeneous from thos
that may be considered homogeneous for all practical purposes.

Concepts and techniques used in studying floods and droughts seem to have bee
petrified in the last couple of decades. As our society places higher and higher
values on solving flood and drought problems, new concepts based on physical
reality and the large amount of hydrologic data accumulated in the world must be
found. A thorough reexamination of our present concepts and techniques are among
those scientific topics that should receive support from research funding
institutions.